ANOTHER TREASURY OF PLAYS
FOR CHILDREN

By Montrose J. Moses

REPRESENTATIVE BRITISH DRAMAS
REPRESENTATIVE CONTINENTAL DRAMAS
REPRESENTATIVE AMERICAN DRAMAS
REPRESENTATIVE CONTINENTAL ONE-ACT PLAYS
HENRIK IBSEN: THE MAN AND HIS PLAYS
A TREASURY OF PLAYS FOR CHILDREN
ANOTHER TREASURY OF PLAYS FOR CHILDREN
THE AMERICAN DRAMATIST

By M. J. Moses and V. Gerson

CLYDE FITCH AND HIS LETTERS

CYNTHIA. Oh! how lovely it is. Where shall I put it?
If that Racketty-Packetty old thing wasn't here—

Racketty-Packetty House.

ANOTHER TREASURY OF PLAYS FOR CHILDREN

EDITED BY

MONTROSE J. MOSES

WITH ILLUSTRATIONS BY
TONY SARG

BOSTON
LITTLE, BROWN, AND COMPANY
1927

Published October, 1926
Reprinted November, 1927

TO MY SON

This is a book of deeds,
Of fine deeds and dreams you will remember;
Herein are seeds
Which, planted now, may harvest in September.

This is a book of fays,
Of brave voyagers and buccaneers —
To color childhood days,
And quiver with a glory riper years.

This is a book of men,
Of gay ladies and boys of bold invention;
Herein are villains when
There's need to savor tales of good intention.

This is a book of acts,
Of high acts and aims of fair endeavor, —
Where fairies abhor facts,
And realms imagined come to stay forever.

This is a book of plays,
Such plays as Mummy would have loved had you,
In those golden days,
Been what you are to-day instead of two.

This is a book of Youth —
Such youth as Mummy lived when "Captain Perry", —
High imaginings and truth,
Grave moments mingled with laughter merry.

This is a book for you —
Builded of memories and of ballads sung,
When Daddy was of your age too,
And Life — the Life of Youth — was very young.

A NOTE OF ACKNOWLEDGMENT

Again we invite a notable company around our Table of Contents. We have sought far and near for guests, and our board being limited, we could not invite every one we would have liked. Our number is twelve, though our hospitality is boundless. The plays of Maeterlinck and Barrie sent word their elders wouldn't let them wander out of the fold, and so we do not find here "The Blue Bird" or "Peter Pan." "The Poor Little Rich Girl" had another engagement; the little boy in Tagore's "The Post Office" considered passage from India too exacting. But we still like them, even if they couldn't come.

Cinderella, with her Slippers, has journeyed all the way from London, with the most cordial greetings of W. Graham Robertson, Esq., and passports from Samuel French. Lord Dunsany's *Tea Kettle* sings temptingly on the Table, with permission to stay from Messrs. G. P. Putnam's Sons. Such a Table as ours is breath of life to the nostrils of *Don Quixote*, whose puppet strings have been put into the Editor's hands with cordial understanding of Mrs. Anne Stoddard and the irresistible Tony Sarg, who has drawn seven menu cards, one color piece, some rollicking end papers, and has housed the Table of Contents in a striking decorative cover. Usually at a feast with twelve guests there are twelve covers. But not so here. There is but one cover, and it is this which makes our party different.

Mr. Goodman and Mr. Hopkins have put Stevenson's "Treasure Island" in shape for any gathering, and sent it to us. Entering, one by one, we note that Messrs. Houghton, Mifflin Company have granted us Mr. Drinkwater's "Abraham Lincoln"; a cable from Mr. A. A. Milne gave us right to set a place for *Make-Believe;* Messrs. D. Appleton and Company have allowed Mr. Stuart Walker's *Infanta* to accept our invitation; Messrs.

Dodd, Mead and Company have told *Snow White* she could be present (not forgetting the *Seven Dwarfs*, whom you will imagine at a side table); Gilbert's *Mikado* and the *Three Little Maids from School* are here with their blossoming kimonos and their kotows, — such different manners from those of Miss Edgeworth's girls and boys (whom we have had to put at another side table). Messrs. Henry Holt and Company have sent us a guest, "The King with the Iron Heart", who is none the less quite at home in such merry company.

The Editor mentions Mr. Vivian Burnett's permission to allow the *Racketty-Packettys* to come, because, now that we are assembled before our Table of Contents, I can imagine all the guests paying a silent tribute to Mrs. Frances Hodgson Burnett, who shall always be with us in the Secret Garden of Memory.

So, here we are again, and the only thing to make the feast complete is to find Readers who believe that, no matter how many years pass, such a Table never grows stale. The Editor is always nervous — what cook is not so? — as the dishes stand ready to be served. Are they to your taste, *Mademoiselles* and *Messieurs?* A fairy tale is not difficult to digest. Our food is from the best market, and it's prepared according to the best literary recipes. There are seasoned things and sweet things, old and new, wise and funny. If you have an imagination I will vouch for good results — I, the Editor, the caterer. But if you haven't, — well — But you have!

MONTROSE J. MOSES

TABLE OF CONTENTS

ILLUSTRATIONS

PANTOMIME

We have all admired the illustrated papers, and noted how boister-ously jolly they become at Christmas time. What wassail-bowls, robin-red-breasts, waits, snow landscapes, bursts of Christmas song! And then to think that these festivities are prepared months before — that these Christmas pieces are prophetic! How kind of artists and poets to devise the festivities beforehand, and serve them pat at the proper time! We ought to be grateful to them, as to the cook who gets up at midnight and sets the pudding a-boiling which is to feast us at six o'clock. I often think with gratitude of the famous Mr. Nelson Lee — the author of I don't know how many hundred glorious pantomimes — walking by the summer wave at Margate, or Brighton perhaps, revolving in his mind the idea of some new gorgeous spectacle of faëry, which the winter shall see complete. He is like cook at midnight (si parva licet). He watches and thinks. He pounds the sparkling sugar of benevolence, the plums of fancy, the sweetmeats of fun, the figs of — well, the figs of fairy fiction, let us say, and pops the whole in the seething cauldron of imagination, and at due season serves up the PANTOMIME.

WILLIAM MAKEPEACE THACKERAY.

TREASURE ISLAND AND PIRATES

To see this play acted is to have an evening with Pirates. Our jealous love of certain books makes us eager to see them on the stage, though we are fearful lest all the things we love about the story are not in the play. Mr. Charles Hopkins planned a very ambitious entertainment when he decided to give a stage version of "Treasure Island" in his little theater, delightfully called The Punch and Judy. I am sure he was prompted by a fervent admiration for Robert Louis Stevenson's Pirates. And he went about his preparations nobly, for his theater was small — all the better, it seemed in the end — for to me I felt as though my evening with Pirates was being spent in the paneled cabin of a ship. Or, if not that, in a public room of an eighteenth-century inn. It would not have surprised me one whit if this dark-wooded auditorium had rocked a little, and I had found myself out at sea. As I was shown to my seat by medievally gowned ushers, or cabin boys, I settled myself comfortably for a real thrill. I looked about me from where I sat in a box — a veritable bunk in the wall — and waited for the ship's gong to tell me we were off!

"Treasure Island" was originally written with a deal of joyousness on the part of Stevenson. "If this don't fetch the kids," he exclaimed, "why, they have gone rotten since my day." Such was the spirit in which he attacked the order given him by his stepson, Lloyd Osbourne, for whom the tale was fortunately written. " No women in the story," he continues; "Lloyd's orders." And who so blithe to obey? "It's awful fun, boys' stories; you just indulge the pleasure of your heart; that's all; no trouble, no strain. The only stiff thing is to get it ended — that I don't see, but I look to a volcano. O sweet, O generous, O human toils! You would like my blind beggar in

Chapter III, I believe; no writing, just drive along as the words come and the pen will scratch. 'R. L. S., Author of Boys' Stories.' "

In this mood Stevenson speaks to his friend, the poet, W. E. Henley, of the beginning of "Treasure Island." Fortunate for the world of letters that this immortal story was written with such enthusiasm, — an enthusiasm which died out after the tale was finished, and which he always longed to experience again. For, hear him in another letter to Henley, in 1884, asking for a good book of adventure.

"I want a book to begin in a good way," he said, "a book, I guess, like 'Treasure Island.' Alas! which I have never read, and cannot though I live to ninety. I would God that some one else had written it! By all that I can learn, it is the very book for my complaint. I like the way I hear it opens; and they tell me *John Silver* is good fun. And to me it is, and must ever be, a dream unrealized, a book unwritten."

Now, it is this very enthusiasm which is contagious about the story of "Treasure Island." It was not only written with joy, but it is read with a relentless pleasure. Mr. Goodman turned the book into a play: and his task was great. Mr. Hopkins put it upon his small stage, and his task was greater still. All the more credit to the two that one saw the book come to life, the actors catching the adventurous spirit of R. L. S., its author.

I have no doubt that romance fixes our conceptions of certain types, and in the realizing of them we are never quite satisfied. Would a real Pirate ever come up to the specifications of an imagined one? That is why imagination is so much greater than reality. In the minds of certain boys, a Pirate is of heroic size, pledged to certain weapons, profuse with certain horrible exclamations, accustomed to cruelty, nonchalantly administered. But if we should ever happen to come face to face with a Pirate, in all likelihood some of his color would have faded. Our imaginations build for us the glamorous color around Pirate life, and those who can find no charm in "Treasure Island" are the very persons who have said that Stevenson failed to make his

Pirates real. Joseph Conrad had been to sea, had met with the real thing, and therefore much preferred Stevenson's other books.

I went to see this play solely with the idea of thrilling once more over certain characters, certain scenes which to me — who have never shipped to the Tropic of Cancer or the Tropic of Capricorn — were typical of a supreme Pirate story. "As for my seamen," exclaimed R. L. S., "did Runciman ever know eighteenth-century Buccaneers?" When the actor who played *Long John Silver* muttered, "Shiver my timbers!" the music of it struck my ears familiarly, as certain strains of "Pinafore" or "The Mikado" strike me when I go a second or third or fourth time to a Gilbert and Sullivan opera. Mr. Goodman was too excellent a dramatist to leave out of his version the *Captain's* song, "Yo-ho, and a bottle of rum!" He would not so cheat the readers of "Treasure Island." The only thing I somehow resented was that the many-colored parrot *John Silver* carried was not trained to shriek across the footlights, "Pieces of Eight! Pieces of Eight!"

The play of "Treasure Island" does not contain all the suspensive movement of the story. But what did I care as I sat there watching it before me — actually seeing *Bill Bones*, the *Captain* and *Doctor Livesey* alive at the "Admiral Benbow Inn." From the very first act — credit alike to Mr. Hopkins and Mr. Goodman — I felt the closeness of the story to my heart. There is no room for criticism when Pirates are near — that is, if you have a tremor of boyhood about you. The more *Bill Jones* called for rum, the less critical I became, and when, in the struggle with *Black Dog*, an actual spark of fire came from his stunted sword, I felt that all the dreams of "Treasure Island" had come true! I ceased to exist in the theater; I was part of the stirring life that faced *Jim Hawkins*. How I wish for you the same capacity to thrill at the playhouse!

One of Stevenson's great concerns, when he had written barely three chapters of his book, was the way he should treat Pirates without oaths. Writing to Henley, he said, "Buccaneers without oaths — bricks without straw, but youth and the fond parent have to be consulted." Yet I challenge any one to find a more expressive exclamation — that runs the whole gamut of terror and vehemence and vengeance — than "Shiver my timbers!" I defy any dramatist to paint for an audience a more graphic picture than that which trembles in the phrase, "A Dead Man's Chest", — which Stevenson confesses he took bodily out of Kingsley's "At Last." "Are they fairly lively on the wires?" asked R. L. S., of the critics of his Pirates. Yes, we say, who have read the story and seen the play.

On the opening night of "Treasure Island", at the Punch and Judy Theater, it was said that Lloyd Osbourne, who was in the audience, was satisfied with what he saw. Here was the lad grown up, who had in his earlier days demanded of his step-father "something craggy to break his mind on." Out of the companionship of these two — painting together, drawing Pirate Maps gaily colored (have you ever drawn a Hidden Treasure Map?), came this classic which is here offered you in a play.

TREASURE ISLAND

Story by ROBERT LOUIS STEVENSON
Play by JULES ECKERT GOODMAN

By Arrangement with Lloyd Osbourne,
Representative of the Robert Louis
Stevenson Estate

Scenes of the Play

Robert Louis Stevenson's introduction will be spoken by *Doctor Livesey*, our play being the *Doctor's* story in which he himself plays an important part.

Act I.   The Admiral Benbow Inn.

Act II.   *Scene 1.* The Quay at Bristol. Early morning.
(The curtain will be lowered to denote the lapse of a few days, between Scenes I and II)
Scene 2. The same — late afternoon.

Act III.   *Scene 1.* The *Hispaniola* at anchor some weeks later off Treasure Island. Night.
Scene 2. Treasure Island at dawn, the following day.
Scene 3. The Stockade. Evening, the following day.
Scene 4. The *Hispaniola* adrift, night of the same day.

Act IV.   *Scene 1.* The Pirates' Camp. Early morning, the following day.
Scene 2. Spyglass Mountain. Midday, the following day.
Scene 3. Ben Gunn's cave.

PROLOGUE

For Prologue, the curtain rises in darkness, a single amber light in foots comes in on dimmer and throws ghostly light on Doctor Livesey's face as he stands before plain dark curtain. After Prologue, light down on dimmer, the Doctor steps through center opening in curtain which is raised in darkness, a blare of trumpets follows, and then the play opens.

If sailor tales to sailor tunes,
    Storm and adventure, heat and cold,
If schooners, islands, and maroons
    And Buccaneers and buried Gold,
And all the old romance, retold
    Exactly in the ancient way,
Can please, as me they pleased of old,
    The wiser youngsters of to-day:

— So be it, and fall on! If not,
    If studious youth no longer crave,
His ancient appetites forgot,
    Kingston, or Ballantyne the brave,
Or Cooper of the wood and wave:
    So be it, also! And may I
And all my pirates share the grave
    Where these and their creations lie!

TREASURE ISLAND

A PLAY BASED ON THE STORY OF ROBERT LOUIS STEVENSON

By JULES ECKERT GOODMAN

As Played by Charles Hopkins, Mrs. Hopkins, and their Punch and Judy Theater Company

Produced by Charles Hopkins at the Punch and Judy Theater (now the Charles Hopkins Theater), New York, December 1, 1915.

CAST

JIM HAWKINS	Mrs. Hopkins
MRS. HAWKINS	Alice Belmore
DR. LIVESEY	David Glassford
SQUIRE TRELAWNEY	Edmund Gurney
CAPTAIN SMOLLETT	Leonard Willey
REDRUTH	Leonard Grey
HUNTER	Marshall Birmingham
JOYCE	Perry Hopper
GREY	F. Cecil Butler
ALAN	Cecil Magnus
A FRUIT SELLER	Agnes Kemble
BILL BONES, THE "CAPTAIN"	Tim Murphy
BLACK DOG	Oswalde Yorke
PEW	Frank Sylvester
LONG JOHN SILVER	Edward Emery
"CAPTAIN FLINT", HIS PARROT	By himself
MORGAN	J. H. Greene
ANDERSON	Lynn Starling
GEORGE MERRY	W. J. Ferguson
ISRAEL HANDS	Herbert Ashton
DIRK	Adin Wilson
O'BRIEN	Chauncy W. Keim
ARROW	Charles Macdonald
DICK	Benjamin Kauser
BEN GUNN, THE MAROON	Charles Hopkins

TREASURE ISLAND

ACT I

TIME: 9:30 P.M.

SCENE: *Interior of "Admiral Benbow Inn."*

Before the curtain goes up Captain Bones is heard singing in loud boisterous voice.

When the curtain rises the Captain is seen seated at table right by fireplace. Four men are seated about the table center.

Stools for table, not chairs. Joyce in fireplace seat, facing Captain, and humoring him in song.

All drinking and talking about the noise the Captain is making.

CAPTAIN (*seated table right, by fireplace, singing before curtain goes up*).

> Fifteen men on the dead man's chest,
>   Yo-ho-ho and a bottle of rum;
> Drink and the devil had done for the rest,
>   Yo-ho-ho and a bottle of rum.

(*Singing at table right to man in fireplace seat. Captain crosses to table between two men, Hunter and Grey, at right of table, putting his arms on their shoulders. They are annoyed at this*)

> "My mates," says he, "you must come wi' me,"
>   Yo-ho-ho and a bottle of rum,
> "Come wi' me, to the depths o' the sea,"
>   Yo-ho-ho and a bottle o' rum.

Now then, we'll sing that over and louder — every one of you sing — sing now — (*Captain draws cutlass and leads song with it. They sing*)

> Fifteen men on the dead man's chest,
>   Yo-ho-ho and a bottle of rum;

(*Captain slaps Grey on back, saying*)   Sing, you lubber, sing!
(*Sings*)

> Drink and the devil had done for the rest,
> Yo-ho-ho and a bottle of rum.

(*Redruth at table continues to sing it over again alone till Captain stops him*)
That's enough!   Silence, I say!   Silence!
(*Poking Redruth back with hand, who turns facing Captain. As Grey gets up from stool right, lower end of table*)   Where are you going?
[*Slapping him across back with cutlass.*

GREY.   I was going home, sir.

CAPTAIN (*thunders at him*).   Sit down!

GREY.   Yes, sir.
[*Moving toward stool fearfully.*

CAPTAIN.   Sit down, sit down!   By thunder, you'll do as I say — (*Grey fearfully sits down*)   Not one of you leaves, do you hear?

THE MEN.   Yes — yes —

CAPTAIN.   It's a foggy evening and I'll have company — company — (*Puts away cutlass*)   Mrs. Hawkins — Mrs. Hawkins, I say —
[*Mrs. Hawkins rushes in from the taproom to foot of stairs.*

MRS. HAWKINS.   Yes — yes — Captain —

CAPTAIN.   Why don't you come when you hear me? — More drinks, Mrs. Hawkins.
[*Indicating men at table.*

MRS. HAWKINS (*pleadingly*).   Oh, please . . . please, sir. . . .

CAPTAIN.   What!   Did you hear what I said!   Did you?
[*Two men, Redruth and Grey, at lower end of table, start to whisper.*

MRS. HAWKINS.   Very well, sir, I'll get it!
[*Goes out to taproom.*

CAPTAIN.   You two there . . . (*Pushing them apart*)   What were you whispering about? . . .   I saw you. . . .   I'll have no whispering, you hear?   Well — why don't you speak?
[*To Grey at end of table.*

ALAN (*seated at head of table*). If you please, sir —
[*Rising.*

CAPTAIN. Who told you to speak? (*Rises and pushes Alan right. Crosses to other man, Hunter, at fireplace, and talks, objecting*) Mrs. Hawkins! Mrs. Hawkins! I'll have that rum! Rum! Rum!
[*Leaning on banister and calling in taproom. Crossing to right of stairs.*

REDRUTH. Let me go get it for you, sir.
[*Rising and crossing to Captain.*

CAPTAIN. Sit down.
[*Pushing Redruth left of stairs.*

GREY (*getting up*). It's late and we must go.
[*Rises from stool lower end of table and backs toward door.*

CAPTAIN. Sit down, I say! (*Drawing cutlass*) Not a man leaves — I'll not be left alone with those faces out there in the fog. . . .

REDRUTH (*standing, facing Captain*). But there are no faces.

CAPTAIN. Who asked you to speak? . . . By thunder, I've seen men run through for less. . . . (*Lunging at him with cutlass*) Rum! Rum! Rum!
[*Sits in chair at head of table, beating on floor with cutlass. Leaving cutlass on floor beside him.*

MRS. HAWKINS. Coming — coming, sir —
[*Comes to right of Captain.*

REDRUTH. But indeed we've had enough —

CAPTAIN. What's that?
[*Grey up near door.*
[*Enter Dr. Livesey, takes in situation, crosses to fireplace, taking off gloves and hat, and greeting men standing there. They salute him.*

MRS. HAWKINS (*pleadingly*). Oh, please, sir — you're driving all my business away.

CAPTAIN. Driving it away? — I'm holding it here, madam. Sit down — (*Captain sees Grey near door going out. He rushes around table, picking up cutlass, and men at fireplace rush out. When Captain gets to left-center of table, Redruth rushes out.*

14   *Another Treasury of Plays for Children*

Dr. Livesey crosses, meeting Captain face to face as he comes around table.   Mrs. Hawkins closes door after men are out, and drops to table at fireplace.)

What, you refuse — you refuse to sit down and drink with me — Then, by thunder, we'll see. . . .

DR. LIVESEY (*at edge of table*).   Hello! What's all this?

CAPTAIN (*thunders at him, putting cutlass up to his face*).   Silence between decks!

DR. LIVESEY.   Are you addressing me, sir!

CAPTAIN.   Aye, that I am! Silence, I said! Silence — or — [*Starts menacing him with cutlass.*

DR. LIVESEY (*firmly*).   Stop that!

CAPTAIN.   What's that? [*Retreating a step.*

MRS. HAWKINS (*comes down right, terribly afraid.   Retreats to former position*).   Oh, please, sir, please —

CAPTAIN (*coming up angrily toward Dr. Livesey and putting cutlass up to his face*).   Now you say that again!

DR. LIVESEY.   I said for you to stop it and I mean it!

CAPTAIN (*retreating*).   Why, you rum puncheon — weak-livered swab, — (*sweeps cups off table with cutlass*) you bandy-legged lubber . . .   I'll show you!
[*Comes up to Doctor, putting cutlass up to his face.*

DR. LIVESEY (*firmly*).   Put down that cutlass —

CAPTAIN.   What you —

DR. LIVESEY (*staring Captain down*).   Put it down, or, upon my honor, you shall hang at the next assizes — Put it down! (*Doctor points to table.   The Captain gives way, and bangs cutlass on table.   He faces audience*)   And now you listen to me — I warned you against drinking before.   You had a stroke, and, much against my will, I dragged you head foremost out of the grave.   And now, Mr. Bones —

CAPTAIN.   That's not my name —

DR. LIVESEY.   Well, it will serve all right — and I tell you this — One glass of rum won't kill you, but, if you take one, you'll take another, and I'll stake my wig you break off short, you'll die — you understand? Die and go to your own place like the man in the Bible —

CAPTAIN. Well, that's my business —

DR. LIVESEY. Yes, and this is mine — I am a magistrate as well as a doctor, and if I find the least complaint about you hereafter, I'll take means to have you routed out of this. Now then, away with you!

CAPTAIN. This is a free inn.

[*Turning on doctor.*

DR. LIVESEY. You heard what I said. Go!

[*Captain picks up cutlass, turns, goes upstairs, and when three steps from head of stairs he turns, speaking this line back up to door. Points cutlass at doctor, feeling the door with other hand.*

CAPTAIN. You'll pay for this — you'll see —

DR. LIVESEY. That's all right. And remember, the very name of rum is death for you.

CAPTAIN (*goes out*). Huh!

[*The doctor comes down stage to fireplace and warms his hands.*

MRS. HAWKINS (*very afraid*). Oh, sir, I'm so glad you came. (*Doctor turns and faces her*) He's got all the people round here so afraid, they'll hardly come to the inn any more. We're all in mortal terror of the man, sir!

DR. LIVESEY. So, in spite of my warning that it would kill him, he's been drinking again, eh?

MRS. HAWKINS. Oh, yes, sir — drinking and singing that horrid song — and blowing his nose so loud it sounds like the report of a cannon. (*Doctor laughs*) You may laugh, but I never knew a man to put such fierceness into the blowing of his nose. And when I asks him for money, sir — why — why — that's when he blows his nose the loudest —

DR. LIVESEY. I dare swear he owes you for the lodgings.

[*Sits in chair at table.*

MRS. HAWKINS (*sitting*). That he does, sir. (*Drawing up-stage stool to right of table*) Oh, I appeal to you as magistrate . . . he's ruining me, sir — ruining me!

DR. LIVESEY. Mrs. Hawkins, Squire Trelawney and I have been watching your lodger for some time. Tell me, does he seem interested in ships and sailors?

MRS. HAWKINS (*mysteriously*). He's given Jim a silver four-penny every month to keep his eye open for a sea-faring man with one leg!

DR. LIVESEY. Ah, has he now!

MRS. HAWKINS. And that's the worst of it . . . the influence he has over my boy. . . .

DR. LIVESEY. Jim's a good boy, I'll be bound. . . .

MRS. HAWKINS. That he is, sir. Jim's the best boy in the world. . . . But the Captain is filling his head with stories. . . . You should have heard the stories as he told about that boat —

[*Indicates picture over mantel.*

DR. LIVESEY (*looks at picture and reads title*). "Flint's Treasure Ship."

[*Rising and looking at picture over fireplace.*

MRS. HAWKINS (*puts back stool to original position*). He's got the boy so worked up, with 'is horrid tales of pirates and sea fights and treasure hunting that the lad is fair bewitched with the idea of going to sea . . . and — oh, sir — he's all I have. I want my money but I don't want my boy in 'is company.

DR. LIVESEY (*turning and facing Mrs. Hawkins*). I think I can promise you both, Mrs. Hawkins. Squire Trelawney is to meet me here to-night.

MRS. HAWKINS. Oh, sir, I hope there ain't going to be no fightin' —

DR. LIVESEY (*coming toward her*). Can you keep a secret, Mrs. Hawkins?

MRS. HAWKINS. As close as the grave, sir —

DR. LIVESEY. You can, eh? Come here to the window. (*Crossing to window, looking out. Mrs. Hawkins crosses to right at following line*) No, it's so foggy you can't see — but there's a little lugger down at Kitt's Hole — I suspect (*turning to Mrs. Hawkins*) that's the boat our friend is looking for —

MRS. HAWKINS. What — what is it?

DR. LIVESEY (*confidentially*). Smuggler —

MRS. HAWKINS. Oh!

[*Retreating a step.*

DR. LIVESEY. That's what your Captain is — that's why he's waiting for one special seaman — and that, Mrs. Hawkins, is what the Squire and I have been waiting for. I've got men all over the countryside. Now, if we can keep an eye on the Captain — (*enter Jim from taproom and goes upstairs*) we'll get the whole crew of them. . . . Oh, you say Jim is close to the Captain?

[*Taking a step towards Mrs. Hawkins.*

MRS. HAWKINS. Hand and glove — more's the pity.

DR. LIVESEY. Jim!

[*Coming down stage a step.*

JIM. Yes, sir.

[*Turning to face doctor on stairs.*

DR. LIVESEY (*crossing to fireplace*). Come over here.

JIM. Yes, sir.

[*Coming down stairs and starting towards doctor.*

MRS. HAWKINS (*crossing to Jim and meeting him*). That horrid man has had enough for to-day. The doctor wants to talk to you —

[*Exits into taproom, leaving rum on table center near window.*

DR. LIVESEY. Sit down, Jim.

[*Indicating stool.*

JIM (*sits on stool*). Thank you, sir.

DR. LIVESEY. Jim, since your father died your mother has had only you to help her —

JIM. I do my best, sir.

DR. LIVESEY. I know you do — quite right, my boy. (*Crossing round table towards Jim*) Jim, your mother tells me the Captain hasn't paid for his board and lodging.

JIM. He hasn't. Not since the first day, sir. He was at that door calling for a glass of rum, and when he had drunk it he says, "This is a handy little cove. Much company?"

DR. LIVESEY. Oh, he asked that, did he?

JIM. And when he heard as how there was very little, he says, "This is the berth for me." So in he comes with his sea-chest, and throws down three pieces of gold. "You can tell me when I've worked through that," says he.

DR. LIVESEY.   Well, he has "worked through" it, hasn't
he?

JIM.   Oh, yes, sir, and much besides.

DR. LIVESEY.   Jim, if your mother is to get what's owing her —
you must watch the Captain's every move to-night —
[*Rising.*

JIM.   Yes, sir.
[*Rises.*

DR. LIVESEY.   I shall be there in the village — the least thing
that looks suspicious — any strangers that call on him —
any attempt of the Captain to leave — you send me word —
by your mother — no matter what happens.   Don't you
leave him for one moment.

JIM.   Yes, sir.

DR. LIVESEY.   Jim!   (*Crossing to door, opening it, and looking
out.   Jim follows*)   There's a nasty fog out there — a fog
that hides things on the sea. — A fog like that is bad for ships
on good business, but it's good for ships on bad business. —
These men are on bad business — (*Closing door and coming
towards Jim, with a sudden change of tone*)   Hawkins, I am
a magistrate.

JIM.   Yes, sir . . .

DR. LIVESEY.   Hawkins, I appoint you an officer of the
crown . . .

JIM (*startled*).   Dr. Livesey . . .

DR. LIVESEY (*salutes him*).   An officer of the crown, Hawkins!

JIM (*awkwardly returns the salute*).   Aye — aye, sir!

DR. LIVESEY.   You're the only one who can watch without
suspicion.   You're not afraid, Hawkins?

JIM.   No — no, sir — I'm not afraid.

DR. LIVESEY.   Then we'll unravel this mystery before midnight. . . .   (*Crosses to table and gets hat and gloves.   Then
to door*)   Keep your eyes open.   Remember, officer of the
crown!
[*Opening door and standing in it, salutes, then exits.*

JIM.   Aye, aye, sir.
[*Salutes.   Closes door after doctor.*

CAPTAIN (*peering out of doorway*). Jim! Jim! Jim! Is he gone?

JIM. Who?

[*Advancing toward him a little.*

CAPTAIN. That swab of a doctor —

JIM. Yes.

CAPTAIN. Then go fetch me some rum, Jim.

JIM. But —

[*Coming nearer to stairs.*

CAPTAIN. Rum . . . a whole tankard of it — fetch it to my room.

[*Starts away.*

JIM. But, Captain — the doctor said —

[*Right to foot of stairs.*

CAPTAIN (*turning on Jim*). The doctor be blowed . . . I . . . (*With sudden change of manner. He now becomes almost winningly kind*) There, there! (*Captain comes down the stairs to him*) I'm not meaning to be hard with you . . . you've been my friend . . . you're the only one I can trust . . . (*Confidentially*) And if ever I need some one it's to-day . . . there's things brewing to-day, Jim. (*Looks fearfully over Jim's shoulder at the window*) I can feel it in the air.

JIM. It's just the fog, Captain.

CAPTAIN. Aye . . . the fog. . . . It's full of faces, Jim . . . the fog . . . (*Keeps looking around furtively at the window*) Every step of the way from the cove I've seen 'em . . . faces, Jim. . . . Like those of Flint's crew up there — they've been all around me; they're . . . (*Suddenly stares at the window*) See — see there at the window — look. . . .

[*Crosses back of banister on stairs.*

JIM (*crosses to window*). Why, there's nothing there.

CAPTAIN. Didn't you see a face — a face with an ugly look on't?

JIM (*goes to the door and looks out*). No, sir. There's not a person on the road.

[*Closes door and watches Captain.*

CAPTAIN. Faces — faces — everywhere in the fog. (*Coming to edge of table and Jim crosses to meet him*) You've kept your eye open for a sea-faring man with one leg?

JIM. Yes, sir . . . though it's no pay I've had these several weeks.

CAPTAIN. What!
[*Roars at him, and taking out handkerchief.*

JIM. I said I'd had no pay — and — (*As Captain blows his nose*) That's all right, sir. You needn't mind.

CAPTAIN. No pay, eh, well-well — (*Kindly*) Well, there's your pay, lad — take it —(*Gives Jim money, — two four-penny pieces*) I'm needing friends to-day. . . . (*As Jim takes the money and puts it in pocket*) There's a little lugger down at Kitt's Hole — keep your eyes open (*backing to foot of stairs*) — watch the road — and — Jim — any one asks for me, you don't know me. You've never heard o' me. Understand?

JIM. Not even the sea-faring man with one leg?

CAPTAIN. No! None of 'em. (*Advancing towards him*) Bring my rum upstairs now — and keep your eyes open. (*Glances at window*) There . . . there he is again . . . see 'im lookin' in that window?
[*Backs halfway upstairs.*

JIM. I tell you there's no one — nothing.
[*Crossing to Captain.*

CAPTAIN (*backs upstairs*). Nothing, eh? It's the whole crew of 'em out there in the fog . . . (*indicates cutlass*) the whole crew of 'em . . . and it's going to be a fight (*indicates cutlass*) . . . but we'll beat 'em yet. . . . Bring me that rum — quick.
[*Goes upstairs.*

[*Jim watches Captain off and exits to taproom. For a moment the stage is empty. Finally a face is seen peering in at the window. Then the face disappears and soon the door opens and a man enters. "A pale tallowy creature, wanting two fingers of the left hand, and though he wore a cutlass he did not look much like a fighter." He is Black Dog. For a moment he stands listening.*

He starts across room, looks at picture of Flint's Ship above mantel over fireplace. As he reaches table Jim makes a noise in the taproom. Startled, he runs behind left of stairs, and watches. Jim enters with rum for the Captain, and is going toward the stairs when Black Dog sees him and comes out from behind stairs.

JIM (*surprised and startled*). I — I didn't hear you come in.

BLACK DOG (*at stairs*). Oh, didn't you now. . . . Tidy little place. . . . Very tidy. Come here, sonny. Come nearer here; and what have you there?

[*Jim goes to him.*

JIM. Some rum, sir —

BLACK DOG (*takes Jim's hand by wrist and lifts rum up to nose and sniffs it*). Um — rum — it is — good strong rum —

JIM (*fearing he is to take it, retreats a step to upper end of table*). It's for the gentleman upstairs, sir.

BLACK DOG. For the gentleman upstairs! (*Turning around in circle, looking at door head of stairs, and finally facing Jim*) Good strong rum for the gentleman upstairs. . . . You know what I think?

JIM. No, sir.

BLACK DOG. I think it is just the sort of stuff that'd suit my old mate Bill. . . . Now what do you think?

JIM. I don't know your mate Bill, and so —

[*Starts towards stairs.*

BLACK DOG. Don't you now! (*stopping him*) that's too bad. . . . What might you call your . . . gentleman upstairs?

JIM. Captain.

BLACK DOG. Well, my mate Bill might be called Captain —

JIM (*starting to go towards stairs*). I'm sure he isn't the same.

BLACK DOG (*stopping him*). We'll put it for argment your Cap'n has a cut on one cheek — and that the right one — (*Jim starts*) Ah, well — I told you. . . . Now is my mate Bill here?

JIM. I'll go upstairs and let him know. . . .

[*Starts toward stairs.*

BLACK DOG. No, you won't. (*As Jim still starts to go, he thunders at him*) Stop, I say, or — Stop!

JIM. But, sir, I must tell the Captain.

BLACK DOG (*fawning again, as Jim stops*). There — there — lad — I'm meaning you no harm. Why, I have a son of my own as like you as two blocks, and he's all the pride of my 'art. But the great thing for boys is discipline, sonny. You see I planned this as a great surprise to Bill — bless his 'art . . . (*takes out his cutlass and tries its edge with fingers*) and I couldn't have you spoil it.

JIM. Oh, sir, I hope there's not going to be any trouble —

CAPTAIN (*upstairs*). Jim! Jim! Where's my rum!

[*Black Dog faces Captain's door.*

BLACK DOG (*motions Jim to keep silent*). Sh-sh! Bill and me's old friends . . . he'll be glad to see me . . . Bill will, bless his 'art. . . .

[*Putting cutlass back in belt.*

CAPTAIN (*still upstairs*). Jim — Jim —

BLACK DOG. Sh-sh — not a word — or I'll wring your neck.

[*As Jim starts, Black Dog grasps him by the throat and urges him back of the stairs.*

JIM. What are you doing, sir?

BLACK DOG. Giving Bill a surprise . . . a little surprise.

[*The Captain comes down the stairs.*

CAPTAIN (*furious*). Jim! Where has he gone . . . Jim, I say . . . Jim. . . .

[*He is just at foot of stairs, turning to go into taproom.*

BLACK DOG (*speaks when Captain gets around right of stairs towards taproom. Steps out as Captain turns*). Hello, Bill!

CAPTAIN (*stops short, as if stunned. Wheels around, resting left hand on newel post*). You . . . you . . .

BLACK DOG. Come, Bill. You know your old shipmate. . . .

CAPTAIN. Black Dog! What do you want?

[*Moves toward him, and Black Dog retreats.*

BLACK DOG. Just come to see my old shipmate Billy, and talk over old times.

CAPTAIN (*bitterly*). Old times, huh!

[*Moves toward Black Dog, and Black Dog retreats.*

BLACK DOG. A sight of times we've seen, Bill, us two, since I lost them talons —
[Holds up mutilated hand.

CAPTAIN. Now, look here, you've runned me down — here I am. Well, then, speak up! What is it?
[Jim crosses to head of table.

BLACK DOG. That's you, Bill — always to the point. (*Significantly to Jim*) I'll have a glass of rum.

JIM. Here, sir.
[Makes as if to offer the tankard.

BLACK DOG (*sinister*). That's for the gentleman upstairs. I'll have my own. (*As Jim hurries toward taproom, leaving Captain's rum on table near window*) Don't hurry back. . . . (*Jim takes hold of the taproom door to go out*) Leave that door open! None of your keyholes for me, sonny.
[Jim goes out at taproom door.

CAPTAIN (*fiercely, sitting left of table*). Well, out with it. . . .

BLACK DOG. Now, we'll talk square, like ole shipmates.

CAPTAIN. Old shipmates, huh!

BLACK DOG. Sure, Bill — we're all here — Morgan and Hands and Pew and O'Brien.

CAPTAIN. Silver?

BLACK DOG. Aye, Silver. He's in command down there on the little lugger. . . .
[Indicating direction of door.

CAPTAIN. A nice little lugger it must be.

BLACK DOG. We all sailed with Flint, and what we got like gentlemen of fortune belonged to . . .

CAPTAIN. Flint. . . .

BLACK DOG. Aye, to Flint!

CAPTAIN. Huh!
[Grunts.

BLACK DOG. And after Flint to Flint's crew, . . . and that's what we've come for . . . what we're going to get.

CAPTAIN. Go on. Out with it all.

BLACK DOG. There's money about you, Bill Jones . . . (*sits right of table on upstage stool*) money as belongs to us all . . .

and more than money there's a little chart . . . Flint's fist . . .
showing where all Flint's Treasure is hid . . . them things
belongs to us all and, by thunder (*banging table with fist*), them
things we're goin' to have. . . . Now you know, Bill.

CAPTAIN. And that's the message they sent by you?

BLACK DOG. Aye —

CAPTAIN (*jumps up from table in rage, and Black Dog jumps up
in fear and backs a step up right*). Then you can go back and
tell 'em I'm still Cap'n — and what I say is law — Why, you
mess of swabs — you think you can give your orders to me
— you . . .

BLACK DOG. It's more than that we'll be giving you . . . the
little Black Spot. . . .

CAPTAIN. Oh, you will, huh? You'll tip me off the Black Spot,
will yer? Well, let's see the one of you that dares . . . send
him along . . . or maybe you've got it. . . . Have you?
Have you? Now hand it over . . . hand it over. . . .
[*Extending right hand to Black Dog.*

BLACK DOG (*advancing a step*). I haven't it . . . but here
it'll be all right . . . and you'll surrender things as don't
belong to you or you'll swing . . .
[*Indicating a rope around neck and knot behind left ear.*

CAPTAIN. I'll swing? Then we'll all swing (*indicating rope*)
— and you can tell that to Silver — to Pew — to Hands —
to O'Brien — to all of them.

BLACK DOG. And that's the answer I'm to take back —

CAPTAIN. Yes. That's the answer and that — that — that —
(*As he speaks, he makes for Black Dog with his cutlass. Black
Dog parries three blows, and then is disarmed, turns tail and runs
out door. The Captain hurls his cutlass at the door in rage, and,
very much shaken, himself follows to the door to pick up his
cutlass, and calls after Black Dog*) And that too. Tell them
whether Bill Jones has lost his arm. (*As he picks up his cutlass*)
Tell that to the one who's to bring the Black Spot and . . .
(*As he comes back into the room, he suddenly totters and falls
into armchair at table by fireplace, sweeping off cups with cutlass and leaving cutlass on floor*) Jim! Jim!

[*The Captain seems about to swoon.*

JIM (*rushes to Captain*).   What is it, Captain?

CAPTAIN.   Rum — rum — quick —

JIM.   The doctor warned you —

CAPTAIN.   Look you, Jim, how my fingers fidget.   I can't keep 'em still, not I.   If I don't have a drain o' rum, I'll have the horrors; I seen some on 'em already.   I seen old Flint in the corner there behind you; as plain as print, and if I get the horrors, I'm a man that has lived rough, and I'll raise Cain. The doctor himself said one glass wouldn't hurt me, and I've hardly had a drop this blessed day.   I'll give you a golden guinea for a noggin, Jim.

JIM (*crosses to little table, gets glass of rum, and gives it to Captain*). There.   (*The Captain drinks, and Jim picks up cutlass, and puts it out of way*)   Oh, sir, hadn't I better call some one.   I fear it's another stroke.

[*Captain has finished drinking; he sinks back in chair with a groan.   Jim runs to him.*

CAPTAIN (*holding on to Jim*).   Don't leave me . . . don't leave me, Jim . . . not now . . . I need you.   You're the only one worth anything . . . and, with your help . . . Jim, (*Jim kneels beside him*)   I'm going to beat 'em yet. . . . I will, Jim . . . I will!

JIM.   You shouldn't touch that stuff, sir.

CAPTAIN.   Eh?

JIM.   The doctor said it was sure death.

[*Sitting back on floor.*

CAPTAIN.   What's he know about it?   Doctors is all swabs. (*Sweeps glass into fireplace with hand, and picks up cutlass, rises and puts it in belt as he crosses.   During this, Jim rises, puts cup back on table, and then watches Captain*)   And that doctor there, why, what does he know about sea-faring men?   I've been in places hot as pitch, and mates dropping round with Yellow Jack, and the blessed land a-heaving like the sea with earthquakes — what do the doctor know of lands like that? I lived on rum, I tell you.   It's been meat and drink, and man and wife, to me, and if 'm not to have me rum now, I'm

a poor old hulk on the lee shore. (*Sits on stool*) My blood'll
be on you, Jim — and on that doctor swab! You will give
me one more noggin, won't you, matey?

[*Seems to grow fainter, holds out hands appealing to Jim.*

JIM (*crosses and gives it to him from table near taproom*). You're
killing yourself.

[*Sits on stool right of table.*

CAPTAIN (*recovering and drinking and setting glass down*). Now
listen, Jim — that man just here — he's a bad 'un — but
there's worse put him on — and they're out there on that ship
— in the fog — waitin' — they're trying to get me, to tip me
the Black Spot.

JIM. The Black Spot — what's that?

CAPTAIN. The Black Spot! It's a summons, matey — the
worst disgrace that can come to a pirate Captain — it means
he must step down — that he's gone — done for — that he's
got to do what his men say instead of them doing what he
says — sometimes it means even worse than that — that's
what I'm fearing from that crowd out there. — Take a look
at the door.

JIM (*rises and crossing, looks out of door*). No one, sir.

CAPTAIN. Close the door. Come here. (*Confidentially pointing to his room*) It's up there in my old sea-chest — what
they're after — but I'm going to try to get away first — and
if I do — I'll promise you — I'll come back for you some day
— and we'll go to sea — aye, as I told you — in a schooner
with a piping boatswain and pigtailed singing seamen — to
sea, Jim, bound for an unknown island, and to seek buried
treasure — you'd like that?

JIM. Oh, yes.

CAPTAIN. Well, I'll promise you — but if they tip me the
Black Spot first, you get word to that doctor magistrate —
tell him to pipe all his hands — and he'll lay 'em aboard
here at the Benbow Inn, all of Flint's crew, all of 'em that's
left —

JIM (*frightened, getting down from table*). Not Flint, the Buccaneer?

CAPTAIN. Flint's crew — I was first mate — aboard that ship there —
[*Looks at painting over mantel.*

JIM. You!
[*Retreating.*

CAPTAIN. Old Flint's first mate — and I'm the only one as knows the place —

JIM. What place?
[*Coming to table and sitting on stool.*

CAPTAIN. The place where Flint hid all his money — the chart's up there in my chest — Flint gave it to me in Savannah as he lay dyin' — but you won't peach, lad, less they get the Black Spot on me, will yer, Jim? — or less you see a sea-faring man with one leg — him above all others — (*gets up, but he is very weak. Jim rises with him. They come in front of table*) and if I get away, I'll pay you well — If I don't — you go to that chest up there — the key is here about my neck — see? (*Shows Jim key*) You takes out the money I owes your mother — and — a little package in oilcloth — it's the chart — take that to the doctor — he'll know what to do.
[*Captain goes to stairs, gets up three steps and totters.*

JIM (*goes to help the Captain, steadying him*). Let me help you —

CAPTAIN. No. (*Turning around and standing alone*) Bill Bones can stand alone — yet — and with your help, sonny, we'll beat 'em — you'll see — we'll beat 'em yet —
[*Ad lib., as Captain goes up stairs and exits. Jim follows him up the stairs to the top of them; calls over banister.*

JIM. Mother — Mother —

MRS. HAWKINS (*enters from taproom, comes to foot of stairs*). What is it?

JIM. Those men down there at the cove —
[*Coming halfway down the stairs.*

MRS. HAWKINS. Yes —

JIM. They — they are pirates.

MRS. HAWKINS. What?

JIM. Flint's crew. They've come for the Captain up there —
(*Whistle*) Hear that?

MRS. HAWKINS. What is it?

JIM. It's a signal. (*Whistle*) There's the answer. (*Noise of Captain in his room saying,* "Ha, ha! What's that?") He's heard it up there.

[*Comes to front of stairs.*

MRS. HAWKINS. Oh, dear, what shall we do? They'll be about our ears. What shall we do?

JIM. We must send word to the doctor.

MRS. HAWKINS. Yes — yes. Come — quick!

JIM. No. I've got to stay — my orders were to watch —

MRS. HAWKINS. But —

JIM. Dr. Livesey made me an officer of the crown and I must stay — so you, Mother, must go —

MRS. HAWKINS. And leave you alone, Jim — no — no — no —

JIM. The doctor is relying on us, Mother.

MRS. HAWKINS. But the fog's so thick!

[*Turns and gets shawl and puts it over her head.*

JIM (*crosses to her and urges her out*). Just to the village, and be sure to tell the doctor they're not smugglers, they're pirates — Flint's crew — quick.

MRS. HAWKINS (*in door. Kissing him*). Oh, Jim! Jim! You close the door — you close it tight —

JIM. There — there, Mother — quick — there's no time to lose — remember —

[*Exits through taproom.*

[*Jim closes the door, and comes back into the room. Then suddenly he gives a start, for there is heard the tapping of a person with a cane. The tapping comes closer and closer, and finally stops outside the door.*

What's that?

[*There is a slight pause. Jim crosses, and gets near door. There is a knock, and, with a gulp, Jim stumbles back. A second knock, and Jim masters his fear and approaches timidly the door. He opens it. There stands a man, "plainly blind. A great green shade over his eyes and nose; he was hunched as if with age and weakness, and wore a tattered old sea-cloak with hood and that made him appear positively deformed. His voice was an odd sing-song."* He is Pew.

PEW (*in doorway*). Will any kind friend inform a poor blind man where or in what part of the country he is?

JIM (*left of door*). You are at the Admiral Benbow Inn, Black Hill Cove.

PEW. I hear a young voice — will you lead me in, my kind young friend?

JIM (*extends hand. Pew puts his hand on Jim's right arm. Jim leads him in*). There, sir — easy now, gently and — Oh! (*He winces with pain as Pew's manner suddenly changes, and he finds his arm gripped tight*). You're hurting my arm, sir — not so tight.

PEW (*hard and menacing*). Take me to the Captain.

JIM (*trying to get away*). Oh, please, sir — please, sir —

PEW. Take me or I'll break your arm —
[*Gripping Jim's arm tighter.*

JIM. The Captain is ill, sir — very ill.

PEW. Lead me straight to him, and then say, "Here's a friend for you, Bill." If you don't this instant — I'll —
[*Gripping his arm again.*
[*As Pew stands listening, noise of Captain upstairs.*

JIM. Please let me go, sir . . . please!

PEW (*gripping Jim's arm again*). Sh! I hear some one coming. . . . Unless Pew's ears trick him, it's our friend the Captain! Is it? Answer! (*Squeezes Jim's arm*) Is it?

JIM. It is, sir.

PEW. Then remember what I said. And I'm holding on to your arm —
[*He tightens his grip upon Jim, who winces. The Captain comes tottering downstairs. He seems very feeble and has on his hat and a telescope in his left hand.*

CAPTAIN. We'll beat 'em yet — we'll beat 'em yet, Jim.
[*Comes to foot of stairs.*

PEW (*whispers to Jim and pinches*). Say it, now!

JIM (*winces under Pew's hold*). Here — here's a friend for you, Bill.

CAPTAIN (*sees Pew*). Pew!

[*Staggers, knocks off hat, drops telescope, draws sword, staggers toward Pew and collapses on table, sitting on stool left of table.*

PEW (*to Jim*). Lead me to him. (*Captain drops cutlass from weakness. As Jim leads Pew to the Captain*) Stay where you are, Bill. Business is business — hold out your hand. . . . Boy, take his hand by the wrist and bring it close to mine. (*Jim does as directed, leading Pew to edge of table, and Pew passes a paper into the hands of the Captain, who seems to crumple up when he receives it*) Now that's done. Boy . . . Lead me to the door, Boy. (*Jim leads him to the door*) Goodday to you, Bill.

[*He goes out. Jim comes running back to the Captain, who sits staring at the paper in his hand.*

JIM (*as the Captain sits looking at the paper in his right hand*). What — what is it?

CAPTAIN. The Black Spot — (*Turns over the paper and reads*) Till ten o'clock — (*With increasing force as if getting an idea*) They've got me, but they sha'n't have that chart . . . (*rises*) — Not Flint's fist . . . Bill Bones is still in command. . . . (*Tearing key from neck and holding it up in defiance*) They sha'n't have it . . . they sha'n't . . . they sha'n't . . .

[*He reels, staggers upstairs, reels back from stairs, turns, then collapses, falling face down near foot of stairs. Jim watches Captain, and when he falls, stoops over him.*

JIM. Captain! (*Rising and retreating*) Captain!

MRS. HAWKINS (*enters taproom door, takes off shawl, and hangs it on peg*). I've seen the doctor. I've told him, and he's coming as soon as he can get his men together.

JIM (*indicating dead Captain*). Mother!

MRS. HAWKINS. Dead, glory be. . . . Oh, Jim, they're such dreadful men out there. . . . (*Crosses to window, draws curtains, blows out lighted lamp*) They come out of the fog like ghosts and now, with him lying there . . . (*Jim is looking for key*) What are you going to do?

JIM. Get our money — the money he owes us, as he told me to, out of his sea-chest — (*Jim lifts Bones' hand which holds key*) Here's the key.

MRS. HAWKINS. Oh, Jim. You're not going to touch that, you're not.

[*Jim gets key and drops hand.*

JIM (*darting upstairs*). Bring the candle, Mother —

[*Exit Jim into Bones' room.*

[*Mrs. Hawkins gets candle from table near taproom, follows Jim upstairs, holding candle in doorway of Captain's room.*

JIM (*off*). Ah!

MRS. HAWKINS. What is it? What is it?

[*Backing on to stairs, keeps to banister.*

JIM (*off stage*). A quadrant — tobacco!

MRS. HAWKINS. But the money, Jim, the money!

JIM (*enters on stairs left of Mrs. Hawkins*). Here it is.

MRS. HAWKINS. I'll take my due, not a penny more. What kind of money is this?

JIM. Pieces of eight, Spanish and French!

MRS. HAWKINS. Spanish and French, Jim? Who was this man?

JIM. A pirate! A buccaneer! He sailed on that ship with Flint.

MRS. HAWKINS. Pirates!

JIM. All of them.

MRS. HAWKINS. Pirates' gold! Put it back! I won't touch it. Lock it up again.

JIM. All right, Mother.

[*Exit with candle Mrs. Hawkins gives him. Trunk slam and lock effect. Reënters. During this Mrs. Hawkins comes down to foot of stairs.*

It's all right. I've got it.

[*Coming down to Mrs. Hawkins.*

MRS. HAWKINS. Got what?

JIM. The package in oilcloth he said I was to take to the doctor. (*Pew's taps*) Listen —

MRS. HAWKINS. What's that?

JIM.   The blind man.   (*Crosses to door, locks it, and back to Mrs. Hawkins*).   He was here before for the Captain.

MRS. HAWKINS.   They'll be murdering us all now.

JIM (*drawing mother towards door left of stairs*).   Come, Mother. Quick.   The back way!

MRS. HAWKINS.   I can't, my legs won't move.

JIM.   Come!   Come!

[*They exit.   Noise outside.*

PEW (*outside*).   Down with the door if they won't open it — beat it down!   (*Shouts*)   Aye — aye!   Will you open? — or must we break it down? — (*When no answer comes*)   Down with the door then, men.

MEN (*without*).   Aye!   Aye!

PEW.   Down with her!   (*The men batter on the door with a large log.   Finally the door is splintered to pieces*)   Aye — that's it!   That's it!   Now in!   In with you!   (*There is a shout as the men rush in.   Hands rushes to head of Captain.   Black Dog rushes upstairs to Captain's room and gets chest ready to drag down.   Merry comes to waistline of Captain, Arrow to feet. Dick rushes into taproom and comes out to corner of wall.   Morgan at head of table.   Anderson by fireplace*).   Now scatter — search everywhere — quick — quick, I say — well — What's the matter? — Why do you stop?   What is it?   What is it?

[*Merry and Hands over body.   Black Dog at steps.*

MERRY (*kneeling by Captain*).   Bill's dead!

PEW.   What!   Well!

HANDS.   He's dead — done for — don't you understand, Pew?

[*Hands takes Captain's head, Arrow his feet, Merry masks him, Arrow hands feet to Morgan, who backs away, and Hands gives head to Dick, and he and Morgan lay Captain in alleyway leading to taproom.   Merry follows them, masking as does Arrow after he passes feet to Morgan.*

PEW.   Search him, you shirking lubbers.   The chart's here somewhere, and we are going to get it — find that chest — look for it —

BLACK DOG (*at head of stairs, dragging down chest*).   It's here, Pew —

PEW. **Bring it down.** (*Black Dog drags chest down the stairs and Hands and Arrow carry it to left of stairs*) Open it quick!

BLACK DOG. It's locked!

[*At foot of stairs beckons Anderson at fireplace. Anderson with fire-irons crosses.*

PEW. Break it open. Smash it open. (*Anderson smashes chest lock hinges off with fire-irons*) Is it there? The chart?

MERRY. They've been here before us.

[*Arrow takes out coat and rummages through it, dropping it on edge of chest.*

BLACK DOG. Some one's turned the chest alow and aloft!

HANDS (*who has been searching through the chest*). There's some money —

PEW. Hang the money . . . it's Flint's fist I want, Flint's fist. . . .

BLACK DOG. We don't see it nowhere.

MERRY. And Bill's been overhauled already . . . nothin' left . . .

PEW. It's that boy. . . . I wish I'd put his eyes out. That chart must be here somewhere. Scatter and look for it. (*Black Dog starts upstairs, Morgan rushes in taproom, and stays in till whistle, and then comes to foot of stairs. Anderson, over to fireplace, knocks over table, upsets candles and plates, etc. Arrow and Dick to window, Arrow pulls down curtains, Dick sweeps off flower-pots. Merry looks under table, etc.*) Look everywhere — under the tables — behind the curtains — turn everything upside down. (*The men turn over the tables, tear down the hangings. Hands tips over the chairs and scatters over the place all the furniture. A whistle is heard*) What's that?

BLACK DOG (*on stairs*). It's Dirk's warning. We'll have to budge, mates.

PEW. Budge, you skulk. We don't stir until we find that chart.

[*Crossing to door and standing in doorway.*

BLACK DOG. But that signal. . . .

PEW. You have your hands on it . . . scatter and look for it, dogs! Shiver my soul, if I had my eyes . . . (*Another*

whistle. Hands rushes towards Pew in door) Well — well
— why are you coming back?

HANDS.   Twice — you heard — Dirk's called — we'd better
go.

PEW *(stands in the doorway).*   Not one of you is going to leave.
Why, you fools, you have your hands on thousands, and you
hang a leg.   You'd be rich as kings, and you stand there malin-
gering.   Am I to lose my chance for you?   If you had the
pluck of a weevil in a biscuit you'd stand your ground.

BLACK DOG.   We're not going to stand here and be caught.

PEW.   Not one of you goes till you find it — or maybe you've
got it — *(Whistle again and sharply.   There is sound of horses
approaching)*   And you're hiding it on me —

HANDS.   Stand out of the way, Pew — we're going —

PEW.   You're not — I believe you've got it, and trying to hide
it from me! — Give it to me — or you don't pass —

BLACK DOG.   Don't you hear them coming — those horses?

HANDS.   Out of the way —

PEW.   Not until you give it —

HANDS.   All right then, men — at him —
[*They make a lunge at Pew, who strikes back with his staff.
They quickly overpower him and throw him into a far corner of
the room to foot of stairs, and then they rush out as the horses
are heard stopping near by.   Dr. Livesey's voice is heard giving
orders without.*

DR. LIVESEY.   There they go — after them.

PEW *(groping blindly towards door).*   Black Dog . . . Hands
. . . you won't leave old Pew . . . you'll save your old
mate — *(Jim glides in door and comes down-stage)*   You'll
save — who's there?   Who is it?   Answer!
[*Near door.*

JIM.   It's I — Jim Hawkins —

PEW.   You!   You stole that chart! — By the living thunder,
if I can get my hands on you, I'll tear your heart out —
[*Rushes at Jim.   He runs into table, and swings it around out
of his way.   Making big sweep with his cane, he rushes at Jim,
who dodges up-stage.*

JIM (*horrified — running around to fireplace*). Help! Squire! Dr. Livesey! Help!

[*Pew follows Jim in the direction of his voice, striking in rage, with his cane. Jim dodges him up near door and Pew, thinking he has gone out, rushes after him.*

PEW. I'll get you, you young rat. I'll get you.

JIM (*as Pew comes nearer*). Squire! Dr. Livesey! Help! Quick!

[*In doorway; then runs over towards taproom in alleyway.*

PEW. I'll get you — I'll wring your neck —

[*He rushes out the door. Then of a sudden there is the report of a pistol and shriek from Pew.*

DR. LIVESEY (*enters with lantern. Squire also enters and stands in door*). Jim! Jim! Are you all right, lad? I came as quickly as possible after I got your message. Tell me, what's happened?

JIM (*coming to doctor*). They were pirates, sir — Flint's crew. The Captain's dead. He was his mate — here's the proof of it. (*Gives doctor the package*) I got it from his sea-chest there; it's a map showing where Flint's Treasure is buried.

DR. LIVESEY (*opening package and laying chart on table*). What!

SQUIRE. If it should be . . .

[*Black Dog appears at window and peers in.*

DR. LIVESEY (*reading map from table with lantern*). "Tall tree, Spy-glass shoulder, bearing a point to the N. of N.N.E. Skeleton Island, E.S.E.; the gold is in the north cache."

SQUIRE. Livesey, that's it! We'll go to Bristol, fit out a ship, and we'll have that Treasure if it takes a year. —(*Black Dog disappears*) Hawkins shall go with us.

[*Turning to Jim and putting hand on his shoulder.*

JIM. Oh! Sir! That's just as the Captain promised, — (*Squire goes back to doctor and map*) to go to sea with piping boatswain — pig-tailed singing seamen — bound for an unknown island to seek buried treasure —

[*Jim returns to Squire and doctor. All looking at map.*

CURTAIN

ACT II

SCENE I

The Quay at Bristol.

Showing Spy-Glass Inn center. Corner of Inn facing front, shows two sides. Small sign hanging from corner of Inn with "Spy-Glass" painted on it. Right side of building are a window and shutters, practical. Left side of Inn is door into building. There is a street left of it, with entrance above and below Inn. The Hispaniola lies moored to sea-wall, her bow being masked by Inn, and stern extending down right. Her name, "Hispaniola", is painted just below poop-deck. Gang-plank comes down from her side. To right of gang-plank is hawser post, to which her hawser is tied. A warehouse, painted with sails and rigging leaning against it, occupies extreme right. Warehouse wing extends extreme left, with small barrel. Small box above door of Inn. Union Jack flying from forward mast of ship, which is seen above the Inn, at back. Aft mast is in full view, and all sails are furled.

At opening, Silver appears through Inn door, with parrot on his shoulder, comes around and opens shutters and window.

SILVER. Well, Cap'n Flint, we'll let in a little sunshine — (*Turns, looks at boat, leans on gang-plank*) Hispaniola! (*Meditatively shakes head as though impossible to solve the problem of her why and wherefore*) Flint, you're wiser than folks give you any credit for; you're mebbe nigh on to two hundred years old — you've sailed with England and you've sailed with Flint, you've been from Madagascar to Malabar, from Providence to Portobello, and now I puts it to you, bein' a wise old pirate Cap'n, will you just cast your blessed deadlights over that there craft and tell me what's 'er game? What's she up to —? It gets me, it do, it beats me all holler . . .

[*Girl enters with apple basket, from behind Inn, sets basket right of box and takes apple.*

GIRL. Good-morning, Mr. Silver.

[*Coming towards Silver, polishing apple.*

SILVER. Mornin' — girl — mornin' !

GIRL. And how is Captain Flint this morning?

SILVER. Well, my lass, I can't rightly say. Captain Flint ain't sayin' much this mornin', which is unusual — he bein' given to swearin' like a B'sin's mate until somebody gives him his mornin' meal.

GIRL. Mebbe he'd like an apple.

[*Gives apple.*

SILVER. Mebbe he would, lass, and thank yer kindly.

[*Girl retires, sits on box for the balance of the scene.*

[*As Silver commences to feed apple to parrot, Hands and Arrow enter and greet Silver, saying, "Mornin', Long John."*

[*During this scene two men, not pirates, enter from boat, and three sailors from street. These five go into Inn, after greeting Silver.*

SILVER. Mornin' — lads — mornin' — you'll find some of the others inside; been there all night — (*Silver, Hands, and Arrow laugh, as Silver is following them into Inn. Black Dog comes down street, and touches Silver on the shoulder. Looks in Inn window, and then faces Silver*) You — Black Dog ! — Where have you been? — A nice turn you did me with your bungling at the Cove — lettin' a fortune slip through your fingers. Where's the chart I sent you to get? Where is it, you bungling numskull?

BLACK DOG. Easy there, Long John — easy — When we all ran away from the Benbow Inn, I got lost in the fog — I must have run in a circle, for I landed up again where I started.

SILVER. The Inn?

[*Coming to corner of Inn and leaning against it, feeding apple to parrot on his left shoulder.*

BLACK DOG (*goes to him — nods*). It was dark and I crept up to the windy.

SILVER (*intense now*). Yes !

BLACK DOG. There was Billy Bones dead, lying upon the floor . . . and at a table . . . three of 'em pawing over a chart. . . .

SILVER (*eagerly*). Flint's fist?

BLACK DOG. Flint's fist.

SILVER (*tense*).   Three of 'em, you say?

BLACK DOG.   One was a boy — he'd got the chart and was showin' it to the men.

SILVER.   And the men?

BLACK DOG.   One they called Doctor.

SILVER.   And the other?

BLACK DOG.   He was older, and looked more like your country gentleman.

SILVER (*excitedly*).   His name?

BLACK DOG.   It was Squire — Squire something — or —

SILVER.   Not Squire — Trelawney?

BLACK DOG (*astonished*).   The very same!

SILVER.   Ha!   I guessed it!   I guessed it!

BLACK DOG.   But . . .

SILVER (*points to Hispaniola*).   See that boat?   That belongs to Squire Trelawney. . . . (*as Black Dog starts*) and she's sailing under sealed orders . . .

BLACK DOG.   Then you know . . .

SILVER.   The Squire and I have already passed the time of day.   I've been watching him — and wondering what all this is about . . . (*With sudden change*)   That's why I have all the men in there now.   (*Indicates Inn*)   Any of 'em see you down at the Cove?

BLACK DOG.   None but the boy — (*enter Squire and Captain Smollett on boat, talking*) and he saw only Pew and me.

SILVER.   Good.   (*Confidentially*)   They haven't shipped their crew yet.   Now I'll try and make our friends here take us to Flint's treasure — in their own ship — aye, find the treasure for us — and then —

BLACK DOG.   What then?

SILVER (*sinister*).   Then we'll pay 'em for it!   (*Silver points to Trelawney and Smollett, and turns Black Dog around*)   Either one of those your Squire?

BLACK DOG.   Aye — the older one —

SILVER.   Good!   Now you go into the Inn; you'll find all of them there.   You tell 'em what you've told me about Flint's fist.   Tell 'em I'm waitin' here to sound the Squire and make sure. Tell 'em all to lay low and be ready the minute I want 'em.

[*Black Dog and Silver exit in Inn.*

[*Squire first drops right of gang-plank and Captain left of it.*

SQUIRE. My dear Captain Smollett, there must be plenty of men.

SMOLLETT. But your requirements are peculiar, sir.

SQUIRE. What! Merely men — not afraid of anything on sea or land? Surely, sir, English manhood has not gone back so far that the spirit of adventure is lost —

SMOLLETT. All very well, sir — but, asking your pardon — I don't know the nature of this voyage.

SQUIRE. And are not to. (*Squire gives Smollett chart*) Here, sir, is the chart you will work the ship by. There is your latitude and longitude. What more does a ship's captain require?

SMOLLETT. Nothing more, sir — this is enough.

[*Examining chart.*

SQUIRE. You're sailing under sealed orders, sir.

SMOLLETT. Quite right. But you must realize this makes it difficult to get men — honest men.

[*Folding chart and putting it in pocket.*

SQUIRE. It shouldn't. . . . England has stood for centuries for her sailors to unknown lands . . . and on unknown seas . . . her Drakes and Raleighs . . . and Hawkes . . . and —

SMOLLETT. Very well, sir — I'll do the best I can.

[*Starts away.*

SQUIRE (*follows him up*). And make haste, Captain . . . my friends come within three days . . . I must be ready, then . . .

SMOLLETT. I'll try, sir.

[*He goes off. The Squire is going toward vessel, when Silver enters from Inn, . . . coughs. Squire turns, just at foot of gang-plank.*

SILVER (*indicates ship*). I never tire of looking at her, sir —

SQUIRE. Pretty, isn't she?

[*Left of gang-plank and looking at ship.*

SILVER. Never saw a sweeter little craft.

SQUIRE (*indicates Silver's loss of leg*). Not a sea-faring man?

SILVER. I lost that, sir, in defense of my country.

SQUIRE (*growing interested*). Did you now?

SILVER. Aye, sir, under the immortal Hawke!

SQUIRE. What! Not really —

SILVER. A fact, sir.

SQUIRE. Pensioned, of course, —

SILVER. No, sir — never asked it — never needed it . . . I keep the Spy-Glass here . . .

SQUIRE. Still, you should have your reward.

SILVER. I have, sir. (*Salutes*) In England . . . my country . . . God bless her!

SQUIRE (*enthusiastically*). A fine spirit . . . the true spirit of an Englishman!
[*Salutes.*

SILVER. There's only one thing — my health's not good ashore (*coming over and leaning on gang-plank's left rail*) — having been to sea so long — that's why I keep my Inn here on the quay — where I can get a bit of salt air and meet sea-faring men. Why, every sailor as comes to port knows Long John Silver —

SQUIRE. Do they now!

SILVER. Aye, and they're all welcome, sir, whether they can pay or no — because of my love of her out there — the sea — (*The Squire starts rather surprised at Silver*) I tell you, when the sea once gets into you, sir — it's hard to ever lose her! May sound queer to you, sir — but it's a fact.

SQUIRE (*studying Silver*). No — no, I think I understand —

SILVER. When I think of the times I've seen . . . dirty weather and clear, fights at close quarters . . . hand to hand . . . and cutlass against cutlass . . . against pirate and buccaneer. (*Squire starts but Silver hurries on*) And then I thinks of me in there doling out grog . . . why, sir, it's like torture. . . . And when I comes out here and sees a trim little craft like that all ready to sail . . . why, I'd give my life, sir, for just one more chance at the old sea . . .

SQUIRE (*who has been thinking and studying Silver*). You say you know every sea-faring man in Bristol?

SILVER. Aye — sir — they all come to the Spy-Glass.

SQUIRE. Well, suppose — just suppose now, I wanted a special sort of crew — men not only sailors, but fighters perhaps — [*Crossing and leaning on rail of gang-plank.*

SILVER (*points to Inn*). There are men in there now — men enough to man this boat — men who have sailed as I have — against Flint hisself!

SQUIRE. You mean to say you have sailed against Flint? [*Retreating a step in surprise.*

SILVER. Aye, sir, it's to him I owe the loss of this — (*Indicates leg*) You see, sir, that's what makes it so hard — to have been through all that, and then to sit idle and hear the sea a-calling — begging for a chance, sir — a chance what might mean life itself, sir —

SQUIRE. Suppose now, just suppose, that you were offered that chance — [*Coming back and leaning on gang-plank again.*

SILVER. You don't mean it, sir?

SQUIRE. Could you help me get together a crew?

SILVER. Yes, sir —

SQUIRE. At once?

SILVER. I'll see to everything, sir. (*As Squire starts, Silver goes on quickly*) There are men in there now, honest men, men ready for any purpose.

SQUIRE. I like your talk, sir — you're engaged.

SILVER. Oh, thank you, sir!

SQUIRE. And now about a crew. My captain has found difficulty —

SILVER. Might I ask, sir, what sort of voyage this is to be?

SQUIRE (*suspiciously*). Why?

SILVER. So I may judge about the men.

SQUIRE. I want tough men . . . such as you just spoke of, men willing to board Flint himself!

SILVER. You shall have 'em! You shall have 'em! Now, you go to your cabin and I'll send them to you. . . .

SQUIRE (*starts up gang-plank and turns to Silver*). Very well.
If I could only get them before Captain Smollett returns . . .

SILVER. I'm sure you can.

SQUIRE. I'll show him. He, with his trouble about getting
honest men . . . Send them along, Silver.
[*Going up gang-plank.*

SILVER. Yes, sir . . . at once, sir . . . and I want to thank
you, sir . . .

SQUIRE (*exits into cabin*). Not at all. Glad we met, Silver. . . .

SILVER. It's a great thing for me, sir . . . a great thing. . . .
(*The Squire disappears in the schooner. Silver's manner
changes at once*) Heaven has sent him to me. (*He turns to
the window of the Inn and calls*) Hands — Arrow — Morgan —
Anderson — Merry — all you men come quick. (*They all
come out*) It's Flint's treasure he's after, all right. [*Hands
makes movement toward ship.*

BLACK DOG. You see I was right.
[*To men.*

SILVER (*there is a slight change of manner*). I'm to engage his
crew. You are to be that crew — (*Much laughter of men,
and they make a move toward gang-plank*) Easy there —
you're to go to him now. You, Arrow, are to be mate —
[*Silver stops them.*

ARROW. Aye, Cap'n.
[*Salutes.*

SILVER. Anderson, coxs'n.

ANDERSON. Coxswain it is.
[*Salutes.*

SILVER. Merry, where's Merry?

MERRY. Aye, aye, sir.

SILVER (*sees Merry*). Merry, you are to be boatswain!

MERRY. Aye, aye, sir. My old job.
[*Comes out from behind men.*

SILVER. The rest of you as he pleases. . . . Act natural.

MEN. Yes!

SILVER. Nothing suspicious.

MEN. No.

SILVER (*as they start away*). Look innocent. (*Men laugh*) Do you think you can?

MEN. Yes.

SILVER. And fierce. Go now, quick — On with you! (*As Morgan passes*) Don't you scare the old gentleman now.

MORGAN. No!

[*And he goes on up.*

[*Silver catches Black Dog by the coat tail, on his way up gang-plank.*

[*Men are all talking and laughing.*

ARROW. Silver's all right.

[*Men exit up gang-plank into cabin aft.*

SILVER (*to Black Dog*). Here you! Wait!

BLACK DOG. Well?

[*Turning to Silver.*

SILVER. He might recognize you.

BLACK DOG (*protestingly*). I told you I saw only the boy.

SILVER (*swinging Black Dog across and into Inn door*). Never mind. We'll take no chances. You'll stay hidden in there till we sail. (*At the Inn door*) I've got him baited — and I'll get him — hook and all.

[*Exits into Inn.*

CURTAIN

ACT II

SCENE II

The Quay at Bristol. The Hispaniola ready to sail.

When the curtain rises, there is a string of men going between the ship and wharf, carrying boxes and barrels upon their shoulders. The pirate crew. At the head of the gang-plank stands Israel Hands with boatswain's whistle, as if directing the men. A little farther away stands Captain Smollett, watching. Arrange for supers to carry on guns, pickaxes, etc., to ship. Parrot discovered on perch between Inn and gang-plank.

HANDS (*as two men go up gang-plank with guns*). Stow them for'd. (*They exit forward. When man passes, carrying picks and shovels*) Picks and shovels, eh? Going to dig for mermaids? (*Man exits forward. Man passes with keg*) Keg o' treacle, — stow that for'ard where I can get it. (*As Anderson comes on board carrying sack*) Is that all?

ANDERSON. Aye, aye, sir.

[*Exits forward.*

MORGAN (*standing at head of gang-plank*). That's all, sir.

[*Exits forward.*

[*Hands turns to Smollett and salutes.*

HANDS. Captain Smollett —

[*Saluting.*

SMOLLETT (*deck right of gang-plank*). Well, Mr. Hands?

HANDS. Everything right, sir!

SMOLLETT. Sure you've missed nothing?

HANDS. Sure, sir.

SMOLLETT. All ready to cast off?

HANDS. All ready. Shall I give the word, sir?

[*Black Dog enters, coming to corner of Inn.*

SMOLLETT. Squire Trelawney is not here yet. . . . Have all the men stand by.

HANDS. Aye, aye, sir.

[*Starts to exit forward after saluting.*

SMOLLETT. Mr. Hands?

HANDS. Yes, sir.

[*Turns and comes back.*

SMOLLETT (*with change*). Who gave the orders for the stowing of those stores?

HANDS. I thought you did, sir.

[*Stammering and confused.*

SMOLLETT (*dismissing him*). Very well.

HANDS. Aye, aye, sir.

[*Goes out forward.*

[*For a moment Smollett stands as if thinking, and then he turns as if to follow Hands. Meanwhile Black Dog has sneaked upon the scene, and is slinking up the gang-plank when Smollett turns and sees him.*

SMOLLETT (*at head of gang-plank*). Well, my man! Who are you?

BLACK DOG (*one foot on gang-plank*). A — a friend of one of the crew, sir. . . . I have a message.

SMOLLETT. This boat is ready to sail — no one boards her now.

BLACK DOG. But, sir, it's important — most important I see him.

SMOLLETT. See who?

BLACK DOG. Silver, sir. Long John Silver.

SMOLLETT (*calls off forward*). Silver. John Silver.

SILVER (*without*). Aye, aye, sir.

[*From forward.*

SMOLLETT. Man to see you.

SILVER (*coming*). Coming, sir, coming. . . . What is it, sir?

[*At right head of gang-plank.*

SMOLLETT. This fellow here says he has a message for you.

SILVER. A message for me? (*Sees Black Dog, starts, and then, quickly recovering, says kindly*) Well, my good man? Speak up — what is it?

BLACK DOG (*indicates Inn*). There's a man over there as would like to talk to you. He said it was most important.

SILVER (*to Smollett*). I don't know who it could be, nor what he wants. . . . Might I go ashore for a minute, sir?

SMOLLETT. We're all ready to cast off.

SILVER. I won't be but a jiffy, sir.

SMOLLETT. Very well.

[*Goes out forward.*

SILVER. Thank you, sir. (*Comes down to Black Dog and turns fiercely upon him. Silver just at foot of gang-plank*) By all the powers, what are you tryin' to do?

BLACK DOG. That boat's sailin'?

[*Advancing a pace toward Silver.*

SILVER. Well?

BLACK DOG. It'll never sail without me! If I don't go — I'll blow the whole gaff. (*As Silver starts to threaten him*) I will. I'm going. You hear?

SILVER. Shiver my timbers, you'll do as I say. . . . What d'ye mean by standing there and defying me that way?

[*Silver advances a pace, hears Hands, and turns to him as he reaches foot of gang-plank.*

HANDS.   That Captain Smollett!

SILVER.   What's he done?

HANDS.   He's down below snooping around —

SILVER.   You put the powder where I told you?

HANDS.   Aye.

SILVER.   And their men — bunked with ours?

HANDS.   Aye.

SILVER.   Did he notice it?

HANDS.   I don't know — he acts suspicious-like.

SILVER (*turns angrily on Black Dog*).   You hear that, Black Dog — you hear? Now you go inside there and wait. Go, I say, or, by thunder, I'll run you through.

BLACK DOG (*driven to the Inn door*).   You'll never go without me. . . . Never!

SILVER.   Go. (*Black Dog goes in. Silver storms*) Hands, Black Dog doesn't go on this cruise.

[*Spoken facing Inn door.*

HANDS.   Aye, aye.

[*Crossing to foot of gang-plank.*

SILVER.   Go inside there — (*Hands crosses to door and faces Silver*) Watch him, don't leave him out of your sight. You've got a toothpick there; use it if you get a chance.

[*Indicating knife.*

HANDS.   Aye, aye, sir.

[*Exits into door of Inn, after indicating knife.*

[*Dr. Livesey and Squire come down.*

SQUIRE.   I don't know what to make of it.

[*Coming near gang-plank.*

DR. LIVESEY.   I'm sure he'll come, Squire.

[*Crossing behind Squire to right of gang-plank.*

SILVER (*comes down from Inn door to left of Squire*).   Everything ready and ship-shape. — Just waiting for you, sir. . . .

SQUIRE (*testily*).   Hawkins hasn't come —

DR. LIVESEY.   You told him he might stay till the last minute with his mother. . . .

SILVER. If we wait — we'll miss the tide. And that means another twelve hours' delay, sir.

SQUIRE (*excitedly*). Look at her there. (*Looking at ship*) Everything ready and to be held up now . . . by Gad, it's hard, sir.

SILVER. Have we got to wait for the boy?

SQUIRE. I'm afraid we must, Silver.

SILVER. If so be we must, we must! (*Sees Parrot*) Oh, beg pardon, sir, might I ask you a favor? — Would you mind if I took my old shipmate, Captain Flint, with us? . . . (*Squire starts, saying "Flint", and exchanges glances with doctor, who also is taken aback. Silver seeing this says*) Oh! that Captain Flint there, sir, (*pointing to parrot on porch near inn*) he always goes on all my voyages with me. (*Squire nods assent*) Thank yer, sir. All right, Flint, you're a-comin' along — I'll take you aboard soon as I get some things inside. [*Exits into Inn.*

SQUIRE. An honest fellow and capable.

DR. LIVESEY. Well, Squire, I don't usually put much faith in your discoveries, but John Silver suits me. [*Following Squire.*

SQUIRE. The man's a perfect trump. . . . We've grown quite familiar.

DR. LIVESEY. Squire, you haven't told him anything? . . .

SQUIRE. Not a word. . . . I have been most discreet. On the contrary . . . I've got all his simple little secrets from him! (*As they start up gang-plank*) He leaves a wife to manage his Inn. [*Turning to doctor who is following.*

DR. LIVESEY. Indeed? [*Following Squire.*

SQUIRE. A lady of color. [*Turning at head of gang-plank.*

DR. LIVESEY. No! [*Squire and doctor laughing exit on boat into cabin aft.* [*Enter Jim with bundle. Sees sign, "Spy-Glass Inn," takes letter out of pocket, compares address with sign, then knocks on door.*

SILVER (*comes to door*). Well, my lad?

JIM.   Silver . . . Mr. Silver . . . I'm looking for . . .

SILVER.   That's my name, lad. . . and who may you be?

JIM (*hands Silver a letter*).   Hawkins, sir.

SILVER.   Hawkins, sir.   I don't know anybody by the name of Hawkins, sir.   (*Crossing near gang-plank, opening letter, and reading it*)   Oh, I see.   You are Jim Hawkins, our new cabin-boy.   Well, pleased I am to see you!   We've been waiting for you.

[*Turning and greeting Jim.*

JIM (*seeing ship*).   Oh, sir, is that the ship we're to sail on?

SILVER.   Aye, lad — that's the *Hispaniola*.

JIM.   Oh, it's wonderful. . . .   I've never been to sea before, and now I'm to go on a real ship, I can hardly wait to start. . . .

SILVER.   No, I suppose you can't, lad.   Ah, boy, boy, it's a great thing to be young and to have ten toes.   You may lay to that.

[*There is a sound of commotion within the Inn.*

JIM (*crossing in front of Silver to window, looking in*).   Oh, sir — what's that?

SILVER (*right of window, reading letter as if paying no attention to it*).   Oh, that — that's nothing, lad — just some men drinking there in my house.

[*As noise in Inn continues.*

JIM (*right of Silver*).   Oh, sir, I think it's a fight.

[*Black Dog pursued by Hands appears at the door.*

BLACK DOG.   I know my rights, and you can't stop me.   I'd fight the whole crew of you.

[*Exit left.*

JIM (*suddenly recognizes Black Dog.   Cries out.   Points excitedly to Black Dog*).   Why, it's Black Dog.   One of the buccaneers.   Stop him, sir, stop him!

SILVER.   Hands!   After that man — quick!

[*Hands rushes out.*

JIM.   It was Black Dog.   I'm sure of it.

SILVER.   I don't care two coppers who he is . . . he hasn't (*looking after Black Dog*) paid his score.   What did you say his name was?   Black what?

JIM.   Black Dog, sir. Hasn't Mr. Trelawney told you of the buccaneers?

SILVER.   What!

JIM.   He was one of them, sir.

SILVER.   So! One of them swabs . . . in my house. . . . (*As Hands returns, comes on from street*) Well?

HANDS.   He got away, sir.

SILVER (*meaningly*).   You know who that was, Hands?

HANDS.   No, sir.

SILVER (*with meaning*).   Black Dog. Isn't it so, Hawkins?

JIM.   Yes, sir.

SILVER.   Hawkins just told me so. And do you know who Black Dog is?

HANDS.   No, sir.

SILVER.   One of Flint's crew. (*As Hands starts*) That's who you've been hob-nobbin' with. . . . You was drinking with him in there. . . . That's who you've let go. . . . I'm glad to see that look of shame on your face, Mr. Hands. (*Jim crosses to right of gang-plank and looks at ship*) Now aboard with you, (*Hands goes up gang-plank*) and be a little more particular who you consort with hereafter.

HANDS.   Aye, aye, sir.

[*At head of gang-plank, winks at Silver with left eye. Exits on ship.*

SILVER.   Now, see here, Hawkins, this is a blessed hard thing on a man like me. There's Squire Trelawney — what's he to think? Here I have this confounded son of a Dutchman sitting in my own house, drinking my own rum — Here you comes and tells me of it plain, and I let him give us the slip before my blessed deadlights.

[*Jim crosses to Silver.*

JIM.   It wasn't your fault.

SILVER.   Nay, that it wasn't — but it might look so —

JIM.   I'll explain it to the Squire.

SILVER.   Will you now?

JIM.   Just as soon as I see him.

SILVER (*anxiously*).   No — no — lad, no, not as soon as yer sees him. You wait till we get out to sea apiece — and then, when he sees how I work, and knows me better — then you ups and tells him — and he'll understand.

JIM. Very well, sir.

SILVER. There's a lad for you — and — (*Stops suddenly and breaks out into a laugh*) Why, what a precious old sea-calf I am.

JIM. What is it, sir?

SILVER. That swab got away without paying his score — three goes of rum — Shiver my timbers if I hadn't forgotten my score! Dash my buttons, but that's a good 'un about my score!

[*As they laugh, Squire and Dr. Livesey come down from ship, the doctor first, followed by Squire.*

DR. LIVESEY. Jim, my lad, we've been anxious about you. [*Greeting him.*

SQUIRE (*foot of gang-plank*). Where have you been?

JIM. It was Mother kept me, sir. She's so afraid — and she's quite alone.

SQUIRE. I sent her a boy to take your place —

JIM (*crossing to Squire*). Yes, sir, and very kind it was — only he can't take my place, sir.

DR. LIVESEY. There's conceit for you, Squire.

JIM (*to doctor*). Oh, no — no, sir — you see there is just Mother and me now — and — (*breaking*) we've never been parted before —

DR. LIVESEY (*pets him*). There — there, Jim, I understand — of course.

SILVER (*significantly to the Squire*). Beggin' your pardon, sir — Lad's beginnin' to pipe his eye a bit on account of his mother — don't you think I'd better take him aboard, sir?

JIM (*mastering himself*). Oh, I'm all right, sir — I'm all right.

SILVER. Course you're all right — Come with me, lad — Silver will show you your quarters. (*Crossing up towards bird*) Here, I know what you can do. You can help me carry Captain Flint aboard.

[*Picks up parrot, handing it to Hawkins.*

JIM (*getting bird and going up gang-plank*). Oh, what a beautiful bird —

SILVER (*following Jim*). Don't call him a bird. He's a sailor man — he don't like to be called a bird, he don't. He's a master mariner, been around the world two or three times — There — there's your way, lad — Forward — that's it — just to your left a bit — Look out for Captain Flint now —
[*Ad lib., to exit.*
[*Enter fruit girl with basket, sits same place as Scene I.*

SQUIRE (*crossing to Dr. Livesey, hears Smollett and turns about*). And now, the ship's company is complete — and — (*Captain Smollett comes hurrying down*) Well, sir, all ready to sail? We mustn't miss this tide, sir.

SMOLLETT. I'd better speak plain at the risk of offense—(*Coming to Squire*) I don't like this cruise and I don't like my crew.

SQUIRE (*startled*). Eh?

SMOLLETT. I was engaged to sail this ship under sealed orders.

SQUIRE. Right.

SMOLLETT. Then, if that is so, how is it every man before the mast knows more than I do?

DR. LIVESEY. Squire!
[*To Squire.*

SQUIRE. That's not true!

SMOLLETT (*meaningly*). I learn we are going after treasure — Now, treasure is ticklish work, and I don't like treasure voyages on any account — but when they're secret and the secret's been blabbed —

SQUIRE. Blabbed!

SMOLLETT. Yes, sir, blabbed — Why, sir, it's life or death and a close run.

SQUIRE. Oh, if you're afraid.
[*Doctor touches Squire on shoulder and urges him left. Squire crosses left in huff, sees girl with fruit, goes up and buys apple.*

DR. LIVESEY. Squire! Captain Smollett! Just what are you aiming at? Come.

SMOLLETT (*with sudden determination*). You gentlemen know the risks you're running?

SQUIRE. We do.

[*At fruit basket.*

SMOLLETT. And you are determined to go?

SQUIRE. We are.

[*Sitting on barrel.*

SMOLLETT. Then I have this to say. Without my orders, those men put all the powder and arms in the forehold. — There's a place under our cabin. Why not put them there?

SQUIRE. But —

DR. LIVESEY. Wait! Wait! (*Stopping the Squire with hand*) All right, Captain, what else?

SMOLLETT. You have some of your own people with you —

SQUIRE. You don't doubt them, too?

SMOLLETT. Berth them beside the cabin.

[*Squire starts to object.*

DR. LIVESEY. Wait. (*Intercepting the Squire as he again starts to answer*) Go on, Captain Smollett.

SMOLLETT (*meaningly*). I've heard you have a certain chart — (*Squire and doctor start*) that there are crosses on that chart.

SQUIRE (*startled*). I never told that to a soul.

[*Rising and advancing a pace toward doctor.*

SMOLLETT. Every man aboard knows it, sir —

SQUIRE. Then, Livesey, it must have been you. . . . [*Doctor crosses up to Inn window, exclaiming " Ah!" and then drops to right of Smollett.*

SMOLLETT. I don't know who has this chart, and I don't want to know — but I insist it be kept secret.

DR. LIVESEY. In short, you fear a mutiny?

SMOLLETT. I deny your right, sir, to put those words into my mouth. No captain would be justified in going to sea if he had ground to say that.

SQUIRE. What, then?

SMOLLETT. Some of these men may be honest — perhaps all are. But I am responsible for the ship's safety, and the life of every man Jack aboard her, and I demand that I be allowed to take these precautions — or I resign!

[*Six bells rung on ship.*

SQUIRE. Well, then — (*Angrily*) You can —
[*Starts to cross to gang-plank and is stopped by doctor.*
DR. LIVESEY (*to Squire*). Wait. I agree with Captain Smollett.
I think it wise to do as Captain Smollett says.
SMOLLETT. Thank you, sir.
[*Saluting.*
SQUIRE. Oh, very well, I'm overruled.
[*Alan comes forward aft and exits forward across ship.*
[*Silver enters on boat from forward and comes down gang-plank.*
[*Hands appears at left of gang-plank, coiling rope.*
(NOTE: *Silver leaves his crutch leaning against rail of ship,
just at right of gang-plank, and gets it later, when he goes up.
He uses gang-plank for support in playing following short scene*)
SILVER (*to Smollett*). Beg pardon, sir, six bells just gone, sir, —
time you set for sailin' sir, —
[*Coming down gang-plank to Smollett. Hands on deck left of
gang-plank.*
SQUIRE. Sailing time. God bless me, doesn't it set you all
a-tingle? Come, Livesey, come!
[*Squire and doctor rush up gang-plank. Silver crosses to left
of gang-plank.*
SMOLLETT (*foot of gang-plank*). Well, sir, do I give the orders
to sail, or do I resign, sir?
SQUIRE. Do as you wish, do as you wish.
[*Squire goes up poop-deck, followed by doctor.*
SMOLLETT. Thank you, sir, you'll find I do my duty. (*To
Hands*) Mr. Hands —
[*Silver goes to window of Inn and motions to people in there
that they're about to sail, and then back to same position.*
HANDS. Aye, aye, sir!
[*Comes down to gang-plank.*
SMOLLETT. As soon as we are under sail, you'll take two or three
men and change the powder from the forehold to the place
beneath our cabin.
HANDS (*startled*). Captain Smollett!
SMOLLETT. My orders, sir.
[*Crossing up gang-plank.*

SILVER (*as Smollett starts up plank*).   But, sir, Squire Trelawney said —

SMOLLETT (*angrily*).   I am Captain of this ship, and you will so recognize, sir.   Without my knowledge or my consent, you have supplied that crew there — but upon that vessel I am in command, and you and every man of you will do exactly as I say or, by heavens, I'll take means to make you. Let that be understood, Mr. Silver!

[*Turns back on Silver and goes aboard.*

SILVER.   Aye, aye, sir, it's understood —

[*Turns facing audience.*

SMOLLETT.   Pipe all hands.

[*At head of gang-plank.   Shouting forward; then goes up on poop-deck.*

MERRY (*forward*).   Aye, aye, sir.

[*Blows whistle and men take position to pull rope.*

[*Dick takes position left of gang-plank, comes from forward. Grey takes position right of gang-plank, comes from forward. Anderson, Hunter, Arrow, and super come from aft and take position to rope.   Morgan, Redruth, two pirates who go up in rigging, come from forward.*

HANDS.   Long John!

[*Crosses to Silver.*

SILVER.   Aye, I heard . . . and we'll do as he says . . . every man of us, but when the time comes . . . we'll cut every honest throat aboard, and sail home with the treasure, laden with crimes and riches.

[*Men start to sing.*

"Fifteen men on the dead man's chest . . . etc."

[*Hands and Silver go up on deck.*

SMOLLETT.   Make sail!   Topmen aloft!

[*Two men climb up in shrouds barefooted and start to unfurl main sail of aft mast.*

Cast off your gang-plank.

[*Dick and Grey untie gang-plank and cast it off.*

FIRST CURTAIN: [*Black Dog comes from Inn and unties ship's hawser on hawser post and crawls half-way up side of ship.*

SECOND CURTAIN : [*Fruit girl calls to two men from street, who come on. One man goes and calls another man from the Inn and all four stand waving "Good-bye."*

SMOLLETT. Haul away there, forward !

[*Men start to haul hawser in time of song.*

[*Jim works his way through crowd forward and joins Silver, talking at head of gang-plank.*

[*Hands leaves Silver and takes place with men on hawser.*

CURTAIN

ACT III

SCENE I

Drop showing the Hispaniola at anchor. The part of ship shown is some of the stern and most of the amidships, the main part of the stage being taken up with what is called the "waist" of the ship. Black cannon left. Apple barrel right.

When the curtain rises the men are discovered in a group at rail of ship. Trelawney, Smollett, and Dr. Livesey are looking off toward island.

SMOLLETT (*using his hands as megaphone*). All fast there forward ?

[*Chart in hand.*

DIRK (*off stage*). All fast, sir. . . .

SMOLLETT. Anchorage good ?

DIRK. Aye, aye, sir.

SMOLLETT. The current's pretty strong here. How's she holding ?

DIRK. Firm in over seven fathoms, sir . . . she hasn't dragged an inch !

SMOLLETT. Good ! (*Turns to crew in waist, who face him in being addressed. Men turn towards island again*) My lads, that Island there is the place we've been sailing to. (*Captain has had chart in his hand from rise of curtain; he now folds it and puts it in his pocket. Squire touches Captain on arm, indicating he wants to speak to crew. Murmurs of satisfaction among crew, etc. Dirk enters and joins men)* Squire Trelawney has a word to say —

[*Men turn to face Squire.*

SQUIRE (*coming forward, taking Captain's place*). Captain Smollett has told me how every man of you has done his duty alow and aloft as I never ask to see it better done, and so, to show my appreciation, I have had Silver here make ready a special mess — and double grog below decks !

SILVER (*turning to men as the crew give murmurs of satisfaction*). My lads, I hold this handsome, and, if you all think as I do, you'll give a good sea cheer for Squire Trelawney. (*As the crew cheer, Pirates say, "Huzzah! Huzzah!" Squire's men say, "Hurrah! Hurrah!"*) Come now — below, and we'll drink a health to these gentlemen. Here's to ourselves and hold your luff — plenty of prizes and plenty of duff !

[*All go off with talking and gesticulating.*

SQUIRE. Well, Captain Smollett, you'll admit now you were wrong.

SMOLLETT. How so, sir ?

SQUIRE. A splendid voyage — a fine brisk crew, and here we are !

SMOLLETT. Aye, sir, we are here, but we're not home again, and I smell trouble brewing. Asking your pardon, sir, you've done your best to spoil this crew. A kick, a curse, a blow are meat and drink to a man before the mast, but you've pampered them up with barrels of apples and double grog, as though they were a pack of schoolgirls. No good will come of it.

SQUIRE (*testily*). By heavens, there's no pleasing you. I'm going below. (*Crosses*) A trifle more of that man and I should explode.

[*Exits.*

SMOLLETT (*advancing to Dr. Livesey*). And you, sir, have you seen nothing suspicious ?

DR. LIVESEY. Yes — much.

SMOLLETT. Then . . . ?

DR. LIVESEY. I believe you're right.

SMOLLETT. I tell you this crew is on the verge of mutiny — and

— (*Stops short as he sees Hands come from men's quarters; he is trying to hear what Smollett and doctor are saying*) What is it, Mr. Hands?

[*Over to Hands.*

HANDS. Some of the men didn't report to mess, sir . . . just looking for 'em, sir. . . . (*As Smollett watches him keenly*) Haven't seen 'em 'bout deck, sir, have you?

SMOLLETT. Not a soul, Hands.

HANDS. Thank you, sir. . . .

[*Crosses back of doctor and Smollett, who watch him. He looks back at them just as he gets near exit. They catch him and he hurries off.*

DR. LIVESEY. You see that?

SMOLLETT. There's something in the air. We'll hear from that crew before the night's over.

DR. LIVESEY. I believe you're right.

SMOLLETT. Then we must take some precautions . . . Squire or no Squire. . . .

DR. LIVESEY. Come below — we must make the Squire listen to reason.

[*They go out, Smollett urged by doctor. The stage is vacant for a moment. Jim enters. Sees barrel, looks in it, takes out apple and begins munching it. Sees Black Dog coming.*

JIM. Black Dog!

[*Ducks behind barrel.*

[*Black Dog enters cautiously, feeling his way along the bulwarks. As he gets toward barrel, Jim works around. Black Dog exits. Noise off.*

HANDS (*off*). You — (*Noise of scuffle off. Jim quickly jumps in barrel. Enter Black Dog and Hands, fighting, on stage*) What are you doing on deck, after all our trouble to keep you hidden. If that boy, Hawkins, sees you, he'll blow the gaff the same as he did on the Quay —

[*Throws Black Dog off.*

BLACK DOG. I don't care if he does. We're here now, and I'll slit his throat if I lay hands on him.

HANDS. You heard Silver's orders —

BLACK DOG.   Aye, I've heard his orders, and I've heard his talk and . . . (*Hands whistles*)   So — you've signaled for him — (*Makes for Hands to stop his whistle*)   Shiver my timbers — but you'll pay for that!

[*Draws knife. Springs at Hands and they struggle, pantingly, without words in fight. All pirates enter, headed by Silver.*

SILVER.   What's all this — Put up those knives!   Who's Cap'n here — I'd like to know.   By thunder, I'll show you — the whole pack of you — Give me that knife — give it to me — (*Black Dog gives up his knife and Silver turns to Hands*)   Here, Hands, I place him in your charge —   At the first word — the first sign — you kill him.   Understand — (*swings Black Dog left of Hands*) kill him!

BLACK DOG.   I'll pay you for this, Long John — (*Hands advances to him threatening*)   If he touches me I'll . . . (*to Hands*) tear him to pieces.

[*Hands hustles him off and Anderson follows.*

[*Silver turns to the men who are in a group.*

MORGAN.   Long John — we want to —

SILVER.   Wait.   (*Stopping him*)   See if any of them are snooping around there.

[*Indicates cabin, and Morgan looks stealthily to see if anyone is about. Crosses back of barrel, looks off, comes down to right of barrel.*

MORGAN.   All clear —

SILVER.   Now then — out with it.

MORGAN.   We men want to know how long we're going to hold off?

SILVER.   By the powers, till the last minute I can manage . . . you'll live hard, you'll speak soft, you'll keep sober till I give the word.   They've got that chart, and until we have it . . . we make no move. . . .

MERRY (*advancing a pace*).   And didn't we see it this very night here in their hands.   Ah, if you had only let us at 'em then . . .

SILVER.   And you think they'll sit still and let you cut their throats while doing it, eh?

DIRK.   We're nineteen to six and —

MERRY. We've taken a vote.

SILVER. Oh, you have, have you?

MERRY. We know our rights, Long John.

SILVER. Another word, George Merry, and — I'll sink this into you?
[*Poising his knife in his hand.*

MERRY. Fo'c's'le council, Long John. Them's rules — rules —

SILVER. Rules, is it? — I'll show ye rules — you'll have all the rules you want —
[*Noise of Black Dog and Hands fighting off.*

ANDERSON (*enters excitedly. Comes to Silver*). It's Hands and Black Dog down below fighting, sir.

SILVER. Stop 'em . . . quick. If the Squire and Captain hears them, we'll be dished. Get below . . . quick . . . all of you. . . .
[*Men rush out. Silver stands by entrance.*
[*Dr. Livesey and Squire and Smollett come in.*

SMOLLETT. What was that noise, Silver?

SILVER (*standing near entrance. Innocently*). Noise, sir? I didn't hear any noise, sir. Perhaps some of the men feelin' a bit lively, sir; you know double grog for all hands — Squire's orders, sir. But if there's anything wrong, I'll soon settle it . . . you can trust me, sir.
[*Goes out quickly.*

SQUIRE. Of course, I trust you. It's only ridiculous (*following Silver*) trouble-seekers who do not. It's —
[*Jim appears from barrel.*

JIM. Doctor! Squire!

DR. LIVESEY. Jim!

JIM. Don't trust Silver, sir. I've been in here and heard. They're after our treasure. They're pirates. The whole crew of 'em. Silver's their captain, and he's the one-leggedest pirate of the lot.

SMOLLETT (*to Jim*). Did you hear anything of their plans?

JIM. They're arguing down there now. (*Getting out of barrel*) The men are all for attack — but Silver is for holding them back.

SMOLLETT. If he only could.   How many men can we count on?

JIM. They said they were nineteen to six.

SMOLLETT. Six — that must be Redruth — Joyce — Hunter and ourselves.

DR. LIVESEY. Then there are some who are doubtful —

SMOLLETT. We'll count on six . . . ammunition and arms are with us. . . .   By Gad, if Silver can only hold them off . . . if we can get a little time.   This ship needs water.   Without it, she can't sail. . . .   Now, according to your chart, there is just one place on that Island where water can be had . . . the stockade.   Now, if we can make the stockade with our arms and provisions, by heaven, sir, they'd have to come to us. . . .   If we could only hold them off for a time. . . (*Hunter rushes in and comes to Smollett*)   How now, Hunter?

HUNTER (*saluting*). Pardon, Captain, there's something come over the crew. . . .   First they tried to make Redruth and Joyce and me join 'em, and, when we refused, they shut themselves in a corner by themselves . . .

SMOLLETT. Well?

HUNTER. I stole back and listened . . . it's all about a map, sir . . . and they're coming to demand it.   If they don't get it . . . I'm afraid it's mutiny, sir . . . and death.
[*Crosses back to entrance, watching.*

SQUIRE (*advancing to Smollett*). What shall we do, Captain Smollett?

JIM (*advancing to Smollett*). I beg your pardon, sir.   You say it's time you want?

SMOLLETT. Yes — yes —

JIM. Well, then, why not give them the map, sir?

DR. LIVESEY. What?

JIM. They think the map that Captain Smollett has to sail the ship by is the right one. . . .   Couldn't we give them that?

SMOLLETT. Jim, I believe you've hit it.   (*Captain takes chart from pocket.   Turns to Squire*)   This chart you gave me to navigate by is an exact copy of the real one, except that the crosses where the treasure is buried were left out.

SQUIRE. True.

SMOLLETT. Jim, take it down to my cabin . . . put some crosses on . . . put them anywhere . . . understand?

JIM. Yes, sir.

SMOLLETT. Then bring it up here and slip it into the Squire's hand. Hurry! —

[*Jim rushes out.*

DR. LIVESEY. I believe the lad has solved it.

SMOLLETT (*turns to Dr. Livesey and Squire*). Now, in case this comes to an issue, are you gentlemen willing to fight them?

DR. LIVESEY. To the last, sir.

SQUIRE. Aye, sir.

SMOLLETT. Very well. Have your pistols primed.

SQUIRE. They are, sir.

[*Joining the doctor.*

DR. LIVESEY. And mine, sir.

SMOLLETT (*to Hunter*). Hunter, as soon as those men come from below, take all the muskets and load them. . . . Drag as much powder and shot into the cabin as you can. . . .

HUNTER. Very well, sir.

SMOLLETT. Stand there on guard. Let no one touch it.

HUNTER. Right, sir.

[*Saluting. Exit.*

SMOLLETT. (*crossing to doctor and Squire*). If it comes to a fight, we'll fight back to the cabin and the ammunition — we've got a chance, gentlemen — just a bare chance, and if we don't make it, we'll sell our lives dear. . . . Steady now! Steady all! (*The pirates, led by Silver, come forward in an angry group*) Well, my men, this looks like a deputation.

SILVER. It is, sir — a depytation.

SMOLLETT (*sternly*). Well, what is it?

SILVER (*hesitates*). These men, sir — these men, sir, have been hearing rumors.

SMOLLETT. Rumors?

SILVER. Rumors, sir, as how this ship is under sealed orders — and them sealed orders are — treasure, sir!

THE MEN. Aye, treasure!

SQUIRE.   And who told you that?

[*Coming down and facing Silver.*

SILVER.   You did, sir, and a whole lot more besides.

SQUIRE.   I?

[*Turns to doctor who censures him, and they talk together.*

SILVER.   Now such things, getting to the ears of men like these, makes them sort of greedy, sir — and —

SMOLLETT.   Do you mean to say that this is mutiny?

SILVER.   You can call it what you want, sir.

[*Men laugh.*

SMOLLETT.   Why, damme, I'll have you put in irons — I'll . . .

SILVER (*as the men with ugly threats go toward Smollett, stops them. To Smollett*).   I think you'd better know, sir — I've counseled peace and fair terms.

SMOLLETT.   Well?

SILVER (*to Smollett*).   We're told that you have a certain chart . . . (*the crew draws nearer in a threatening manner*) with certain crosses on it . . . we want that chart.

SQUIRE (*turning to Silver*).   Silver, I've trusted you.

SILVER.   The chart, sir . . . do we get it . . . do we?

SMOLLETT (*as Squire goes to answer*).   Wait.   Suppose we give this chart to you.   What then?

SILVER.   What then?

SMOLLETT.   Aye, what then?   What happens to us?

SILVER.   Why — why — nothing, sir.

SMOLLETT.   You mean you'll not harm us?

SILVER.   No . . .

SMOLLETT.   Your solemn promise?

SILVER.   Solemn promise.

SMOLLETT.   Here.   (*To the men*)   You — you give your word, too?   (*Cries of "Aye, aye"*)   Very well, then . . . much as I think you are a pack of scoundrels . . . (*Men, "Huh!"*) and hope to see you all hanged — (*Men, "Huh!"   They come threateningly at him.   Silver stops them*)   Why . . . I know when I'm beaten . . . (*Men grunt satisfactorily*)   Squire, get the chart.

SQUIRE.   Very well.   (*Crosses to entrance, calls*)   Jim!

JIM (*without*).   Yes, sir?

SQUIRE (*calls*).   You know where that chart is, Jim?

JIM (*without*).   Aye, aye, sir.

SQUIRE (*calls*).   Bring it here.

JIM (*without*).   In a jiffy, sir.

SILVER (*as the men press forward*).   Now then, ready with the boats, men . . . quick . . . get them ready. . . . (*Merry directs two men to get boats, who exit, and men move up to drop in group*) I'll stand guard and watch . . . for I tell you I don't trust you, Captain Smollett.

[*Down near entrance.*

SMOLLETT (*advancing*).   Well, I can't say as I trust you either, Silver. (*As Jim comes on with chart, he goes to give it to Silver. Smollett stops him*) Wait! Remember your promise?

SILVER.   Aye . . . aye . . . aye . . . aye. . . .

SMOLLETT.   Then let them have it, Jim.

[*As Jim gives Silver the chart, all the men with a cry spring forward. Arrow pushes Jim back out of the way.*

ARROW.   Now then, let's settle with them.

[*When the men see they have the chart, they make a rush for Smollett and the doctor and Squire.*

SMOLLETT.   Back! Back! (*Squire and Dr. Livesey and Smollett all draw their guns*) Your promise — by heavens, gentlemen, if you come a step further —

SILVER (*crossing between men and Smollett. Turns to men*). Stop! Stop, I say! You fools, you blockheads —

ARROW.   Well, haven't we got the chart?

SMOLLETT.   So you're not going to keep your word?

SILVER.   You may as well know, that was Flint's crew . . . Flint was Cap'n, I was quartermaster. I've seen Flint's ship amuck with blood, and fit to sink with gold . . . aye . . . gold that's buried there . . . gold that's ours by rights . . . belongs to us . . . who have sailed with Flint . . . (*As he sees the men again threatening, he goes closer to Smollett and speaks low*) They're a rough lot . . . there . . . it's all I can do to hold 'em. . . . You'd better go below . . . quick . . . go!

SMOLLETT. I warn you!

SILVER. Go.

[*Smollett, Squire, and doctor exit. Silver crosses after them.*

MERRY. Now then, men, after them . . . we'll finish this up. . . .

[*Men start for exit.*

[*Black Dog enters and works his way to Hand's side.*

SILVER. Wait!

[*Stops men.*

MERRY. Haven't we got the chart? — haven't we . . .

SILVER. Yes . . . and we got it too easy.

MORGAN. Aye, too easy. . . .

SILVER. It don't look nat'ral . . . there's something behind it. . . .

DIRK. A trick . . . maybe a wrong chart.

MERRY. Then we'll find out soon enough. . . . Come, lads . . . come . . .

[*All start.*

JIM (*stepping forward*). Wait. (*The men, surprised, stop and turn and face Jim*) You go down there and attack, and you'll lose everything. They're waiting for you — their muskets and pistols primed. — They've got all the guns and ammunition. — You go down there and you'll lose your ship — your chart — and your lives!

SILVER. So! You say this is the right chart? Do you, sonny? (*Crossing to Jim, taking him by his wrist*) Well, we'll just let you risk your life on that. Lads, — we'll take this boy along . . . (*to men*) as a hostage. (*As Jim starts*) That makes you start, eh?

[*To Jim.*

JIM (*recovering himself*). No! I'm willing to go.

SILVER. All right, you shall go whether you're willing or not! What do you think of that! (*To men*) Come on, get this boy in the boat here. Hands!

HANDS. Aye, aye, sir.

SILVER. And you, Black Dog. (*Hands and Black Dog come forward*) You stay here and watch this ship. At the first sign of any trouble from them down below, you fire a shot, and tell the Squire from me — that the first shot from this boat will be a signal for Hawkins' death.

JIM (*crossing to Hands*).   And tell the Squire from me that Jim Hawkins is not afraid.

SILVER.   All right, Jim Hawkins.   (*Takes Jim by collar and shoves him into midst of pirates who close around him and exit, followed by Silver*)   In with him!
[*Song heard, oar-lock effect.*
[*Black Dog and Hands looking off.*

DR. LIVESEY (*offstage, as he enters.   Comes below barrel*).   Jim! Jim!   Where's Jim Hawkins?

HANDS.   Silver's taken him along as a hostage.
[*As Smollett, Squire, Redruth, Grey, and Squire's man enter with leveled revolvers.*

DR. LIVESEY.   What!

SMOLLETT.   Up with your hands — up with them, or I shoot!

HANDS (*puts up hands, as does Black Dog*).   I warn you, you fire one shot and it will be the signal for that boy's death!

SMOLLETT.   Come, Livesey, to the boats —
[*Crossing to left of Black Dog.*

HANDS.   Where are you going?
[*Both turning and facing Captain.*

SMOLLETT.   By all the stars, we're going to rescue that boy. — We've tricked you and we're going to fight you to the end . . . and I tell you this much, and you can tell Silver, God help you if anything happens to that boy!

CURTAIN

ACT III

SCENE II

Treasure Island

Transparent drop at back showing sea and outline of island's shore and mountains; effect of sun rising in mountains shown through drop.

When the curtain rises the stage is in darkness, the darkness just before dawn. Then gradually the light comes stealing in, turning the black to gray, and until this melts into tones of early dawn, the whole reaching a sort of climactic effulgence with the rise of the sun. Ben Gunn is discovered asleep, his head on his coracle or little boat he has made. He yawns, stretches, and gets up rubbing his eyes, looks towards the sea, shakes his head, wanders slowly down extreme right. As he reaches right he stops and listens, as if hearing some strange sound; then he turns and looks off through trees; he starts and quickly jumps behind one of the trees. Jim enters almost at once. For a moment he looks about wonderingly. He seems weary and tired, and wanders down past Gunn, when suddenly he catches sight of him hiding. All alert now, he stops.

"My eyes turned instinctively in that direction, and I saw a figure leap with great rapidity behind the trunk of a pine. What it was, whether bear or man or monkey, I could in nowise tell. It seemed dark and shaggy; more I knew not. But the terror of this new apparition brought me to a stand. I was now, it seemed, cut off upon both sides; behind me the murderers, before me this lurking nondescript. And immediately I began to prefer the dangers that I knew to those I knew not. Silver himself appeared less terrible in contrast with this creature of the woods, and I turned on my heels, and, looking sharply behind me over my shoulder, began to retrace my steps in the direction of the boats. Instantly the figure reappeared and, making a wide circuit, began to head me off. I was tired, at any rate; but had I been as fresh as when I rose, I could see it was in vain for me to contend in speed with such an adversary. From trunk to trunk the creature flitted like a deer, running man-like on two legs, but, unlike any man that I had ever seen, stooping almost double as it ran. Yet a man it was, I could no longer be in doubt about that. I began to recall what I had heard of cannibals. I was within an ace of calling for help. But the mere fact that he was a man, however wild, had somewhat reassured me, and my fear of Silver began to revive in proportion. I stood still therefore and cast about for some method of escape; and as I was so thinking, the recollection of my pistol flashed into my mind. As soon as I remembered I was not defenseless, courage glowed again

*in my heart; and I set my face resolutely for this man of the island,
and walked briskly toward him. He was concealed by this time
behind another tree-trunk; but he must have been watching me
closely, for, as soon as I began to move in his direction, he reappeared and took a step to meet me. Then he hesitated, drew back,
came forward again, and, at last, to my wonder and confusion,
threw himself on his knees and held out his clasped hands in sup-
plication."*

JIM. Who are you?

GUNN. Ben Gunn. . . . (*On knees*) I am poor Ben Gunn, I
am, and haven't spoke with a Christian these three years.

JIM. Three years . . .

GUNN. Aye, three blessed years . . .

JIM. Shipwrecked here?

GUNN. Nay, mate . . . marooned . . .

JIM. Marooned . . .

GUNN. Aye, mate, marooned, left here, cast away to live or
die (*rises*), and lived on goats, since then, and berries and
oysters. But, mate, my heart is sore for Christian diet. Now,
you mightn't have a piece of cheese about you . . . eh? . . .
[*Comes a step toward Jim.*

JIM. No!

GUNN. No! (*turns, shaking head. Jim follows to right of
stump*) and it's many the long nights I have dreamed of
cheese, toasted mostly — (*turns to Jim again*) and woke up
again, and here I were. Now you — what do you call yourself, mate?

JIM. Jim —

GUNN (*advances to Jim, who retreats a step*). Jim? There, there,
now don't you be afeared.

JIM. I'm not afraid of you. (*Coming toward him*) It's them
I'm afraid of. I've been running all night from the pirates.

GUNN. Pirates, says you — pirates?

JIM. Aye, such they prove to be, all of them. Pirates who
sailed with Flint.

GUNN. Flint's crew?

JIM.   Yes, all of 'em.

GUNN.   Not a man with one leg?

JIM.   Silver?

GUNN.   Aye, Silver.

JIM.   He's cook and ring-leader too.

GUNN.   If Long John's on this island I am as good as pork and I know it.

[*Looking off through trees.*

JIM.   He's down there on the beach.   There's been a mutiny, and they've come ashore to search for — Flint's treasure. But they can't find it — because the Squire gave them the wrong chart.

GUNN.   What chart might you be speaking of, matey?

JIM.   Flint's fist . . . I got it from Bill Bones when he died.

GUNN.   Billy Bones dead too!   So your Squire gave Silver a false chart, and kept Flint's fist?   Is that it, matey?

JIM.   Yes —

GUNN.   Haw!   That's a good 'un.   That's a good one!   (*Sits on stump*)   You're all in a clove hitch, ain't yer?   But Ben Gunn will help you agin them pirates.

JIM.   You will?   Oh, you will? —

[*Advancing to him.*

GUNN.   Aye, lad, agin all the pirates in the world, for Ben Gunn has been a gentleman of fortune hisself, and, such being the case, he knows how to grapple with such.

JIM.   You!   One of the buccaneers?

[*Retreats a pace.*

GUNN.   There, there, lad.   I won't harm you.   I've thought it all out on this lonely island . . . and I'm back on piety . . . you don't catch me tasting rum again, but just a thimble full for luck, of course, the first chance I gets.   I'm bound I'll be good, and I see the way to.   But d'ye think it likely now, that your Squire would prove a liberal-minded one . . . in case of help . . . him being in a clove hitch?

JIM.   The Squire is the most liberal of men.

GUNN.   Aye, but you see I didn't mean giving me a gate to keep and a (*rises and comes to Jim*) soot of livery clothes and such . . . that's not my mark, Jim. What I mean is, would he be likely to come down to the toon of, say, one thousand pounds or so out of money that's as good as a man's own, already? And a passage home? And a passage home?

JIM. Why, if we come out on top, we should need you to help us work the vessel home.

GUNN. Ah, so you would! (*Taking Jim by arm*) Just you mention them words to your Squire, and then you'll give him a nip like I do . . . and say this to him . . . Gunn has something to propose and reasons of his own.

JIM. What am I to tell the Squire?

GUNN (*turning to him*). That Gunn's a good man now. . . . You'd never think, to look at me, that I had a pious mother . . . would you now?

JIM. Why no, not particularly.

GUNN. Ah, well, I had, remarkable pious, an' I were a civil pious boy as could rattle off my catechism that fast, as you couldn't tell one word from another, an' here's what it come to, Jim, and it began with chucking farthings on the blessed gravestones — that's what it begun with, but, it went further'n that, an' so my mother told me and predicked the whole, she did, the pious woman, and that, Jim, is what I'd have your Squire to know, and that's what you'll tell him as soon as you see him.

JIM. As soon as I see him? With Long John Silver between him and me — I'm afraid it's all up with me now.
[*Sitting on stump.*

GUNN (*crossing to Jim and kneeling left of him*). There, there, matey . . . wherever man is, says I, man can do for hisself. You'll be all right, lad, and Ben Gunn's here to help you. . . . I've got a little boat I made with my two hands, and I'll let you have it to get back to your friends. (*Jim crosses to boat, and comes down and meets Gunn, who is following him*) Come nightfall, we'll steal down to the beach under cover of them trees, through the cetemary. You see them mounds? (*Looks off*) — I goes there and prays now and

then, when I thinks maybe a Sunday would be about due.
It ain't quite a chapel, but it seems more solemn like.

[*The report of a cannon is heard from the right.*

JIM.   What's that firing?

GUNN.   See — see there through the clearing — they're firing
on the old stockade.

[*Pointing off.*

JIM.   The stockade?

[*Looking off.*

GUNN.   Aye, lad.   Flint's old stockade.

JIM.   Yes, yes, I see — where our colors are flyin' — the Union
Jack — the Union Jack!

[*Turning to Gunn.*

GUNN.   There's your friends, Jim — they've come ashore, and
now you can go to your Squire — Jim.

JIM.   Yes, yes.

GUNN.   And when you sees him, you won't forget to give him a
nip, like I do, and tell him Ben Gunn has something to propose, — something most important to propose and reasons
of his own. . . .

JIM.   All right, I'll tell him.

[*Trying to get away.*

GUNN (*stopping him*).   An' when Ben Gunn's wanted, you
know where to find him, Jim. . . .

JIM.   No!   Where?

GUNN.   Why, just where you found him to-day.   An' him that
comes is to have a white flag in his hand, and he's to come
alone, you understand, eh?

JIM.   Yes, yes, I think so.

GUNN.   An' when, says you?   Why, from noon observation to
about six bells.

JIM.   Good!

GUNN.   Jim, if you was to see Silver, you wouldn't go to sell
Ben Gunn, would you?   Wild horses wouldn't draw it from
you?

JIM.   No, no, I swear it!

GUNN.   God bless you, lad! — (*Puts right hand on Jim's right* shoulder, *and takes his right hand with his left*) You'll thank your stars, you will, you was the first that found me. (*The cannon booms. Jim runs off right*) Keep to the left through the cetemary . . . remember . . .

JIM (*off stage*). I'll tell him. . . .

GUNN. Reasons of his own. If them pirates camp ashore, there'll be widders in the morning.

CURTAIN

ACT III

SCENE III

The Stockade

Upon two sides, wherever visible, high walls, made of rude planks, spike-shaped at top. At left the front of a log house, with door and small window down stage, with torn curtain in it. Back of house tall, large trees. At right, a wooden gate with wooden bar to fasten it. At several places about the walls, port-holes. At upstage corner of house a tree stump, and, on corresponding corner of roof, the Union Jack is flying.

At rise of curtain, cannon shot is heard and sand flies up outside wall of stockade.

DR. LIVESEY (*near door of house*). Another cannon-ball from the ship.

SMOLLETT (*looking through port-hole at door with spy-glass*). Blaze away — blaze away — you've little enough powder left.

SQUIRE. It seems to be our flag they're aiming at. Wouldn't it be wiser to take it in?

SMOLLETT. Strike my colors! No, sir, not I.
[*Turning to Squire.*

SQUIRE. We shall have to do it sooner or later. They've got us like rats in a trap. Let's give up, — give them the chart and make terms.

SMOLLETT. No, sir! not if Hunter and Grey out there find a way to reach that ship.

DR. LIVESEY. They've been gone an hour.

SMOLLETT (*to Joyce at port-hole right of door*). See anything, Joyce?

JOYCE. Not a thing.

SMOLLETT. They must reach that ship and cut her adrift so that the tide will beach her. It's our only chance — they must — (*Shots off*) It's all up. (*Looking through port-hole at door*) They've got 'em. Hunter's wounded, Grey is dragging him back. Stand by, Doctor, to help.

[*Captain Smollett opens stockade door. Grey enters with Hunter leaning on his shoulder for support.*

GREY (*right of Hunter*). They're all in the woods on every side. I got one of 'em, I think.

SMOLLETT. Is he badly hurt, Doctor?

DR. LIVESEY. Yes, very.

HUNTER. Be I going, Doctor?

DR. LIVESEY. Tom, my man, you're going home.

HUNTER. I wish I'd had a shot at 'em first.

SQUIRE (*coming between Grey and Hunter, takes Grey's place*). Tom — Tom —

HUNTER. Yes, sir —

SQUIRE. Say you forgive me, Tom, for bringing you along?

HUNTER. Would that be respectful, sir?

SQUIRE. Aye, do, Tom!

HUNTER. All right — howsoever, so be it — amen — [*Falls back.*

DR. LIVESEY. Grey, lend a hand here. We'll carry him in.
[*Grey takes Hunter's right arm around his neck, and they carry him into log house.*

SQUIRE. And it's all my fault for bringing him.

SMOLLETT. No time for that now, sir. Those men out there are planning an attack, — that's it, waiting to creep up in the dusk.

SQUIRE. All the better for us.

SMOLLETT. If we win . . . yes . . . if not . . . (*Grey and doctor return from house. To doctor*) Well?

DR. LIVESEY. He's gone, sir. . . .

SQUIRE. Poor lad. . . .

[*Joyce shoots through port-hole.*

SMOLLETT. What's that?

[*Grey goes to port-hole near house.*

JOYCE. I thought I saw something.

SMOLLETT (*comes and looks through port-hole at gate*). Hit him?

JOYCE. Don't know, sir.

SMOLLETT. Wait — easy now —

[*Peers out intently.*

JOYCE. There — in the trees to the right — don't you see something moving?

SMOLLETT. Yes — wait — he's coming nearer — get ready — now — wait till he gets to the open. Now then, ready an' — (*Suddenly stumbles back*) Oh, my God! It's Jim.

DR. LIVESEY. What's that?

SMOLLETT. Don't call. See — to the left — they're watching — shoot to the left when I call — ready —

JOYCE. Ready.

SMOLLETT (*throwing gate open*). Jim, come, come now — lad — (*To Joyce*) Shoot now! Shoot! (*Joyce shoots and there is a rattle of musketry off*) My God — did they get him — did they?

[*Jim comes rushing in out of breath.*

DR. LIVESEY (*left of Jim*). Thank God you're safe, lad.

JIM. Did 'em that time, sir.

[*Squire comes right of Jim.*

DR. LIVESEY. Where have you been?

JIM. I've met a man, Ben Gunn, who's been here three years; he has something to propose — says if you're in a clove hitch, you're to go to him with a white flag — and he'll help you against the pirates.

SILVER (*off*). Ahoy!

[*Jim goes into house and stands in doorway.*

SMOLLETT. What's that! Listen!

[*Doctor crosses to port-hole left and Squire to port-hole center.*

SILVER (*without*). Log-house ahoy! Log-house ahoy!

SMOLLETT. Silver, as I live.

DR. LIVESEY. With a flag of truce.

SQUIRE.   What do you suppose? —

SMOLLETT.   Some trick — they know we've discovered their presence — (*Then turns to men*)   All stand ready and watch — (*The men take their places about the stockade and peer out through the port-holes*)   Grey, stand by the gates. (*Grey takes his place at the gate*)   Wait till I give the word.

SILVER (*without*).   Ahoy!   Log-house ahoy!

SMOLLETT.   Who goes?   Stand or we fire!

SILVER (*without*).   Flag of truce!

SMOLLETT (*calls*).   What do you want with your flag of truce?

SILVER (*without*).   Captain Silver, come aboard to make terms.

SQUIRE.   What?

SMOLLETT.   Easy! (*To Squire*)   It's a trick, I tell you. (*To Silver*)   You come alone?

SILVER.   Alone.   Flag of truce — you respect a flag of truce? [*Appears above wall of stockade with white rag tied on crutch. Shoves crutch over first.   Squire crosses to upstage of log house door.   Doctor below it.   Men turn and cover him with rifles.*

SMOLLETT (*severely*).   If there's any treachery, Silver — it will be on your side — and the Lord help you!

SILVER.   Right you are, Cap'n.   A word from you's enough. (*Looks about*)   Ah, Squire, the top of the morning to you. Doctor, my respects.

SMOLLETT (*severely*).   If you have anything to say —

SILVER.   Well, then, we're willing to come to terms.

SQUIRE (*eagerly*).   What, you —

SMOLLETT (*to Squire*).   Wait — (*To Silver*)   What terms?

SILVER.   That was a good lay of yours, sending us on that wild-goose chase, with that false chart, while you reached here — only —

SMOLLETT (*men come to rest with rifles*).   Well!

SILVER.   It won't work twice. . . .   I suspected you even then . . . that's why I took Hawkins.   But now, here you are . . . and there's your ship with the Jolly Roger flying at her masthead.   You lost most of your provisions and ammunition coming here.

SMOLLETT. That's our affair.

SILVER. And ours — (*With sudden fierceness*) We've got you, I tell you, and you've got to do what I say! We want that treasure and we want it now. That's our point.

SMOLLETT. Point enough.

SILVER. You want your lives, and that's your point.

SMOLLETT. Well?

SILVER. Now, you give us that chart and then, as soon as the treasure is shipped, you can come aboard along with us, and I'll give you my affy-davy, upon my sacred word of honor, to clap you somewhere safe ashore.

SMOLLETT (*sarcastically*). Of course we can trust you. . . .

SILVER. Well, then, if that ain't to your fancy, some of my hands being rough, you can stay here, and we'll divide stores with you, and I give you my affy-davy, as before, to speak the first ship we sight, and send 'em here to pick you up. Now, you'll own that's talkin' handsome. (*Turns round to the men*) I hope all hands will overhaul my words, for what is spoke to one is spoke to all.

SMOLLETT. And is that all?

SILVER. Every last word, by thunder. Refuse, and you've seen the last of me but musket-balls.

SMOLLETT (*coming to wall*). Then hear me. If you'll come one by one — I'll engage to clap you all in irons —

SILVER. Oh —

SMOLLETT. And take you home for trial.

SILVER. You will, will you?

SMOLLETT. You can't find that treasure without us . . . you can't work that ship without us. . . .

SILVER. Look out, I warn you!

SMOLLETT. You need us more than we need you.

SILVER. Oh, we do, do we? You wouldn't stand there and defy me if we still had that boy. If Hawkins hadn't got away, I'd have you on your knees fast enough. (*Smollett laughs*) Laugh, by thunder, laugh! But before a quarter of an hour is out, I'll have you laughing on the other side of your mouth.

SMOLLETT. Now, bundle out of this, double-quick. I'll put a bullet in your back when next we meet.

SILVER. That's your last word?

SMOLLETT. It is.

SILVER. All right. In less than two minutes I'll stave your old blockhouse in like a rum puncheon. (*Turns and looks at men*) And them that die'll be the lucky ones.

[*Disappears.*

[*Jim comes out of house.*

SMOLLETT (*turns to men*). Now, lads, I've given Silver a broadside . . . pitched it in red-hot on purpose, and, before many minutes are out, as he said, we'll be boarded. We're outnumbered, but we fight in shelter, and I believe we can drub 'em. That's why I put it on so thick . . . to make 'em fight. We can stand anything but what he threatened . . . a siege or being marooned . . . so let them come, lads, let them come. (*Faces men. They all get ready*) Doctor, you take the rear there.

DR. LIVESEY (*as he goes to his position at port-hole left*). Aye, aye, sir.

SMOLLETT. Joyce, the east side. (*Joyce stays at port-hole above door and Redruth crosses to port-hole left, near log house*) Mr. Trelawney, you and Grey will take the south.

SQUIRE. Right, Captain. We'll make it hot for them. They'll not find us unprepared.

SMOLLETT (*crossing. Men all turn from their place to Captain except Grey*). Now listen, if we can beat them to-night, one or two of us will steal down to the beach, row out, cut the *Hispaniola* adrift. Once beached and we've got 'em.

GREY. I see them moving, sir.

SMOLLETT. Back to your places. (*Men turn to port-holes again*) Jim, you get under cover. Go into the house.

JIM. No, sir, I'll help you load.

[*Jim goes into house.*

JOYCE. I think I see them over here, too, sir.

DR. LIVESEY. Aye, and here, too —

GRAY. And here, sir —

SMOLLETT.   It'll be from all sides — They're getting ready for a charge. — Now hold steady.

SQUIRE.   They're starting!

SMOLLETT.   Save your ammunition until they reach the open —

[*Pirates off stage, "Huzzar! Huzzar! Huzzar!" Three shots fired, followed by a volley.*

[*Jim runs across to Squire, looks through port-hole, and runs back into house.*

DR. LIVESEY.   Here they come.

SMOLLETT.   Then let them have it!

[*There are cries and shouts, with shots from outside; those within the stockade return the fire.*

SQUIRE.   I got one of them.

[*Fires through port-hole.*

GRAY.   And I, sir —

[*Fires through port-hole.*

DR. LIVESEY.   Four of them on this side. — They're making for the wall!

SMOLLETT.   Shoot — keep 'em away.   Don't let 'em over — at 'em, lads.   (*The sounds increase.   Cries, curses, and musket shots are heard*)   Look out there — you, Redruth — over your head —

[*Pirate appears over wall with musket. He shoots Redruth at port-hole left, who falls. Grey shoots pirate who has first shot Redruth, and pirate falls back. After shooting Dirk, Grey rushes back into house, and Smollett center cries, "That's it! Look to your weapons!" Dick appears above wall center, and is shot by doctor left and Squire right with pistols. Joyce, at port-hole above gate, Squire at gate and doctor at port-hole left center, cry, "Pistols." Beattie starts to push in gate, against which Squire is putting his weight, crying, "They're bursting in the door — A pistol!" Cannon shot. Jim rushes from house with four pistols of period, drops them at Smollett's feet, and rushes back to house. At this Thompson counts two and comes over wall, center, and Glocker appears with cutlass over wall right. Crittenden rushes from house and wrestles with Thompson for dagger, and Grey, with cutlass, rushes from house* and meets Glocker, who has jumped down, right center. Crittenden wrests dagger from Thompson's hand, kills him, and he falls, left center, against wall; Crittenden, who has been wounded in the fight, staggers back to house, and Grey fights Glocker into house. Glocker's arm and cutlass come through window of house as he cries, drops cutlass, and falls dead half through door. During all this, Smollett rushes with pistol to Squire, who shoots it through port-hole in gate. Joyce rushes center, picks pistol up and rushes back, firing it through port-hole above gate. Beattie forces open gate, and Squire grapples with him. Dr. Livesey, seeing this, rushes across to aid Squire, picking up pistol center as he does so, and they both force Beattie out of gate, fighting off after him. Cannon effect and volley. As Captain sees Squire and Dr. Livesey force Beattie out, he cries, rushing to the house, " My cutlass, Jim! " Jim hands it to him through window of house, and he rushes off right through gate, crying, " That's right, lads, we'll fight 'em in the open." As Captain makes rush to window for cutlass, Beecroft appears on roof of house, and Joyce rushes over and climbs up to meet him. They fight for flag on roof, which is thrown down as Jim rushes out of house with more pistols. Joyce kills Beecroft. Jim drops pistols center and, rushing over, hands one to Joyce, who jumps over stockade wall to outside. At first blow of Glocker's and Grey's fight, Anderson comes over wall center crying, "On, men, don't leave one of 'em — not one." Jim, after handing Joyce pistol, makes towards gate as if to escape, when Anderson jumps down and catches him right center upper, saying, "So! it's you, you young rat! " Jim cries out, "Let me go, let me go." Anderson, with dagger in left hand above Jim's head, says, "Let you go! Aye, here's where you go — a long, long way, lad!" Grey rushes from house with cutlass as Anderson says, "Aye," is about to kill Jim, — and runs him through, crying, "Anderson! " Anderson falls right center against wall. Grey says, "I was just in time, lad." Cannon and volley of shots. Jim retreats towards house, and Grey, exhausted, leans against stockade center; at this, Captain Smollett and Pons enter through gate, wrestling with cutlass, and Mayer and Hanauer appear on wall.

Hanauer, with dagger in left hand, jumps down and makes towards Smollett, and Mayer is half over when Squire and doctor enter gate and shoot them. Mayer hangs over wall dead, and Hanauer falls near wall center with head down stage and dagger in left hand for Jim to pick up later. By this time, Smollett has taken cutlass from Pons, and fights him off through gate; running him through with cutlass. Pons, with shriek, falls outside gate, Smollett comes back and closes gate, leaning against it.
[*At end of fight, Captain comes through door after killing pirate outside.*

SQUIRE. We've won! We've won!

JIM (*putting up flag again that has been knocked down by pirate on roof*). Hurrah!

SMOLLETT (*leaning against door*). That's right, lad, we'll never strike our colors.

[*All on stage shout "Hurrah" twice.*

DR. LIVESEY (*near log house door*). There's five of them that will never run again.

SMOLLETT. That leaves us four against nine. That's better odds than we had at starting.

[*Falls. Doctor catches him.*

DR. LIVESEY. Captain! You're wounded!

SMOLLETT (*sinking on right knee, looking up at doctor*). Now listen . . . quick . . . before they can reach the beach . . . beat 'em to the *Hispaniola* . . . cut her adrift, and you've got 'em, I tell you . . . you've got 'em. . . . Go . . . save the ship . . .

[*Falls back.*

[*Jim, who during speech takes dagger from dead pirate's hand, listens to what Smollett says, and exits through gate.*

CURTAIN

ACT III

SCENE IV

The Hispaniola tossing at sea with Jolly Roger flying at her forward mast. The ship itself is in motion, but evidently not

*under control.   The boat tosses and pitches as the sea runs high.
Black Dog and Hands are seen upon the deck of the ship, "locked
together" in deadly wrestle, each with a hand upon the other's
throat.   Finally they separate for a moment, and then knives
flash.   Black Dog by a quick movement wounds Hands in the
leg.   As he starts to follow up his advantage, Hands turns quickly,
catches Black Dog by the neck and holds him back against the
rigging, his knife at his throat.   Both are drunk.   Jim is seen
clinging to rope ladder at stern of ship, climbing up.*

HANDS (*as he gets wounded*).   Oh!   You would, would you?   Now
   you'll do as I say.
BLACK DOG.   Oh, I will, will I?
HANDS.   Them's Silver's orders.
BLACK DOG.   I'll take no orders from you.
HANDS.   Then for the last time — there — (*Kills Black Dog*)
   He's got me, got me in the leg.   I can't stand, I can't move
   — (*Sinks against mast forward.   Jim climbs on deck, comes to
   center of ship*)   Jim Hawkins!   Where'd you come from?
JIM.   I've cut this ship adrift, and I'm going to beach her in
   the north inlet.
HANDS.   Oh, you are — are you?
JIM.   Yes.
[*Goes up to tiller.*
HANDS.   Then you'll have to fight me for it, my friend.   It's
   you and me now, lad, for this ship — your life or mine!
[*During this speech, Hands crawls to upper side of mast aft.
Jim comes down from tiller.   Hands slips and falls to down-
stage side of ship.   Jim rushes around upstage side of mast
and makes for rigging of mast forward, which he climbs up.
When he is about half-way up, Hands regains his feet and follows
him.   As Jim gets to crosstree of mast, Hands starts to climb
up after him.*
HANDS.   That's right, run, but I'll get you — (*as he slips*)   By
   thunder, if this leg was right it would be quick work — but
   I've got you now.   You got away from Long John, but you
   won't get away from me.   I got a score to settle with you,

you young rat! You cut this ship adrift. It's you and me
for it. I got you up a tree, my young friend!

JIM (*in crosstrees*). Drop that knife, Mr. Hands, drop it!

HANDS (*in rigging*). All right then, take it —

[*Jim shoots Hands, who falls limp in the rigging.*

JIM (*after shooting Hands*). I've got the ship — I've got the
ship!

CURTAIN

ACT IV

SCENE I

Pirates in Camp.

*Drop showing seashore of island and camp-fire. Sea in dis-
tance. Trees. Pirates discovered asleep — only five left. Merry
sitting on barrel asleep, other pirates on ground. Picks and shovels
lying left. Silver is off stage. Jim comes on, sees Pirates, is
startled, and starts to run back, when Merry, who is awakened by
this time, catches hold of him.*

MERRY. No, you don't — no, you don't —

JIM (*pulling*). Let me be — let me be —

[*Pirates are awakening and get up, making group right of Merry.*

MERRY. Silver — Silver!

SILVER. Well!

[*Coming on.*

MERRY. Here's a nice little catch.

SILVER. Shiver my timbers!

MERRY. Jim Hawkins — and looking as brash as ever!

SILVER. Just dropped in for an early morning call. Well,
lad, speak up — speak up. I'm going to know what you've
been up to. Your friends thought they'd done for me, that
they'd get the ship and leave us here. But I fooled 'em! I've
got the only boat to reach that ship, and I've got it hidden —
I've beaten 'em — fooled 'em at every turn. . . .

JIM. Oh, have you?

SILVER. Aye, by gum, I have. . . .

JIM. Well, then, look there — The ship's gone!

[*All pirates look off.*

SILVER. Well, shiver my timbers!

MORGAN. Marooned!

[*All turn and face Jim.*

MERRY. Cockle-shells and goat skins for the rest of our lives.

MORGAN. Tricked! — beaten! — fooled!

JIM. Oh, I'm not such a fool that I don't know what I have to look for. Well, let the worst come . . . it's little I care . . . but there's a thing or two I have to tell you first. . . . You're in a bad way . . . ship's lost . . . treasure's lost . . . men lost . . . your whole business gone to wreck. . . . And do you want to know who did it? It was I.

MORGAN. You!

JIM. When I was in the apple barrel . . . I heard you, all of you . . . and told every word of it. And as for the *Hispaniola* — it was I who cut her hawser. . . . It was I who killed the men you had aboard her!

SILVER. You . . . you! . . .

JIM. I killed them, I tell you, and I brought that ship where you'll never see her more, not one of you. The laugh's on my side. I've had the top of this business from the first, and I no more fear you than I do a fly! (*As the men threaten but are held back by Silver*) Kill me, if you please, and do yourselves no good, or spare me, and keep a witness to save you from the gallows.

[*The men, with the exception of Silver, are in a little group, whispering together. Silver stands and stares at Jim.*

SILVER (*his manner has changed. He is no longer threatening, but rather sly as if feeling his way*). So you cut that boat adrift?

JIM. Yes.

MORGAN. Then, by thunder, here goes —

[*Morgan, with knife drawn, springs toward Jim, but Silver suddenly jumps in front of the boy, and stands between him and the men.*

SILVER. Avast there, Tom Morgan. Maybe you think you're

cap'n here. By the powers, I'll teach you better. Have I
lived this many years, and a son of a rum puncheon cock his
hat athwart my hawser at the latter end of it? Take a cutlass — him as dares — and I'll see the color of his insides!
(*Draws cutlass. As the men all draw away in a group and
whisper together*) So, you won't fight! Then, by thunder,
you'll obey! — I like that boy — he's more a man than any
pair of rats of you here, and — let me see him that'll lay a hand
on him. (*During this part of the speech, the men have come
back, with Merry at their head*) Well, Merry, you seem to
have something to say. Pipe up and let me hear it.
[*Puts cutlass back.*

MERRY. Ax your pardon, sir, you're pretty free with some of
the rules; maybe you'll kindly keep your eye on the rest —

SILVER. Meanin' by that?

MERRY. This crew's dissatisfied. This crew don't vally bully-
ing a marlinspike. This crew has rights — and by your own
rules we can talk together. I ax your pardon, sir, acknowledging you as cap'n at this present, but I claim my right
and step aside for a council.
[*Exit, after saluting Silver elaborately and motioning men with
head to follow him.*

ARROW. Crew's right.
[*Salutes and exits.*

MORGAN. Fo'c's'le council.
[*Salutes and exits.*

DIRK. Aye — fo'c's'le council —
[*Exits, shaking fist at Silver.*

SILVER (*intensely and confidentially as soon as they're gone*).
Boy, you're within half a plank of death and worse —

JIM (*coming to Silver's left*). What are they going to do?

SILVER. First they're going to tip me the Black Spot.

JIM. Same as Billy Bones?

SILVER. Aye — (*Takes Jim by the arm*) But I'm going to
stand by you, lad, through thick and thin.

JIM (*surprised*). What?

SILVER. I'll confess I didn't mean to till you spoke up and told

about that ship. . . .   Once I looked into the bay and seen
her gone . . . well, I'm tough, but I gave out . . . ship
gone . . . neck gone . . . that's about the size of it.   (*Intensely to Jim*)   Sure you've got her hidden?

JIM.   Yes, but I'll not tell where —

SILVER.   And I'm not going to ask — but — (*With intensity*)
You're sure she's safe?

JIM.   Yes — sure —

SILVER.   That being the case, why did the doctor give me that
chart?

[*Draws out the chart surreptitiously.*

JIM.   What?

SILVER (*as Jim looks startled*).   Aye, look at it! — Is that the
right one? — is it?

JIM (*impassioned*).   I don't know how you got this . . . what
torture you put them to . . . to make them give it to you
. . . but you'll never get that treasure home. . . .

SILVER.   Aye, lad . . . a proper spirit, but just now I'm thinking I'm your last card here, and, by the livin' thunder, you're
mine . . . I'll save your life, if so be I can . . . from them
in there . . . but tit for tat . . . you save Long John from
swinging when the time comes.

JIM.   I'll do what I can!

SILVER.   A bargain. . . .   Now understand . . . I'm on the
Squire's side, from now on.   I know when a game's up, I do,
and I know a lad as is staunch. . . .   Ah, you what's young
— you and me might have done a power of good together.

JIM.   Here they come!

[*Men come in and form group.*

SILVER.   Stand up plucky — and, by thunder, I still have a
shot in my locker for these lubbers.   (*As buccaneers hesitate to
approach*)   Well, step up.   I won't eat you.   Which has it?
You, George Merry?

MERRY (*comes timidly forward, urged by men*).   Aye, aye,
sir.

SILVER.   You always was a friend of mine, wasn't you, George?
Well, hand it over, lubber. . . .   I know the rules. . . .   I

won't hurt a depytation. (*Merry hands Silver the Black Spot. Silver glances at it and then holds it to Jim, right of him*) Jim, do you know what that is?

JIM. The Black Spot.

SILVER. Right you was. Jim, boy — (*taking Spot and examining it closely*) look here now — where would you say that was out from?

JIM. The Bible, sir. See, it reads, "Without are dogs and murderers" —

SILVER. Dogs and murderers. And very fitting, too. Look at 'em. What fool's cut a Bible . . . you . . . Merry? Well, no good'll come of it . . . you'll swing now . . . it ain't lucky.

MERRY (*advancing a little*). Oh, ain't it? This crew has tipped you the Black Spot in full council, as in dooty bound. . . . Just you look underneath, and see what's wrote there. . . .

SILVER. Thanky, George — you always was brisk for business. Well, what is it? (*Reads*) D-e-p-p-o-s-e-d — Dep-posed, and very pretty wrote, too.

MERRY. Come, you don't fool this crew no more. You're over now.

SILVER. Thought you said you knowed rules?

MERRY. Well?

SILVER. Well, according to rules, I'm still your cap'n till you outs with your grievances, and I reply.

MERRY. All right, then. First and last you made a hash of this cruise. And now, for some reason, you're holding back that boy from us. You've bungled the whole thing.

SILVER. Bungled? You say — bungled? By the powers, if you only knew how bad it's bungled. We're that near the gibbet my neck's stiff with thinking on it. And do you know all that stands between us and to swing and sun-dry? That boy. He may be our last chance. By thunder, you've neither sense nor memory. I let the Squire and his friends go. All right. And do you want to know why? Well, that's why. (*Takes out the chart and throws it to pirates. Morgan catches it*) I got what I wanted — I got the chart! (*As*

the men look at chart)   Aye, look at it.   Mull it over, you rum
puncheons — is it the real one this time or not?

MORGAN.   J. F., and a score below.

ARROW.   Flint's fist . . . blood and bones, mates.   The chart,
we've got the chart!

ALL.   Long John . . . Long John Silver! . . .

SILVER.   So that's your toon now?

ALL.   Captain Silver . . . Captain Silver! . . .

MORGAN.   Come, mates, picks and shovels.

[*Takes shovel.   Dirk takes pick.   Arrow and Dick take shovels.*

DICK.   Aye, the treasure — Flint's treasure-chest!

MERRY (*as they get things*).   Hold on!   Hold on!

MORGAN.   Well?

MERRY.   Supposin' we do find the treasure with this here —
(*pointing to chart*) how are we to get home with it, and us no
ship.

MORGAN.   By the powers, that's right.

ARROW (*appealing to Silver*).   Long John . . .

MERRY.   Aye . . . tell us that. . . . Silver, tell us that . . .

ALL.   Aye, how, how!

SILVER.   By the powers, but you ain't got the invention of a
cockroach. . . .   You can't find a way to get that money
home . . . not   you. . . .   It's   Silver . . . Silver. . . .
Well, then, I tell you . . . there's your chart, and that's the
way to Flint's treasure-chest . . . picks and shovels it is . . .
and once we find it . . . then, by thunder . . . (*turning to
Jim and grabbing him by collar*) if this boy doesn't lead us to
that boat I'll cut his heart out.

ALL.   That's right — kill the brat.

[*Ad lib., till off, menacing Jim.*

JIM.   Long John!

SILVER.   It's you and me now, lad, agin the five.   We'll save
our necks in spite of fate and fortune.

[*Starts to exit.*

CURTAIN

ACT IV

Scene II

The Spy-glass Mountain, a heavily wooded mountain side, with trees and shrubs, and a thick undergrowth, terminating in a large tree at center and up, the base of which alone can be seen. In front of this tree there is a small plateau, grown up on every side with shrubs. At bottom of tree, among the shrubs and partly concealed by them, a skeleton, with hands over its head, pointing to left, and feet extended in opposite direction. Ten feet to left of skeleton's hands is a cache, covered over with shrubs, the place where Flint buried the treasure; at foot of tree is broken pick, covered over with shrubbery; between cache and skeleton a small board with "Walrus" painted on it. Below cache is a two-guinea piece.

When the curtain rises, the pirates, with the exception of Dick, are seen grouped around Silver, studying the map. Dick sits upon ground, a little apart, his head in his hands, as if sick.

SILVER (*reads from map*). "Tall tree — Spy-glass shoulder, bearing a point to the N. of N.N.E. Skeleton Island, E.S.E., and by E., ten feet."

MERRY. This is Spy-glass shoulder.

[*Turning and looking around.*

ARROW. He buried it well — Flint did — in a wicked spot.

DICK (*sitting on ground. Starts up, looking off*). Listen —

SILVER. What?

DICK. It sounds like some one crying —

SILVER. Oh, go on! go on! It's a touch of the sun you've got, lad —

[*Turns to study his map.*

DICK. I tell you I heard it — heard it clear —

SILVER (*reading from the map*). "Tall — tree — Spy-glass shoulder, bearing a point to the N. of N.N.E." (*Turns to the men*) Well, lads, here we are — scatter — and look — try every tree. Keep an eye for some sign — scatter with you! (*The men spread about the mountain, looking at different trees. Dick looking off left listening*) Come, lad, come. We're getting near the treasure-chest.   Keep a sharp watch for whatever happens —

DICK (*suddenly cries out*).   There — there — it is again.   Don't you hear it?   Don't you?   (*As Silver stares at him*)   It isn't the sun — I did hear it, I tell you —

[*Suddenly Morgan gives a shout, uncovering the skeleton.*

SILVER.   What is it, Tom?   (*He and all the men rush to where stands Morgan, who is regarding a skeleton he has found*)   What is it?

MORGAN.   Look there —

[*The men all look and then draw back.*

MERRY.   By the powers — a skeleton!

DICK.   I knew I heard something.

[*Right of cache.*

ARROW.   Now, who d'ye think that might be?

MORGAN (*bends over, picking up a bit of sea-cloth from skeleton*). He was a seaman — leastways, this is good sea-cloth.

MERRY.   You wouldn't think to find a bishop here, would you?

SILVER (*who has been studying skeleton*).   Aye, — but what sort of a way is that for bones to lie?

MORGAN.   Hands pointing one way . . . feet t'other . . .

MERRY.   Like a blessed diver he is.

SILVER.   'Tain't in natur'.

MORGAN.   It ain't, and that's a fact.

SILVER.   Lads, I'm thinkin' if this could be one of Flint's jokes now?   (*As the men question*)   Six came ashore when he buried the treasure — none came back.   (*Examines the skeleton*) Long bones . . . and hair's been yellow . . .

DIRK.   Allerdyce!

SILVER.   Aye, that might be Allerdyce . . . you mind him, Merry?

MERRY.   Aye, that I do . . . he owed me money, he did . . . and took my knife ashore with him . . .

MORGAN.   Well, there's little enough about him now . . . not a thing left . . . not a copper doit . . . nor a baccy box.

MERRY.   That's queer. . . .   Flint weren't a man to pick a seaman's pocket.

SILVER. By thunder, that's right.

MERRY. It don't look nat'ral to me.

SILVER. No, by gum, it don't . . . not nat'ral and not nice.
. . . Great guns, messmates, but if Flint was living now, this
would be a hot spot for you and me. Six they were and six
are we; and bones is what they are now.

[*Men cover up skeleton during the speech and drop down
stage.*

DICK (*starts up*). There. . . . There it is again. . . .

SILVER. Avast there, Dick! Flint's dead.

MERRY. Aye, I saw him with these here deadlights . . . Billy
Bones took me in. And there he lay with penny pieces on
his eyes.

DICK. Aye, but if ever sperrit walked it would be Flint's . . .

MERRY. Dear heart, but he died hard.

MORGAN. Raged and hollered for rum, and sang "Fifteen Men."

MERRY. It was main hot, and the windy was open, and I hear
that old song comin' out as clear as clear . . . and him with
the death-haul on him already.

SILVER. Come, stow that talk . . . Flint's dead and he won't
walk.

DIRK. He's wise who could say that.

[*Song starts center, behind drop.*

DICK (*suddenly*). You must hear it now . . . you must . . .

[*From the distance and in a weird voice there is heard:*
    "Fifteen men on a dead man's chest,
        Yo-ho-ho and a bottle of rum," etc.

[*There is sudden consternation among the pirates as they stop,
stunned.*

[*Jim goes and looks off right.*

MERRY. Bottle o' rum. (*In awed whisper*) Flint's voice.

MORGAN. Aye, and his song!

DICK. I told you I heard something . . . I told you . . .

MERRY. He were an ugly debil, were Flint . . . and that blue
in the face . . .

MORGAN. Blue . . . that's the word.

ARROW (*coming down*). That was how the rum took him!

SILVER (*suddenly recovering*).   Come . . . come . . . this won't do. . . .   Stand by to go about!

MERRY.   No — no, Long John.

SILVER.   This is only some one what's sky-larking . . . some one what's flesh and blood.

MORGAN.   It was Flint's way of singing . . .

MERRY.   Aye, and his wery tones . . . I'll swear to that.

SILVER.   I tell you it's flesh and blood, and I'll prove it to you . . .

DICK.   Stop! Oh, stop!

SILVER.   Now, by the powers, Dick, another word and I'll crack your skull with this. . . .
[*Raising crutch.*

DICK.   Listen.
[*In terror they all stop and there comes from the distance a wailing voice.*

VOICE.   Darby M'Graw . . . Darby M'Graw . . . Darby M'Graw. . . .

MERRY (*in terrified whisper sinks to the ground*).   Oh, listen to that!!!

VOICE.   Fetch aft the rum, Darby.

MERRY.   Fetch aft the rum! That fixes it! Them was his last words!

MORGAN.   No one on this island ever heard of Darby but us here.

MERRY.   It's Flint, mates. Oh, I'm all over goose-flesh. Oh!

SILVER.   What's the matter with you now!

MERRY (*indicating skeleton*).   I think he bit me! I'm going back!

SILVER.   No, I never feared Flint alive, and, by the powers, I'll face him dead!

MERRY.   Oh, no . . . no, John . . . don't go . . . it ar'n't lucky. . . .   I think it's Friday. . . . No, don't you cross the sperrit.
[*On his knees, hands clasped.*

SILVER.   Sperrit . . . well, maybe. . . . Why, you rum puncheon, if you had listened, you'd ha'e noticed an echo.

TREASURE ISLAND

Act IV. Scene ii

Silver.—"No! No! No! I'm here to get that stuff, and I'll not be
beat by man or devil . . . ."

MERRY. Well?

[*Rising.*

SILVER. Well, no man has ever seen a sperrit with a shadow. Well, then what's he doin' with an echo to him, eh? And as for that voice, it may be like Flint's, but it's a deal more like another's.

MORGAN. Whose?

SILVER. Ben Gunn's.

MEN. Ben Gunn!

MERRY. By the powers, it is.

JIM (*left of Silver, startled*). Ben Gunn?

SILVER. Aye, Ben Gunn! That's who it is.

DICK. But Ben Gunn ain't alive any more'n Flint.

MERRY. Sho! Nobody minds Ben Gunn . . . dead or alive.

DICK. Let's turn back, Silver.

MORGAN. Aye . . . back it is. . . .

SILVER. No! No! No! I'm here to get that stuff, and I'll not be beat by man or devil. . . . There's 700,000 pounds buried here . . . and when did ever a gentleman of fortune show his stern to that much dollars, for a boozy old seaman with a blue mug, and him dead. And as for this fellow here . . . (*Points to skeleton. All look at it*) I've taken a notion in my old numskull, as how Flint hauled him here and laid him down by compass.

MORGAN. What for?

SILVER. For a p'inter.

MERRY. What!

[*There is general excitement among the men.*

SILVER (*to Morgan*). Tom, here's a compass . . . just take a bearing along the line of them bones. . . . I'm thinking maybe this here's the sign we're looking for. Well?

[*Morgan gets compass and then takes bearing of bones.*

MORGAN (*while the men wait eagerly*). E. S. E. and by E.

SILVER (*reads from map*). And the chart reads E. S. E. and by E., ten feet. It was one of Flint's jokes, and no mistake. . . . Now scatter, lads, and look . . . ten feet, search . . . search with you. . . .

[*All search.*

[*Arrow works towards board with "Walrus" on it.*

[*Dirk works around upper head of cache, leaving pick.*

[*Morgan counts ten and walks a few paces right and then back till he discovers pick.*

[*Dick crawls around, looking on ground.*

ARROW.   Ah, a board with "Walrus" on it!

ALL.   Ah!

SILVER.   You're getting near it.   Go on, go on, hurry. . . .

DICK.   A two-guinea piece.

[*All look at it from respective positions, then continue search.*

SILVER.   We've got it!   We've got it!   There's 700,000 more. . . .

DIRK (*at left of cache*).   By the powers, we'll take it home with us, all of it.

ALL.   Silver, Silver forever!

ARROW (*with shout of delight discovers cache*).   Ah, look here. Flint's treasure-chest, it's here, lads, it's here!   (*Yell of delight from all, and they kneel around brink.   They shout, "Huzzah! Huzzah!"*)   We're rich, lads, we're rich.

SILVER.   Aye, lads, rich, rich. . . .   Kings. . . .

ARROW (*rising*).   Ah!   Empty.

MORGAN.   What?

DICK.   What?

MERRY.   Empty!

ARROW.   Aye, empty! . . . rifled . . . don't yer see . . . can't you understand?

DIRK.   And this what we've risked our lives for?

MORGAN.   Swing for nothing.

DICK.   And twenty of us have died for.

MERRY.   Aye, lads, done, and do you want to know whose done it?   Look there — (*pointing to Silver*) it's that old cripple there as has done it.   That's why he's protected the boy.

MORGAN.   And wouldn't give him up.

ARROW.   He's going for the ship with him.

SILVER (*puts Jim behind him*).   Stand by for trouble, lad.

MERRY. Look at him, lads, — see it in the face of him; he's sold us, mates, sold us!

ARROW. Tear him to pieces!

[*Advancing toward Silver.*

DICK. I'll have his heart's blood!

[*Advancing toward Silver.*

DIRK. Tear his heart out!

[*Advancing toward Silver.*

MORGAN. Kill him, kill him!

[*Advancing toward Silver.*

SILVER. Stop. The first man that takes a step in this direction, I'll fire.

[*Drawing his pistol and covering men.*

MERRY. Then you'll have to fire. Here goes. . . .

[*Merry advances on Silver, who shoots him.*

ARROW. He's fired his last shot. We've got 'em now.

[*Silver throws pistol away and draws cutlass as pirates advance. Ben Gunn comes on and shoots.*

[*Arrow falls left, half off in entrance. Dick falls left of cache.*

[*Morgan right of cache. Dirk falls left off out of sight.*

[*Dr. Livesey and Grey enter, shooting two pirates. Shots off stage. Other pirates fall.*

DR. LIVESEY. Jim — Jim —

SILVER. He's safe, sir. I've got the lad safe. You were just about in the nick, I guess, for me and Hawkins.

DR. LIVESEY. And we have this man to thank for saving you, lad.

JIM. Ben Gunn.

[*Crossing to Gunn.*

SILVER. Ben Gunn!

GUNN. Aye, I'm poor Ben Gunn, I am. How d'ye do, Mr. Silver? Pretty well, I thank you, says you.

SILVER. But one man of her crew alive what put to sea with seventy-five, and to think it's you who's done me, Ben Gunn!

DR. LIVESEY. Aye, Silver — that he has.

JIM. But, Doctor, the treasure . . . it's gone!

BEN GUNN. Aye, gone! that it is, and do you want to know

where its gone? (*Silver advances towards Gunn*) Well, come along with me, mates, and I'll show you . . . come. . . .

SILVER.   Aye, come, mates — come. . . .   He'll show us.
[*Laughs.*

CURTAIN

ACT IV

SCENE III

Drop showing Ben Gunn's cave. Transparent center, showing sea in distance, and entrance of cave. At right is smouldering fire, at left is pile of gold, of gold bars, of bags of gold, etc., representing Flint's treasure.

Gunn and Jim enter. Gunn lights torch in fire, and crosses to pile of gold, holding torch above it.

GUNN.   I told you, lad, you'd bless the day you was the first to find Ben Gunn, for, Jim, I'll make you rich, lad, rich.
[*Shows Jim treasure.*

JIM.   Oh!
[*Crossing to gold.*

GUNN.   Three years, day by day, it took Ben Gunn to fetch it here.
[*Taking up money and letting it stream through his hands.*

JIM.   Oh, it's wonderful! Wonderful! More than I ever dreamed of!

SILVER (*without*).   Ahoy! Ship-ahoy! Shipmates, ahoy!

JIM.   Squire . . . Dr. Livesey . . . Captain . . . we've got it. . . .   We've got it!
[*Rushing up stage to meet Dr. Livesey. Squire and others come on with lanterns. Silver comes on with parrot, and Smollett and Grey enter.*
[*Jim runs back to gold.*

SQUIRE.   Well, bless my soul. . . .

DR. LIVESEY.   Flint's treasure. . . .

SQUIRE.   Our search is at an end, gentlemen. Here's fortunes for us all.

SILV[...]

SQUIRE[...]

retreats[...]

DR. LIVESEY[...]

JIM (*crossing to*[...]

DR. LIVESEY.   Jim,[...]
if we have found t[...]
we owe it all to you! [...]
on Jim's shoulder)   Gentl[...]
Hawkins — officer of the crown[...]

ALL (*saluting*).   Jim Hawkins, officer[...]
Hurrah!   Hurrah!

CURTAIN

brought to his such characters as *A* *Winter* and *Mr* *Conscious Thought*, *Melancholy* and *Vain Thought*. And though the pageant itself was written for persons old and young, there were parts in this charming little play...

THE SLIPPERS OF CINDERELLA

No one is in more proper mood when he writes a play than
W. Graham Robertson. Give him an occasion like a birthday, or
a local celebration, like his pageant of Guilford, and his whole heart
is tumultuous, his whole strength is given to the task. I have
encountered no writer who is more on the side of young folk than
he. Like the present Editor, I am inclined to believe that he views
girls and boys as if they had some ideas as to what they themselves
liked or didn't like in the way of drama. He writes:

"Of what interest to my volcanic Leading Lady, a strong emotional actress rising ten and already with an eye on *Lady Macbeth*,
were the pastoral but puny woes of *Little Bo-Peep?* What in
common had my elegantly fastidious *Jeune Premier* of eight with
Tommy Tucker or *Little Jack Horner*, whose table manners had long
since caused him to drop their acquaintance? All had left the
Nursery far, far behind, from the youngest Extra Lady to the
Veteran tottering soberly into her teens, and their point of view
seemed identical with that of the adult Thespian."

I can imagine, from the correspondence I have had with Mr.
Graham Robertson, that he must live in a country where the
children, as they grow older, make their elders grow young. I can
imagine him among his little actors, who have played so many years
in his dramas, as Lewis Carroll was with the girls among whom he
found the key to "Alice in Wonderland." He says in a letter,
describing the beautiful pictorial colors of his pageant of Guilford:

"The early training of my 'Children's Troupe' came in very
usefully. 'Jimmy' (aged ten when in 'The Slippers of Cinderella')
at seventeen made a lovely *Elaine*, and 'Myra' developed into
Faithful."

In that Surrey country, with all its historical association, what
richness of pageantry may one not have. And so "The Town of
the Ford ", as written by him, gave a panorama of Guilford, which

brought to life such characters as *St. Martha* and *St. Catherine*, *Launcelot* and *Elaine*, *Alfred the Great*, *Geoffrey Chaucer*, *Queen Elizabeth*, and *John Bunyan*. And, though the pageant as a whole was written for a local celebration, I know of several scenes in this charming decoration which might, in themselves, prove excellent separate pictures. There could be no prettier glimpse than that given of Chaucer with the flower children. He enters, just after the passing of some devout Pilgrims. These have been so intent on their journey that they have brushed aside the posies proffered them. The directions follow :

Children crowd round Chaucer with their posies. A little girl, who has followed the first band of Pilgrims, returns weeping. She carries some wilted daisies.

CHAUCER

. . . Nay, stynt thee, my litel oone ; what harmeth thee ?

CHILD

The Pilgrims wol not of my floures lest they withdraw their thoughtes from Hevene.

(*Chaucer glances at her flowers, then kneels beside her*)

CHAUCER

What thinke you of al floures I love most ?

CHILD

(*Sobbing*)   The violete — the oxlip ?

CHAUCER

Nay, I love
That floure whyte al other floures above
Swich as men callen daysies in oure toun :
For these I keep my great affeccioun.
This dayesye, of alle floures flour,
Fulfild of vertu and of alle honour,
And even ylyke faire and fresh of hewe
As wel in wynter as in somer newe.

CHILD

(*Joyfully*) And I have none but daysies!

CHAUCER

Then, pardee,
This posye was ygadered al for me.

(*Chaucer goes up with the children, to whom he seems to tell stories*)

Indeed, this gives us a view of Graham Robertson's simplicity, and of Chaucer's human sunniness. The more I read of plays the more I believe in the unpretentious scene, not only because it is easy to give, easy to memorize, easy to understand; but because it reaches the heart so directly. That is one of the chief beauties about Mr. Drinkwater's "Abraham Lincoln." It is surprising how a small flash like the scene I have just quoted would make a moment on the school platform, if acted before simple gray curtains, with delicate colors of costumes and flowers, which one would remember long after the ordinary tableau dialogue is forgotten. With a little imagination, with the training of the voice to be beautifully musical, think of what might be done with even such a love lyric (question and answer) as the following, written by the poet, Robert Herrick.

UPON LOVE, BY WAY OF QUESTION AND ANSWER

I bring ye love. *Quest.* What will Love do?
Ans. Like and dislike ye.
I bring ye Love. *Quest.* What will Love do?
Ans. Stroake ye to strike ye.
I bring ye Love. *Quest.* What will Love do?
Ans. Love will befoole ye.
I bring ye Love. *Quest.* What will Love do?
Ans. Heate ye to coole ye.
I bring ye Love. *Quest.* What will Love do?
Ans. Love gifts will send ye.
I bring ye Love. *Quest.* What will Love do?
Ans. Stock ye to spend ye.

I bring ye Love.   *Quest.* What will Love do?
   Ans. Love will fulfill ye.
I bring ye Love.   *Quest.* What will Love do?
   Ans. Kisse ye, to kill ye.

It does not take so very much ferreting to select the most beautiful thing to do rather than the wooden thing. If only one has the imagination and enthusiasm of a Graham Robertson, one can find at hand matter for any sort of pageant. I came across a glowing essay by Charles Lamb, wherein the Months are described so much in detail that any person dressed according to his plan would be the very embodiment of the season. I looked through Lamb's "The Masque of Days", as illustrated by Walter Crane, and the delicate tints of the pictures were challenging of all sorts of stage possibilities.

So, Mr. Graham Robertson's letters always suggest excellent freshness to me. "The Slippers of Cinderella" is just such a play as his Troupe wanted. His Troupe were children in 1919, and children the English-speaking world over are just the same in 1926 or any other year.

THE SLIPPERS OF CINDERELLA

AN IMPOSSIBILITY IN ONE ACT

By W. GRAHAM ROBERTSON

CHARACTERS

MYRA TREMAINE

POLLY TREMAINE ⎱ *Twins*
DOLLY TREMAINE ⎰

JIMMY TREMAINE

BELINDA TREMAINE

AGATHA-NEXT-DOOR

JANE

ELIZA

THE FAIRY GODMOTHER

THE SLIPPERS OF CINDERELLA

SCENE. *A very shabby parlour. At back is a curtained window on one side of which stands a bookcase, on the other a Grandfather clock stopped at twenty minutes past eleven. A fireplace right with mirror over mantelpiece. Doors right and left. Myra, a tall girl of fourteeen, sits at a table mending Jimmy's coat while he stands in his shirt sleeves watching the operation. Belinda sits on a stool by the fire absorbed in a book. The curtains are drawn and the room lit. It is about five o'clock on the 31st of October.*

MYRA. There. That's the best I can do with it. Really, Jimmy, anyone would think that you walked on your elbows.

JIMMY (*putting on coat*). Thanks awfully. Does it look very patchy?

MYRA. Not so bad. You must try and keep full face when there's company, and sit with your back to the wall.

JIMMY. I don't do much sitting in these knickers; they're at their last gasp.

MYRA. I suppose we're a very discontented family. When we had all the nice things we didn't particularly notice them; now we haven't got them we miss them dreadfully.

JIMMY. It's not so much having no nice things as having nasty ones that I object to.

BELINDA (*holding out her frock*). I know. I never cared for this when it was Myra's, and when it was cut up for Dolly I hated it. Now it's mine I simply loathe it.

JIMMY. At any rate you don't run the risk of going off with a bang whenever you sit down. (*Walks drearily to the window, draws aside curtain and stares into the darkness*) What time will the Old Dears be back, Myra?

MYRA. I don't quite know; mother said she would telegraph. O Jimmy, I do hope to goodness th⬛⬛⬛⬛⬛⬛ this appointment.

JIMMY. Estate Agent to Lord What's-his-name, isn't it?

MYRA. Yes. What exactly are the duties of an Estate Agent, Jimmy?

JIMMY. O — you wear riding breeches, you know, and — well, you tell the other fellows to do the rest.

BELINDA. I'm sure father could do that beautifully.

MYRA. And it would show off his nice legs. I've always recommended the ballet or a Bishopric.

JIMMY. I suppose it wouldn't exactly restore the fallen fortunes of our house?

MYRA. Not quite, of course, but we should be in the country again and poor Jane would be able to remember whether she's nurse or parlourmaid or cook. (*Enter right Polly and Dolly in hats and coats. They carry satchels which they throw down*) Hullo, Tweenies, late aren't you?

POLLY. Not particularly. It's so dark; there's a fog coming on, I think.

DOLLY. A good, thick yellow one. Ugh. (*Shivers. The Twins take off hats and coats and throw them down*) And lots of the girls have got parties. It's Hallowe'en, you know.

BELINDA. O Dolly — Hallowe'en, when all the Fairies are abroad?

POLLY. Little silly with your Fairies.

DOLLY. What are you stodging over? (*Looking over Belinda's shoulder*) Cinderella, of course.

MYRA. Fairies won't come our way, I'm afraid. Now, children, you must clear away all that litter (*pointing to coats*) and then try to get yourselves decently clean.

TWINS (*open-mouthed*). Clean? What ever for?

MYRA. Have you forgotten High Tea and Aunt Maria?

JIMMY. I say, Myra — it isn't *this* evening?

POLLY. And the Old Dears away, and just us — we, I mean?

MYRA. It is — worse luck. She's going to take me to a Lecture.

JIMMY. Oughtn't we to have run to dinner for Aunt? She's one of the idle rich, you know.

MYRA. The .... besides, I thought High Tea rather a good .... without the opulence of dinner.

JIMMY.   Filling, but not fashionable, eh?

POLLY.   What's the Lecture about?

MYRA.   Economy.

DOLLY.   What is economy?

MYRA.   I believe it teaches you how to spend very little money.

JIMMY.   We don't find much difficulty in doing *that*. Now, if it taught you how to spend a great deal of money when you haven't got any, then there'd be sense in it.

MYRA.   I'm not sure, but I can't help fancying that father looks to Aunt Maria to do that.

TWINS.   Aunt Maria?

MYRA.   She's tremendously rich, you know. Simply frightfully. And you see, if she took a fancy to one of us —

JIMMY.   Or even two — we could offer the pair of Twins at a reduction.

DOLLY.   O do chuck it, Jimmy. I don't know why there should be anything absurd about being a twin — but there *is*.

POLLY.   Yes. You needn't rub it in.

JIMMY.   Well, unless I'm much mistaken she'll go in for quality, not quantity. A stalwart nephew to support her tottering steps will about fill her bill, I should say.

MYRA.   Or a sensible, elderly niece who would be a companion to her.

BELINDA.   Or a dear little girl to brighten her declining — O don't, Jimmy.

[*Jimmy shies a cushion at her.*

POLLY.   But why Aunt Maria *now?* She has hardly ever come near us.

JIMMY.   She doesn't like us; and she's only a half Aunt really, you know.

BELINDA.   O Jimmy, how dreadful. Which half?

JIMMY.   Shut up.

MYRA.   She saw Jimmy and me when we were little and loathed us; now, I suppose, she's coming back with a fresh eye to see if she likes us any better.

JIMMY (*gloomily*).   She won't.

MYRA.   No, I don't suppose she will. Of course, from the

pathetic point of view, we should have made a better show as orphans.

DOLLY. We can't very well work that.

MYRA. Hardly, with a brace of parents in robust health on the premises. If we only knew her taste we could play up better.

POLLY. If we each take a different line she may find one of us sympathetic.

MYRA. Good idea, Polly. Now — who shall be what? How about the Tweenies?

JIMMY. One can be pretty and the other good.

POLLY. Bags I being pretty.

DOLLY. No, Polly, you're ever so much better than I am. *I'll* be pretty.

JIMMY. Toss up — your call, Polly.

POLLY. Heads.

JIMMY (*tossing a penny*). Tails. Dolly's pretty, you're good. Then there must be a clever one who swots over lessons — Auntie may like that sort — and we ought to have an angel child.

MYRA. I'm the clever one, I suppose: that leaves Belinda for the angel child.

JIMMY. Belinda, forward please.

BELINDA (*advancing bashfully*). O Jimmy —

JIMMY (*sternly*). No back answers. You'll be sitting at the window, your wistful gaze fixed upon the distant hills.

BELINDA. You can't see anything but chimney-pots from this window — and it's pitch dark.

JIMMY. S-sh. And when she comes in you'll look up with a sad smile.

MYRA. Let's try it once over and see how it works out. (*Group formed. Belinda at window, Myra sitting at table and the Twins gracefully posed at her feet*) I ought to be reading aloud something improving.

JIMMY (*at bookcase*). Try "Flowering Plants of Great Britain"; some of the words in that are a fair treat. Catch. (*Myra fields a heavy volume with difficulty*) Now — picture; the

Poor but Virtuous Family. H'm-m. Not bad. Why are you making those silly faces, Dolly?

DOLLY. I'm looking pretty; you told me to.

JIMMY. Better cut out the prettiness — it would put any Aunt off. That's better. Don't grin, Belinda.

BELINDA. You told me to. That's the sad smile.

JIMMY. Cut out the sad smile. What utter poops you girls are. You've no more notion of — I say, here *is* somebody! Now then, Myra — and don't look up any one when the door opens. Let it all soak in.

MYRA (*reading*). "In plants of the Umbelliferous Tribe the floral leaves, grown in a whorl and forming what is termed an Involucre, often grow at the base of the general and partial umbels —"

[*Jane appears at door.*

JANE. If you please, Miss Myra, could I speak to you for a minute?

MYRA. Jane! *Not* the kitchen flue?

JANE. No, Miss.

MYRA. Then I can bear it. What's the matter?

JANE. Nothing, Miss, leastways no more than usual; but was you wishful that I should be dressed for the door, seeing I'm to dish up the minute your Aunt comes and everything so to speak trembling in the balance?

MYRA. O Jane, I'm afraid so. Mother made such a point of it.

JANE. Then 'Eaven 'elp the lemon soles, Miss, that's all I can say. No, Miss Myra, I can open a door with anyone in the land and I can cook you a sole as wouldn't have disgraced your Pa's table in the Dogwood Park days, but I can't do 'em both at once and keep my reason and so I tell you.

MYRA (*rising, and taking Jane's hand*). Jane, dear, we must forget the Dogwood Park days. We've all come down in the world now, and you were a dear old silly to come with us.

JANE (*tearfully*). And do I ever complain, Miss Myra? Do I mind being engaged as a General and doing the work of a Commander-in-Chief? Do I mind sleeping in what you may

well call the pantry, for pant you do with a window the size of a sixpence and arm-in-arm with the boiler — but dress for the door and leave them blessed soles, lemon though they be, and never would Mrs. Silverside have allowed such things to breathe the air of Dogwood Park while *she* was housekeeper — Well, Miss Myra, we lives and we learns, and I *may* learn to be in two places at once and do a dozen things at the same time — I may or I may *not*, but — (*Myra looks anxiously at Jane and sniffs suspiciously. Jane sniffs*) Something burning? There! If I turn my back half a minute — though I suppose we should reckon it as one of the blessings of living in a rabbit hutch; what's done in the kitchen you smell in the attic.
[*She dashes from the room.*

MYRA (*laughing*). Poor, dear Jane. I always smell burning when she gets a little long winded; it sends her off like a shot. But now, seriously, children, this is *my* evening, and the important question is — what *am* I to wear? Mother particularly said that it was to be "quiet and appropriate." What would be appropriate for an Economy Lecture?

JIMMY. Your oldest frock, or none at all, I should say.

MYRA. But you couldn't call that quiet. As a fact, I haven't got anything. Agatha-next-Door offered me the loan of a purple velvet trimmed with swansdown, but I thought *not*.

DOLLY. What on earth made you tell *her* about it?

JIMMY. If there is one thing beastlier than the general beastliness of everything it's the continued patronage of Agatha-next-Door.

POLLY. And her habit of "dropping in to play with us" as she puts it.

DOLLY. At all hours.

MYRA. She's really quite a good sort, and it's nice of her to offer her frocks. The mere fact that one wouldn't be found dead in them ought not to weigh with us. But I *do* wish that I had something decent.

DOLLY. What we want is a little woman to come in.

BELINDA (*suddenly*). What we want is a Fairy Godmother.

ALL (*in scorn*). A Fairy Godmother?

BELINDA. Yes, and the Old Dears ought to have seen about it long ago.

MYRA. Belinda, you are not to call father and mother the Old Dears. I've told you over and over again.

BELINDA. But you and Jimmy — O!

JIMMY (*shying another cushion*). Shut it, Belinda.

MYRA. All the same there's something in the idea. The Fairy Godmother would merely wave her wand and there should I be, "quiet and appropriate."

POLLY. And a lovely Motor to take you to the Lecture.

MYRA. And a splendid person to open the door in a gold laced coat and canary coloured knee-breeches.

DOLLY. My dear Myra, Jane would die first.

MYRA (*laughing*). So she would: I forgot Jane. Well, then a beautiful Greek maiden in flowing raiment and wreathed with roses.

JIMMY. And the High Tea. Peacock pasties, haunches of venison, grapes, pineapples — my eye!

MYRA. Ah, Jimmy, I'm afraid that Fairy Days are over. It is not for us poor moderns to stand in the slippers of Cinderella.

[*A knock at the door.*

POLLY (*in horror*). Not Aunt? Not yet?

A VOICE (*without*). May I come in?

JIMMY. Worse. Agatha. (*Shouting*) O, come in.

[*Enter Agatha, a very pretty girl but showily and badly dressed.*

AGATHA. Jane had the door open, so I thought I would just drop in to —

JIMMY. I know. To play with us. We are feeling particularly sportive this evening. Let me introduce Miss Myra Tremaine, the Champion Kiss-in-the-Ring player, and Miss Belinda Tremaine, who holds the cup for Hop Scotch.

MYRA (*taking Agatha's hand and looking her up and down*). Dear me, Agatha, another smart frock. You look like a bridesmaid.

POLLY. Sorry to disappoint you but Belinda's engagement to the Archbishop of Canterbury is off.

DOLLY. Because she objects to his smoking all over the house.

AGATHA (*sinking into a chair and holding out her frock*). This smart? My dear, my maid ran this up for me ages ago: it's as old as the hills and washes like a rag. By-the-bye, I came upon something that might be useful to you for to-night. I know you're such a one for the quiet shades. It's that very soft tone of pink; frazy crazy the French call it.

MYRA (*puzzled*). What? O, I see. Fraise écrasée — crushed strawberry. It's ever so kind of you, Agatha dear, but you really mustn't trouble.

AGATHA. Trouble's a pleasure, I'm sure. My little maid shall run for it — she's waiting outside. (*Calling*) Faites monter le carton, Elise — tut — stupid of me. It seems so natural to speak to one's fum de chambre in French. (*Calling*) Bring up the box I left in our hall, Elise.

JIMMY. What's your — er — fum de chambre doing here?

AGATHA. She came round with me, of course; Mamma would not dream of letting me go out unattended. So you are entertaining this evening?

MYRA. Only Lady Errington.

AGATHA (*eagerly*). Lady Errington?

POLLY. That's Aunt Maria.

AGATHA. Lady Errington. O — but oughtn't you to smarten up a bit? With a yard or two of Art Muslin and a few pins I could make this a different room. Mamma always says I am such a one for the delicate touches. Have you got the right cards to the top in the card plate?

DOLLY. We haven't a card plate.

POLLY. And only the Sweep's card to put in it if we had.

AGATHA. Ah, well, you're newcomers, you see, and perhaps we *are* a little exclusive. How would it be if *I* stayed to dinner so as to give a tone and to show her Ladyship that you visit with the *better* houses in the neighbourhood?

JIMMY. But next door is just like this house.

AGATHA (*gently*). We come at the end of the row, you see, dear. That makes us Semi-detached, doesn't it?

MYRA (*smiling*). And is that very distinguished? We're dreadfully ignorant.

AGATHA. Well, after the Semi you come to the Detached — in gardens — and there you practically touch the County.

MYRA. Do you?

AGATHA. At any rate the Landed Gentry. (*A knock. Enter a very small child in cap and apron, carrying a large dress box*) There. Now we'll just have a peep and then you must let Elise get you into it. So much depends upon the way a thing's worn.

MYRA. O, but — please Agatha, I couldn't think of troubling — er — Elise.

AGATHA. My dear, what has she to do? A little light fancy work —

ELIZA (*anxiously*). Please, Miss —

AGATHA. A little lace to mend — what is it, Elise?

ELIZA. If you please, Miss, I was to get back to the potatoes the very minute you'd finished with me.

AGATHA (*hastily*). Open the box at once, Elise. There! (*An appalling garment is disclosed*) Now, won't that be just the thing? Dressy, you know, and yet only a simple little demi-toilette.

[*Myra gazes in stricken silence, then kisses Agatha.*

MYRA. Thank you, Agatha. It's wonderful. It's — it's wonderful. Isn't it, girls?

AWED CHORUS. Quite — quite wonderful.

MYRA. And I'm sure it would be *just* right for *some* occasions —

JIMMY (*very politely*). The Fifth of November, for instance.

MYRA. Jimmy! But I'm afraid it's a little too smart for me.

AGATHA. Ah, but wait till you see it on. Take the box upstairs, Elise.

[*Agatha opens door left for Eliza who staggers out with box.*

JIMMY (*softly*). Myra, you can't. You'd look like a Sweep on May Day.

MYRA. Of course I can't, but we mustn't hurt her feelings.

AGATHA (*at door*). Come along, Myra.

MYRA (*to Jimmy*). You come too, and we'll work it somehow.

AGATHA (*archly*). Yes, Mr. Jimmy, you come too and give your opinion. We all know how particular the gentlemen are. [*Exeunt Myra, Agatha and Jimmy.*

POLLY (*giggling*). "The gentlemen." Why not "gents"?

DOLLY. "There you touch the County."

BELINDA (*looking up suddenly from her book*). Brutes, both of you.

POLLY. Brutes?

BELINDA. She's nice and kind and pretty, and you're always horrid to her. And Myra told you to clear up the room and wash yourselves.

POLLY. Well — I — never.

DOLLY. For the first time I realize the feelings of Balaam.

POLLY (*severely*). Belinda clears up the room for sheer, unprovoked cheek.

DOLLY (*twitching away Belinda's book*). Step lively, Belinda.

BELINDA (*rising*). All right. I don't mind. I may as well fag for you as for Jimmy. (*She takes up Polly's coat. Three small objects fall from the pocket*) Hullo. Chestnuts. (*Picking them up*) Only three?

DOLLY. Hand them over. We'll roast them now — there'll be one each. (*She arranges the three chestnuts on the bars of the grate*) That's mine, that's Polly's and that's Belinda's — if she behaves herself.

POLLY. One of the girls gave them to me because it's Hallowe'en. I forget why.

DOLLY (*kneeling on the rug*). I know. If your chestnut pops and jumps off the bar you get a wish — your Heart's Desire, as some silly book calls it. What's your Heart's Desire, Polly?

POLLY (*with a sigh*). I couldn't possibly stuff 'em into one chestnut; I've got so many.

DOLLY (*clearing the fire with the poker*). So have I. And of course it *is* all nonsense: Jane might just as well expect to get her Heart's Desire from a lemon sole.

BELINDA. Dolly, you mustn't talk like that on Hallowe'en. It's the great Fairy night, and I'm sure we *ought* to wish.

POLLY. Well, there's your chestnut. Wish away and see what your Fairies can do for you.

BELINDA (*with closed eyes and tightly clenched hands*). Then I wish — O, I *do* wish — that a Fairy Godmother would appear and give us *all* our wishes. Why shouldn't she come to us as well as to Cinderella? *She* only wanted to go to a silly ball; *we* want such lots of things.

[*The room darkens and a loud pop is heard.*

POLLY. There goes a chestnut. Whose is it?

DOLLY (*raking among the ashes*). Belinda's I think. What's wrong with the light? I can hardly see.

BELINDA. It *is* mine. O Polly, you — you don't *really* think that anything's going to happen, do you? I almost wish that we *hadn't* wished.

[*The room darkens still more, leaving only the dull glow of the fire.*

DOLLY (*looking nervously round*). Don't be absurd, child. It's — it's some stupid trick of Jimmy's, I expect.

[*A sound of music is heard; soft, rippling arpeggios which seem to come from immense distance.*

POLLY (*loudly*). Stop it, Jimmy. We're not a bit frightened. (*Clinging to Dolly*) O — oh, Dolly.

[*The music sounds nearer and now voices can be heard, faint but shrill, blent in a wild, wordless chant. The three children huddle together on the hearthrug.*

DOLLY. O — oh — look there.

[*Out of the darkness grows a pale silvery light. The window curtains wave as if in a strong gale, then sweep aside disclosing the tiny shining figure of the Fairy. She wears a long red robe and a steeple-crowned hat; her little face is that of a child but long grey hair flows over her shoulders, and she leans upon a crutch of ebony. She peers into the room with drowsy eyes while the music sinks to a whisper, then ceases.*

FAIRY (*in a faint, far-away voice*). Who calls upon the Name Forgotten? Who wakes the Faerie from their dream?

BELINDA. We — we didn't know you were asleep. We're *so* sorry.

FAIRY. What should we do but sleep in a world which knows us no longer? My eyes are grown dim. (*She draws from her robe and puts on a huge pair of horn spectacles*) Are you not my little Cinderella?

BELINDA. Please — I'm Belinda, please.

FAIRY (*peering at her*). I know not Belinda. But (*passing her hand over her brows*) I have slumbered long. (*Her eyes fall upon the prostrate twins*) And these — these should be your sisters. (*Shaking her crutch with a menacing gesture*) Ugly and cruel, doubtless.

BELINDA (*hastily*). Yes, they're my sisters, but they aren't ugly — at least, not particularly — and they're quite nice.

TWINS (*piteously*). O, we *are* — we really *are*, dear Fairy; quite.

FAIRY. Then what ails the child? Has the King, your father, brought you home a Cruel Stepmother?

POLLY. Mother is quite well, thank you.

DOLLY. And father isn't a king.

FAIRY. Strange. Strange. Then perchance he is a poor Woodcutter?

BELINDA. He's poor but he isn't a Woodcutter.

POLLY. He wants to be an Estate Agent.

FAIRY. I know not the Estate Agent. Is it a noble calling?

DOLLY. They look after land, I think.

FAIRY. Ah, the Governor of a Province. A modest ambition truly, and he shall attain it. (*She waves her crutch*) He is an Estate Agent from henceforth. (*To Belinda*) And now for you, my child. What boon would you ask of the Faerie?

BELINDA (*overcoming her nervousness and advancing a few steps*). O, dear Fairy, it isn't for me — it's for Myra.

FAIRY. Myra?

BELINDA. She's my eldest sister, you know.

FAIRY. The Princess Royal? Yes.

BELINDA. She's going out to-night with Aunt Maria and she hasn't a single decent frock.

FAIRY. Is she good and true, this Myra?

BELINDA. She's a perfect dear.

DOLLY. Everybody likes Myra.

FAIRY. Then to-night she shall be fairest of the fair. Shall hers be the robe that blazes like the sun, that shines like the moon, or that glitters like the stars?

POLLY. I think — if you wouldn't mind — something a little quieter.

DOLLY. Yes, she said "quiet and appropriate."

FAIRY. Modest and wise Myra. White shall be her raiment; white as the Dawn before the Sun has kissed her. What more?

BELINDA. Well — if she *could* have something to take her to the hall.

POLLY. A taxi, you know —

DOLLY. Or even the station fly —

FAIRY. A Suitable Equipage. Good.

BELINDA. Then — what was it she wanted for poor Jane?

POLLY. A neat gown to open the door in.

FAIRY. A Bower Maiden in fair apparel. Yes. But you have then bidden guests hither? I will transform this hovel to Halls of Splendour.

[*Raises her crutch.*

DOLLY (*hastily*). No, no, please. You mustn't. This is a furnished house — and we mayn't transform anything.

POLLY. They won't even let us shift the bookcase.

FAIRY. Then at least I will provide a Banquet.

BELINDA (*doubtfully*). We've got lemon soles.

POLLY. Of course, a cold chicken *would* be nice.

FAIRY (*sharply*). Tut, tut. Leave that to me, child.

POLLY. I beg your pardon, dear Fairy — and we're ever so much obliged. Now Agatha-next-Door won't be able to wave her frightful frocks at Myra any more.

FAIRY. What is this malapert Agatha that she should taunt the Lady Myra? Shall I cause toads to fall from her lips with her every word?

BELINDA. Oh, no, *please* don't.

POLLY (*regretfully*). Perhaps it would be better not. She never leaves off talking so the place would be *full* of toads.

DOLLY. And she doesn't exactly taunt, you know, only she has such heaps of frocks and there's Myra without one to her back.

FAIRY. This at least shall be remedied. (*She describes a circle round herself in the air with her crutch, then with arms uplifted, she chants*)

> This to That and That to This,
> One shall find what one shall miss:
> Black to white and white to black,
> This shall gain what That shall lack;
> This shall lose what That shall hold
> Till the Strokes of Twelve be told — a — ah!

[*As she speaks the last line she totters as if faint.*

CHILDREN. O, what is it? Aren't you well?

[*The Fairy recovers herself and stands leaning on her crutch but her speech is faint and breathless.*

FAIRY. I have spoken no Spell this many a day. Now the Great Words come slowly to my lips and my feet falter on the Ancient Way. I am weary, my children: let me go.

[*The brightness about her begins to fade.*

POLLY. We are so sorry that you should have tired yourself for us.

DOLLY. But, dear Fairy, why are you so old and weak? I thought that Fairies were always young and dancing in the moonbeams.

[*The far-away music sounds again as the Fairy answers slowly.*

FAIRY. We are the world's first babies, dear; the children of its youth and innocence: now it grows grim and over wise and cares to play with us no longer. It is falling — falling, the Twilight of the Fairies: soon the Midsummer moon will look on us no more.

[*There is now only a pale glimmer of light round the little figure.*

POLLY. Oh — she's going.

DOLLY. She's putting herself out.

BELINDA (*darting forward*). One minute, please, Fairy! Must Myra be careful about twelve o'clock — like Cinderella, you know?

[*Through the shadows the last words of the Fairy fall faintly.*

FAIRY.

> This shall lose what That shall hold
> Till the Strokes of Twelve be told.

[*Complete darkness. The music once more swells to a chorus of wild voices, then dies away to a mere breath — the sigh of an Æolian harp. Suddenly the room flashes again into brightness: the normal atmosphere has again returned, the window curtains are closed and the Fairy has vanished.*

BELINDA.   "Till the Strokes of Twelve be told." That means till twelve o'clock, doesn't it?

POLLY (*dreamily*).   I — suppose so.

BELINDA.   They'll be home long before that, but I'm glad I remembered to ask. Aunt Maria would be dreadfully annoyed to find herself bouncing down High Street in a pumpkin.

POLLY (*suddenly*).   Dolly — pinch me. Harder. I *can't* be awake.

DOLLY.   Polly — then it really did happen? It's true?

POLLY.   The — the Fairy? I — suppose so.

BELINDA (*clapping her hands and skipping*).   Of course it's true, and we've got all these nice things for Myra. A fly to take her to the Lecture —

POLLY.   A cold chicken — That was *my* idea.

BELINDA.   A new frock.

DOLLY.   I suppose the — (*looking nervously over her shoulder*) the Old Lady knows the sort of thing that girls wear now?

POLLY.   She said "white": you can't go far wrong with plain white. When will this Spell affair begin to work?

DOLLY.   Don't talk as if it were a mustard poultice. Almost at once, I should think. I wonder that we haven't heard cries of joy already.

POLLY.   S-sh. Listen.

[*A distant commotion is heard, voices raised in alarm, the upsetting of chairs, a door violently slammed. Hurried footsteps draw near and Eliza bursts in left and dashes across to the opposite door. She is pale and breathless.*

DOLLY AND BELINDA. What is it?

POLLY (*between Eliza and the door right*). What's the matter?

ELIZA (*wildly*). Don't you stop me! — I wouldn't stay another minute in this house, not — not if it was *ever* so. Don't you stop me, Miss Polly!

[*She slips past Polly and out right. As the children stare at each other the front door is heard to bang.*

DOLLY. Can anything be wrong upstairs?

POLLY. Perhaps I'd better go and see.

DOLLY. Wait — here comes someone else. Agatha!

[*Agatha runs in left, a terrified and dishevelled Agatha, dressed only in her bodice and petticoat. Her hair, freed from ribbons and combs, falls over her shoulders, all her affectations have vanished; she is a pretty and pathetic little figure.*

AGATHA (*in a choked voice*). Girls — I — I didn't leave my clothes down here, did I?

POLLY. Clothes? Of course not.

DOLLY. What on earth has happened?

AGATHA. I — I don't know. Oh, poor Myra! (*Covering her face with her hands*) I believe I'm going out of my mind.

DOLLY (*severely*). You've gone out of quite enough already, seems to me. Where's your frock?

AGATHA. I — I don't know.

POLLY. Don't *know?*

AGATHA (*wildly*). O, don't ask questions or I shall scream! Who's that? (*The door left bursts open and Jimmy runs in. Agatha rushes to him*) Jimmy. Is she any better?

JIMMY (*panting*). Worse. It's awful. Why did you cut away?

AGATHA. I couldn't stand it — when she began to sprout.

CHILDREN. *Sprout?* Myra? What's she sprouting?

JIMMY. It looks like feathers.

CHILDREN. *Feathers?*

JIMMY. And now her tail's growing — there are yards and yards of it on the floor.

CHILDREN. Her *tail?*

AGATHA (*faintly*). O don't! Jimmy — couldn't you run for the doctor?

JIMMY. I suppose I'd better : Dr. Raynor at the corner?

AGATHA. No, no, he's homœopathic : I'm sure she wants violent treatment. Dr. Bargrave in Milford Street.

JIMMY. Right-O. (*Turning to Twins*) And you girls standing there like gaping geese, why don't you *do* something? Take her up a cup of tea — or a hot water bottle — or *something*.

MYRA (*without*). Jimmy. Jimmy.

POLLY. Hush. I believe she's coming.

[*Belinda runs to the door left and flings it open.*

BELINDA (*staring in ecstasy*). O Myra! How lovely!

JIMMY. O Myra! How awful!

ALL. O my good gracious Goodness, Myra!!

[*Myra totters in, supporting herself from chair to chair, until she reaches the table, against which she leans trembling. A beam of Fairy radiance falls upon her, emphasizing the glories of her toilette. She is in full evening dress of white satin with a heavy Court train falling from the shoulders, and embroidered with pearl and diamond flowers. Diamonds blaze at her throat and on her corsage, ropes of pearls hang from her neck, and her arms and fingers are loaded with bracelets and rings. On her head is a diamond tiara from which waves a forest of white ostrich plumes.*

MYRA. Jimmy — How could you leave me, Jimmy?

JIMMY. I'm going for the doctor.

MYRA (*clutching him*). No, no. Let's all keep together. I don't know what may be going to happen next.

AGATHA. I don't know what has happened *now*. I can't understand.

MYRA. Well — you *saw*. I was just trying on that frock of yours when all of a sudden it — it went.

TWINS. *Went?*

MYRA. It wasn't there. And then *her* frock went — and then I began to break out like this. Don't come near me, children ; it's probably catching.

AGATHA. O, Myra, the jewels! I shouldn't mind catching some of them. *Look* at the diamonds — and aren't those pearls — pearls as big as marbles?

JIMMY. And they're stuck all over her. My word, if we could spout her as she stands she'd fetch pounds and pounds.

AGATHA. Pounds? That dress is worth hundreds — thousands!

MYRA. But it won't come off — I've tried. Not a thing will come off.

JIMMY (*aghast*). Won't come off? But it *must*. You can't go about like that. I'll tell you plainly you don't come tagging after me down town in white satin and feathers.

BELINDA (*solemnly*). It will all vanish at twelve o'clock, just like Cinderella's ball dress.

JIMMY. O, shut your head, Belinda.

MYRA. Look here, Belinda, we've got enough to worry us without *your* twaddle. Don't talk of what you know nothing about.

POLLY. But she *does* know.

DOLLY. She's trying to tell you. It's true.

MYRA. One at a time, children. *What's* true?

JIMMY. Come on, cough it up, Belinda.

BELINDA. True that a Fairy came and —

MYRA. A *what?*

POLLY. A Fairy.

DOLLY. Yes, really a Fairy. We saw her too.

BELINDA. It's Hallowe'en, you know. She gave us all wishes, and I wanted you to have a nice new frock for the Economy Lecture.

MYRA. And — is this it?

JIMMY (*going into guffaws of laughter*). O my eye, the Economy Lecture! Quiet and appropriate — eh, Myra?

BELINDA. We said it was to be quiet and appropriate, didn't we?

TWINS. Yes, yes, we did.

MYRA (*with the calm of despair*). I should like to see the Fairy's notion of something a little dressy. But what about poor Agatha? Is your Fairy responsible for *her* present — er — costume?

AGATHA (*ruefully*). It seems to be all or nothing with her.

BELINDA. That was Polly.

POLLY. Sneak. I may have hinted that Agatha had too many frocks, but I never asked the Old Lady to take away every stitch the girl stands up in.

DOLLY. How were we to know that Fairies are so beastly literal?

JIMMY (*taking off his coat*). I call it a shame. Here, Agatha, put this on. It won't look quite so — so evening dress.
[*Helps Agatha into the coat.*

MYRA. Well, there's only one thing to be done. Polly must go to the Lecture, Agatha must go to bed, and I must shut myself into the boot cupboard until twelve o'clock. Now I hope this is all, Belinda — no more wishes.

BELINDA. No.

DOLLY (*feebly*). N-no — except Jane.

POLLY. — and the cold chicken.
[*A loud crash is heard as of breaking crockery.*

MYRA. Belinda — That wretched Fairy isn't starting on *Jane* now — when you know as well as I do how the least thing upsets her?

CHILDREN. But we only asked —

JANE (*without*). If you please, Miss —
[*The door right is kicked violently open and Jane staggers in, bearing upon a silver dish a monstrous gilded pasty from which emerge the head and tail of a well-grown peacock. Jane is attired in flowing robes of pale almond pink, and decked with gold bracelets and a necklet of gold coins; on her head is a wreath of pink roses entwined with golden leaves.*

JANE. If you please, Miss Myra, was it by your orders that *this* was sent in? (*She slams down the Pasty on the table and stands gazing at it as though fascinated*) When I see the creature staring at me it give me such a turn I dropped a pile o' plates — and never would your Ma approve of any such French fallals and kickshaws from the pastrycook, Miss Myra; plain roast and boiled was good enough for Dogwood Park and — (*her glance falls upon Agatha*) Lor', Miss Agatha! (*Realizing Myra*) Sakes alive, Miss Myra!

CHORUS. Jane!

JANE. Ah, Jane indeed. No, Miss Myra, it's not my place to pass remarks and none shall be passed : I merely *ask* you whether *this* is what your Ma would have ordered for High Tea for six, let alone the hares and pheasants, shot in like coals they were, and there's a whole stag in the passage and two swans in the sink.

MYRA (*hopelessly*). It's quite useless to explain. A — a friend has sent us a little present of game, Jane.

JANE. Then there's been some mistake in delivery, you mark my words; it's the Lord Mayor's Banquet we've got, Miss Myra, and our brace o'rabbits has gone to the Mansion House.

BELINDA. O, Jane, you do look lovely.

JIMMY (*struggling with laughter*). I say, Jane, have you seen yourself lately ?

JANE. Seen myself, Master Jimmy ? Ah, some of us *ought* to see ourselves — you standing there a disgrace in your shirt sleeves and Miss Agatha dressed — well, I won't say how — and as to Miss Myra, it's not for me to pass remarks, but her Ma wouldn't like it, no more her Aunt won't neither. *My* tastes was always quiet, thanks be ; plain washin' print for week days and a nice bit o' black for Sunday —

MYRA. Jane, dear — I think you had better take a look at yourself.

JANE. Me, Miss Myra ? Is my cap crooked ? (*Raising her hands to her wreath*) Why — what's all this ? (*Seeing her gold-clasped arms*) Oh ! (*She cautiously approaches the mirror above the mantelpiece and takes one glance at it*) Oh !! (*She sinks into a chair by the table*) What is it, Miss Myra ? What's done it ? Oh — Oh, it's crool. Dressed for the door I was by your Ma's wish and now (*extending her bare arms*) I might be going to do the week's washing.

[*Flings her arms along the table, buries her face in them and sobs.*

MYRA. Now she's going into hysterics. I hope you're satisfied, Belinda.

JIMMY. Yes, Belinda, you and your footling Fairy have got us into a rotten mess between you.

THE SLIPPERS OF CINDERELLA

Jane. — "It's the Lord Mayor's Banquet we've got, Miss Myra, and our brace o' rabbits has gone to the Mansion House."

POLLY. Don't speak of her like that, Jimmy.

DOLLY. You might remember that she could turn us all into white rats or guinea-pigs.

MYRA (*wildly*). I'd *rather* be a guinea-pig. I shouldn't feel nearly such a f-fool as a guinea-pig.

[*Drops into chair opposite Jane and hides her face on the table.*

[*A fanfare of trumpets. Myra and Jane simultaneously raise their heads.*

MYRA AND JANE. What's that?

JIMMY. It sounded just outside.

AGATHA (*running to the window and peeping out*). Good gracious, look!

[*She draws the curtains, the street is seen to be brilliantly lit up. Shouts are heard and a distant hum of voices.*

JIMMY (*running to the window*). I say! Look at those chaps with torches — Linkmen, don't they call them?

[*The three children run to the window.*

AGATHA. And here come Outriders in crimson and silver and — O Myra, do look — (*A louder flourish of trumpets. The shouts and uproar increase*) — look at this coming round the corner — (*Jane jumps up and runs to the window*) — six milk white horses with Postilions in cloth of silver and — O my goodness — (*trumpets and an outburst of cheering*) — such a Coach, all gold and crystal and as big as a haystack.

JANE. It's the Free Foresters' Feet.

JIMMY. It's the King and Queen.

BELINDA (*dancing with excitement*). No, it isn't. It's the Suitable Equipage. Wait a minute — there. (*A thunderous knock at the front door*) It's the carriage come for Myra.

MYRA (*faintly*). I knew it. The Fairy has done things thoroughly.

DOLLY. And we only asked for the station fly.

A TREMENDOUS VOICE (*from the street*). THE PRINCESS MYRA'S CARRIAGE STOPS THE WAY.

JIMMY. Stops the way — I should think it *did*: it's the size of a brewer's van.

THE VOICE. THE PRINCESS MYRA'S CARRIAGE.

MYRA. If that creature keeps on bawling out my name I shall go silly.

A MAN'S VOICE (*in the crowd*). Cheers for the Princess Myra. Hip-hip-hip —

[*A burst of cheering.*

AGATHA. Myra — you'll have to come to the window and bow — Royalties always do.

MYRA. No, no. I can't — I won't.

JIMMY (*at window*). Myra, you jolly well *must*. They're packed like sardines in the street. Come on.

TWINS. Yes, come on, Myra.

[*They drag the reluctant Myra to the window.*

JIMMY. Coat, Agatha, quick.

[*Agatha snatches off coat and helps Jimmy into it. Jimmy flings up the sash of window. Loud cheers.*

JIMMY. Ladies and Gentlemen. (*Dead silence*) Her Royal Highness the Princess Myra has graciously consented to appear.

[*Bows elaborately. Trumpets. Roars of applause, amidst which Myra steps to the window and bows gravely right and left. She then slams down the sash and draws the curtains quickly. The hubbub sinks to a continuous murmur.*

MYRA (*leaning exhausted against the curtains*). Will anyone kindly tell me what we're going to do *now?*

JIMMY (*scratching his head*). *I* don't know. And Aunt may blow in at any minute.

POLLY. Perhaps she won't notice anything.

JIMMY. Perhaps not — with a full fledged Circus at the door and Jane looking like the "Last Days of Pompeii."

[*Enter Eliza right hastily. At sight of Myra she hesitates and makes for the door again.*

ELIZA. Please Miss —

MYRA. What's the matter, Eliza? Don't be frightened.

ELIZA. O, if you please, Miss — Missus's compliments and Miss Agatha's to come home this very minute.

AGATHA. I can't, Eliza, you must *see* that I can't.

ELIZA (*with increasing nervousness*). And please Miss, Number Fifteen desires 'is compliments and — and —

MYRA (*coming towards her*). Yes? And what?

ELIZA (*desperately*). And 'e's gone for the P'LICE.

[*Dashes from the room.*

CHILDREN. The Police.

JANE. The *Police!*

JIMMY. That about puts the lid on.

MYRA (*calmly*). Yes. I think we may regard the Police as the finishing touch.

JIMMY. Let's see. Five minutes to the station, five minutes back — (*Agatha glances at the clock*) That clock's no good: it has been at twenty past eleven ever since we came here. We've got about ten minutes. What's to be done?

MYRA (*advancing with tragic dignity*). I have quite decided what is to be done. I am the eldest and therefore responsible; if the Police arrive I shall give myself up — "go quiet" I believe is the expression. You, Polly, will take my place as hostess. Jane, it is too late for the soles; you had better serve that dreadful bird (*pointing to Peacock*) but for goodness sake let it be carved off the table. And you, children, at the height of your High Tea, think of your unhappy sister sitting in white satin and diamonds in the Police Station, and (*almost breaking down*) don't make greater fools of yourselves than is absolutely necessary.

[*She passes slowly out left with hanging head.*

JIMMY. She's handing out the sob stuff pretty thick, isn't she?

AGATHA. I think it is very affecting: it's like Mary Queen of Scots going to execution.

JIMMY. Of course we can't let her get jugged. Now — what price medal for distinguished service? Jane, will you lead the forlorn hope — run down and tell those chaps with the Coach to go away?

AGATHA. Yes. Say it's the wrong house — they've mistaken the day — anything.

JANE. What, *me*, Master Jimmy? Not like this?

JIMMY. Slip on Mother's mackintosh.

AGATHA. Put up an umbrella. And if the Police come —

JIMMY (*wildly*). If the Police come, just give the whole bally
Show in charge. That ought to keep them busy for a
bit.

JANE (*picking up the great dish*). If the Police come I shall
give 'em *this:* that's the way to keep 'em busy. Don't you
worry, Master Jimmy : I'll see what I can do.

TWINS. And we'll come with you, Jane.

[*Exeunt right Jane with the pasty, Polly and Dolly.*

JIMMY (*stopping Belinda*). Not you, Belinda ; I want a word
with you. (*Slaps Agatha on the back*) Good old Agatha.
Still sticking to the ship, eh ?

AGATHA. Of course ; but when the Policemen come I shall nip
behind those curtains ; I'm not — er — dressed to receive.

JIMMY. Then you'd better nip : they'll be here directly. (*Agatha hides behind the window curtains*) Now, Belinda.

[*Belinda advances timidly, her hands behind her.*

BELINDA. Yes, Jimmy.

JIMMY (*sternly*). You're at the bottom of all this, you know.

BELINDA. Jimmy, I will not be bullied. I've got any amount
of people their Heart's Desire, and if they don't like it, it's
not my fault.

JIMMY. But d'you mean to say that this Variety Entertainment
of yours is going to last till midnight ?

BELINDA. Yes, till twelve o'clock. The Fairy told me so.

JIMMY. Are you *sure ?*

AGATHA (*poking her head out between the curtains*). Repeat what
she said.

BELINDA. It was all in poetry : I can't remember.

JIMMY (*catching her by the shoulders and shaking her*). But you
must. Think, you little ass, *think.*

BELINDA (*in gasps*). I — can only — remember — the last
two lines. She said them twice.

JIMMY (*releasing her*). Well — let's have 'em.

BELINDA. "This shall — shall —" O yes. "This shall lose
what That shall hold —"

JIMMY. This shall lose —

AGATHA. That's me. That's all right. Goodness knows I've lost enough.

JIMMY. What That shall hold. That's Myra, I suppose : she's got away with the goods. Go on, child.

BELINDA. "Till the strokes of twelve be told."

JIMMY (*hopelessly*). Till twelve o'clock. That's plain enough. That does us in.

AGATHA (*eagerly*). Well, but Jimmy, *does* it? She didn't exactly say till twelve o'clock; she said "Until the clock strikes twelve."

JIMMY (*staring at the clock*). By Jove! I believe you've hit upon the weak spot. (*The trumpets begin to sound again*) O shut your heads! I'll make the clock strike twelve in half a jiff.

[*Jumps on a chair, opens the clock face and seizes the minute hand.*

AGATHA. No, no, Jimmy, not yet! I'm frightened. It may start something else off — do wait a minute.

JIMMY. What for?

AGATHA. Let's think — let's consult —

JIMMY. If we don't look slippy we shall do our consulting in the Station. (*A loud ring, followed by a knock at the front door*) There! The Police. Agatha, it's now or never. Risk it?

AGATHA (*nodding*). Risk it.

[*Her head disappears within the curtains. Jimmy whirls the minute hand round to the hour and the clock slowly strikes twelve. As the last stroke falls all sounds from the street cease.*

JIMMY (*breathlessly*). Well?

AGATHA. The street is all dark again and — Jimmy — I can't see the Coach : I believe it has gone away.

JIMMY. Let's have a look. (*Draws the curtains, showing Agatha dressed as at first*) Why — yes. The whole Show has done a bunk. The street's quite empty and — (*seeing Agatha*) — Hullo!

AGATHA. — And here's my frock! Jimmy — it worked. O Jimmy!

[*Embraces him violently.*

JIMMY (*struggling*). Here, I say — drop it.
[*The Twins rush in right.*

DOLLY. Jimmy, Jimmy! Jane has come right again.

POLLY. And we couldn't find the Coach — it's not there.

JIMMY. Good business. My word, what a narrow squeak. Now then for the Police — let 'em all come!

DOLLY. The Police?

JIMMY. They rang just now. Didn't you let them in?

POLLY. That wasn't the Police: it was this telegram for Myra.
[*Holds up a telegram.*

JIMMY (*taking it*). Give it here.
[*Myra bursts in left. Her fairy robes have disappeared and she is dressed as before.*

MYRA. Look. Look at me! I'm all right again! What has happened?

JIMMY (*solemnly*). The clock has struck twelve.

ALL THE GIRLS (*after a pause*). O — Oh — you clever boy!
[*They all rush at him.*

JIMMY. Now, drop it, drop it. It was Agatha's idea. Myra, here's a telegram for you.

MYRA (*tearing it open and reading*). "All settled, home this evening, Dad Mother." Children — he has got it. Dad has really got the appointment.

JIMMY. Well played, the Governor.

TWINS. Hip hurray!

BELINDA. Of course he has. The Fairy said most particularly —

JIMMY. O, *hop* it, Belinda.

MYRA. Belinda — if you so much as mention that Fairy again I'll — I'll slap you.

AGATHA. Listen. Isn't that a taxi stopping?

JIMMY. Aunt, you bet. Agatha, you must stay to tea. I say, Myra, don't you rather wish you hadn't been shorn of all your splendour?

MYRA. Not a bit. I wouldn't stand in Cinderella's shoes again for anything you liked to offer. Yes, here comes Aunt.

JIMMY. Now, girls, pull yourselves together. 'Tention! Fall in behind there.

[*Buttons his coat and shoots his cuffs. The girls arrange their frocks and pat their hair.*

[*Enter Jane in neat black dress, white cap and apron.*

JANE. Lady Errington.

ALL (*advancing with outstretched hands*). How d'you do, Aunt Maria?

QUICK CURTAIN

DON QUIXOTE

About the time our English Will
Was writing plays in which we glory,
There lived a man of subtle skill
Who wrote for Spain her greatest story.

He wasn't much on early learning,
He wasn't much on fancy prattle;
His heart adventureward was burning,
His arm was eager to do battle.

He traveled much on land and sea,
No man e'er met with trouble harder;
He fought the pirates valiantly,
And took a hand in Spain's Armada.

He downed the Turks with Christian zeal,
He courted wounds and boasted of them;
On foreign soil, come woe or weal,
He showed his hurts and seemed to love them.

He fell into some corsairs' hands,
Held fast a captive in Algeria;
He tried in vain to snap his bands — .
A weary prisoner growing wearier.

By chance, the money being found
To pay the bandits for their burden,
He once more stood on native ground
And held a public job as guerdon.

So poor was he, he had to eke
His slim means in whatever fashion;
And so requital he did seek
In letters which were e'er his passion.

Cervantes was the Spaniard's name —
Cervantes, whom the world claimed master —
Whose mind in colors was aflame
With brilliance like the flow'ring aster.

His quill, become an active pen,
Made note in drama, tale and poem
The strength and weaknesses of men, —
And so he left the world to owe him

An unrequited debt to pay,
A debt which age on age will note he
Fashioned so, from day to day
'Twould increase in his "Don Quixote."

Here is a tale of ceaseless fun,
Eccentric bubbling through its pages;
Here is a tale which scarce begun,
Begins to breathe of knightly ages.

Lo, it's a tale of hero lean, —
With ancient lance and rusty armor, —
A sort of Spanish palatine,
Who dreams he is the ladies' charmer.

So steeped in lore, chivalric, he,
With figure gaunt and face all wizened,
Declared himself for errantry
And hied him forth, bedight, bedizened.

He knew the laws to knights pertain;
He quoted books by rule and rote; he
Was the native flower of Spain,
The dear quixotic Don Quixote.

With foot in stirrup, forth he went,
Armed cap-a-pie on Rosinante —
He was a perfect Spanish "gent",
Who rode him forth in pace andante.

He thought he saw what wasn't there;
He knew he faced an army near him;
He charged upon a windmill fair,
As though a cavalcade did fear him.

So bruised his head, so stiff his back, —
So hither, thither tossed and battered,
He hurried home, alas, alack,
Pretending there was nothing mattered!

And soon he turned afield once more,
This time with servant, Sancho Panza —
A roly-poly country boor,
A very unimaginative man, sir.

They journeyed far, companions they,
And what befell, Cervantes wrote he
The full adventures, night and day,
Of Sancho's master, Don Quixote.

Dulcinea was his lady's name
(Oh, not forgetting del Toboso),
His mistress fair, his love, his flame,
Who made his heart go tremolo so.

Did ever history know a knight
With chivalry so touched by madness?
Did ever history indite
A tale so fraught with human sadness?

So full was Don Quixote's mind
Of fancies free and deeds historic,
His eyes were filled with every kind
Of joust and tourney meteoric.

"Behold," Cervantes seemed to say,
"Is very knighthood in these pages;
I give you sentiments the way
They spake them in the Middle Ages.

"I make my hero such an one
To live by rules as records list 'em;
I make him brave and yet undone
By brooding on a worn-out system.

"I give you mirth in all his pranks,
I make him utter wisdom mellow;
I draw him Peer among all cranks, —
Absurdly lovable old fellow!

"I tint his life with Spanish flame —
I spice his deeds with comments clever —
I give the world a Spanish name
To live, by grace of God, forever!"

As a matter of record, here is reproduced part of the program for "Don Quixote", as given its first performance on Wednesday evening, November 8, 1922, at the Salmagundi Club, New York.

[Note: After the performance, Mr. Sarg raised his curtain and allowed his audience to peep behind stage; in other words, he showed exactly how expertly the strings of his dolls were handled by his assistants. The descriptions of these assistants are so good-naturedly vivid that the Editor reproduces them here as they were given on the evening's program. They suggest the life that goes into the creation of a puppet-show.]

Tony Sarg

Designed and supervised every detail of the production. He produced the play, made the scenery, including the curtain of the small puppet-stage at the Inn, and taught the puppeteers how to pull the 433 strings used in "Don Quixote." He also collaborated with Anne Stoddard in the writing of the play.

Charles E. Searle (Mat)

Is an artist and does a good deal of everything. He is in charge of the show and has taken it from coast to coast. He pulls the strings and speaks the lines for Don Quixote and Dr.

Perez, the Curate. He also manages the lights, made most of the small properties and adapted most of the puppets to their present use. So you see, without "Mat," there simply would be no show!

AMY HAMLIN

Is the star puppeteer. She has been with Tony Sarg's marionettes ever since they made their first bow to Broadway. She operates and speaks for Maria and the Duchess of Barataria; and, single-handed, she manages the flock of sheep. She also pulls the strings for Sancho Panza's dance, and acts as Mistress of the Robes.

BRONSON GOBE

Speaks for and operates the Barber, the Shepherd, the Officer of the Law, the Puppet-Showman, and the Inn-Keeper. He has helped tremendously in making the dolls and stage properties. He has worked hard and loves it!

JEAN GROS

Who has a little marionette show of his own, pulls the strings and speaks the lines for Sancho Panza and the Duke of Barataria. He also sings the toreador song in the last scene.

IRENE GROS

Plays the guitar, the piano, mandolin, castanets and tambourine. She has selected the music for the production, too, and, at one time or another, pulls the strings of almost every puppet in the show.

HELEN LYVERS

Has a sweet singing voice. She acts for Dulcinea, puts one of the lambs through his little dance, and has had a hand in the making of the costumes.

HENRY CASEY

Is a very important member of the cast. He pulls the curtain; he makes the lightning to flash, and the thunder to roll;

he plays the flute and the xylophone; he throws stones for the Shepherd. And, when any of the puppets are ill or injured, he becomes their doctor and mends their broken arms or legs and patches up their broken heads.

Many of the costumes and some of the figures used in this production were made years ago by Spanish artists in Barcelona and were adapted to Mr. Sarg's needs. Special attention is called to the small puppets in Scene Four. These are from the famous Palazzio Carminotti in Venice and are very old.

DON QUIXOTE

A PLAY IN SEVEN SCENES

Based on the "Don Quixote" of Miguel de Cervantes

WRITTEN FOR MARIONETTES BY
ANNE STODDARD AND TONY SARG

THE CHARACTERS IN ORDER OF APPEARANCE

NICHOLAS . . . . *A Barber*
SANCHO PANZA . . . . *Servant to Don Quixote*
DR. PEREZ . . . . *The Curate of La Mancha*
MARIA . . . . *Housekeeper for Don Quixote*
DON QUIXOTE . . . . *A Gentleman of La Mancha*
(Whose real name is Alonzo Quixano)
A SHEPHERD
ROSINANTE . . . . *Don Quixote's Horse*
DULCINEA . . . . *A Peasant Girl*
(Whose real name is Aldonza Lorenzo)
A MILLER
DAPPLE . . . . *Sancho Panza's Ass*
THE DUKE OF BARATARIA
THE DUCHESS OF BARATARIA
AN INNKEEPER
AN OFFICER OF THE HOLY BROTHERHOOD OF TOLEDO
PETER . . . . *A Puppet Showman*
Apparitions, sheep and lambs, a dancing bear, a dog, little
puppets on Peter's stage, toreadors, villagers, etc.

THE SCENES

1. Don Quixote's House at La Mancha
2. A Hillside near Toboso
3. A Road
4. An Inn near La Mancha
5. Outside the Inn
6. A Forest
7. A Street in La Mancha

DON QUIXOTE

SCENE I

Don Quixote's library in his house at La Mancha. It is late afternoon. At the center, back, a large window; before it a table, upon which lies an immense book. Two chairs are placed, left and right. An ancient suit of armor hangs on the wall.

Sancho Panza is discovered, seated in a chair; Nicholas, the barber, is clipping his hair.

BARBER. By my faith, Sancho, I am sorry to hear it. There is not a more devout, kindly, or charitable man in La Mancha than Alonzo Quixano, your master. For my part, I think he has gone mad.

SANCHO. You do wrong to call him mad. My master is no more mad than my mother. He is in his sober senses; he eats and drinks like other folks and as he used to do. And yet, forsooth, you must call him mad.

BARBER. Mad as a doodle, if you ask me! It all comes of his reading those books of magic and knight-errantry he is so fond of, day in and day out, night in and night out — forty-eight hours together sometimes, they do say, without stopping for a sup, or a bite, or a whiff of sleep. Curses on his books, I say! They have cracked the best headpiece in La Mancha.

SANCHO. Ouch! Pray, mind yourself, Master Shave-beard. That time you well-nigh nicked my ear.

BARBER. Your pardon, Sancho. The shears slipped because my thoughts were with my poor friend.

[Enter Dr. Perez, the curate.

BARBER. Good morrow, your reverence.

CURATE. Good morrow, Nicholas. What — *you*, Sancho Panza? What are you doing here, turning your master's library into a barber shop? Is that your notion of conduct becoming to a servant?

SANCHO. Marry, your reverence, my motto is, "Waste not, want not." And when Master Nicholas, here, drops in to cut my master's hair and finds him sleeping — why, then, I say, "After the master, the man," and bid him cut mine instead. That was the way of it.

CURATE. You are a saucy fellow, Sancho Panza; and I wonder at Alonzo Quixano for keeping such an impertinent servant in his house. Wait until Mistress Maria catches you at this!

SANCHO. I ain't afraid of her, for all she digs and hammers at a man, like a cooper at a tub. She be but a woman and the weaker vessel — and I be a man, every inch of me!

CURATE. All the same, you would better look to yourself. Where is your master?

SANCHO. Why, asleep and snoring, as I told your reverence a moment a-gone. And Mistress Maria's orders is, he is not to be disturbed for no one, for he was up all night reading his books, and needs his rest. But I will go and see if he is awake yet.

[*Exit Sancho.*

CURATE. Nicholas, is it true, the tale I hear in La Mancha, that our poor friend has taken leave of his wits from reading so many tales of knight-errantry? And that he proposes to — but, no, it is too absurd!

BARBER. Absurd or no, it appears to be the truth. The poor gentleman is clean besotted.

CURATE. Good-lack-a-day! By my holy orders, I am grieved to learn of it. What form does his disorder take?

BARBER. A most strange form, forsooth. He has given himself a new name. "Don Quixote" he calls himself, and swears he is a knight errant — or whatever you call those roving fellows he reads of in his books. He says it is his duty to go out and ride about the world, doing good works and rescuing distressed damsels. Heard you ever the like of that?

CURATE. Strange! Strange! "Don Quixote" — where does he get that "Don Quixote"?

BARBER. Indeed, I know not, unless it is some kind of a name he has made out of Quixano, which is not good enough for one of these pestilent knights errant, I suppose.

CURATE. Knight errant! And vowed to redress all wrongs, especially those of distressed ladies! I swear there is humor in that! First thing you know, Nicholas, our fanciful neighbor will be bestriding that flea-bitten old nag of his and setting out on a quest for adventures, like the knights of old. It makes me laugh to think of it.

BARBER. In sooth, Doctor, that is what he proposes to do. It is, in truth. And that same flea-bitten nag you speak of, that rack-a-bones with his ribs clean through his ragged hide, has a fine new name, too, as befits the steed of a knight errant. He calls the old rattle-trap — (*bursts out laughing*) — "Rosinante!"

CURATE (*laughs*). "Rosinante!" That's good — "Rosinante!"

BARBER. The same, sir! "Rosinante," he calls the horse, as sure as I'm a sinner. And there is more to it, too.

CURATE. Pray tell me all.

BARBER. Yonder hangs an old suit of armor that once belonged to his great-grandfather. Yesterday — I have it from Mistress Maria, the housekeeper — he spent the live-long day scouring and cleaning that armor; and mending it, too, as well as he was able.

CURATE. What is his notion in doing that, pray tell me?

[*Enter Sancho.*

BARBER. Look you, when our friend rides out on his quest for adventures, he means to ride in armor. But here is Sancho Panza. He will know the straight of it. How about it, Sancho?

SANCHO. Aye, truly. My master means to arm himself from top to toe.

CURATE. Armed cap-a-pie! Surely, it is the most fantastic notion that a madman ever conceived. But I must be off, Nicholas, since I am not permitted to see our friend. In truth, he must be mad indeed!

BARBER. Mad as ever I saw a lunatic!

SANCHO. Pray, Master Barber, mind what you say, for all consists not in the shaving of beards; and there is some difference between a hawk and a hand-saw. I say so, because we all know each other, and nobody shall put a false card on me. As to my master's madness, let it stand as it is!

CURATE. What is the fellow talking about? What have you to do with Alonzo Quixano's business, Sancho Panza?

SANCHO. "Don Quixote," if it please your reverence! And him you see before you is Don Quixote's squire, Sancho Panza, who will ride with him to seek adventures and to do a world of good deeds.

CURATE (*laughing*). By my faith, you are a comical fellow, Sancho! Farewell to you! Nicholas, we shall speak more of this matter presently.

BARBER. Farewell, Doctor!

SANCHO. Good even to your reverence.

[*Exit the Curate.*

BARBER. When does your master propose to set out on this ridiculous quest of his?

SANCHO. To-morrow, at cock-crow, if the saints are willing. I am to saddle Rosinante — so he bade me — and to bring Dapple, my little gray ass (that is for me to ride, as I am but a poor body afoot) and meet him at the gate at daybreak.

BARBER. Holy Virgin!

MARIA (*off-stage*). Good even to your reverence.

BARBER. I hear somebody coming. You would better brush up the floor, Sancho, before Maria catches you.

SANCHO. Maria!

[*He brushes frantically at the floor with his hands.*
[*Enter Maria, the housekeeper.*

MARIA. Good even, Master Nicholas. My master has been abed and asleep all day, poor gentleman — and, faith, he needs his sleep. (*She catches sight of Sancho Panza*) What have you been doing here, Sancho Panza, you bundle of impudence? What? Getting your hair trimmed in Master Quixano's library? What? What, I say?

SANCHO (*trembles with fright*).   B-b-b — yes, ma'am!

MARIA.   You wretch!   You sackful of wickedness!   Look at the mess you have made!   Clippings all over the floor — a fine servant you are!   As if a body hadn't enough work to do, and enough to worry about, with all the goings on in this house, without a country lout like you getting his beard trimmed in the library!   You belong in the pig-sty, you do, and not in a gentleman's house!   What?   What?

SANCHO.   Y-y-y-yes, ma'am.

MARIA.   It is all because of you and nobody else that my master is distracted and debauched and wants to go rambling the country over!   Idle rogue!   Dumble-head!

SANCHO.   Y-y-y-yes, ma'am.

MARIA.   Begone — and bring me a broom!

[*Exit Sancho.*

BARBER.   How does your master seem to-day, Maria?   Is he still bent on setting out on this fool's errand?

MARIA.   Oh, neighbor, I am fair distracted!   He does nothing but mumble and dumble over his books; and he speaks all wildly about his duty to be off, away from his home, a-scouring the world to help needy folk and relieve them that's in trouble.   And that's all right, sir, and like him, too, for my master is a kind man — but there is more — oh, woe, that I should have to tell it!

BARBER.   Tell us, Maria.

MARIA.   Magic — that's what it is!   Spells — that's what it is!   Witchcraft, I say!   Enchantments!   (*She weeps noisily*) Last eve I came into his study of a sudden, and there he sat, his big book open before him, mumbling strange words with a heathen sound to them.   Talking to himself, I thought he was — but no, sir, no!   *There was others present!*

BARBER.   What do you mean?

MARIA.   Spirits!

BARBER.   Nonsense!

MARIA.   Nonsense, or no nonsense, there was spirits there, for I heard him talking to them.   Spirits, and he raised them out of that big black book of his, that ought to be burnt in the stove — that it ought. You should have seen him, your worship, and have heard the goings on. It was fair horrible. I felt my scalp prickle, though I could not see anything myself; and that is a sure sign, as you know.

BARBER. Be calm, mistress. Our friend has delusions, and imagines, no doubt, that he is conversing with those he reads of in his books. . . . We have been talking of your master, our good curate and I. Leave it to us to devise some means of bringing him to his senses.

MARIA. Heaven grant you may! But I have not told you all. There is some wench he calls "Dulcinea" mixed up in this affair.

BARBER. I never heard tell of any Dulcinea in these parts.

MARIA. She lives in Toboso, this Dulcinea, so he says, and the way he talks of her is a fair scandal, and him a bachelor. "Princess", he calls her, "Empress of La Mancha", "Sovereign Lady", "Dulcinea del Toboso", and the like; and swears there is not so beautiful a lady in the universe as this Dulcinea of his — a murrain on her!

[*Enter Sancho with a broom.*

SANCHO. Here is the broom, mistress.

MARIA. Well, use it then! Don't you know what a broom is for? Do you expect me to sweep up after you?

SANCHO. Y-yes, ma'am. N-no, ma'am!

[*He sweeps.*

BARBER. Did you ever see this remarkable lady, Dulcinea of Toboso, Maria?

MARIA. That I did not. And I doubt my master ever saw her, either; for, as your worship knows, he was ever too respectful to ladies to take any pleasure in their company. For my part, I do not think he knows any of them. Dulcinea, indeed! If there be a Dulcinea, I'll warrant her a hussy to have so bemuddled my poor master!

SANCHO. Heigh-day! Did you ever hear the like? My Lady Dulcinea del Toboso is no other than the daughter of Lorenzo Corchuelo, the farmer — she that is otherwise called Aldonza Lorenzo. "Dulcinea" — that is just a highfalutin

name the master has given her, though I have his own word for
it that he only saw her twice in his life and that at a distance.

MARIA. Much you know about it, indeed!

SANCHO (*doubles up with laughter*). Udsniggers! I know her
full well. It is a strapping wench, i' faith, and pitches the
bar with any lusty fellow in our parish. By the mass, it is a
notable, strong-built, sizable, sturdy, manly lass, and one
that will keep her chin out of the mire, I'll warrant her!

BARBER. Peace, ignorant coxcomb! How could so high a lady
as Dulcinea del Toboso be such a wench as you prate of?

SANCHO (*rocks with laughter*). There you hit it! She is a high
lady, indeed, for she is taller than I am by a foot and a half!
[*Enter Don Quixote, unnoticed by the others.*

BARBER. I would I had you for a servant, Sancho Panza,
though it were but for one short hour. Belike I should beat
a more respectful tongue into your head!

SANCHO. Aye, you may talk, but I a'n't afraid of words. And
when it comes to beating — why, "where there is no hook,
there will hang no bacon," as the proverb says.

MARIA. Go! And take your saucy tongue home with you.

SANCHO. Going I be — for I ain't had a bite of supper yet!

DON QUIXOTE (*coughs*). Ahem! Good even, friends.

MARIA. Good evening, master.

BARBER. Good evening, sir.

DON QUIXOTE (*to Sancho*). Get you gone, Sancho, and make
all ready for our departure on the morrow. Saddle Rosinante, as I bade you, and meet me at daybreak at the city
gate.

SANCHO. Aye, master.

DON QUIXOTE. May Heaven and the Lady Dulcinea prosper
our journey!
[*Exit Sancho.*

MARIA. Oh, my dear master, can nothing persuade you to stay
at home? I fear for your life on this terrible journey. Bide
in your own house, I do beseech you!

DON QUIXOTE. Stay me not, good Maria. I must e'en go where
honor leads the way.

MARIA. Pray, sir, are there not a-many knights at the king's court?

DON QUIXOTE. I doubt not there are many knights maintained at court for the ornament and pomp of royalty.

MARIA. Why, then, would it not be better for your worship to be one of those brave knights who serve the king afoot at court, than to go gallivanting around the country horseback? And, dear knows, I fear you will fall off, with all that armor on your back.

DON QUIXOTE. You do not understand, woman. All knights cannot be courtiers, nor all courtiers, knights. Arms, I have chosen; and the planet Mars, that presided at my nativity, has led me to that adventurous road. All your attempts to shake my resolution are in vain. I will pursue what Heaven has fated, fortune ordained, and reason requires. Look well to my house, and the saints keep you, whilst I am gone.

MARIA. Alack-a-day!

[*Exit Maria.*

BARBER. Oh, my dear neighbor, I do implore you not to start out upon this ridiculous quest!

DON QUIXOTE. Thou art a dullard, Nicholas, and have no understanding of the path of honor.

BARBER (*shakes his head*). Alas! my poor friend. What will become of you?

[*Exit barber.*

DON QUIXOTE (*seats himself at the table and begins to turn the pages of the great book. The room darkens*). Let me see — where was I? Yes, this is the place. Yes — yes — (*He reads, mumbling at first, then in growing excitement*) "*The Green Sword Knight sailed with his company towards Constantinople, but suddenly the wind changed, and the sea became so high that neither the strength of the ship, nor the skill of the mariners, could withstand it, and they were in great peril of death. At length the vessel was driven ashore, it being night, and they were all greatly comforted to reach land in safety; but when they saw that they were upon the Devil's Island, they began*

*to beat their breasts and lament that they were fallen into a worse
danger than that they had escaped, the lord of the island being a
monster called the Endriago, whose delight it was to kill and
devour men and living animals. At morning the master sung
mass and the Knight of the Green Sword armed himself and made
his horse to be landed on the Devil's Island, saying to the sailors,
'Friends, I go to yonder castle, and if I find the Endriago, I shall
fight him.'"* Ah, brave Amadis! Peerless Knight of the
Green Sword! Flower of Chivalry! (*He continues his reading*) *"It was not long before the knight beheld the Endriago
come bounding over the rocks, breathing smoke and flames of
fire in its fury, gnashing its teeth, and foaming and clapping its
wings. The monster's face was all hairy and its body covered
with scales, one lying over the other, so hard that no weapon
could pierce them. From its shoulders grew two wings so large
that they covered it down to the feet, not of feathers, but of a shaggy
leather, black as pitch and shining. Its hands were like eagle's
claws and its eyes red like fire. Its stench was rank poison and,
as it ruffled its scales, and gnashed its teeth, and shook its wings,
it was as if the earth trembled.*

*"The Green Sword Knight then grasped his lance and, covering
himself with his shield, rode forth against the Endriago."*

(*He breaks off, as an apparition of the Endriago appears, opening its wings and blowing smoke from its nostrils*) Ha! What
art thou, diabolical and monstrous vision? What dost thou
here? Art thou that demon, Endriago, whom the brave
Amadis of Gaul overcame in battle by the strength of his
sword? Get thee gone, thou blasting dream! (*As he recoils
from the Endriago, a giant appears. He wheels about*) How
now! Thy bulk is unfolding to a giant's size! I know thee
well enough, infernal spirit! Thou art Brocabruno, surnamed
"the Strong." (*A magician and a skeleton appear*) Thou,
too, Archelaus, prince of enchanters! I know thee well and
all thy curséd brood. (*The skeleton dances*) Ghastly phan-
tasm, begone! Know that once again a knight, mighty as
Amadis, shall roam the world, dealing death, as he did, to
demons, giants and enchanters! Get you gone, get you

gone, false spirits! Don Quixote de la Mancha fears you not. (*An apparition of a lady appears and stretches out her arms to Don Quixote in appeal. He falls upon his knees*) Oh, lady of my soul, Dulcinea! Flower of all beauty, great and illustrious princess, vouchsafe to assist thy champion in the dangerous quest which he is about to undertake, to rid the world of the doers of evil, and to do honor to thy worth and peerless beauty! (*He rises and cries in a loud voice*) Ho, brave Amadis, prince and pattern of chivalry, Don Quixote de la Mancha follows in your footsteps! (*Enter Maria with a lantern. The apparitions disappear as the light of the lantern illuminates the room. He sinks into his chair, gasping*) Ah—h—ah—ah!

MARIA. What is the matter? What is all this noise? Oh, my poor master, what has brought you to this pass?

DON QUIXOTE (*feebly*). Is it you, then, good Maria? I pray you, fetch me some wine, for I have seen strange sights here — here in this room — which have turned my blood to water.

MARIA. Alack-a-day, Master Quixano, do not talk so wildly. You look fair mazed.

DON QUIXOTE. This house is enchanted, Maria. By my honor, I swear to you that within these four walls —

MARIA. Spirits! Spirits! Spirits!

[*She runs screaming from the room.*

CURTAIN

SCENE II

A hill near Toboso. It is early morning. Birds are singing and butterflies dancing over the flowers. A shepherd is discovered, seated under a tree. He plays on a rustic flute. A frisky lamb dances to his piping.

SHEPHERD (*to the lamb*). What now, little wanton, little woolly elf, what has made thee trip it so much of late? Dost feel the spring in thy blood, eh? Thou art a pretty hussy, that thou art! (*Shouting and barking of dogs is heard off-stage. Several sheep run across the stage, followed by the shepherd dog)* The wolves are after them! (*He tries to quiet the sheep*) Hey, hey! What ails thee, then? Hey, hey!

[*More sheep run across stage.*

DON QUIXOTE (*off-stage*). Courage, brave knights! March up, fall on, all you who fight under the standard of the valiant Pentapolin! Follow me! Up! At them! (*Enter Don Quixote on horseback, charging the sheep. He pulls up Rosinante and strikes an attitude*) Where art thou, proud Alifanfaron? Appear! I challenge thee, insolent tyrant! Let thy life pay the penalty for the unjust war thou hast waged against the gallant Pentapolin!

SHEPHERD. I'll Pentapolin thee, for frightening my sheep! Take that — and may the saints curse thee!

[*He throws a volley of stones at Don Quixote, hitting him in the jaw. Don Quixote falls from his horse.*

DON QUIXOTE. Holy Virgin! I am wounded. Help, good Sancho, help! They have knocked my teeth out.

SHEPHERD. I would I had knocked thy head off as well. Sheep-killer! Pig-snout. May you be slit like a cucumber, if you have destroyed any of my sheep!

DON QUIXOTE. Sancho! Help! Help, I say, I am sorely wounded.

SHEPHERD. May I give up the ghost, if I have not the law on thee! Mayhap thou'lt sing a different tune when the Holy Brotherhood of Toledo call thee to account. Mayhap 'twill cool thy hot head to row in the galleys a season — though, by the mass, I have a mind to beat your dogship to a jelly without waiting for the officers!

DON QUIXOTE. Sancho! Where art thou?

[*Enter Sancho, afoot.*

SANCHO. Hold, sir! For Heaven's sake, what ails you? What do you mean? Are you mad, sir? Why do you maul a poor harmless flock of sheep?

SHEPHERD. I'll have the law on thee, never fear. Thou shalt pay dear for this piece of folly.

[*Exit shepherd.*

DON QUIXOTE. My enemies have wounded me sorely, Sancho. I pray thee look how many teeth I lack in my upper jaw on the right side — for there I feel the most pain.
[*He opens his mouth wide and Sancho looks in, squatting with his hands on his knees. Don Quixote groans.*

SANCHO. How many grinders did your worship use to have on that side?

DON QUIXOTE. Four, besides the eyetooth, all whole and sound.

SANCHO. Bless me! Why, you have in this nether jaw on this side but two grinders and a stump; and never a grinder in your upper jaw — never a stump. All is leveled there as smooth as the palm of your hand.

DON QUIXOTE. Alas! I had rather have lost an arm, so it were not my sword-arm; for a mouth without cheek-teeth is like a mill without a millstone. Every tooth in a man's head is more valuable than a diamond.

SANCHO. Thou sayest well, master, but what I want to know is: how came you to be overhauling a flock of sheep, and frightening the poor creatures out of their silly wits? Belike you would have kept your teeth, if it were not for such foolishness.

DON QUIXOTE. "Flock of sheep" indeed! There thou art wrong, Sancho! Sawest thou not the armies that met here in combat — the knights in gilded armor, with their banners and devices?

SANCHO (*busies himself with Rosinante*). Armies? Burn my beard, if I saw any armies!

DON QUIXOTE. How! Didst thou not hear the neighing of their horses, the shrilling of their trumpets, nor the beat of their drums?

SANCHO. Not I! I pricked up my ears, like a sow in the beans, and yet heard naught but the bleating of sheep.

DON QUIXOTE. My enemies, the magicians, have disturbed thy senses, Sancho; and keep thee from seeing and hearing aright.

SANCHO. Huh! That's all very well, master, but I think my own thoughts. It is as plain as the nose on one's face these same adventures which we have set out to hunt for, up and down, are like to bring us into a peck of troubles!

DON QUIXOTE. Poor Sancho! How ignorant thou art in matters of chivalry!

SANCHO. What are we like to get out of it, pray, but blows and more blows; and bruises and more bruises?

DON QUIXOTE. Hast thou so base a mind that glory means nothing to thee? And what is as sweet withal, as to triumph over an enemy?

SANCHO. Huh! (*He grunts sceptically*) Methinks I shall drive Rosinante out to grass and myself gather such herbs as grow hereabout to make a poultice for your worship's jaw. (*He spanks the animal on his flank, driving him off stage*) Off, with you! Out you go!

[*Exit Rosinante. Sancho Panza starts to follow, but stops short, catching sight of Dulcinea, off-stage, who approaches, pushing a cart, loaded with oranges. She is a strapping country wench.*

SANCHO. Hist, master! Who could ever have thought it? Of all the luck in the world, this is the best!

DON QUIXOTE. Out with it, Sancho Panza.

SANCHO. What think you? Aldonza Lorenzo, herself, approaches, coming this way, as I am a sinner.

DON QUIXOTE. Blessèd Heaven! What art thou saying, my dear Sancho?

SANCHO. Why, beshrew me, thou hast but to look! (*He points off-stage*) Seeing is believing, the world over.

DON QUIXOTE. I see naught but a damsel, trundling a cart full of oranges.

SANCHO. 'Tis thy Dulcinea, nevertheless. Come, sir, snuff your eyes, and go pay your homage to the lady of your soul, for she is near at hand.

DON QUIXOTE (*claps his hand to his mouth*). My teeth!

[*Enter Dulcinea.*

SANCHO. Halt, mistress! And permit my master, the noble Don Quixote de la Mancha, to pay his respects to your high-and-mightiness.

DULCINEA. Sancho Panza, as I live!

DON QUIXOTE (*falls on one knee before Dulcinea*). Princess, and Universal Lady of Toboso, take pity, I pray thee, upon thy humble adorer. Masterpiece of all human perfections, and only comfort of this afflicted heart —

DULCINEA. What nonsense is this? Pray spare your breath to cool your porridge! I like not such gibberish.

DON QUIXOTE (*leans his elbows on the cart*). Peerless Dulcinea, look upon thy knight with favoring eyes, I do beseech thee; and, in the worship which I pay to thy beauty, read the humility with which my soul adores thee.

DULCINEA. I do not know you, sir! And you should take shame to yourself — you should, indeed, — to make game of an honest country lass. Is this the way you small gentry jeer and flout us poor rustics — as if we could not give you as good as you bring! Go, get about your business, and let me go about mine. (*She jerks the cart and Don Quixote falls sprawling*) Let be, Sancho Panza, — and the next time I see you, may you be in better company!

[*She kicks Sancho and he, too, sprawls on the ground.*

CURTAIN

SCENE III

A road near Toboso. A windmill is placed, left; a church spire is seen in the distance, right. The stage is almost dark; there is an occasional flash of lightning and rumble of thunder.

Don Quixote and Sancho Panza are seen in the distance in silhouette, passing across the stage and disappearing at a bend of the road.

A miller with a sack on his back enters. Business of adjusting pulleys and working about the mill. Exit miller. Enter Don Quixote and Sancho on horseback.

DON QUIXOTE. Halt, Sancho! Pray you, see to Rosinante, for he is limping sorely. I fear he has picked up a stone along the road.

SANCHO. Aye, master. (*He dismounts*) Faith, I am glad to stretch my legs again! Where does your worship locate the trouble? That is to say, which foot?

DON QUIXOTE. The left hind foot, as it seems to me.

SANCHO (*slaps Rosinante on the flank*). Move yourself, old bag-a-bones! (*Rosinante rears*) Whoa, there! Whoa!

DON QUIXOTE (*lurches in the saddle*). Have a care, Sancho.

SANCHO (*lifts Rosinante's hoof — Rosinante kicks him*). A plague take thee! Whatever ails thee, then? Dost think thyself a don, as well as thy master — huh?

DON QUIXOTE (*sighs heavily*). I am an unhappy man, Sancho, when I think of our encounter with the Lady Dulcinea! What do you make of it?

SANCHO. Well, your eternity, it seems to me that these enchanters you have told me of, have bewitched the Lady Dulcinea, so that she did not know your worship. But, cheer up, sir! Aldonza Lorenzo is a kind wench and will not hold anything against thee, I promise it.

DON QUIXOTE. Truly, thou art right. The blame is not upon Dulcinea, matchless and immaculate princess, but rather upon the wiles of the base enchanters that have bewitched her. How extensive is their spite to deprive me of happiness in a meeting with the lady of my heart.

SANCHO. Huh-uh!

[*He picks up Rosinante's hoof again.*

DON QUIXOTE. Hast found the stone?

SANCHO. Aye, marry, that I have, blessings on the saints! No wonder the poor beast was so full of chivalry!

DON QUIXOTE (*looks up at the sky*). The sky is dark and overcast. We must find shelter quickly, or we shall get a wetting.

SANCHO. There you have the right of it, sir. We are in for a shower, as sure as I am a sinner!

DON QUIXOTE. Be quick, Sancho. To horse!

SANCHO (*attempts to catch the ass*). Come now, Dapple — Come, my precious! (*Dapple backs away*) A murrain on thee! (*He approaches again*) Come, my darling! Come now! (*He is about to catch Dapple's bridle, when the ass switches his head and backs away again*) Thou art a saucy little ass, Dapple, and had ought to be well punished for thy capers. (*Dapple dashes off stage*) May the curse of Heaven light upon thee!

[*There is a faint sound of rising wind and a rumble of thunder. The sails of the windmill begin to turn creakingly.*

DON QUIXOTE (*points at the windmill and cries out in a loud voice*). Ha! Look yonder, friend! Look, I say! What see you there?

SANCHO. I see a windmill.

DON QUIXOTE. The giant, fool! (*The thunder rumbles*) Hark to him!

SANCHO (*looks here and there*). What giant? Where?

DON QUIXOTE (*points to the windmill*). He, whom thou seest yonder, with his long, extended arms — the same, I make no doubt, that so recently bewitched the Lady Dulcinea.

SANCHO. Now, in truth, thou art mad, as our good curate said. Look again, sir. That is no giant, but a windmill; the things that you fancy to be arms are sails, which, being whirled by the wind, make the mill go.

DON QUIXOTE. I tell thee, stupid fellow, it is a giant. And, if thou art afraid, go aside and say thy prayers, for I intend to do battle with him. (*He makes a pass at the windmill with his lance, crying in a loud voice*) Stand your ground, ignoble creature! Base miscreant, though you move more arms than Briareus, you shall pay for your arrogance!

[*He rushes upon the windmill, with upraised lance. The windmill catches both horse and rider in its sails, raises them aloft and holds them there, struggling. There is a flash of lightning and a great clap of thunder.*

SANCHO (*falls to his knees*). Alas! That I was ever born to see this day.

CURTAIN

Scene IV

An Inn near La Mancha, several days later. Back-stage, center, a crude puppet-stage is set up. Stage left is a table, set for a meal, with three stools beside it; staircase right. Back-stage, left, is a cupboard in the wall, like a "dumb waiter." A drum stands in front of the puppet-stage.

The Duke of Barataria, the Duchess, and the Innkeeper are discovered.

INNKEEPER. Most rare sport, your grace! Your worships will not believe what is going on outside!

DUKE. Does it concern the long, lean, gloomy-visaged fellow we saw just now in the courtyard? He had set up an old suit of armor in the horse trough and — by my faith! — it appeared as if he were performing his devotions before it. A madman, surely!

INNKEEPER. It does concern him, in sooth, your grace. And you say well when you say "madman" — but there's a pair of them. The long-favored fellow is the noble Don Quixote de la Mancha, a knight errant, an' it please your eternities! You have not seen the other, I take it. He is the squire — a saucy rustic, a fat pudding-bag of a fellow, called Sancho Panza.

DUCHESS. This is too comical! And why is the noble Don Quixote de la Mancha watching his armor in the horse trough?

INNKEEPER. For the drollest of reasons, your grace. Being quite out of his wits, the poor gentleman takes my humble house for a castle — and myself for a great lord, the governor of the stronghold. It troubles his mind, he says, that he has never been knighted after the custom of chivalry; and he begs me — *me* — to confer the honor of knighthood upon him after he has kept watch before his arms, as they used to do in olden times, in the chapel of the castle. Is it not a strange whimsy, my lady?

DUKE. What said you, landlord?

INNKEEPER. May Heaven pardon my sins! I told him the

chapel was but recently burned down and not yet re-built; but, said I, in case of emergency, 'twould be lawful to watch the armor in any other place; and he might do so in the castle courtyard. So down he plumps upon his knees before the horse trough!

DUCHESS. 'Tis a sweet jest! We must have speech with this amusing lunatic — and with the pudding-bag, too. Can you bring it about, landlord?

[*Shouts and noise of fighting are heard outside.*

INNKEEPER. How now! What is all this brawling?

DUCHESS. Oh! Oh! What a clatter!

DUKE. By my troth, they must be fighting!

INNKEEPER. I must put a stop to this. If I cut not the matter short, milord, no telling what mischief this Don Quixote will fall into! For it is he, you may be sure, who is raising the disturbance. The sooner the better for Sir Knight, say I.

[*Enter Don Quixote.*

DON QUIXOTE (*to the Innkeeper*). You do great wrong, sir, to permit your uncivil retainers to insult a guest in your castle — and especially one who keeps the holy vigil in preparation for knighthood!

INNKEEPER. Most illustrious Don Quixote, what has occurred to disturb your highness?

DON QUIXOTE. Matter enough, milord! Your rascally varlets have thrown my armor out of the horse trough, that they might give their mules to drink. Sacrilege! And when I clouted them over the head, they fell to stoning me!

INNKEEPER (*bows low*). It is with the utmost regret, most noble lord, that I learn of the misdemeanors of my servants. Believe me, they shall be punished.

DON QUIXOTE. I have myself seen to that.

INNKEEPER. It is come upon me, gentle sir, that you have already kept the vigil so long as the laws of chivalry require; and that, in this hour, I shall dub thee knight without further delay.

DON QUIXOTE. Permit me to thank you for your magnanimity. It is no more than I expected from your magnificence.

DUCHESS (*to the Innkeeper*).   Pray present the noble Don Quixote, sir.

INNKEEPER (*bows*).   Her grace, the Duchess of Barataria — the illustrious Don Quixote de la Mancha.

[*The Duchess extends her hand and Don Quixote kisses it.*

DON QUIXOTE.   Also called, "The Knight of the Lions."

INNKEEPER.   His grace, the Duke of Barataria — the valorous Don Quixote de la Mancha.

[*The Duke and Don Quixote both bow low.*

DON QUIXOTE.   Also known as "The Knight of the Woful Figure !"

INNKEEPER.   My poor house is honored by the presence of such distinguished guests.   An' your worships be pleased to excuse me, I will now bring the — er — implements for the ceremony.

DUCHESS.   Pray do so.

[*Exit the Innkeeper.*

DUKE.   I am sorry, Sir Knight of the Woful Figure, that you should have suffered a mischance while stopping at this castle.

DON QUIXOTE.   Most generous prince, I can think of nothing ill that could befall me here, since I have had the happiness of seeing your grace.

[*Enter the Innkeeper, carrying an account book and a staff.*

INNKEEPER.   Is all in readiness?   (*To the Duke and Duchess*) Pray seat yourselves, eternities.   (*To Don Quixote*)   To your knees, illustrious Quixote !

[*Don Quixote kneels and the Innkeeper reads in a chanting singsong from the account book,*

Five measures of barley	*Ten reals.*
Five measures of wheat	*Ten reals.*
Six loads of hay	*Four ducats, twelve-pence.*
Six loads of chopped straw	*Six-and-thirty pence.*
One dozen cheeses of Seville	*Half-a-crown.*
One dozen cruses of olive oil . . .	*One-and-thirty pence, half-penny.*
One measure of salt	*Two reals.*
One dozen skins Amontillado . . .	*Twelve ducats.*

(*He gives Don Quixote a blow on the neck; and a slap on the back with the staff*) Herewith I dub thee knight! Arise, Don Quixote de la Mancha, Knight of the Woful Figure, Knight of the Lions!
[*Don Quixote rises.*

DUKE.   Congratulations, brave knight!

DUCHESS.   May Heaven prosper you, wherever you go!

DON QUIXOTE.   I thank you, fair lady and noble lords.

INNKEEPER.   Pray excuse me, gentles. I must step into the kitchen and see how your worships' dinner is progressing.
[*Exit landlord.*

DUKE.   Will the illustrious Quixote honor us by partaking of refreshment?

DON QUIXOTE.   With the utmost pleasure, your grace. (*They seat themselves at the table*) Permit me to summon my squire. (*He calls*) Sancho! Sancho Panza! What, Sancho, I say!
[*Enter Sancho.*

DUCHESS.   Ah! Indeed! So this is your squire, sir? Thou shalt serve us, Sancho Panza. I'll warrant thee a man of sense.

SANCHO.   May your holiness live many years, Madam Duchess, for your good opinion of me.

DON QUIXOTE.   You will find my squire very handy in these matters. He can serve at table with the same neatness and dispatch with which he performs his duties in the field.
[*Sancho knocks a tray of dishes off the table. They land with a crash.*

SANCHO.   May the saints preserve us!
[*He makes a motion, as if to pick up the dishes.*

DUCHESS.   Let them alone, good Sancho. 'Tis a matter of no consequence. Make haste to fetch us the royal, red-legged partridges that milord has ordered to be roasted, in honor of your master — and forget not the wine, I beg of you.

SANCHO.   Right, Madam Duchess. I shall be as nimble as a frog.
[*Sancho gets a tray full of food from the "dumb waiter."*

DUKE (*to Don Quixote*).   Pray tell us of your adventures, Sir Knight. We have heard brave tales of your encounters on the highroad, and would fain have the truth of them from your own mouth.

DUCHESS. Do tell us, great Knight of the Lions!

DON QUIXOTE. If it please you to listen to my adventures, gracious lady, — why, then it is a pleasure to tell of them.

[*Sancho offers the tray of food to Don Quixote first.*

DON QUIXOTE (*half rises in his chair in annoyance*). Mind yourself, Sancho. Serve her grace first. Have you no manners, buffle-head? Do you not know that ladies must come first in everything?

[*Sancho presents the dish to the Duchess on the right side.*

DON QUIXOTE. Clod-pate! The other side! Left — to the *left*, I tell you!

SANCHO. Left or right, what matters it, so long as each gets himself the tidbit he .desires? (*To the Duchess*) Try the leg, ma'am. That's a dainty trifle.

DON QUIXOTE (*to the Duchess*). Your grace must know that no knight errant had ever such an eternal babbler, such a bundle of conceit, for a squire, as I have.

DUCHESS. Nay, nay! I am glad honest Sancho has his conceits; it is a sign he is wise, for merry conceits are never the offspring of a dull brain, I do assure you.

[*Sancho passes the tray to the Duke and Don Quixote, who serve themselves.*

SANCHO (*to Don Quixote, in a loud whisper*). Take this piece, master. 'Tis the best on the dish. I put it one side for you in the pantry.

DON QUIXOTE. Be quiet, sirrah!

DUCHESS. Hast forgotten the wine, Sancho Panza?

SANCHO. Before George, yes, lady!

[*Sancho gets rid of the tray at the " dumb waiter " and takes out a wine jug, from which he drinks unseen by the company.*

DUKE. Pray continue, brave Don Quixote. You were about to relate your adventures when we were — er — interrupted.

DON QUIXOTE. Ah, yes! One day, upon this very road that leads out of Toboso, I met twelve prisoners, trudging along in a row — one behind the other, like a string of beads. These poor wretches were linked together by the neck to a huge iron chain — and they were attended by four keepers, armed with carbines and javelins. I fell upon the guards, your grace, with my good sword! I smote them hip and thigh — and set the prisoners free!

DUKE. Ha!

DUCHESS. Bless me! You amaze me, sir.

SANCHO (*pours the wine*). Whatever you set those gaol-birds free for, master, I h'an't no idea; for they was a pack of crack-ropes and slip-strings on the way to the galleys, to serve out their terms for cattle stealing, highway robbery and the like. And I misdoubt me we are in for a peck of trouble for it, too. Like as not we shall go to the galleys ourselves, because of this fine business — with a taste of the cat-o'-nine-tails, as well.

DON QUIXOTE. Hold thy tongue, Sancho. On another occasion, your grace, I encountered a giant—a monstrous and very evil giant — with long, extended arms, which he whirled about constantly, seeking to catch and crush me in his embrace. I fell upon him, madam, and slew him with my sword!

SANCHO. A giant, eh? (*He laughs derisively*) 'Twas no more a giant than I be! 'Twas a windmill — that is what it was — and nobody could think otherwise, unless he had windmills in his head!

[*Sancho is somewhat tipsy and tilts the wine jug so that its contents spill down the Duchess's neck. The Duchess screams and jumps up from her chair.*

DON QUIXOTE. Dunce! Addle-pate! Unmannerly looby! What hast thou done?

SANCHO (*begins to bawl*). I will take my corporal oath, master, that I did not go for to do it!

[*He bawls yet louder.*

DON QUIXOTE. Sew up thy mouth, insufferable rustic!

DUCHESS. Nay, reprove him not. I will answer for him that he will do no more mischief. Cease your crying, friend Sancho, and let us have a little music. It will cheer us up. What say you all?

DUKE. Excellent! I will fetch my lute.

SANCHO. And I will bring my castanets and dance for you.

[*Exit Duke and Sancho.*

DUCHESS (*to Don Quixote*). Forgive my curiosity, sir, but I would know if there is not some fair lady, to whom you dedicate your career in arms?

DON QUIXOTE. Aye, madam. The knights had ever a beauteous mistress to whom they paid their devotions. But among them all was none so high, so beautiful and so virtuous as the peerless Dulcinea del Toboso, the lady of my heart!

DUCHESS. And none so fortunate in her champion, noble knight.

[*Enter the Duke and Sancho, with lute and castanets.*

SANCHO (*capers about*). Well, here we are! Let us dance and sing and make merry! I know a fine song and one that is a favorite in the taverns. Do your worships know "La Cachuca"?

DUKE. Let me see — how goes it?

SANCHO. Why, this way.

[*He hums the tune.*

DUKE. Ah, yes. I know. (*He strums on the lute*) Now, then, Sancho.

[*They sing. Sancho dances tipsily.*

DON QUIXOTE. Have a care, Sancho. Mind thyself!

DUKE. Bravo! Bravo!

DUCHESS. Well done, Sancho Panza. Thou art a very prince of dancers!

DUKE. 'Tis our Sancho's favorite dance, I'll warrant it.

SANCHO. Yes, by the mass. 'Tis the same I danced at the village fair at La Mancha last May-day; and whether your worships believe it or not, it was the hit of the business and set the tongues wagging all over the town.

DUCHESS. Noble Knight of the Lions, I would beg a boon of thee.

DON QUIXOTE. Speak, highness, and it shall be done. Don Quixote de la Mancha never yet refused to comply with the wishes of a lady.

DUCHESS. You are too gallant, sir! I beg of you, put on that magnificent suit of armor which we saw but now in the court-yard. I am sure it must become you — and I pine to see a handsome gentleman armed cap-a-pie! It is a sight which seldom gladdens our eyes nowadays.

DON QUIXOTE. Your grace does me too much honor. It will give me all possible pleasure to oblige your grace.

[*Exit Don Quixote.*

DUKE. And what do you think of the profession of knight-errantry, friend Sancho?

SANCHO. Ods-bodikins, I think little enough of it; and I would be out of it in a trice, but that I love my master, and for the hopes I have of getting me an island to govern.

DUCHESS. An island! How interesting!

SANCHO. So my master, Don Quixote, has promised it. If I will be squire to him, so he says, he will give me the governor-ship of some island he is a-going to conquer with his sword.

[*A knock is heard at the door.*

DUKE. Enter!

[*Enter an Officer of the Holy Brotherhood of Toledo.*

OFFICER. I salute you, gentlemen! (*To the Duchess*) Your pardon, madam, for this intrusion. (*To the Duke*) I am an officer of the Holy Brotherhood of Toledo, milord, whose duty it is to apprehend thieves, robbers and disturbers of the peace, as your worship knows. In the King's name, sir, I bid you give assistance to the Holy Brotherhood.

SANCHO (*trembles with fear*). Now, may Heaven have mercy!

[*He hides himself under the stairs, in view of the audience.*

DUKE. Pray tell me in what way I may serve the Holy Brother-hood?

OFFICER. Why, in this way, milord. Here is a warrant for the arrest of one Alonzo Quixano of La Mancha — also known as Don Quixote de la Mancha — for many and various crimes upon the King's Highway. He is wanted by the law for the wanton slaughter of three sheep near Toboso — and for damage done to a windmill in the same vicinity. But the worst of all was his setting free a party of galley slaves, notorious rogues; and murderously assaulting their keepers! He will get ten years in the galleys for that, sir; and a hundred jerks with the cat-o'-nine-tails, into the bargain.

DUKE. Extraordinary!

SANCHO (*mumbles under his breath*). Oh, blessèd saints! If ever you helped us out of trouble, help us now!

OFFICER (*shows his warrant, a roll of parchment*). Here is the warrant for the arrest of this rogue, as I have said; and this, which I am about to read you, is a description of the offender. (*He scans the warrant*) Ah — let me see! Yes — here it is. (*He reads*) "*A tall, wither-faced, lantern-jawed fellow, scragged, grizzle-haired, hawk-nosed, and wears long, lank mustachios. Dressed in full armor; rides a raw-boned old horse; has for a servant one Sancho Panza, a laboring man.*"

SANCHO. I am a dead man!

OFFICER. Have you seen any such person as this Don Quixote de la Mancha, milord? Or Sancho Panza, his servant? They have been reported in these parts.

DUKE. Aye, marry, that I have. I have seen the pair you speak of in this very inn.

SANCHO (*rocks himself to and fro*). Oh, my blood and bones!

DUCHESS (*imploringly*). That was some time ago, sweet husband.

DUKE. Not two hours past, good sir, a pair such as you describe stopped here at the inn — and raised a fine disturbance in the courtyard, too, until the landlord put an end to it. Without doubt it was this Don Quixote you are after — and Sancho Panza, his squire, as well.

OFFICER. Belike the very persons! Where are they now, sir?

DUKE. How should I know where they have got to, by this time? But if you pursue them at once, officer, and ride fast and furious, no doubt you will overtake the vagabonds before many hours!

SANCHO (*comes boldly out of his hiding-place*). This gentleman here, his grace of Barataria, has the straight on't, sir. You have the right sow by the ear! I watched them ride away from the inn myself, sir, and I heard them say they were headed straight for the Sierra Morena.

DUKE. Better make haste, officer! That is a swift steed of the Don's. You must e'en ride at a good pace to overtake him.

OFFICER. I will do so, sir. My thanks to your grace. (*To the Duchess*) By your leave, madam.

[*He bows. Exit officer.*

DUCHESS. Incomparable husband! My heart would have broken if the law were to overtake these amusing friends of ours — and for such serious crimes, too. Surely the punishment will be terrible, if they are caught. Down on your knees, Sancho, and kiss his grace's feet for getting you out of this muddle.

SANCHO (*falls to his knees*). Heaven bless your worship's grace! I do not know how to thank your highnesses for what you have done; but if in any matter like squiring, or ploughing, or the care of poultry, that I am familiar with, I can do you any good, you have but to make your wishes known to Sancho Panza.

DUKE. You have learned civility in the school of courtesy itself, good Sancho!

[*Enter Don Quixote in armor, sword in hand. He descends the stairs.*

SANCHO. Body o' me, here comes my master, all trinkum-trankumed up in armor, as fine as a tin-shop on wheels.

DUKE (*to Sancho*). Not a word about this disturbance.

SANCHO. Not so much as a wink, your worship. Mum as a new-laid egg. And now, if your eternities please, I'd like to go and get my dinner.

DUKE. You may go.

[*Exit Sancho.*

DUCHESS (*to Don Quixote*). Splendid, sir! How the armor sets you off, to be sure! La, la! You will be turning all the pretty ladies' heads, most noble Don! Look here, milord! Behold the brave Don Quixote, what a fine figure he cuts!

DUKE. How commanding he looks! What majesty has its seat upon his brow! Austere, yet clement! Words fail me, noble knight.

DON QUIXOTE (*coughs affectedly*). Ahem! Your graces give me honor beyond my deserts!

[*Enter the Innkeeper, with Master Peter, the puppet-showman.*

INNKEEPER (*to Peter*). This way, Master Peter! Is everything to your taste, gentles? The wine? The cheese? The fowl? I trust you found all satisfactory?

DUCHESS. All was as it should be, landlord.

INNKEEPER. Perchance your worships have been wondering about the little stage you see set up here in the tavern — the castle, I should say. To speak truth, I have a surprise for you. This is Master Peter, the celebrated puppet-showman, who has strolled about the country this long time, with his curious manikins; and I have persuaded him to show his motion for your pleasure this evening — if that is agreeable to the company?

DUCHESS. Excellent! I have heard of Master Peter, and should like nothing so much as to see his puppets.

PETER. I thank your grace.

INNKEEPER. Pray seat yourselves where you can best view the stage. As your worships know, perhaps, Master Peter speaks for the marionettes, and tells your highnesses what it is all about. I myself am going back of the stage to observe how the affair is managed.

[*They seat themselves. Exit Innkeeper.*

PETER (*stands beside the stage*). First, I shall show you my little juggler, manipulating his balls.

[*He beats a drum and the curtain goes up. A juggler is seen upon the stage. He goes through his little performance.*

DUCHESS. Marvelous, is it not, milord?

PETER. Now, you shall see a pair of dancers, performing the fandango.

[*He beats the drum. Marionettes appear and dance with castanets.*

DUKE. Bravo! Thou shalt have a rich reward, good Peter.

PETER. Now, you shall see the play of Melisandra and Don Gayferos. It is a true history, taken out of the Chronicles of France and the Spanish ballads; and tells how Don Gayferos

rescued his wife, Melisandra, that was a prisoner among the
Moors in the city of Saragossa. (*He beats the drum.   A lady
and a Moor are seen on the stage*)   Now, gentles, cast your
eyes upon this lady, whom you see in a Moorish habit, for this
is the peerless Melisandra, she that is held a prisoner by the
Moors.   But now — silence, your worships, pray, silence!
— who is he, that comes a-tip-toe, creeping and stealing along,
with his finger in his mouth, behind Melisandra?   Don't you
see that it is a curséd Moor?

DON QUIXOTE (*shouts*).   Watch yourself, madam!   Look behind
you, Madam Melisandra!   This is monstrous!   Monstrous!
[*He half rises in his seat.*

PETER.   Hear what a smack he gives her!   See how she spits
and wipes her mouth with her white sleeve!

DON QUIXOTE (*draws his sword*).   Villain!   Infidel!   Dost
thou presume to lay hands on the Lady Melisandra?

PETER.   See how she takes on, and tears her lovely hair for
very madness!   Behold the Moor, how he catches her up,
tosses her over his shoulder and makes off with her!

DON QUIXOTE.   Shall Don Quixote stand by, and see a curséd
infidel abduct a Christian lady?   No, by the Mass!   Take
that!   And that!   And that, thou base-born dog!
[*He smashes the puppet-show with his sword.   The Duchess
screams.*

CURTAIN

SCENE V

*Outside the inn, the following morning.   There is a wall with
an open gate, which leads into the courtyard of the inn.*
The barber is discovered, looking about.   He beckons off stage.

BARBER (*speaks in a loud whisper*).   Hist!   Hist!   This way,
sir!
[*Enter the Curate.*

BARBER.   This is the place, your reverence.   The goatherd, who
brought news of our friend's whereabouts last evening, said

that he had seen Master Quixano, along with Sancho Panza, riding into an inn that was midway between La Mancha and Toboso. This is that very inn, beyond the shadow of a doubt.

CURATE. What do you make of our errand, Nicholas? Will Alonzo Quixano come home without argument, or the use of force, think you?

BARBER. By the Mass, I know not. But get him home we must, or good Mistress Maria will fret herself into her grave, belike, with fearing this, or that, has happened to her master. And if what the goatherd told me of his carryings-on be true, why, sure, it is high time that he was brought home — by force, if need be.

CURATE. Truly, we must get this madman home.

BARBER. And the law is after him, too, for sheep-killing and other damage on the King's highway! He could be thrown into the galleys for such doings. Heard you —— Hist!

[*Voices are heard behind the wall. The Innkeeper and Don Quixote are speaking, unseen by the audience.*

DON QUIXOTE. My lord governor, the favors I have received in your castle are so great that they bind my grateful soul to an eternal acknowledgment. If there is any proud mortal on whom you wish to be revenged for some affront, or injury, pray acquaint me with it now; and, by my order of knighthood, I promise you that you shall receive satisfaction.

BARBER. Hist!

CURATE. It is Alonzo Quixano's voice.

BARBER. Let us hide ourselves around the corner of the wall and see what takes place.

CURATE. An excellent idea!

[*Exit Curate and barber.*

INNKEEPER. Sir Knight, I shall not need your assistance to revenge any wrong that may be offered to my person; and all the satisfaction I desire is that you will pay for the damage you did to Master Peter's puppet-show — and your reckoning for horse meat and man's meat, and all your expenses in my inn.

[*Enter, through the gate, Don Quixote in armor and mounted upon Rosinante.   He is followed by the Innkeeper.*

DON QUIXOTE.   How?   Is this an inn?

INNKEEPER.   It is, in truth, and one of the best upon the road, I do assure you.

DON QUIXOTE.   How strangely have I been mistaken, then. For, upon my honor, I mistook this inn for a castle — and a considerable one, too.   But if it be an inn, indeed, — why, then, I shall pay thee naught, for the laws of chivalry forbid it.

INNKEEPER.   What is that?   "Pay me naught?"   Indeed, thou shalt pay me what thou owest, sir!   And Master Peter, too, by the Mass!

DON QUIXOTE.   Knights errant never paid in any inn whatsoever, landlord — and this is the least recompense that can be allowed them, in return for the dangers and labors and inconveniences they endure.   No, I will not break through the customs of chivalry because of any beggarly innkeeper, forsooth.

INNKEEPER.   I have nothing to do with this chivalry nonsense. Pay your reckoning and tell me no more cock-and-bull stories. How do you think I can afford to keep house at this rate?

DON QUIXOTE (*threatens the landlord with his lance*).   Thou fool and knave!   Out of my way!

INNKEEPER.   Pay your reckoning!

[*He tries to catch Rosinante by the bridle.*

DON QUIXOTE.   What!   Wouldst thou hinder me?   Let me pass, infamous poltroon, or it shall be the worse for thee!   By the sun that shines, I have a mind to run thee through with my lance!

INNKEEPER.   Now may the Evil One belabor and rib-roast and bastinado thee, thou crack-brained cut-throat!   Thy paper skull is full of empty rooms!   Wouldst cheat me out of what thou owest?   Four ducats, I say!   Four ducats!

DON QUIXOTE (*makes a pass at the Innkeeper with his lance*). Out of my way, thou monster of nature!   Magazine of lies, cupboard of deceits, granary of guile, foe of all honor!   Thou villainous, ignorant, rash, unmannerly, blasphemous detractor, away, and never let me see thy face again!

INNKEEPER. Lizard! Ape! Spawn of Satan!

DON QUIXOTE. Out of my way!

[*He puts spurs to Rosinante and rides out.*

INNKEEPER (*shouts after the departing knight*). Very well, then, old skinflint, scurvy dog! Wait till I catch thy squire, forsooth, and I will get the reckoning out of him, or make him sweat for it!

[*Exit landlord, through the gate. He closes and bars it after him. The Curate and the barber come out of their hiding place.*

CURATE. Now Heaven assist thee, poor Don Quixote! I am afraid thou art tumbling from the top of thy madness to the very bottom of simplicity!

BARBER. All this flim-flam about knight-errantry! Do you know, Dr. Perez, there came into my mind a plan as we stood there in hiding, listening to our poor friend's ravings — a plan to bring him home peaceable, and keep him there!

CURATE. Out with it, Goodman Shaver.

BARBER. It came into my head on the moment, your reverence — and perhaps the Holy Virgin put it there, who can say? — "Why not," said something inside my head — plain as a voice it was — "why not find another suit of armor and put it on? Another helmet and shield and sword, also?" In short, why not be another knight errant, myself, and meet our Don Quixote on the road and challenge him to a duel — as the knights used to do in the days of old? He would never know me, your reverence, with the visor of the helmet down.

CURATE. Good! Good! And what is to be the condition of this duel?

BARBER. Why, marry, the condition of it will be that the conquered shall be wholly at the mercy of the conqueror. I cannot help but win, Master Curate, since I be the heavier, and the stronger, and the younger! And winning — as Our Lady grant I may be able to do! — I shall bid our valiant Don go to his home and stay there.

CURATE. It is an inspiration, Nicholas! Alonzo Quixano will never suspect the trick. And, by my holy orders, I will get me a false nose and go along with you, as squire, to see the fun! A pair of knights errant in combat! It will be a rare sight.

[*Voices in altercation are heard behind the wall. The Innkeeper, Sancho Panza, Peter and others are speaking, unseen by the audience.*

INNKEEPER. Here's the saucy rascal! Here is Sancho Panza! Now, by the saints, if the master refuses to pay, the man shall settle the reckoning. Four ducats is the charge, Sir Squire, and four ducats I will have, ere thou leavest my house — that I swear!

SANCHO. Easy, now! Easy, sir! Leave go of me! Be not so hasty, sir.

CURATE. It is Sancho Panza they are berating. Oh, I would I could see over the wall.

BARBER. Climb up on my back — so! Up, doctor, and take a look into the courtyard!

[*The barber bends over and the Curate climbs up on his back and looks over the wall.*

INNKEEPER. Four ducats and not a *real* less — horse meat and man's meat!

PETER. How about my puppet-show? A'n't I to be paid for the Moor that the gentleman hacked up with his sword? And all the damage to my stage as well? Forty *reals* would no more than cover the cost!

SANCHO. Thou art a pack of rascals. My master would have paid thee, if the knights thought proper to do so. And I a'n't a-going to do what my master would not have me — that I a'n't.

INNKEEPER. What! Thou wilt not pay, either?

BARBER. What is going on there, doctor? Can you see what they do?

CURATE. Aye, marry. They are badgering Sancho Panza for the reckoning. Look you now! They have got him by the jacket.

BARBER. How many are there? Are there two or three?

CURATE. Three stout fellows, besides the landlord. By Our

Lady, they are shaking him, for all he struggles. It will go ill with him.

INNKEEPER. Get his wallet, then! Pull off his jacket!

SANCHO. I a'n't got no wallet. There's not a *real* on me — I swear it! Leave go of me! Leave go, I say!

INNKEEPER. Ho, carriers! Fetch a blanket! That horse blanket will do — give me that! We'll give this fellow a tossing.

CURATE. Nicholas! They are going to toss Sancho Panza in a blanket!

SANCHO. Help, Holy Virgin! Help! Help!

VOICES. Ho, then! Tumble him in! So much for you! Up you go!

[*Sancho appears and disappears above the wall, as he is tossed in the blanket. He bawls lustily and the carriers laugh.*

CURTAIN

Scene VI

A Forest

Don Quixote and Sancho Panza are discovered, asleep at the foot of a tree. The Knight is in armor. They snore. A bumble-bee buzzes about and annoys them. It lights on Don Quixote's nose and wakens him. He slaps at it.

DON QUIXOTE. Wake up, Sancho! Wake up! I am amazed at the insensibility of thy temper. Thou art certainly made of marble, or of solid brass, that thou liest so, without either motion or feeling.

SANCHO (*is half asleep*). Leave off clapper-clawing my back, I do beseech thee!

[*The bee returns and buzzes around Don Quixote's head.*

DON QUIXOTE. Pestiferous insect! Sancho! Rouse thyself and kill this perfidious bumblebee that is disturbing my slumbers.

SANCHO. What ails your worship? What bee? Where?

[*He scrambles to his feet.*

DON QUIXOTE. There! There! There it goes

SANCHO (*runs about, trying to catch the bee*). What, thou infidel! What, thou plaguey pest! I'll get thee! I'll get thee!

DON QUIXOTE. Kill it! Kill it! There!

[*Sancho catches and kills the bee.*

SANCHO. So much for thee, then!

DON QUIXOTE. Well done! So may all our enemies perish! (*He sighs heavily and assumes a dejected attitude*) My heart is heavy, Sancho.

SANCHO. Why, come, cheer up, master! Better take a dose of that magic balsam you have the receipt for. It will put you right in a twinkling.

DON QUIXOTE. Nay, nay, Sancho. My sorrows are of the heart and such as no balsam can cure. I dreamed just now of my Lady Dulcinea; and I am sorely afflicted, thinking of the harsh words she spoke to me that day we met her on the road. I would my enemies, the enchanters, were bumblebees, that we might so easily destroy them.

SANCHO. Again I say, cheer up! Better that all the Dulcineas in the world be enchanted than that one knight errant should be cast down at this rate.

DON QUIXOTE. Truly, I am the most unfortunate man in the universe.

SANCHO. Not so unfortunate as me, neither — black and blue as I be from that accursèd blanket-tossing they gave me at the castle we visited last. But hark! — here's company.

[*A doleful song is heard off-stage.*

BARBER (*sings, but is not yet seen by the audience*).

> *Say, must I die, or hopeless live?*
> *I'll act as you ordain;*
> *Despair a silent death shall give,*
> *Or love himself complain.*

DON QUIXOTE. Some one is singing!

SANCHO. Aye, and a fair doleful song it is! Whosoever he may be, he seems in tune to moan a month together.

DON QUIXOTE. This promises to be an adventure; I must get
me to horse!

[*Exit Don Quixote.*

BARBER (*off-stage. He sings*).

> *Bright queen, how shall your loving slave*
> *Be sure not to displease?*
> *Some rule of duty let him crave,*
> *He begs no other ease!*

[*Sancho mimics the song.*

[*Enter Don Quixote in full armor. He is mounted and carries*
a lance.

SANCHO. Hark to him! I'll warrant him in love, that fellow
— if that down-in-the-mouth song of his be any token!

DON QUIXOTE (*looks off-stage*). A knight, Sancho — a knight
errant in full armor, with his squire by his side. Now, this
is indeed good fortune.

SANCHO. That squire-fellow — I seem to have seen him before.
If it were not for that great nose of his, I should say he was
main like our curate, Dr. Perez, in La Mancha. Save for
the beak, he is as like him as one egg is like another.

[*Enter the barber, on horseback and in full armor. His shield is*
blazoned with a white moon and the vizor of his helmet is down.
He is accompanied by the Curate, afoot, as squire, disguised by
a false nose.

DON QUIXOTE (*to the barber*). Greeting, noble Knight of the
Wood!

BARBER. Good morrow, Sir Knight! Whither goest thou?
Art thou numbered among the happy, or the miserable?

DON QUIXOTE (*sighs heavily*). The miserable!

BARBER. Then thou art well met.

DON QUIXOTE. Is it your fortune to be in love?

BARBER. It is my misfortune to have fallen in love with a dis-
dainful mistress.

DON QUIXOTE. I should never have felt my mistress's disdain,
were it not for the wiles of my enemies, the enchanters, who
have laid a spell on her.

SANCHO.   No, truly, for our lady is as gentle as a lamb.

BARBER.   Is that your squire?   I never saw a squire before that durst presume to interrupt his master.   That is my fellow, yonder; he is as big as his father and yet no man can say that he was ever so saucy as to open his lips when I spoke.

SANCHO.   Well, well, so it goes!   I have talked before and may talk again — but I have done for the present.

DON QUIXOTE.   Sancho, retire!   And cease to trouble the conversation of your betters with your insolent tongue.

CURATE (*to Sancho*).   Come, brother!   Let us go where we may chat freely, like the downright squires we are — and let our masters get head-over-heels into the story of their loves.

SANCHO.   With all my heart!   And then I will tell you who I am, and what I am, and you shall judge whether I am not fit to make one among the talking squires!

[*Exit Sancho and Curate.*

BARBER.   You must know, sir, that I am the Knight of the White Moon, and that I am in love with the matchless Casildea de Vandalia; but this lady has been pleased to take no notice of my passion beyond employing me in a series of perilous adventures.

DON QUIXOTE.   Unhappy knight!

BARBER.   Not altogether unhappy, sir, in spite of my lady's disdain.   For, in these adventures I have earned for myself much fame and glory.   The name of the Knight of the White Moon is on every tongue in Spain!

DON QUIXOTE.   I, myself, have not been lacking in adventures and glories.

BARBER.   But the perfection of my glory lies in my victory over the renowed champion, Don Quixote de la Mancha, whom I conquered in single combat — and compelled to acknowledge that the beauty of his Dulcinea in no way equals that of my Casildea.

DON QUIXOTE.   What?   How?   What is this?   I do not question, Sir Knight, that thy prowess has brought down all other knights in Spain; but that thou hast vanquished Don Quixote de la Mancha — why, that, indeed, I must dispute!

BARBER. What d'ye mean? By the spangled skies, I fought
Don Quixote hand to hand, vanquished him and made him
submit!

DON QUIXOTE. Thou liest in thy throat! Behold Don Quixote,
himself, in person — that stands here before you, ready to
maintain his words with arms! And prepared to attest his
lady's beauty in any manner you may think convenient.

BARBER. Thou sayest "liar" to me? What! Wouldst fight
me, then? So be it! We shall settle our differences in combat!

DON QUIXOTE. Aye — you have my meaning, sir! I pray
you, state the terms of the encounter.

BARBER. Why, marry, then, these shall be the terms. If the
victory be on my side, thou shalt be obliged immediately to
forsake thy arms and the quest of adventures; and to return
to thy own house where thou shalt live peaceably henceforth.
But, if *thou* comest off conqueror, my life is at thy mercy; my
horse and arms shall be thy trophy; and the fame of all my
former exploits shall be vested in thee, as victor.

DON QUIXOTE. Knight of the White Moon, I accept thy challenge! And to whom God gives the victory, may Saint Peter
add his blessing!

BARBER. Make ready, then!
[*They take positions facing each other.*

DON QUIXOTE. Now, Lady Dulcinea, queen of beauty and
lodestar of this heart, protect thy knight and guide his arms to
victory!

BARBER. Beauteous Casildea, aid thy champion in this mortal
combat!

DON QUIXOTE. Advance! And may Heaven show the right!
[*They advance and pass each other several times, thrusting with
their lances and parrying the blows with their shields.*

BARBER. Have at thee, now!

DON QUIXOTE. Ah! Now thou shalt eat thy words!

BARBER (*wounds Don Quixote slightly*). Ha! I have thee!

DON QUIXOTE. Aid me, Lady!

BARBER. Take that, for Saint Peter! Take that for Our Lady!

[*The barber unhorses Don Quixote, both horse and rider falling heavily to the ground. Don Quixote groans. The barber points his lance at the breast of his fallen adversary.*

BARBER. Fulfill the terms of the combat — or thou art a dead man!

CURTAIN

SCENE VII

A Street in La Mancha

The front of a house is shown, decked with flags and bright hangings. A balcony center, above a barred door. Benches are placed to left and right of the door. Several villagers are discovered, seated on the balcony: the shepherd (Scene II) sits on one of the benches and Maria on the other. All watch a dancing bear, whose master plays a flute. The bear dances lumberingly.

SHEPHERD. Well done! You have a fine animal there, my friend.

VILLAGER (*tosses a coin from the balcony*). Here is a *real* for you, my good fellow.

MASTER. Thank 'ee, sir.

MARIA. It is my master — Alonzo Quixano, that you have heard tell of — that all this celebration is about. It is a kind of welcome home to him — and a fine man he is!

MASTER. Indeed, mistress! (*He waves his hand*) Good day to ye, gentles! I must be on my way. As you well know, 'tis Corpus Christi-tide, and we go to join the mummers at Toboso, where they are acting a mystery — very fine! — called "The Parliament of Death." Heaven willing, we shall pick up a good bit of money.

VILLAGER. Farewell, friend!

MARIA. The saints keep you!

[*Exit master and bear.*

VILLAGER (*to Maria*). You must be fair proud to-day, mistress, at all these goings-on in honor of your master's homecoming.

MARIA. I am, indeed, thank ye, neighbor — but I cannot help wondering in what shape the poor gentleman finds himself.

[Enter the Curate and the barber in their usual guise.

CURATE. Good morrow, neighbors. Alonzo Quixano may be expected now at any minute.

BARBER. Look ye, friends, let us make this a royal home-coming for our good neighbor. When he comes riding in, you shall all cry, every man jack of you, "Welcome home, Don Quixote de la Mancha!" "Bravo, noble knight!" or whatever like sentiment fits itself to your tongues.

CURATE. As we all know, our friend has delusions. Humor him, I beg of you — and he will never doubt that you think him as great as you say.

SHEPHERD. Truly, this is a dainty jest! "Welcome, Don Quixote de la Mancha! Hail, renowned killer of sheep! Welcome home to La Mancha, where your neighbors and kinsfolk wait with their tongues a-hanging out for eagerness to see the hero that ran a-tilt with old Corchuelo's windmill!" Bah!

BARBER. Who is this fellow?

SHEPHERD. Who I may be, is no concern of yours.

CURATE. Come now, friend, conduct yourself more mannerly, I beg of you.

BARBER (*to villagers in balcony*). I see you have flowers. Pelt our knight errant with them! Shower him with blossoms! And let there be no lag-a-bones in raising the cheers, neither.

CURATE (*to Maria*). Is all in readiness at the house, Maria?

MARIA. Everything is prepared, your reverence. A fowl in the pot and the wine drawn.

CURATE. Come then, or your master will arrive before us and find no one in the house to greet him. Haste, Nicholas!

[Exit Maria, Curate, and barber. Music sounds off-stage.

VILLAGER. I hear music.

ANOTHER. They are coming. Hark!

[Enter Don Quixote in armor, mounted on Rosinante.

VILLAGERS. Welcome home, Don Quixote de la Mancha!

Brava, noble knight! Hail, brave champion. Brava, brava, brava!

DON QUIXOTE (*bows right and left in acknowledgment of the greetings*). Thank you, friends. Thank you for this royal welcome. It is no more, indeed, than I expected from your generosity.

VILLAGERS. Brava! Brava!

[*Enter Officer of the Holy Brotherhood.*

OFFICER. Don Quixote de la Mancha, I arrest you in the King's name. (*To all*) Gentlemen, I command you to assist the Holy Brotherhood. (*To Don Quixote*) Alonzo Quixano, you are the King's prisoner.

DON QUIXOTE. How! What is the meaning of this, most insolent varlet?

OFFICER (*shows a parchment*). Here is the warrant for your arrest on a charge of sheep-killing ——

SHEPHERD. Didn't I say I would have the law on you, old crack-brain? Did I not say you should pay dear for killing my sheep, eh?

OFFICER. Out of the way, fellow. This business has gone out of your hands. Be off! (*Exit shepherd. To Don Quixote*) You are held for other charges, also, Alonzo Quixano: for damage to property, namely one windmill in the vicinity of Toboso; on a charge of refusing to pay your just reckoning at an inn and threatening the landlord; on a charge of destroying one puppet-show; and on a charge of freeing a band of prisoners on their way to the galleys, and assaulting the guards.

VILLAGERS. Oh! Ah! What a shame! He will get ten years in the galleys for this! Alack, poor Master Quixano!

OFFICER. This way, Master Quixano. You will do well to come peaceably.

[*Enter the Duke of Barataria.*

DUKE (*to the officer*). Hold, sir! Hold! Not so fast, my zealous friend.

OFFICER. I salute your grace. Stay me not, I beg of you, in the performance of my duty.

DUKE. Can you not see for yourself that this is a madman?
If, in mistaken zeal, you carry this poor lunatic before a magistrate, he will be speedily acquitted because of his malady —
and yourself be made a fool of for your pains. There is no
law in Spain that holds a madman accountable for his
acts.

OFFICER (*doubtfully*). How am I to know that he is mad?

DUKE. Read your warrant, man. Does any one in his sober
senses ride about duelling with windmills? Use your own
wits, my friend.

OFFICER. But the damages, milord?

DUKE. I, myself, will be responsible for any damage the noble
knight may have done in his encounters. Pray assure those
whom he has injured that I will settle their accounts. And
tell that rascally landlord that I will crack his wretched
poll, if I hear any more of the matter. Do you understand
me, sir?

OFFICER. It shall be done, your grace. I beg that you will
overlook my officiousness in performing what I thought to
be my duty.

DUKE. There you show a right sensible spirit. Belike you
know that you should make yourself ridiculous by hailing a
madman into court.

OFFICER (*bows*). As your highness wishes.

[*Exit officer.*

DUKE. Don Quixote is a free man! And, while I live, he
shall not lack for a friend.

ALL. Brava! Long live the noble Duke of Barataria! Long
live Don Quixote de la Mancha!

[*The Duke bows his thanks.*

DON QUIXOTE. I thank you, my lord Duke, for extricating me
from a dilemma, invoked no doubt by my enemies, the enchanters; but I must say, sir, that it suits your courtesy but
ill to call me a madman. A jest, perhaps? I know your
grace's sprightly humor.

DUKE. Your pardon, illustrious Knight of the Lions. It was,
indeed, a jest.

DON QUIXOTE. You have given me a royal welcome, neighbors, and believe me, your loyalty shall not go unrewarded. Come presently to my castle where there shall be a tankard of ale for every faithful retainer, and such largesse as I shall know how to distribute. (*To a villager*) You, sir, shall be my Master of the Horse! (*To another*) You shall be Major-domo! (*To another*) And you shall be Cup-bearer. I have fine new names for each one of you, besides, and we shall all enjoy the glories of peace together forevermore!

[*Music sounds. All burst into prolonged cheers and shower Don Quixote with flowers.*

CURTAIN

THE LADY OF THE SECRET GARDEN

THERE was a year in New York — 1913, to be exact — when it seemed as though our parents were going to the theater to see nothing but children's plays. Then, if ever, was an opportunity, so it seemed to many, for some one to begin a Children's Theater, and one manager was even so far successful that he awakened the interest of a wealthy man to help him start one. It was on the roof of our largest playhouse in New York, a garret-shaped place, with decorations from the fables of La Fontaine and Æsop, and here Mrs. Burnett's "Racketty-Packetty House" was given with gusto — perhaps too much gusto, for Master Gabriel, the midget actor who headed the doll inhabitants of the discarded doll house, fairly shouted his head off.

Then, at the Little Theater, under the artistic guidance of Mr. Winthrop Ames, Jessie White's "Snow White" gave a tremulous audience exciting thrills, the Seven Dwarfs being a dream come true, — wonder and delight marked by gasps and gurgles of young hearts.

In that year, also, there were "Hansel and Gretel" at the opera and "Puss in Boots" in vaudeville, while Rostand's son was the author of "The Good Little Devil" (adapted for America by Mr. Austin Strong), and Eleanor Gates delighted every one with her fanciful "The Poor Little Rich Girl."

But none of these efforts seemed to convince managers that a Children's Theater was necessary. Curls bobbed in the auditoriums, suppressed whispers rose above the playing orchestras, there was excitement everywhere as on the eve of a private peep into fairyland. But the theater managers did not find it profitable, — in dollars and cents; and so bows-in-the-hair, bibs-and-tuckers, lace-collars and open-mouths went a-begging.

There is an empty theater now in New York called "The Children's Theater"; there are exciting mural pictures on all the walls, and clambering over the proscenium arch, done in glowing colors; there are comfortable seats for chubby legs; but it is an old-fashioned theater, and no one seems to know exactly what to give in it. There's another Children's Theater that makes a brave attempt to weather the storm of indifference. And there have been sporadic attempts to give shadow plays and puppet-shows. But there is no entertainment guaranteed every season for young folks; there is not even the expectancy of pantomime — such pantomime as Thackeray so lovingly describes.

There may be many reasons for this which do not concern us here. For we know by experience that when such plays as "Peter Pan" and "The Blue Bird" strike fire, houses are filled with young and old alike. And so we have every reason to believe that a good children's play is the one children may take their parents to without any fear of boring them. For what did Eleanor Gates say, when "The Poor Little Rich Girl" was vociferously greeted? "My play is one of fact and fancy for any one who has the imagination and child-heart to understand it."

It was Mr. George Tyler who produced "Racketty-Packetty House", and Mr. Vivian Burnett — the original for *Lord Fauntleroy* — who wrote the music for it. The play necessitated the use of many children. When it was taken traveling to the big cities, it was decided that the youngsters of these different places should have a chance to act in it themselves. This saved the necessity of having a large company on the road; it assured a lot of fun to those who were willing to be rehearsed. Thus "Racketty-Packetty House" lived its life on the stage, and then was put away. From its manuscript covers it has been rescued, by kind consent of Mr. Burnett, for this "Treasury."

Frances Hodgson Burnett (1849–1924) had that rare touch which caught the fancy of her young readers. It was true of her that a doll in her hands was not a doll but a hero or heroine. It was also true, as Mr. W. F. Clarke, of *St. Nicholas*, said of her, that she was whole-heartedly a lover of children. And he quoted her in answer to a question, "What characteristics do you consider the cause of your success?" — "The fact that I am interested in everything in the world — from emperors and prime ministers to swineherds and cats and dogs and every smallest blade of grass that grows. I *care* about them."

"Racketty-Packetty House" — a story, before it was turned into a play — belongs to a series of which the other miniature volumes are "The Cozy Lion", "Spring Cleaning", and "Queen Silver Bell."

During a long and busy life, Mrs. Burnett wrote many stories for young and old alike : they all had about them the glamour of romance, they were all carefully etched. From her early years, she was closely connected with the stage, and both Mr. William Gillette and Mr. Augustus Thomas — one an actor, the other a playwright — found themselves associated with her in putting her early pieces into plays. She wrote a story with a most alluring title, "The Secret Garden", and if dreams come true, her friend, Miss Marguerite Merington — whose play, "The Testing of Sir Gawayne", graced our first "Treasury", — may yet perpetuate for New York the name of Mrs. Burnett in marble, bronze, and a "host of dancing daffodils." For, when there was talk of starting a Frances Hodgson Burnett Memorial, it was she who proposed a Secret Garden in Central Park, tucked away within reach of the great Fifth Avenue, yet so hidden by rock and shrubbery that one needs must seek for it in earnest in its nook. The plans took shape, and there grew into a landscape gardener's plans the grace of a pool in the center of the Garden, which will serve as a bird bath, and a bronze boy to pipe them to their laving, and a bronze girl with a shell in her hands to offer crystal-clear water to the thirsty visitor.

Such a fairy spot must have a fence, so high that no mischievous peanut shell will have the opportunity of falling within the magic flower beds, no colored supplements of the Sunday papers of littering the flagged paths. There are planned stone benches and a gate with a password every one shall have who loves the idea of a Secret Garden, and who pledges to maintain

its sweet integrity. The Park Commissioner has shown his
interest — that's a great point in its favor when an all-powerful
Park Commissioner nods approval! It was he who insisted on
the high fence, for, alas, a Park Commissioner knows only too
well what mischief is done by the unthinking to city trees and
shrubs and flowers by those who would never care if there was a
Secret Garden or not. Perhaps, as Miss Merington said to me,
when she told of her dream, it will be well to close the gate for a
few hours every day — to give the flowers and the grass time to
grow.

Now, whether New York be the first or the last to act on such
a perfectly feasible dream as this, it is an excellent suggestion for
any community where children desire to pay tribute to one of
their memorable writers. I can imagine a whole line of Secret
Gardens from the waters of the Atlantic to the waters of the
Pacific, so wide were the pleasure and happiness Mrs. Burnett
gave to the young of this land. Both she and Mrs. Kate
Douglas Wiggin are long to be treasured as friends of childhood,
and if a Secret Garden can stand as symbol of youthful tribute
to one who thus served them, the flowers in it may serve as
votive thanks to as many more writers as memory recalls. I
have already written in the first "Treasury", which contains
Mrs. Burnett's "The Little Princess", that the Boy I knew will
always regard tenderly "Little Lord Fauntleroy" because it was
the first book he read to himself. So I say to any Secret Garden,
where'er it be, "There's rosemary, that's for remembrance."

RACKETTY–PACKETTY HOUSE

A PLAY IN PROLOGUE AND THREE ACTS

By FRANCES HODGSON BURNETT

CHARACTERS

CYNTHIA
PRINCESS
QUEEN CROSSPATCH — *Fairy*
OLD NURSE
NEW NURSE
NIP }
FLIP }
TRIP } *Green Workers*
SKIP }
PETER PIPER } *Boys of Racketty-Packetty House*
GUSTIBUS }
MEG }
PEG }
KILMANSKEGG } *Girls of Racketty-Packetty House*
RIDICKLIS }
THE DUCHESS OF TIDY CASTLE
LADY PATSY
LADY DORIS
LADY MURIEL
LADY GWENDOLYN } *Her Children*
LORD HUBERT
LORD RUPERT
LORD FRANCIS
JAMES }
JOHN } *Footmen*
CHARLES }

Green Workers, Herald, Ladies-in-Waiting, Footmen, etc.

SCENES

PROLOGUE : *Cynthia's Nursery.*
ACT I. *Sitting-room in Racketty-Packetty House.*
ACT II. *Drawing-room in Racketty-Packetty House.*
ACT III. Scene I. *Cynthia's Nursery.*
Scene II. *Outside Toy Church.*

RACKETTY–PACKETTY HOUSE

PROLOGUE

SCENE. *Cynthia's nursery. — Large shabby doll's house standing in prominent position. Before the fire in Grandfather's chair sits the Old Nurse knitting. She wears an old-fashioned dress, a big apron and a white cap with a broad frill. She stops knitting and speaks in cracked voice.*

OLD NURSE. Hoity-toity, mercy me! Things is changed — things is changed since my young days! When I was Young Nurse instead of Old Nurse, we paid some respect to our elders. We thought they was our betters and knew something. Now everything that's old gets pushed aside. (*Lays down her knitting on her knee and bridles*) Look at me! Me as nursed little Miss Cynthia's mother, and her grandmother, for that matter — here I sits in the corner, and Miss Cynthia is waited on by a flighty minx with a bit of lace and ribbon on her head instead of a decent cap. Hoity-toity! things is changed. (*Stops as if she heard something — turns head sideways towards nursery door*) Eh! (*Pauses a second listening — puts hand up to her ear*) What's that? Who's there? (*Pauses again*) I thought I heard something. My hearing's not as bad as Miss New Nurse pretends.

[*Knits.*

[*The door is pushed slowly open and Queen Crosspatch flutters into the room — four of her Green Workers stealing after her, but lagging behind as if they were afraid to be seen. Queen Crosspatch must be obviously a Fairy, carrying a tiny gold bugle swung over her shoulder — winged and gauzy and pretty, but with a fussy, consequential air and a dictatorial and magnificent manner. The Green Workers wear green smocks and pointed green caps, and carry little kits of tools on their backs.*

QUEEN CROSSPATCH (*turning and seeing her Green Workers, beckons to them authoritatively*). Come on, you silly things! Flip! Trip! Nip! Skip! She can't see us or hear us. (*Contemptuously*) Can't you remember that PEOPLE — (*disdainfully — emphasis on the word*) never can see Fairies? (*The Green Workers steal more forward — giggling and nudging and peeping over each other's shoulders*) You might sit on her lap and she wouldn't know you were there. (*Nip and Flip and Trip and Skip giggle still more, and push each other and hop from foot to foot as if they were full of mischief. They begin to dance about Old Nurse, who goes on knitting, evidently not seeing them at all*) You see she neither sees nor hears you! That's the way with *people!* They can't see any of the things worth seeing. If you can believe it, they don't know there are such things as Fairies. That old woman doesn't even know anything about ME! (*Green Workers start and stare incredulously*) And I've been Queen of the Fairies for millions of years! People are the most ignorant things in the world. (*Indignantly*) Beetles know more than they do!

NIP (*hops up to Old Nurse and tweaks her cap on one side*).

OLD NURSE (*crossly — setting her cap straight*). Drat this cap! It won't never stay in its place. (*Flip tweaks her knitting off on to the floor*) Drat that knitting! Now how did that drop! It's as bad as the cap. (*As she bends stiffly to pick up knitting, Tip holds her back by her sleeve*) What's the matter? (*Pulling*) Has my sleeve caught on a tack? (*As she raises herself, Skip jumps on her knee. Old Nurse waves her arms about*) What's happening, I say! I feel as if the cat had jumped on my knee — and there's no cat there. There's nothing there. [*Skip jumps down and dances with the others about her chair in contortions of mirth.*

QUEEN CROSSPATCH. Stop teasing her, you silly things. Come and look at the doll's house. That's your business. (*They all go to the doll's house. Old Nurse settles back in her chair, and presently begins to nod and drop into a nap. Grandly*) Now listen to me! There are doll families I like and doll families I don't like. The doll family in this shabby old house I DO like.

TRIP (*pokes Nip who pokes Trip who pokes Skip to signify that they should bow, and they all bow profoundly*). They must be very much obliged, your Majesty. Who does the house belong to, please, your Majesty?

QUEEN CROSSPATCH. It belongs to the little girl who lives in the nursery. Her name is Cynthia, and I don't care about her a bit.

TRIP (*pokes and bows — all bow*). That's very sad for her, your Majesty.

QUEEN CROSSPATCH. It is! I don't see how she bears it! But she does. In the days when Queen Victoria was a little girl this doll's house belonged to Cynthia's grandmother. (*Shakes her head in regretful reflection*) Oh! I can tell you the dolls in it lived a gay and fashionable life then. They had parties and balls and were married and had families and scarlet fever and whooping-cough and funerals and every luxury. (*Shakes head again*) But that was long, long ago, and now everything is changed. Their house has grown shabbier and shabbier, the paint has been rubbed off and their clothes are simply awful.

SKIP. Poor things.

QUEEN CROSSPATCH. Poor things indeed! They've gone through such troubles and reverses that if they hadn't been such a jolly lot they would have had fits and appendicitis and died of grief. But not a bit of it! They get fun out of everything. It's a pleasure to know them. And I am going to stand by them in their trouble.

TRIP. What is going to happen to them, your Majesty?

QUEEN CROSSPATCH (*grandiloquently*). If it were not for ME there is no knowing WHAT would happen to them. Listen to Old Nurse — she's waking up.

OLD NURSE (*wakes up — rubs her eyes — rises and hobbles over to doll's house. Green Workers giggle and jump out of her way. She stands before doll's house with her hands on her hips — grumbling*). Oh! It's there yet, is it? I dreamed it had been took away and thrown on to the dust heap. That's what'll come of it. Times is changed, indeed! Miss Cynthia's Grandma's fine doll's house looked down on like as if it was rubbidge! 'That old Racketty-Packetty doll's house,' says she (*mimicking*). 'It's too shabby! I won't play with it. I want a new one. That old Racketty-Packetty House,' says she. (*With snappish indignation. The Green Workers dance round her giggling. Old Nurse turning, puts her hand behind ear as if listening irritatedly*) What's that? Eh! (*Green Workers catch at her skirt and then run away and hide behind chairs. Old Nurse shakes her skirt*) Scat! Scat! It sounds like mice — but it's kittens. Must be — clawing a person's skirt like that. I can't see them but I'll drive them out. (*Spreads her dress*) Shoo! Scat! Get away! [*Listens a moment — then hobbles back to her chair. The Green Workers come out and return to the doll's house.*

NIP (*kneels down and looks in at window*). Well, it does look shabby. I never saw such a tumbled-down old place. [*Business — lights showing dolls peering out of windows.*

QUEEN CROSSPATCH (*stamping her foot*). What do you mean by looking in at people's windows as if they had no feelings, just because they are dolls! So would *you* look shabby if you'd been played with by careless children for fifty years.

NIP (*scrambling up and bowing several times as fast as ever he can*). Beg your Majesty's pardon.

QUEEN CROSSPATCH. You act as if you were just like PEOPLE and don't know any more! People think dolls never do anything they don't see them do. (*Scathingly*) They're very much mistaken.

SKIP. You don't say so, your Majesty. What can they do?

QUEEN CROSSPATCH. When people are not looking at them, they can do anything they choose. They can dance and sing and play on the piano and have all sorts of fun.

NIP AND TRIP. Oh — O-h-h-oo!

QUEEN CROSSPATCH. You are a Fairy, though you are only a Green Worker, and you ought to know.

NIP (*making more hurried bows*). I forgot, your Majesty! I forgot!

QUEEN CROSSPATCH. Don't forget again! That old house belongs to dolls who are friends of mine. It's their home, and goodness knows what that empty-headed little Cynthia will do to it if I don't interfere. Those dolls have had their noses broken and their heads broken, but they shall not have their hearts broken so long as I'm a Fairy Queen, with all you lazy louts to find work for.

GREEN WORKERS. Certainly, your Majesty! What shall we do?

QUEEN CROSSPATCH (*puts her finger on her lips and thinks. Then speaks suddenly*). I believe I'll call up the others. (*Goes to the window — puts gold bugle to her lips and blows call on it. Then sings*)

> Green Workers, Green Workers —
>   Halloa!
> Green Workers, Green Workers,
>   Ho! Ho!
> Come East and come West,
> Come over the hill crest,
> Come ready for friend —
>   Or for foe!
> Come ready to polish
>   And sweep!
> Come ready to crawl
>   Or to creep!
> Come ready to sing,
> To laugh and to spring,
> Come ready to bound,
>   Hop and leap!

[*Blows bugle call again. Old Nurse listens — hand up to ear.*

OLD NURSE (*listening*). There's the Auty-mobeel — some-wheres. It's a good way off yet. But they're coming back — Miss Cynthia and Miss New Nurse is.

[*Many other Green Workers come flocking in through the door. They stand before Queen Crosspatch in line, making bows, and sing.*

GREEN WORKERS.

> All steady — all steady —
>   Fly we!
> All ready — all ready —
>   You see!

From East and from West
To do your best
What ever it chances
To be.

[*More bows.*

QUEEN CROSSPATCH. Very right and proper of you to come so quickly. I have something important to tell you. Now stand at attention and listen — (*Green Workers arrange themselves, using picks as if they were rifles*) Look at that Doll's House. (*Green Workers wheel about and look at Racketty-Packetty House*) A nice, cheerful, disrespectable family lives in there, and I'm very fond of them. They used to be grand and rich, and now they are poor and shabby, but it hasn't spoiled their tempers a bit. That's why I like them. Just now they are in great danger. The trouble is that they have a hard landlady. Her name is Cynthia, and she is nine years old. She has not done any decorating since she owned the house. She doesn't care about it or about her tenants.

GREEN WORKERS. Shame! Shame! S-h-a-a-a-me!

QUEEN CROSSPATCH. That's what I say! She lets things go to rack and ruin, and then complains that they're shabby, and wants to throw them away. I'm here now because I found out something. When she went out with her nurse this morning, I followed her. They went to a toy-shop — (*fearful significance*) and they looked — at — dolls' houses! She's going to buy a *new one!*

GREEN WORKERS. Oh! Oh! Oh!

QUEEN CROSSPATCH. It's the worst thing that could happen for those poor creatures. But here's where I come in (*very grandly*) as usual. I'm always doing things other people can't do. I'm going to save them!

GREEN WORKERS. Hooray! Hooray!

QUEEN CROSSPATCH. That's why I called you. To tell you that you are to keep near this place and be ready any minute to do *anything*.

GREEN WORKERS (*saluting with picks*). Anything, your Majesty! ANYTHING!

QUEEN CROSSPATCH. As nobody has sense enough to see Fairies, even when they're right under their noses, we can come in and out as we like. And we can give the silly things advice, and push them and pull them about, and they'll think they are doing it all themselves.

GREEN WORKERS (*laugh*). Ha! Ha!

[*Automobile horn heard outside.*

QUEEN CROSSPATCH (*runs to window*). Here they are! Here they are! And they've brought something with them! (*Turns and looks at Green Workers. Turns again to window and, after a glance, turns to Green Workers again*) The biggest footman is lifting it out. *It is a New Doll's House!* (*More solemnly than before — turns and walks towards Green Workers. Waves hand*) Now scatter yourselves in corners. We'll stay and listen.

[*The Green Workers get under sofas and tables, leaving their heads sticking out; they perch here and there and sit dangling their feet. Queen Crosspatch places herself in dominant position.*

OLD NURSE (*takes off spectacles — polishes them — puts them on nose again and looks around her*). What a buzzin' and a flutterin' there is in this room. Has some bees got in? I can't see nothin'!

[*Business — gets up and hobbles about, flapping apron. Green Workers' business of dodging, jumping and laughing. Cynthia is heard calling excitedly as she runs upstairs.*

CYNTHIA. Old Nurse! Old Nurse! (*She bursts open door and runs in*) Old Nurse! I've bought the most beautiful Doll's House you ever saw in your life. (*Dances about*) It isn't a doll's *house* — it's a doll's *castle*.

OLD NURSE. I knowed it! I knowed it! I knowed some such highfalutin' rubbidge would be brought into your Grandma's nursery. I knowed you'd be just egged on to it!

CYNTHIA (*jumping on to chair and bouncing up and down on its springs*). Don't be such a cross old thing. Papa said I might have it for my birthday and New Nurse took me to the shop. She picked it out for me.

NEW NURSE (*smart young woman, enters*). John will bring it up in a few minutes, Miss Cynthia.

CYNTHIA. It's perfectly beautiful! (*To Old Nurse*) It's called Tidy Castle, and it's got all the modern improvements in it. The Duchess of Tidyshire lives in it, and her children are called — What are they called, New Nurse? You made up their names. I can't remember.

NEW NURSE (*in a fine manner*). Lord Hubert and Lord Rupert and Lord Francis Vere de Vere and Lady Gwendolen and Lady Muriel and Lady Doris and Lady Patricia.

OLD NURSE (*sniffing*). I'll warrant they'll be Lords and Ladies! Your Grandma's dolls had grand names once. They was Amelia and Charlotte and Victoria Leopoldina and Aurelia Matilda and Rosiland and Vincent and Charles Edward Stuart.

NEW NURSE. Aurelia Matilda was broken to bits and thrown into the dust-bin, and Victoria Leopoldina was dragged out on the hearth rug one night and had her paint licked off by the Newfoundland puppy. She used to be the beauty, but she's not a beauty now.

CYNTHIA (*giggling*). Cousin Charlie painted her a pair of saucer eyes and a turned-up nose, and now she's called Ridicklis. The rest are called Meg and Peg and Kilmanskegg and Gustibus and Peter Piper. The other ones were lost — (*Jumps off her chair*) That reminds me. What shall we do with that old Racketty-Packetty House when Tidy Castle is brought up? It's too shabby and old-fashioned to stand near it. Where shall we put it?

[*Queen Crosspatch waves her wand and the Green Workers begin to creep out from their places and gather round Racketty-Packetty House.*

OLD NURSE (*trembling with rage, and half crying*). Oh! Yes! Oh! Yes! Throw it in the ashes. Break it up in bits. Your very own Grandma's very own doll house as was given her for a birthday present when her and Queen Victoria was children. Why don't you throw me in the dust-bin?

[*Wipes her eyes. Some of the Green Workers run to her chair and begin to pat her and soothe her. Trip jumps on her knee, puts his arm around her neck and cuddles her.*

CYNTHIA (*rudely*). You're such a silly old thing — always talking about Grandma and Queen Victoria — (*Aside to New Nurse*) I wish Mamma would send her away.

[*Queen Crosspatch slaps her sharply on her cheek with her wand.*

CYNTHIA (*jumps*). Oh! I believe I am going to have the toothache. I had such a pain in my cheek!

[*Rubs her face. The Green Workers giggle.*

NEW NURSE (*grandly*). John and James are bringing up Tidy Castle, Miss Cynthia. It will make you forget all about your toothache.

CYNTHIA. Yes, it will. But it was such a funny pain. It seemed almost as if something had hit me. (*Green Workers giggle. Enter two footmen, carefully carrying the new doll's house. It is very large and built in the form of a castle. Cynthia dances about them*) Isn't it beautiful! Oh, I do love it! Be careful — be careful!

[*To the footmen.*

QUEEN CROSSPATCH (*quickly to Green Workers*). Push Racketty-Packetty House gently out of the way. Push it into that alcove. Nobody is looking. (*Green Workers push Racketty-Packetty House into alcove*) Push that chair before it.

[*They do as they are told.*

CYNTHIA (*to footmen*). Put it down for a minute. (*They set Tidy Castle down in the middle of nursery*) I want to think where it shall stand. Oh! how lovely it is. Where shall I put it? If that Racketty-Packetty old thing wasn't there — (*She turns round and looks at the place where the old doll's house stood, and starts at seeing its place empty*) Why, it's not there! It's gone! I thought it was here when we came in.

NEW NURSE. So did I — but we were so full of Tidy Castle that perhaps we only thought it was there. (*Looks round and catches sight of it behind chair*) Oh! It's been pushed into the alcove and the armchair is before it. Perhaps one of the housemaids did it.

CYNTHIA. I'm glad she did. Tidy Castle shall be put in its

place, and John and James can carry the old thing down-stairs and burn it up.

OLD NURSE. Miss Cynthia, now don't you do it! It'd be a wicked thing. Your Grandma played with it and your Mamma played with it and you've played with it. Perhaps them dolls has feelings. They was here when your Grandma and Queen Victoria ——

CYNTHIA (*flouncing*). Oh! bother Grandma and Queen Victoria!

[*Queen Crosspatch pinches her sharply and she jumps.*

CYNTHIA. Oh! Oh! What a pain! I felt as if something pinched me. (*Rubs her arm*) Put Tidy Castle here. (*To footmen, pointing out place where Racketty-Packetty House previously stood. Footmen obey her*) That is just the right place for it.

OLD NURSE (*still resentfully*). That part of the nursery was called Belgrave Square in your Grandma's time, and Belgravia was the most fashionable part of London.

NEW NURSE (*tossing her head*). It's not fashionable now!

OLD NURSE. Suppose you'd know what was fashionable and what was not! Nursemaids always does.

CYNTHIA (*to footmen*). You can take the old doll's house away.

QUEEN CROSSPATCH (*to Green Workers*). Some of you hold the house down and some of you drag at their coat tails ——

[*As footmen try to move house, Green Workers hang on to their coats and hold on to doll's house.*

JOHN (*trying to move Racketty-Packetty House*). It's the heaviest doll's house I ever lifted.

JAMES (*tugging*). Seems as if it was nailed to the floor.

CYNTHIA. Why can't you lift it?

JOHN. It weighs a ton, Miss.

QUEEN CROSSPATCH (*speaks to Cynthia close to her ear*). You'd better let it stay where it is. Think how nice it would be to play that it is a hospital or a poorhouse.

CYNTHIA (*stands as if thinking the matter over — of course not seeing her*). Wait! I believe I will let it stay. I've just thought of something. Some day I might like to pretend it is a poorhouse or a hospital. Leave it where it is. (*Green Workers let go, and the doll's house drops back into its place with a bang. Cynthia laughing*) What a noise! Meg and Peg and Kilmanskegg and Peter Piper must nearly have had their heads shaken off.

JOHN. Anything else, Miss?

CYNTHIA. No, nothing else. (*Footmen exit. Cynthia goes and kneels on floor before Tidy Castle. New Nurse has opened the front door. Cynthia clasps her hands in ecstasy*) No one ever had a more beautiful doll's house! There are carpets and curtains and ornaments and pictures and beds and baths and boudoirs and lamps and bookcases, and just look at the Duchess of Tidyshire and Lord Hubert and Lord Rupert and Lady Gwendolyn and Lady Muriel and Lady Doris — but where's Lady Patricia? (*Excited*) I don't see Lady Patricia! New Nurse, where is Lady Patricia?

NEW NURSE (*hurrying forward to look*). Which one was she, Miss?

CYNTHIA (*increased excitement*). She was the prettiest one of all. She had curly hair and such a laughing little face. Where is she? She's lost! I won't have her lost.

NEW NURSE. She may have got behind something. Perhaps she's rolled under the bed.

CYNTHIA (*almost crying*). No! she hasn't. I know she's lost! (*Takes out dolls*) See, here's the Duchess — and here are Lord Hubert and Lord Rupert and Lord Francis, and here are Lady Gwendolyn and Lady Doris and Lady Muriel — but there's no Lady Patricia. If she's lost I shall scream! Ring the bell for the footman. I know it was James who lost her. He's so fat and stupid, and he's always forgetting things. Ring the bell.

[*New Nurse runs and rings the bell. Almost immediately the fat footman, James, enters — out of breath with running. He has a note in his hand.*

JAMES (*panting*). If you please, Miss, I was just coming. I ran as fast as I could. I forgot to give you this note. It was left with the doll's house.

CYNTHIA (*snatches it from him*). You're always forgetting things, you stupid creature. I shall tell Mamma. (*She tears open note*) It may be about Lady Patricia. (*Reads*) Yes, it is. It's from the doll's house toy-shop. (*Reads*) "Dear Madam: We are very sorry to inform you that at the last moment we found that Lady Patricia had broken her leg. We took her at once to the doll's Nursing Home to have it set. She will be sent back as soon as possible." (*Cynthia relieved*) Well, at all events she's not lost! James, the moment she comes, bring her up, and mind you don't forget anything else. (*Goes back to Tidy Castle and begins to return dolls to their places*) How beautifully dressed they are. How different from those shabby old Racketty-Packettys. (*Sudden thought — sitting back on her heels as she sits on floor*) I believe I will have the Racketty-Packettys burnt up! They're too shabby to live in the same nursery with Tidy Castle.

QUEEN CROSSPATCH (*runs to her and speaks in her ear*). No, you won't! No, you won't! No, you won't! Think of the hospital. (*She makes a sign to Green Workers and they all join in murmuring the same words*) Think of the poorhouse.

GREEN WORKERS (*dancing round her with joined hands*). No, you won't! No, you won't! You won't! You won't! You won't!

CYNTHIA (*stops as if to think again. Changing her mind*). No, I won't, after all. They will do for the hospital or the poor-house!

OLD NURSE (*lifting hands in horror*). Pushed in a corner and used for a poorhouse, them that has lived in Belgravia when her Grandma and Queen Victoria was little girls.

QUEEN CROSSPATCH (*to Green Workers*). Come along. She is safe for to-day.

[*They form in Indian file behind Queen. Dutch doll's march begins — played delicately and staccato. They march round room — with business. As they near door, march music hurries its time and they run out laughing.*

CURTAIN

ACT I

SCENE.   *Sitting-room of Racketty-Packetty House just after the footmen have set the house down with a bang in Cynthia's nursery. Everything is in greatest disorder.   Furniture turned upside down, pictures still swinging on walls.   Peter Piper has broken through top of table, through which his head sticks — surrounded by a large white frill — table hangs on his shoulders.   Gustibus is sitting doubled up in the coal-scuttle.   Meg and Peg are lying under an overturned sofa, — Meg's head sticking out one way, Peg's legs sticking out beside it.   Kilmanskegg is not in sight.*

PETER PIPER *(is first to move, struggles to his feet, walks forward with table hanging on shoulders).*   Halloa ! You !
[*To Gustibus.*

GUSTIBUS *(struggling to get up).*   Halloa yourself — till I get out of this coal box.

PETER PIPER *(business with table).*   Come and help me off with this thing.

GUSTIBUS *(manages to get up).*   My eye ! That was a shake. What happened ?

PETER PIPER.   I think we moved into a new neighborhood. There's nothing so upsetting as moving, and earthquake-moving particularly.   I say ! — help me to get this thing off.

GUSTIBUS *(walks round to look at him).*   How did you get it on ?

PETER PIPER.   There was a broken place in the middle, and I was standing on the edge of it mending the chandelier, and when the shock came I just went through and sat down.   It wasn't difficult for a clever person like me.   I just went through — *(waves hand fantastically)* like that, you know. *(Gustibus bursts out laughing and doubles up)*   That's right. Go to it, old chap.   I know it's becoming.   I'd keep it on and wear it for an overcoat if it was raining.   But it isn't. Lend a hand, if you're not too busy.

GUSTIBUS *(still giggling — tries to lift table off).*   It's almost a pity to take it off.

PETER PIPER.   It would be very convenient at meal times . . .

if I could get my arms through. Halloa! (*Sudden inspiration*)
There's an invention. Get this thing off quick. I must
write it down. (*They get the table over his head. Peter Piper
greatly excited*) Where's the Invention Book? Quick!
Quick! I might forget it! There it is! (*Darts at big book
lying on floor. Picks up book, which is large. On back of it
is printed unevenly in immense black letters on white ground,*
INVENTIONS, BY PETER PIPER. *He snatches fountain pen
from his pocket, shakes it, sucks it, tries to write — shakes again
— scribbles:* "INVENTION 950,999 — Portable Table!"
To Gustibus) This is the cleverest one of all. You wear it
round your waist like a belt, and eat your dinner off it. You
could keep it set all day if you liked, and then you'd never be
late for meals. Hooray! (*Slams book — jumps up, looks
around*) Where are the girls? (*Runs to overturned sofa*)
Here's Meg's head! Whose legs are these?

PEG (*from other side of sofa*). P-e-e-g's!

PETER PIPER (*to Gustibus*). The sofa fell on them when we
moved. Come and help. (*They lift sofa and Meg and Peg get
up*) Are you chipped anywhere? Any sawdust running out?

MEG (*shaking herself*). No.

PEG. I'm all right. But that *was* a jolt! I hope the sofa's
not broken.

MEG. I'm glad we're not broken.

PETER PIPER. We are not a family that breaks easily. But
the sofa had four legs — (*examines sofa*) and as it's the only
thing in the house that has four legs it would be a shock if it
lost one. Where's Kilmanskegg?

[*They all look around.*

GUSTIBUS (*calls*). Helloa, Killy?

PETER PIPER. Hello! Skeggy?

[*Knocking heard inside Grandfather's clock. They all rush
towards it. Peter Piper opens door and Kilmanskegg's feet are
seen sticking up and kicking. Peter Piper and Gustibus drag
her out.*

KILMANSKEGG (*panting*). My goodness gracious mercy me!
I've been standing on my head for ten minutes. I was just

looking into the clock, and I was shot right in — as if I was a load of coal. We move far too often — (*indignantly*) and too suddenly.

PETER PIPER. We've not moved much lately. Cynthia has taken no notice of us for two weeks. I think something's up.

KILMANSKEGG (*picks up chair and flounces into it, fanning herself with her apron*). The next time I'm born I don't believe I'll be a doll at all.

MEG (*horrified*). Would you be a *child* — like Cynthia?

KILMANSKEGG. I'd have more sense than Cynthia, even if I *was* a child.

PETER PIPER. Dolls have twice the sense PEOPLE have. But if I wasn't a doll I'd be a fairy like Queen Crosspatch.

MEG. I hope you wouldn't be as peppery as she is.

PETER PIPER (*good-naturedly*). Oh! well, she wasn't always like that. She used to be as sweet as I am, and that's saying a good deal, isn't it? (*Grins from ear to ear and looks round at them*) Now, don't all speak at once!

MEG. We're not going to. But what happened to her?

PETER PIPER (*solemnly*). One day she lost her Temper.

KILMANSKEGG. What is a Temper?

PETER PIPER (*stammering uncertainly*). Well — it's a kind — it's a kind of thing. We haven't got them, so it isn't easy to explain. It's a kind of thing that — that you must *keep*. It's all right as long as you *keep* it. But if you lose it — My hat! It plays the very Harry O!

PEG (*the others all interested*). How did she lose hers?

PETER PIPER. She lost it the day she found out that Fairies had gone out of fashion and that no one could see them or hear them. It didn't matter how clever they were. Fairyland had begun to go to the dogs. The Fairies were getting all out of practise. They were forgetting how to turn things into something else. One morning a hateful little boy was teasing a kitten and a fairy wanted to change him into a kitten himself, just to let him see how he liked it, and when she had got as far as the claws and the Meow she forgot the rest and he ran away meowing and scratching his face when he rubbed his eyes —

but all the rest of him was little boy, and the Queen got so angry that she stamped and screamed and her little Temper broke his chain and flew away, and she's never seen him since. That's why she can't help scolding. (*Suddenly*) Horray! (*Puts finger to forehead*) There's an invention! (*Looks all round excitedly*) Where's the Invention Book! I must put it down this minute.

[*They all begin to run about and look, saying:*

TOGETHER. Where is it? Where is it? Where is it?

PETER PIPER (*sees book on floor*). Oh! I forgot! It's here! (*Sits down on floor as before, opens book, business with fountain pen — beams with delight*) This is cleverer than the other. (*Writes — the rest all look on enraptured*) "INVENTION No. 951,000: The way to always keep your Temper. Never — lose it. Keep it in a Cage tied round your waist." (*Sudden new idea — looks round at rest*) Why, you might keep it on the Portable Table I just invented — the one that prevents you from being late to dinner.

[*All Racketty-Packettys clap hands.*

RACKETTY-PACKETTYS. Splendid! You'll make a fortune by it.

PETER PIPER (*very busy writing*). Keep it in a Cage. On the P. Piper Portable Table. (*Looks up with new inspiration*) You might teach it to sing. And feed it on bird seed — and lump sugar. I'll write that down. (*Scribbles. Then shuts book and draws long breath of triumph*) The way I invent things is marvelous! (*Puts back Invention Book proudly*) When I sell all these inventions, we shall all have fortunes. We shall be rich beyond all dreams of Alice — whoever she was. (*Jumps up as suddenly as he had sat down*) Now let's go and look out the windows and see where we have moved to.

MEG (*as they go to the window*). I hope it's a nice neighborhood.

GUSTIBUS. I hope it's near the Golf Links on the hearthrug.

PEG (*bridling*). I hope it's near the mouse hole so that Mr. Mouse can often run in to tea. I do like a bit of society.

PETER PIPER (*at window*). Hello! We've been pushed into the alcove where the book-shelves are.

MEG. It's not a fashionable neighborhood.

PETER PIPER. Oh! Isn't it! You just look out here, then. Where we used to stand.

[*Meg and Peg and Kilmanskegg and Gustibus crowd about the two windows.*

ALL. Oh! Oh!

MEG. There's a Castle there!

PEG. A splendid Castle!

PETER PIPER (*struts up and down with his thumbs in the armholes of his ragged coat*). Talk about fashionable neighborhoods. We mayn't live in one, but we can SEE one. We're regular swells. I think I'll put a pin or so in my trousers. (*Begins to pin up holes in his rags*) There! That's a bit more tasty. (*Strides about with hands in his pockets*) Who knows but what we're living next to Dooks — and they've moved here just to make my acquaintance.

MEG (*from window*). Oh! it's such a *grand* place!

PEG. It's built out of stone, and it has turrets and battlements and a flag flying.

PETER PIPER (*swaggers to window and looks out*). I'll tell you what I think of it. It's a lot too grand. I shouldn't want to live in it.

PEG. You wouldn't?

PETER PIPER. Not on your life. I'd rather live here. Just look at the comforts. (*Wheels about and looks round room — as they all do*) Look at the jolly old holes in the carpet — and the jolly old stuffing coming out of the chairs — and the jolly old legs tumbling off the tables. Think of the cheerful occupation it provides. There's something to knock nails into — or patch up — or stick on with glue every hour of the day. They've got nothing as entertaining as that over there — (*Disdainfully*) I'd almost bet you as much as half a quarter of a cent — (*Hurriedly with waving gesture*) I can't pay it if I lose, of course. Don't expect that. I've not got half a quarter of a cent.

GUSTIBUS. Neither have I.

MEG. Neither have I.

PEG. Neither have I.

PETER PIPER. Neither has any of us. Think of the wear and tear and responsibility we're saved. Just think of it. (*Sudden inspiration*) Let's all join hands and dance round and round and kick up our heels and laugh as hard as we can.

[*They join hands in ring and dance round and round, kicking up heels and laughing until they all fall down and roll about.*

PETER PIPER (*sitting up on the floor, panting, holding on to his ankles*). That's the kind of thing you can do when you haven't half a quarter of a cent! If any of us had it, we'd just be worn to a frazzle with the anxiety of taking care of it. Thinking where we could hide it — or what bank we could put it in where the cashier wouldn't run away — or what sort of a Trust we could work up. (*The door suddenly bursts open and Ridicklis falls into the room headlong — her market-basket and two old frying-pans rolling over the floor. Peter Piper jumps up — so do all the others*) Hello! Here's Ridicklis home from market! (*He picks her up — they all help her pick up vegetables and basket. Peter puts her into a chair where she sits and mops her face with her ragged apron*) What made you so sudden?

RIDICKLIS (*mopping and settling her old bonnet — out of breath — speaks with gasps*). The Nurse — swept me — in — with a broom.

MEG. The careless thing!

PEG. I'm sure it was New Nurse.

RIDICKLIS. It was. There now. I've got my breath again. I'd been to market to get some slightly soiled second-hand bones to make a Near-Meat Pie. I could wash them, you know, and put a great deal of salt and pepper in.

PETER PIPER. I should think so. Why, there's nothing on earth like one of your second-hand bone salt-and-pepper pies — Nothing on earth!

RIDICKLIS. I thought I could get across the room while her back was turned and nobody could see me — and suddenly she turned round, and of course I had to drop down on the floor

and pretend I couldn't move; and the minute she saw me
she said: "Oh, bother! There's one of those old dolls!"
And she swept me right into the alcove and into the house.

GUSTIBUS. That's a nice way to treat a lady — even if she is
made of wood.

PETER PIPER (*suddenly*). Hello! Look out! Legs passing the
window. 'Tention! (*They all stand stock-still for a moment.
Legs are seen passing window. When they disappear, all resume
activity. Peter Piper draws long breath*) The only objection
to being a Doll is this having to stand stock-still every minute
a human being looks at you. I find it a bit wearing.

GUSTIBUS (*anxiously*). But if they found out we could do things
they'd work us to death making us amuse them. Think of
Cynthia.

PETER PIPER. If they found out that a talented creature like
ME could do things, what would happen! Why! They'd
be making me into a King or something, and I should have
no peace. No (*solemnly*), we've got to keep it a dead
secret.

RIDICKLIS. It's very tiresome when you're just in the middle
of stirring a pudding on the fire and Cynthia looks in at the
window and you have to stop and let it burn. But that's
not the worst.

PETER PIPER. I didn't know there was anything worse than
Cynthia.

RIDICKLIS. Tidy Castle is worse. It's full of enemies. The
Duchess of Tidyshire hates us — Lord Hubert and Lord
Rupert and Lord Francis and Lady Gwendolyn and Lady
Doris and Lady Muriel DESPISE — they just SCORN us!
[*All look at each other aghast.*

PETER PIPER. Hello! (*Immediately pulls himself together val-
orously. Swaggers about with hands in his pockets*) Well,
let 'em scorn away. We've never been "scorned" before. It's
a sort of novelty. How do they do it? I'd like to see them.

RIDICKLIS. Oh! they look DOWN on us!

PETER PIPER. Let 'em look down. We'll look up. Like this!
[*Sticks his face up — as he struts about.*

RIDICKLIS. They turn up their noses and they sniff. The Duchess says we make the neighborhood low, and she won't live in it.

PETER PIPER (*suddenly looking at window*). Legs! 'Tention!
[*All strike attitude and remain stiff. Top of ceiling is removed, large hand, surmounted by scarlet cuff of footman's livery, sets down in middle of floor a large box, — then disappears, replacing ceiling.*
[*Racketty-Packettys all come to life and rush to box.*

ALL. What is it? What's in it?
[*Business of kneeling down and poking and pushing and peeping.*

MEG. It looks like a present. But nobody ever sends us a present.

PETER PIPER (*walks about box, inspecting with grand air*). I'll tell you what, Rackettys! It's not really meant for us at all. It's meant for Tidy Castle.

MEG AND PEG (*disappointed*). Oh!

GUSTIBUS. It was the fat footman who put it in, and he never remembers anything, and besides, he's flirting with New Nurse. He's made a mistake in the address.

PETER PIPER. That's it. I wonder what's in it? (*Sudden movement towards it as if he heard something*) Hello! What's that? There's something alive in it. I hear little kicks on the lid.

VOICE FROM INSIDE BOX. Let me out! Let me out! This minute!
[*Excitement of Racketty-Packettys. Peter Piper kneels down by box; so does Gustibus. They both lift top, which comes off — and a beautifully dressed little person sits up in it at once. It is Lady Patsy.*

RACKETTY-PACKETTYS. Oh! Oh! Oh!

LADY PATSY. I am Lady Patricia Vere de Vere. (*Looks round the room*) THIS isn't Tidy Castle?

PETER PIPER. No, your ladyship. Shall I help you out?

LADY PATSY (*smiling*). Yes, please. (*He helps her out and she looks round again*) What a funny place! I thought it couldn't be Tidy Castle.

PETER PIPER. Far from it, your ladyship. It's Racketty-Packetty House — and we are the Racketty-Packettys.

[*Lady Patsy looks at him and then at the others and begins to laugh. She laughs and laughs and rocks backwards and forwards, and clasps her little hands. The Rackettys are rather embarrassed and look at each other. Suddenly Peter Piper throws back his head and begins to laugh too — the others catch the infection and begin to laugh also. They laugh until Lady Patsy stops herself and Peter Piper stops also.*

PETER PIPER. We ARE funny, aren't we?

LADY PATSY. Yes, you are. I never saw anything so funny in my life. That's why I like you so. You all look so amusing and nice.

PETER PIPER (*eagerly*). Oh! we are, my lady. We're perfect Turkish Delights. It's laughing that does it. And I'm the most fascinating one of the lot. But would you mind telling us where you came from?

LADY PATSY. I came from the Dolls' Nursing Home. I have to live at Tidy Castle — bother it! It's so dull there, I just had to pretend to break my leg to get a change. I cried all the way home because I didn't want to come. (*Clasps her hands*) I'm so glad that silly footman put me in the wrong house. It must be so nice to be you. I'm sure you laugh all the time.

PETER PIPER. We laugh till we nearly split our sides. That's why we're in such rags. Look at this.

[*Shows large slit in the side of his coat.*

LADY PATSY (*coquettishly*). I like your rags. They look so amusing. I wish I had some. (*Takes hold of his torn sleeve and strokes it flirtatiously*) You don't look exactly like the gentlemen I have known, but I think you are VERY interesting.

PETER PIPER. Oh! I am! You never knew anything like it. You girls — (*authoritative gesture towards Meg and Peg and Ridicklis*) tell her what a treasure I am, and how I help you to wile the hours away with my brilliant repartees. I just sparkle — that's what *I* do, Lady Patricia Vere de Vere.

LADY PATSY (*coyly*). Don't call me that. It's my name, of course, but — the people who are really FOND of me call me — Lady Patsy.

PETER PIPER (*with sentimental ardor*). Then everybody in the world must call you Lady Patsy — because everybody that has ever seen you MUST be fond of you. They couldn't help it. Look at ME!

LADY PATSY (*coquettishly*). Are YOU fond of me — already? How SUDDEN!

PETER PIPER. Oh! we are sudden in Racketty-Packetty House! We have to be. We may have our house burnt over our heads any moment.

LADY PATSY. Why! Why! How dreadful!

MEG. Because we're shabby, low and common, your ladyship — and Cynthia's tired of us — and New Nurse thinks we are a disgrace to the nursery.

RIDICKLIS (*mopping her eyes with her apron*). And it's really quite a nice home, my lady, though it mayn't seem so to you. And the kitchen range is such a convenient one — when you don't try to cook anything on it.

PEG. And we've had such fun here — trying to mend the furniture and seeing it come to pieces again.

LADY PATSY (*rushes to Ridicklis and Meg and Peg and hugs them*). You poor darling dears, I don't see how even Cynthia can have the heart to think of burning your house up.

RIDICKLIS (*drawing back*). I'm afraid our rags will spoil your beautiful lace frock.

LADY PATSY. Oh! bother my beautiful lace frock! I want to see your nice house. Nothing is ever funny at the Castle — nothing ever sticks out or hangs down or tumbles off — it's all so stiff and bare and grand.

PETER PIPER. There's nothing stiff here — and nothing bare and nothing grand but ME! I'm the only grand thing.
[*Makes a splendid bow — sweeping floor with his old hat.*

LADY PATSY (*giggles and claps hands*). Oh! You are funny! I do like you. Nobody could ever burn your house up. They'll never do it.

PETER PIPER (*elatedly*). Don't let's think about it. I'll tell you what let's do. Let's all join hands and dance round and round and kick up our heels and laugh as hard as ever we can.

LADY PATSY (*clasps hands excitedly*). Lovely! Lovely! Oh, let's! I never saw any one do it!

PETER PIPER. We do it — when anything nice happens, and we do it when anything horrid happens — and we do it when nothing happens at all. It's a little way of ours. Come along. [*They all join hands and begin to dance and kick up their heels and laugh. Lady Patsy is delighted. Just when they all drop sitting on the floor, a loud knock is heard at the door. Terror of all. Peter Piper scrambles up and runs to door — others scramble up and stand staring. Peter Piper opens door and bows low, as the Duchess of Tidyshire sails into the room. A footman in livery follows her, carrying a tall gold stave with which he has knocked at the door. The Duchess walks into the middle of the room, stands quite stiff as if transfixed with disgust and horror, holds her head high with her nose up in the air and sniffs violently. She holds immensely long eye-glass up.*

DUCHESS. Pu-gh-h! Persons of the very lowest order! Pugh-h! [*Glances with great disdain slowly all round the room.*

PETER PIPER (*walks up to her — strikes an attitude — leg bent and crossed — hand on his hip*). Don't you like it — ma'am?

DUCHESS (*stares at him through her glasses*). Like it — Person!

PETER PIPER. Thank you, ma'am. Did you come to make a call?

DUCHESS. I call — Vagabond!

PETER PIPER. Thank you, ma'am — Really very much obliged. Thank you kindly, ma'am. Did you come to borrow a pound of soap — or — a — a — few eggs or some trifle of that sort? Because we haven't got any!

DUCHESS. Do not insult me by suggesting that I could desire your low eggs or your degraded soap. I am the Duchess of Tidyshire.

PETER PIPER (*making low bow*). You don't say so, ma'am. I'm very pleased to allow you to make my acquaintance. I am the Duke of Tags. This is Lord Gustibus Rags. (*Gusti-*

bus bows) And these are our sisters, Lady Meg and Lady Peg and Lady Kilmanskegg and Lady Ridicklis Ragbag, of Racketty-Packettyshire.

LADY PATSY (*has been hiding behind Meg and Peg, giggling*). Oh! how funny he is. And how funny Mamma is. I never knew she was so funny before.

PETER PIPER. It's so delightful to have pleasant neighbors, your Grace. You can run in and out and see us any time. It'll cheer us up.

DUCHESS. Audacious scoundrel! I come to search for my poor child, Lady Patricia Vere de Vere, who I hear was left here by mistake.

PETER PIPER. Yes, she came in a box. I unpacked her myself.

DUCHESS. Where is she — low villain! I demand her at once.

LADY PATSY (*comes forward, giggling*). Here I am, Mamma!

DUCHESS (*indignantly*). Here you are! In this disgraceful household — among these vagabonds — and laughing! As if you had been enjoying yourself! Can I believe my eyes?

LADY PATSY. Yes, Mamma, I HAVE been enjoying myself. I never laughed as much before in my life. I think I should like to stay!

DUCHESS (*utters a scream.— calls out*). Lord Hubert! Lord Rupert! Lord Francis! Lady Gwendolyn! Lady Muriel! Lady Doris! (*Falls into a chair*) Charles! (*To footman*) Run and call them all — I am swooning!
[*Charles runs out of the door. Ridicklis runs to Duchess and fans her with her apron, Meg and Peg slap her hands. Gustibus runs about and gets cruet stand.*

PETER PIPER (*getting ink bottle*). Give her some ink to drink. Give her the pepper and mustard to smell at. Pluck the feather out of her head and burn it under her nose.
[*Snatches at the ostrich feather in her hair.*

DUCHESS (*springs up*). Don't dare to touch my plume. Don't dare to touch it.
[*Door opens and Lord Hubert and Lord Rupert, etc., etc., rush into the room. All strike attitudes of horror at sight of Racketty-Packettys.*

LADY MURIEL (*rushes to Duchess*). Mamma! Mamma! Why did you come to this horrible place?

DUCHESS (*tragic manner*). I heard the footman confess that he had left your sister here by mistake. I rushed to rescue her. I found her laughing. Lord Hubert, Lord Rupert, Lord Francis, form a guard around her and march her home. Bring her back to the Castle by force. At once! She says she would like to STAY!

[*Stalks out of door.*

LADY PATSY (*as her brothers seize her*). I would! I would! (*Kisses her hand, laughing, as they take her away*) Good-bye, Peter Piper! Good-bye, Meg and Peg and Kilmanskegg. I'm in love with you every one.

[*She is taken out.*

PETER PIPER (*stands in center after she is gone*). I'M in love with HER! I'm going to MARRY her!

QUEEN CROSSPATCH (*appears, rising out of a big vase in a corner*). Well, if you do, you'll have to thank me for it, because I was the person who made the footman bring her here. I jumped on his shoulder and whispered in his ear until he didn't know what he was doing.

GREEN WORKERS (*suddenly appearing*). And we pulled him and pushed him until we dragged him to the wrong house.

QUEEN CROSSPATCH. So that's where *I* come in.

PETER PIPER. Let's all join hands and dance round and round and kick up our heels and laugh as hard as ever we can.

[*They all join hands and dance. Queen and Green Workers form ring and dance also.*

CURTAIN

ACT II

SCENE. *Drawing-room of Racketty-Packetty House. Peter Piper is languishing in an armchair which is propped up by books because one of its back legs is missing. Meg and Peg are fanning him with tattered palm-leaf fans. Kilmanskegg has his feet in hot water.   Gustibus has on spectacles and is holding a huge turnip watch in one hand and Peter Piper's wrist in the other.*

GUSTIBUS (*shakes his watch violently — puts it to his ear — shakes his head*).   I wish this watch would go.   (*Knocking it against his heel*)   It's so much better in a serious case like this — if a doctor's watch will go.

MEG.   But it's a very GOOD watch.   We've played ball with it for years.

PEG.   Ridicklis says it's the best thing she ever had to bake eggs in.

GUSTIBUS.   It's a PERFECT watch.   The only one little tiny, trifling, insignificant flaw in it is that it has no works.   Peter Piper took all the wheels out to invent a flying-machine with. And there are SOME watches that will NOT go if they have no wheels inside.

PETER PIPER (*faintly*).   It will go if you carry it.   That is one of my sparkling jokes.   Ha!   Ha!   Ha!   (*Spectral laugh*) Listen to my hollow laugh.   It is the laughter of a dying Doll. (*Raises himself, hand on chest, and coughs — hollow cough. Looks round at them proudly*)   Listen to that!   (*Coughs again, mournfully*)   Ah!   How I am changed!

MEG.   Don't you think you EVER can get well, Peter Piper?

PETER PIPER (*firmly*).   Never!   This is the effect of a broken heart upon a person like me.   I am dying of love.   I am fading away like a beautiful flower.   Soon I shall be lying beneath a pure white marble monument — with these lines written on it : "Peter Piper — who died of a broken heart in all his youth and beauty.   Slain by the falseness of Lady Patricia Vere de Vere."   Then crowds — CROWDS — will gather to weep over my tomb — and scatter expensive orchids all over it.   (*Ridicklis comes bustling in, carrying a kettle of boiling water.   She pours it into Peter Piper's foot bath.   Peter Piper cries out*)   Ouch!

[*Loudly, and jerks his feet up in the air.*

RIDICKLIS (*surprised*).   What are you saying "ouch" for?

PETER PIPER (*rubbing his legs*).   Are you sure the medicine book said "BOILING water" — QUITE boiling?

RIDICKLIS (*indignantly*). Of course it did. Read it aloud, Gustibus.

GUSTIBUS (*drops watch on floor, takes book from under arm and reads*). "In case of very severe dying of love — very severe — pour boiling water on the feet and boiling water on the head. If it is QUITE boiling and is repeated every ten minutes, the patient will forget his troubles."

RIDICKLIS. You see, it says "quite boiling." I'll go and get some for your head.

[*Hurries towards door.*

PETER PIPER (*hastily looks round*). No, don't! I wouldn't, if I were you. I am a little better already — (*she turns back. He sinks back in chair*) though of course I am still dying. Just bring my Invention Book and I will invent a prescription which may support me for a few hours. (*They rush about and bring the Invention Book, put book on his knee, give him his pen. He shakes it, sucks it, etc., etc.*) Billions of money will be made by other people out of these inventions when the nation is mourning my loss. I write — with my trembling hand — this last one : "Invention No. 952,000 — Prescription for distinguished persons dying of love." Let me see. (*Thinks*) "A good strengthening cup of hot Shoe Polish."

[*Others crowd around him.*

RIDICKLIS. That sounds nourishing.

PETER PIPER. Ah! What a doctor I should have made if I had not died of Love! "Add one penny package of the best brass-headed tacks — a tin whistle, well chopped up — seventeen and three-quarters boot laces minced fine — flavor with lucifer matches and door knobs — (*solemn deliberation*) Boil twenty-four years, three minutes, two seconds and a half. Keep cool for seventy-five years and one minute — EXACTLY! Then give to the patient as often as he will take it. P. Piper, M.D., F.R.C.S." There, Ridicklis, study that well before you prepare it.

[*Triumphantly.*

RIDICKLIS. But it takes so long to make. You mightn't be here when it is ready.

PETER PIPER. That's why I invented it. (*Sudden thought —
finger on brow*) Here! Give me that book again! I must
put this down. (*Hurriedly scratching down*) "Invention
953,000 — Never invent a prescription in time to take it
yourself." (*Shuts book — shakes head in disappointment —
mournful*) But I'm afraid that's not quite a new one. All
the most distinguished medical men know about that invention. I mightn't be able to get a safe patent.
[*Sinks back in chair.*

RIDICKLIS (*anxiously*). How do you feel now, Peter?

PETER PIPER. Very — very weak and fragile. I wish she could
see me. But she sits in her proud baronial halls and decks herself with jewels. She thought to break a country heart for
pastime ere she went to town, — I mean to Tidy Castle.

GUSTIBUS. Cheer up, old chap. I wouldn't die, if I was you.
You might repent it — when it was too late.

PETER PIPER. Lady Patricia will repent it. That's what I'm
doing it for. I want her to feel the bitterness of losing me.

RIDICKLIS. But, after all, perhaps she can't help it. You know,
when they carried her away, she said she was in love with
every one of us.

PETER PIPER. That's what I complain of. She comes here in
all her lace and jewels, and laughs and giggles, and says I'm
interesting, and dances round and round, and kicks up her
little heels, and then, when she goes away, she says she's in
love *with every one of us.* She doesn't say like this — (*coy
grimace*) "I'm in love with —" (*pointing as if he were Lady
Patsy pointing coyly at himself*) Looking at me like this —
[*Ogles with his head on one side, finger in mouth.*

MEG. But you didn't seem to think of that at first.

PETER PIPER. I only thought of it this morning at ten-thirty.
It was my death-blow. You may have noticed I only began to
die of love at ten-thirty.

RIDICKLIS. So he did.

GUSTIBUS. So he did.

MEG AND PEG (*weeping*). It's true.

PETER PIPER. I'm one who begins things promptly. I began

without one second's delay. By ten-thirty to-morrow morning my lifeless corpse may be borne past her window to be committed to the tomb.

[*All begin to exclaim and weep.*

MEG AND PEG. Oh! Please don't, Peter Piper. Please don't die of love.

KILMANSKEGG. Oh, don't leave us, Peter!

RIDICKLIS. We shall all feel like widows. Let me try pouring boiling water on your head.

PETER PIPER. No. It would do no good. Nothing will save me. I am perishing in my prime. I think I will do it now. (*Lies back in his chair and stretches out his legs*) Cover me with snow-white blossoms, and tell her that she will never know what rapture she has missed.

ALL. Ow! Ow! Ow! Peter! Don't! Don't!

[*They run about. — Gustibus rushes to pick up watch, and feels his pulse. Ridicklis, wildly agitated, snatches up one thing after another.*

RIDICKLIS (*wildly excited*). Give him some glue! Give him some blotting-paper! Pour a few lead pencils down his throat!

QUEEN CROSSPATCH (*comes out of drawer in table — or big broken umbrella lying in corner — or from under pile of mending — or anything. Green Workers detach themselves from various before unobserved places. Queen Crosspatch goes to Peter Piper*). What's all this ridiculous nonsense about?

GUSTIBUS. He's dying of love. If this watch was going, it would tell me that his pulse has ceased to beat at all. At least I think —

QUEEN CROSSPATCH. Dying of love! Oh! Fudge! Nobody does that in these days. It's as much out of fashion as crinoline! Rubbish!

PETER PIPER (*starting up*). What! It isn't fashionable!

QUEEN CROSSPATCH. It's not been done for fifty years. I don't believe people really did it then — except in novels. Pooh! (*Contemptuously*) Get up and stop dying this minute!

PETER PIPER (*complete change of manner — jumps up and begins to settle his collar and swagger a little*). Well, of course I can't do anything that's not fashionable — under the circumstances. You see, I've fallen in love with a very fashionable young lady — one of the — er — young ladies — er — at Tidy Castle.

QUEEN CROSSPATCH. That pretty little baggage of a Patsy — the giggling one, of course.

PETER PIPER (*coy grin*). Isn't she a little love?

QUEEN CROSSPATCH. She's a little duck — though I'm rather afraid she'll giggle her little head off some time. Of course, I know all about it, really — I always know things — that's my business.

PETER PIPER (*obsequiously*). So you do, your Majesty. I'm so glad you have condescended to come. Where is she now? What has she been doing since they took her away? Is she pining for me as she ought?

QUEEN CROSSPATCH (*laughs*). She's been pretending that she had to stay in bed with her broken leg, because she thought she might creep to the window and see you if the nurse would leave her alone.

MEG. Oh! the darling little thing!

KILMANSKEGG. I knew she liked us.

RIDICKLIS. I was sure she liked *Peter Piper!*

QUEEN CROSSPATCH. But the Duchess won't let the nurse leave her, and she's bored to death.

PETER PIPER (*settling his collar*). It's plain she's not forgetting me. Though I don't really see how she *could* forget me. Do you?

QUEEN CROSSPATCH. She won't forget you if you don't waste your time in dying of love. Begin to remind her of yourself as soon as possible.

PETER PIPER. How can I? How can I? (*Suddenly*) Wait a moment! An invention! (*Gets book*) "No. 956,000. To make titled ladies remember you. Don't let them forget you!"

QUEEN CROSSPATCH. That's quite a good one! I've thought of two plans. I'll tell you one at a time. (*Calls*) Nip. Trip.

Skip. Flip. (*Green Workers come near*) Go over to the Castle and tell the Trained Nurse that the servants are having a Tea Party in the Servants' Hall — and tell her that her young man is there and that she must slip downstairs and leave Lady Patsy alone. (*Green Workers fly*) Now, I'll tell you the other plan which is a great deal more important.

[*All crowd about her.*

PEG. Oh! Your Majesty.

MEG. Your most gracious Majesty.

RIDICKLIS. Your Majesty can do anything.

PETER PIPER. What is it, your most Gracious Majestical Majesty?

QUEEN CROSSPATCH. That silly little Cynthia is playing with Tidy Castle, of course. She never stops playing with it. And before I came away I whispered in her ear that it would be a lovely idea to pretend that scarlet fever had broken out in the family, and they must all be put to bed. Of course, she thought she had made it all up herself — the conceited thing! — and she put them all in bed in a minute — with mustard plasters on their chests and poultices round their throats and blisters on their heads.

PETER PIPER. Oh! Scrump! They can't get away! (*Turns several somersaults — when he stands on feet again*) Lady Patsy can have all the fun she wants if Cynthia only lets them stay ill long enough.

QUEEN CROSSPATCH (*nodding head gravely*). You don't suppose I couldn't manage that?

PETER PIPER. How! How!

QUEEN CROSSPATCH. Cynthia's Mamma used to be a lady-in-waiting to the Queen, and a little girl Princess is going to do Cynthia the honor of coming to see her and her new doll's house to-morrow. I made Cynthia put the Tidy Castle people to bed with scarlet fever just before her Mamma sent for her to tell her what is going to happen, and to teach her what she is to say and do. She went away and forgot all about them, and she'll not remember them for days. She's worse than the fat footman for forgetting.

PETER PIPER (*turns another somersault*). Oh! Scrump! I can make a rope ladder and run up and make love to Lady Patsy. I can ask her to run away and marry me.

RIDICKLIS. But she's a lady of high degree.

PETER PIPER. That's why she'll have me. Ladies of high degree always marry the good-looking ones in rags and tatters. I'm very good-looking, you know.

[*Green Workers run into the room. They all quickly form in line and bow low to Crosspatch.*

TRIP. The nurse has gone downstairs, your Majesty. Lady Patsy is looking out of her casement.

QUEEN CROSSPATCH. Open that window so that she can see in. (*They run and open window*) Now, light your torches. (*They light torches*) Now, Peter Piper — begin to amuse her so that she'll want to come here more than ever. I'll just go over and keep Cynthia forgetting.

[*Exit.*

PETER PIPER. Oh! If she sees me — if she just sees me she will never forget me again. She can't! She will have seen me twice then. And no titled lady could get over that. Now, girls! Now, girls! Begin to get me things.

ALL. What shall we get? What shall we do? What do you want?

PETER PIPER (*thinks a moment — finger on forehead*). Oh! I know! Meg! That ball of string Cynthia's kitten made us a present of. (*Meg and Peg and Kilmanskegg run about wildly until they find it and bring it to him. He gives it to Gustibus*) Gustibus, go outside and make it into a rope ladder immediately. (*Gustibus runs outside*) Kilmanskegg, two of our richest antimacassars. Peg, some pins. (*Kilmanskegg runs and pulls two torn antimacassars off chairs and brings them. Peg brings pins and begins to pin antimacassars round the edge of his torn trousers' legs as if they were trimming*) These are for lace ruffles. Ridicklis, bring your best frying-pan. (*Ridicklis brings frying-pan*) My best cocked hat, Meg. (*She snatches it out of the fireplace and gives it to him. He puts it on with great jauntiness and strikes an attitude with his leg bent and his hand in his breast*) First I'm going to attract her attention and then I'm going to *do things*. (*To Green Workers*) Throw all the light on me you can. (*Their torches flare up*) Now — (*Grandly*) Draw aside the curtains and let me burst on her suddenly. (*Meg and Peg at each side of window dramatically draw aside ragged curtains. Tidy Castle is seen all dark but one window at which Lady Patsy is seated looking out*) There she is. She *sees* me. She's beginning to laugh. She can't stand it. (*He turns three stately somersaults and then, standing on his feet, makes a magnificent bow. Lady Patsy laughs harder*) If we were married, how she would enjoy me. All through the long summer evenings I could turn handsprings for her. (*Racketty-Packettys all admiring him*) Now, I'm going to walk like a Duke. (*Cocks hat still more jauntily — folds arms on chest, strides about before windows. While doing it, falls over footstool; exclaims*) Oh! Scrump! (*Gets up, kicks footstool about room, resumes his stride, makes another somersault, stands up, kisses his hand, takes off hat, waves it, kisses both hands. Lady Patsy is seen covering her face and rocking backwards and forwards with laughter*) Now! I have attracted her attention! Give me the frying-pan, Ridicklis. I am going to play the guitar on it and serenade her. (*Strikes attitude with frying-pan and sings*)

From Racketty-Packetty House I come,
It stands, dear Lady, in a slum,
A low, low slum behind the door,
The stout armchair is placed before,
    Just take a look at it, my lady.

The house itself is a perfect sight,
And everyone's dressed like a perfect fright,
But no one cares a single jot,
And each one giggles over his lot,
And as for me, I'm in love with you, my lady.

I can't make up another verse,
And if I did it would be worse,

But I could stand and sing all day,
If I could think of things to say —
But the fact is I just wanted to make you look at me.

(*Then he dances a lively jig so that his rags and tags fly about him; then he makes another bow, kisses his hand and speaks to Green Workers*) Put out your torches — quick! (*Torches go out. Meg and Peg close the curtains. He drops into a chair, panting and fanning himself with the frying-pan*) Now, that she has had the pleasure of seeing me — I'm going to let her miss me for a few moments — not very long. Just long enough to make her realize that life without me would be a howling wilderness. When she begins to weep bitterly I'll go out and just run up the rope ladder and ask her to elope with me. She'll come — like a shot. Wait a minute. (*Gets up and creeps towards door; speaks in hollow whisper through it to Gustibus who is outside*) Have you made the rope ladder yet?

GUSTIBUS (*comes to door, mopping his brow; answers same voice*). Yes! But it was hard work to do it so fast. I couldn't have finished it if the Queen hadn't sent me some Green Workers.

PETER PIPER. Have you fastened a ball of string to it so that I can throw it through her window and she can pull it up?

GUSTIBUS. The Green Workers did that.

PETER PIPER (*stealing across room to window*). All right! Now I'm going to peep at her through the window to see if she is weeping bitterly. (*Draws aside curtain and looks. Lady Patsy is to be seen at her lighted window with her head on her arms, her arms hanging over the sill, crying*) Yes! She's weeping bitterly! She's missed me enough. You see what it is to be a fascinating person? She'd probably die of a broken heart — if it were fashionable.

[*Goes out. Racketty-Packettys crowd around the windows. Peter Piper is to be heard whistling.*

GUSTIBUS. He's whistling to attract her attention.

KILMANSKEGG (*excited*). She's heard him!

PEG. She's looking up!

MEG. She's wiping her eyes and beginning to laugh again. Listen! He's speaking to her!

[*Peter Piper heard speaking in hollow attempt at loud whisper.*

PETER PIPER. Hello! Could you catch this ball of string if I threw it up to you?

LADY PATSY. Yes.

PETER PIPER. Then catch it.

ALL (*dancing for joy*). She's caught it.

PETER PIPER. Now, pull till the rope ladder comes up.

MEG. She's pulling!

PEG. She's got it up!

RIDICKLIS. She's fastening it to her bed-post!

GUSTIBUS. He's running up the ladder — as fast as lightning!

KILMANSKEGG. He's asking her to elope with him. I know he is!

MEG AND PEG. She's saying she will. They've got their arms around each other's necks!

[*They fall on each other's neck in ecstasy.*

GUSTIBUS. He's helping her to go through the window.

RIDICKLIS. My goodness gracious mercy me! He's carrying her down the ladder. They'll be here in a minute. There's going to be a wedding in the family, and we've got nothing but shavings to make the wedding cake of.

[*Falls into chair and fans herself with apron.*

[*Door opens. Peter Piper strides in, grander than ever, with Lady Patsy on his arm, giggling with delight.*

PETER PIPER (*magnificent low bow*). My dear Lady Meg, Lady Peg, Lady Kilmanskegg, Lady Ridicklis and Lord Gustibus Rags, allow me to present to you your future sister-in-law, the Duchess of Tags. She has consented to be mine. Lord Gustibus, write at once to announce the engagement to the *Morning Post.* (*He leads her to the largest armchair with a flourish. She sits down — the back legs give way, and she falls with her little feet kicking in the air, but laughing more than ever. They all rush to help her up, Peter Piper raising her*) A mere trifle, my darling. The merest trifle in the world. It almost always happens when we sit down in a chair or put anything on a table.　But legs will come off, even in the best regulated families.　The library, Gustibus —

[*Waving his hand towards the book-shelves.　Gustibus gets an armful of books and brings them to support chair with.　Meg and Peg and Kilmanskegg gather round Lady Patsy, admiring her.*

KILMANSKEGG.　Oh!　We're so glad!

[*Hugs her.*

MEG.　You sweet darling!

[*Hugs her.*

PEG.　Don't you mind our being low at all?

LADY PATSY.　Not a bit.　I want to be low myself.　It makes me laugh.

RIDICKLIS (*anxiously*).　But since Cynthia began to despise us, she never gives us anything to eat.　We scarcely ever have anything for dinner but shavings.

LADY PATSY.　Peter told me all about that.　I eat very little, even at the Castle where they serve us painted Plaster-of-Paris dinners in seventeen courses.　Chickens with paint gravy don't agree with me.　And I'd do without anything if I can be married to Peter and live in your funny old shabby house.

PETER PIPER (*ogling her — arm round her waist*).　You couldn't resist me, could you, Angel?

LADY PATSY.　I never tried.　You're *such fun!* (*Looks round at sofa*)　What a lovely battered old sofa.　What's that running about on top of it?

PETER PIPER.　Only a few mice, darling.　They make nests in the furniture and pay their rent in crumbs.

RIDICKLIS (*shaking her head*).　*When they can spare them!*

PETER PIPER (*cheerfully*).　Which they *never* can.　They're *unpaying* guests!

RIDICKLIS (*goes to chair on which lies large coal-scuttle bonnet; picks it up with great care and brings it to show to Lady Patsy — lace veil dangles from it in tatters*).　There's a beautiful family of them in this.　It's my best bonnet.　It's a little inconvenient.　I have to be so careful in putting it on that I scarcely ever wear it.　(*Lifts it up and puts it on very slowly*)　I can only put it on like this.　(*Holds out lace tatters*)　You

see they needed the lace for sheets and pillow-cases. (*Squeaks
are heard*) Hear them squeak! They think I'm going to
market and they're a little frightened.

PETER PIPER (*proudly*). It's not everybody who has a bonnet
trimmed with mice.

RIDICKLIS (*holds head carefully on one side*). Give them a crumb
to keep them quiet, Peter. There's one on the mantelpiece.

PETER PIPER (*gets crumb and feeds it to mice in crown of bonnet*).
It's quite a new fashion. I don't believe they have it even
in Paris yet.

[*Ridicklis carefully removes bonnet and puts it back in corner.*

LADY PATSY (*jumps about and claps her hands for joy*). I must
have one in my bridal trousseau!

PETER PIPER. You shall, dearest. You shall — if it takes
my last mouse.

LADY PATSY (*throws herself into his arms*). Oh! I'm so happy.
(*Suddenly*) What's that?

[*They all listen. Shouts of "Ou! Ou! Ouch!" are heard coming from Tidy Castle.*

GUSTIBUS. What a noise! It's coming from outside!

[*All run to window. Peter Piper throws it open, puts head out.*

PETER PIPER. Hello! You! What's the matter? (*Draws
head in*) It's in Tidy Castle!

RIDICKLIS. I know what it is. Cynthia left them all raving in
delirium with mustard plasters on — and poultries and blisters,
and they're all groaning and screaming.

PETER PIPER. Well, her Majesty, Queen Crosspatch, told her
to do it so that I could elope with Patsy — but — I didn't
know it was going to hurt them as much as that. I — I — I
don't know what to do.

QUEEN CROSSPATCH (*suddenly appearing*). Well, go over and
cure them. I knew you'd want to do it, you shabby, kind-
hearted things!

PETER PIPER. Well, your most Gracious Majestical Imperial
Majesty, we shouldn't like it ourselves, you know. Should
we?

QUEEN CROSSPATCH. No, you wouldn't. And you belong to

the "Do as you'd be done bys." That's why I like you. Bundle over there as fast as you can, and take off their plasters and blisters. But don't *quite* cure them. Just leave them comfortably bedridden until you've married Patsy. You can tell them it's awfully dangerous for scarlet fever patients to get up until they're peeled. Off with you.

[*Racketty-Packettys rush off, tumbling over each other to get out of the door.*

[*Stage darkens. When it lightens again, audience see a room in Tidy Castle — no furniture — row of pallets on floor, on which lie Duchess and rest of Tidy Castle family.*

DUCHESS (*sitting up in her pallet, with large poultice tied round throat and bandage on head*). Ow — w! The lady took away all the furniture for fear of infection. She didn't even leave a glass of water. The servants ran away and we're nearly all of us raving in delirium. Ow — this blister on my head!

LORD HUBERT (*rising and rocking backwards and forwards*). Ow — this mustard plaster on my stomach.

LORD RUPERT (*rises also, twisting round to get his hand on his back*). Ow — this red-hot poultice on my back!

LORD FRANCIS. I'm raving in delirium. I think I'm a mad dog! Bow! Wow! Wow! Wow! Wow!

LADY GWENDOLYN. I'm raving too. I think I'm a cat. Meow! Meow! Me-ow-ow!

LADY MURIEL. I think I'm a hen that's just laid an egg. Cluck-cluck — cluck — cluck. Coo-ch! Tuch — tuch — tuch — too — oh!

LADY DORIS (*sits up, bright red all over, and nose swollen enormously*). I've broken out in a violent rash — and look at my lovely nose — that I used to turn up so haughtily.

[*All rock backwards and forwards.*

DUCHESS. Oh! my poor children, I wish some one would come! Oh, if some one would only come. (*Door opens*) Some one is coming.

[*All stop and stare as Racketty-Packettys appear: Ridicklis with large basket on arm — Meg and Peg with kettles full of hot water, bottles of medicine, etc.*

PETER PIPER (*advances to middle of room*). Hello! Hello! Cheer up! Cheer up! It's US! Look at ME! (*Turns somersault — strikes attitude — kisses tips of fingers to each patient in turn. They stare and Lord Hubert begins to laugh*) That's right! It'll do you good! Nothing cures scarlet fever like cheering up. (*Meg and Peg, etc., are bustling about, taking off plasters, pouring out medicine, putting ice on heads. Gustibus goes round with his watch, feeling pulses*) Go ahead, Racketty-Packettys. Give them everything you can think of.

RIDICKLIS (*coming forward panting, and ticking off on her fingers*). They'll all be quite out of pain directly. I'm giving them hot water and cold water and ice and brandy and castor-oil and gruel and ipecacuanha — and I'm going to massage them and osteopath them and electrocute them.

PETER PIPER. You mean electrify them. Well, that may help. But mind you don't *forget* anything. We must do our best. (*Duchess staring at him*) Hello! Your grace! What's the matter?

DUCHESS. Who are you?

PETER PIPER (*bows*). The Duke of Tags, ma'am. You had the pleasure of making my acquaintance when you came to find Lady Patsy.

DUCHESS. Villain! I rescued her from you. She is shut up in the tower chamber.

PETER PIPER. No, she isn't, ma'am. She's looking out of the window at Racketty-Packetty House — waiting to marry me the minute I get back, after we've cured you.

DUCHESS. Monster! She sha'n't! I'm going to her this instant to drag her away.

[*Tries to get up.*

PETER PIPER (*holds her back*). No, ma'am! You can't do that. You're not peeled yet. The most dangerous thing a scarlet fever patient can do is to get up before she's peeled. Any distinguished physician will tell you that. Gustibus, come here.

GUSTIBUS (*runs with watch, dragging after him a long watch ribbon*). Is she delirious?

PETER PIPER. Tell her what will happen to her if she gets up before she's peeled.

GUSTIBUS (*opens book he has under arm — reads*). The patient who gets up before she is peeled will drop down dead instantly — besides which she will have fits — go quite insane — foam at the mouth — and have lockjaw and hydrophobia.

PETER PIPER. *Now* will you be good.

DUCHESS (*throws up arms and stiffens out*). Let me perish where I lie. My daughter! Oh! My daughter!

PETER PIPER. That's what Lord Ullin said — across the stormy water. My daughter! Oh! My daughter! Take my tip, ma'am — don't you perish. You might live to regret it ever afterwards.

LADY MURIEL (*faintly*). Mamma! What was it the New Nurse said when she heard that the little girl Princess was coming to-morrow?

DUCHESS (*starts up*). Oh! Why did I forget! She said that she did not know whether she stood on her head or her heels, and she must tidy up the nursery and have that Racketty-Packetty old doll's house carried downstairs and burned early in the morning. That was what she said.

[*Triumphantly.*

[*Meg and Peg and Kilmanskegg and Ridicklis, who are working over their patients, rise from the different bedsides and clutch at their hearts and gasp. Gustibus drops his watch and book with a bang and sits down on the floor. Peter Piper clutches his brow. There is a moment's silence.*

LORD HUBERT (*speaks faintly in affected tones*). I don't really want the shabby and good-natured things to be burned up. This one — (*pointing to Meg, who stands near him*) took my mustard plaster off.

LORD RUPERT (*motions to Peg*). This one removed my red-hot poultice.

LORD FRANCIS (*looking at Kilmanskegg*). This one put ice on my head until I stopped barking.

LADY GWENDOLYN (*pointing to Gustibus*). This dear funny old thing has taken the swelling out of my nose. Just look at it.

DUCHESS (*furious*). What are these things in comparison with your sister's degradation. (*To Peter*) Before breakfast to-morrow morning your wretched hovel will be in flames.

RACKETTY-PACKETTYS. Ow! Ow! Ow!

PETER PIPER (*sudden hope*). Perhaps it isn't true! Perhaps she's only raving in delirium!

RIDICKLIS. No, she isn't! I've given her hot water and cold and gruel and broth and castor-oil and ipecacuahana and put ice almost all over her. She's as sensible as any of us.

KILMANSKEGG. This time to-morrow we shall not have a house over our heads.

PETER PIPER. If she isn't raving in delirium we sha'n't have any heads. We had better go home. I must tell Lady Patsy.

LADY PATSY (*rushing in*). I heard it all! I heard it all! I was hiding behind the door. Oh! my darling Peter Piper. [*Throws herself in his arms.*

PETER PIPER (*releasing himself*). Farewell, my beloved Patsy. You will never know the happiness of being married to me. You must stay here to-night. Racketty-Packetty House is no place for you.

LADY PATSY (*drawing herself up to her full height*). I — will — never — leave — you!

PETER PIPER. You won't?

LADY PATSY. *NEVER!*

PETER PIPER (*to Rackettys*). You see that. She won't. I knew she wouldn't. I don't blame you, my ducky darling! I wouldn't leave myself, if I were you. Come to my arms! (*They are clasped in each other's arms. Pause. Then Peter Piper looks up and speaks solemnly, holding her hand*) We will now go home to Racketty-Packetty House, and all go over it together. We will look for the last time at every hole in the carpet, and every piece of stuffing sticking out of the dear old shabby sofa, and every broken window and chair leg and table and ragged blanket, and bid them all farewell. Patsy and I will lead the way.

[*March in line out of the room slowly to Doll's March, played with pathos. The Tidy Castle dolls all watch them as they go out, and lights gradually lower until they go out also.*

CURTAIN

ACT III

SCENE : *Cynthia's Nursery.*

AT RISE : *Green Workers flying about, making it untidy, overturning footstools, snatching off table covers, upsetting Nurse's workbasket, etc., etc., sweeping ashes out of fireplace on to floor.*

TRIP. Hurry! Hurry! Hurry! We must make it all as untidy as possible.
[*Runs about.*

FLIP (*business*). Skurry! Skurry! Skurry! Upset everything! Put everything in the wrong place.

NIP. Flurry! Flurry! Flurry! What are we doing it for?

TRIP. So that New Nurse won't be able to make it straight and have time to burn Racketty-Packetty House before the Princess comes! Upset that bowl of flowers and spill the water on the carpet! Hurry! Hurry! Hurry!

QUEEN CROSSPATCH (*appears. Green Workers all draw up, present brooms*). You have obeyed my commands pretty well. It's nice and untidy. New Nurse is coming upstairs. Now, when she begins to try to put things straight, hold on to her skirts and snatch her broom and duster, — and upset things as soon as her back is turned. After that, I'll tell you what to do next.

NEW NURSE (*hurries into the room in great excitement. Lifts up hands at sight of disorder*). Good gracious! What has Cynthia been doing! I never saw the place in such a state before! And the Princess may come any minute! Oh, dear! Oh, dear! (*Catches sight of Racketty-Packetty House*) There's that old Racketty-Packetty thing to be taken down stairs and burned. I must ring for James and John.

QUEEN CROSSPATCH (*hurries to Green Workers*). Hang on to the bell, so that it won't ring when she thinks it does.

[*Green Workers hang on to bell and on to New Nurse's arm.*

NEW NURSE (*pulling at bell rope*). There's something the matter with it. (*Jerks it*) I don't believe it rang.

QUEEN CROSSPATCH (*to Trip*). Cut the rope.

[*Trip cuts it as Nurse jerks it. She falls backward on the floor.*

NEW NURSE. The rope's broken and I haven't time to go and call anyone. Oh, dear! Oh, dear! I must get this place straightened. (*She flies from one thing to another. This scene must be lengthened or shortened as seems best to stage manager. Nurse straightens things; Green Workers unstraighten them; they drag her back. New Nurse fanning with apron*) Oh, dear! Oh, dear! I can't get on. I feel as if weights were dragging on me! What shall I do. I'm sure I hear a carriage in the street. And that Racketty-Packetty House isn't burned! I'll push the armchair quite in front of it and hide it. (*She rushes and pushes chair. Green Workers help her. Listens*) It *is* a carriage! (*Runs to window and looks out*) It's the Princess — and two ladies-in-waiting! They're getting out. I'm not fit to be seen. I must run!

[*Hurried exit.*

[*Enter Old Nurse, hobbling.*

OLD NURSE (*clean cap and apron, knitting in her hand*). I've got on my best gown — and my best cap and apron. I'll just sit in that chair behind the window curtain and I can see her — bless her little royal heart — and she'll never see me. My goodness mercy me! Won't it be a treat to see blessed Queen Victoria's grandchild.

[*Green Workers help her to her chair in the bay window — help her to sit down — give her her knitting and spectacles and draw the curtains.*

[*Enter Cynthia with little girl Princess, followed by two ladies-in-waiting. Cynthia is very shy and quiet. She evidently does not know what to say — neither does the little Princess. They stare at each other child fashion.*

PRINCESS (*politely after pause*). This is a very nice nursery.

CYNTHIA. Thank you, your Highness.

[*They stare again.*

PRINCESS (*looks about her — sees Tidy Castle*).   Is that the new doll's house?

CYNTHIA.   Yes, your Highness.

[*They stare again.*

PRINCESS (*after another pause*).   Will you show it to me?

CYNTHIA.   Yes, your Highness — with — with great pleasure. (*She opens Tidy Castle. The Princess gets up and goes to look. Cynthia explains*)   This is the Banquetting Hall — and this is the Grand Salon — and this is the Picture Gallery.   And that is Lord Hubert and that is Lord Rupert — and that is Lord Francis — and these are Lady Gwendolyn and Lady Muriel and Lady Doris, and this is the Duchess of Tidyshire.

PRINCESS (*giggling a little — turning Duchess over in her hand*).   Isn't she a ridiculous old woman?   She looks so cross.

CYNTHIA (*looking into Castle*).   Where's Lady Patsy?   She's the funny, pretty one.   I've lost her again.   I wonder where she is!

[*Green Workers giggle and nudge each other.*

QUEEN CROSSPATCH.   Pull aside the window curtain a little.

[*Green Workers pull it aside and Princess sees Old Nurse knitting.*

PRINCESS.   Who is that nice old woman knitting in the window?

CYNTHIA (*sudden turn*).   Oh!   It's Old Nurse.   What are you doing here, Old Nurse?

OLD NURSE (*getting up from her chair, quite trembling with alarm. Makes a low stiff curtsey to Princess*).   I beg your pardon, your Royal Highness.   I beg your pardon, Miss Cynthia.   I never thought as anyone could see me.   I just hid behind the curtain so that I could just get a peep at her little Royal Highness as is blessed Queen Victoria's grandchild.

PRINCESS (*prettily to Cynthia*).   What a nice old woman.   (*Goes to Old Nurse and holds out her hand to shake hands with her*)   How do you do?   I hope you are very well?

OLD NURSE (*curtseying as she takes her hand*).   Bless you, your kind little Highness.   I'm very well for my years — if my old bones was not so stiff.   I hope I haven't took too great a liberty, your Highness.   I'll hobble away now.

PRINCESS. Oh, no! Please don't go away. Please sit down again — and go on with your knitting.

[*Helps Old Nurse to sit down and picks up her knitting for her.*

CYNTHIA (*to herself, discontentedly*). I never saw such a Princess. She likes quite common things. I don't believe she cares for Tidy Castle at all.

PRINCESS (*turning to Cynthia*). She's such a sweetie old thing. I do so like her funny clean cap with the big frill.

QUEEN CROSSPATCH (*to Green Workers*). Push the armchair away from before Racketty-Packetty House. Push it very slowly — nobody's looking.

[*Green Workers push chair slowly aside until Racketty-Packetty House stands revealed just as the Princess turns towards it.*

PRINCESS (*starting forward, exclaiming*). Oh! What is that?

CYNTHIA (*stammering and horrified*). Oh! It's nothing, your Highness! It's nothing worth looking at. It's only a shabby old doll's house.

PRINCESS. A shabby old doll's house!

CYNTHIA. It belonged to my Grandmamma and it ought not to be in the nursery. (*To Old Nurse*) I told New Nurse to have it carried downstairs and burned.

PRINCESS. Burned! Why, if it were mine I wouldn't have it burned for worlds! Oh! Please let me look at it. There are no doll's houses like it anywhere in these days.

[*She kneels down and looks inside delightedly.*

CYNTHIA. Do you *like* it?

PRINCESS (*exclaiming*). Oh! Yes! It's so dear. It's shabby and wants mending, of course, but it's almost exactly like one my Grandmamma had, and she kept it among her treasures, and only let me look at it as a great, great treat.

[*Cynthia turns towards Old Nurse.*

OLD NURSE (*cracked triumphant voice*). Yes, and her Grandmamma was the Queen of England, and people knelt down and kissed her hand — and had to go out of the room backwards before her. That's what they had to do!

PRINCESS (*picking up dolls one after another*). The darling dears!

Look at their nice funny clothes. Only they do want some new ones. How I should like to dress them all up again, and have the house made just as it was when it was new.
[*Sits back on her little Royal heels and gazes at them in rapture, with clasped hands.*

CYNTHIA. That old Racketty-Packetty House!

PRINCESS. If it were mine I should love it more than any doll's house I have ever had. I never saw anything as laughing and good-natured as the dolls' faces. Oh! If you were to burn them and their home I — never *could* forgive you!

CYNTHIA (*stammering*). I — never — never — will — your Highness. (*Darts forward and picks up Lady Patsy*) Why, here's Lady Patsy! How did she get into Racketty-Packetty House?

PRINCESS. Perhaps she went to see them because they were poor and shabby. Perhaps she likes this one. (*Holds up Peter Piper*) When I picked them up, their arms were round each other. Please let her stay with him. Oh! (*Little startled jump*) I felt as if the boy one kicked his ragged leg for joy. I wonder if he did?

OLD NURSE (*to Cynthia, whispering*). Ask her if she'll let you make her a present of it? Ask her, — think of her a-takin' it off to Buckham Palace!

CYNTHIA (*timidly stammers*). If you like it so — your Highness — would you please accept it as a — a present. I — I — I wish you'd let me give it to you.

PRINCESS (*rising*). How kind of you. Thank you very much. (*Looks at lady-in-waiting*) I should so like to have it and make it new again.

LADY-IN-WAITING. Perhaps your Highness might ask permission from her Majesty.

PRINCESS (*to Cynthia*). I hope I shall be allowed to accept it. I hope I shall — I do so love it. Thank you very much.

LADY-IN-WAITING (*draws near and speaks respectfully*). Your Royal Highness — I think —

PRINCESS (*to Cynthia*). I must say good-morning to you now. I have enjoyed myself very much.

CYNTHIA (*curtseys*).   Thank your Royal Highness.

PRINCESS.   You have been so kind to me.   I shall be so glad if I am allowed to have the doll's house.

CYNTHIA (*curtseys*).   Thank your Royal Highness.

LADY-IN-WAITING (*opens the door and stands beside it*).

PRINCESS.   Good-by, Old Nurse.   Some day, when your bones are not so stiff, you must come and see me at the Palace.   I am sure Mamma would be pleased.   (*Old Nurse hobbles to feet.   Green Workers help her.   She curtseys again and again*) Good-by and thank you again —
[*To Cynthia.   Cynthia curtseys.*
[*Green Workers bow and scrape and posture and present arms as she goes out of the room.   Then they form line and follow her to Dutch Dolls' March.*

CYNTHIA (*staring*).   That old Racketty-Packetty House!

CURTAIN

or Stage Darkening.

FINAL SCENE

Outside toy church — toy wedding chimes ringing.   Stage crowded with dolls fashionably dressed.   Green Workers bustling about.   Dolls crowd each other in lines before the church door, peeping over each other's shoulders — great excitement as if watching for somebody.   Tidy Castle crowd all dressed up; all wear coronets — even Lord Hubert, Lord Rupert and Lord Francis, but they are kept in background by footmen in scarlet and gold — powdered hair and long gold staves.   They keep pushing and struggling and are pushed back.

DUCHESS (*struggling to the front with her train bundled over her arm and her coronet on one side*).   I ought to be at the front. We ought all to be in the church.   I'm the Duchess of Tidy-shire, of Tidy Castle.

FOOTMAN (*pushing her back*).   Doesn't matter, your grace.   You don't belong to the Royal Nursery.

DUCHESS. But I'm a relation. We're all relations.

FOOTMAN. Don't know anything about that, your grace. You don't live in the Royal Nursery. Stand back.

SOME ONE IN CROWD. The Heralds are coming out to announce that the wedding is over.

HERALD (*comes out of church and stands on church steps : blows his trumpet*). By order of Her Royal Highness, I announce the marriage, in the Royal Nursery Church, of His Grace the Duke of Tags, of Racketty-Packetty House in Racketty-Packettyshire to the Lady Patricia Vere de Vere, of Tidy Castle in Cynthia's nursery. (*The bridal party approach*) Three cheers !

[*All cheer loudly.*

[*Enter from church Peter Piper, grandly dressed, with Lady Patsy in bridal costume, followed by Gustibus with Lady Meg, Peg, Kilmanskegg and Ridicklis, all mended and painted and beautifully dressed in Early Victorian fashion. When they reach bottom of steps, Duchess stretches her arms out wildly across the white silk rope dividing the crowd from the party.*

DUCHESS (*to Peter*). Your grace ! My adored Duke ! Speak — speak to your wonty, donty mother-in-law.

PETER PIPER (*putting up glass cheerfully*). I say, Patsy ! It's Maw !

LADY PATSY. It's all the family.

PETER PIPER (*to footman*). Let them through.

[*Footman drops white rope and they rush through, almost tumbling over each other.*

DUCHESS. My darling Peter. What happiness ! What joy ! What rapture ! And to think that once I scorned you. How could I scorn you ?

PETER PIPER (*cheerful advice*). I don't know. Never did. You take my tip. Never scorn any one. It's always a mistake — and sometimes you find it out. (*People are bowing and curtseying on all sides. Peter bows back flourishingly*) Patsy, I can't stand this. All these people bowing to us makes me feel as if I should have to stand on my head — and that wouldn't be dignified for a Royal Doll. (*Sudden inspiration*) Suppose we all join hands and dance round and round and kick up our heels as hard as ever we can. Suppose everybody does it. [*Racketty-Packettys, Tidy Castle family and Crowd make separate rings and dance madly to the music of Dutch Doll's Dance.*

CURTAIN

WAS THE EVIL KETTLE REALLY EVIL?

THERE still may be some people in the world who deplore the fact that the steam-engine was ever invented. Some years ago I made a visit to a very beautiful University town in the Great Smoky Mountain section of Tennessee. The railway wound itself amidst the most ravishing scenery; it took the most precipitous curves, which brought to view zigzagging paths leading farther into the dense forests. Yonder I could imagine the mountain folk, who never saw a newspaper, never heard a telephone, never were near a telegraph ticker — living their own lives, speaking their own language — an English very near to Shakespeare's.

The conductor stood by me and spoke. "They didn't like the railroad breaking into this section," he said, meaning by "they" the mountain clans, — "they thought it intrusion; they were real mad. So, what did they do when we ran the first engine and cars through but hide behind the trees and shoot at us as we passed."

It was wrong of them thus to defy Progress and break the law. There was much ignorance shown by them, for they did not realize that one reason why they were such strange Americans, so resentful of modern ways, was that they were far removed from cities. This locomotive, with its sputtering steam, its wail of a whistle, its smoking stack, and its clanging bell, was to break the silence of the hills, but was at the same time to bring nearer the mail and some of the comforts of civilization.

In New York, not so long ago, an old gentleman — the head of a prosperous Wall Street firm — scowled upon all new inventions. He had gotten along pretty well without them: he could go on a little longer without them. "Bah!" he exclaimed, "the telephones are pesky!" And he wouldn't have one of the things in his large office. "Nonsense," he declared, when it was suggested that he have some push buttons on his desk to summon his clerks, "no such thing. I'll call when I want one!" And he went home every evening in an old-fashioned cab, sniffing impatiently at hastening motor cars.

The history of Progress is full of such fights against change. Ask the average person, in these young days of airships, if we'll ever think it an ordinary event to fly across the ocean, and the answer will be, "Not in great numbers. That's not practical!" Yet, only recently, a very timid lady described enthusiastically a most beautiful trip she took on the Continent in one of the latest style passenger airships, and she wrote letters, seated at a desk in the cabin, while she passed over the ridges of the steepest Alps. Messages sent with wires : the telephone and telegraph; messages sent without wires and radioed! "It can't be done!" That is always the first cry.

So the stories connected with the discovery of the power of steam, by James Watt (1736–1819), and the application of steam to the locomotive by George Stephenson (1781–1848), are full of opposition from those who doubted. Here were two boys, without the opportunities of education, who became — of their own will — master mechanics, and who picked up learning as best they could. The one created wonders by merely watching the antics of a boiling teakettle, the steam from which clattered the kettle top and made the whole kettle tremble and sing most cheerfully. If the pent-up vapor could do such a thing to a teakettle, what might it not do as a motive power in a steam-engine?

Watt had better luck than Stephenson in convincing people of the serviceableness of his discovery. But the latter proposed to revolutionize travel : he proposed to construct a locomotive that would have driving force and speed. He dared to suggest that people go faster than three or four miles an hour! And his generation cried out against him, "Think of the danger; think how unnecessary!" They even declared, in an attempt to break up his schemes, that the very air would be so polluted with smoke from the dreadful monster that hens would refuse to lay eggs! But still the two persisted in their experiments and gave to the modern world the two greatest factors which have helped to weld the world closer together.

Lord Dunsany has taken Watt as his small hero in "The Evil Kettle", and has woven a very beautiful story about a simple incident. He gives us two boys in one : the Watt who is sensitive and shy, poetic and dreamy, who fears — as the mountaineers feared in Tennessee — that what might follow from the steam of his fireside kettle would eventually rob the world of much of its quiet beauty : make cities grow faster and thus help the work of the world to become more complicated. The other picture we have of the boy is the Inventor, full of will and enthusiasm to aid Progress by ferreting out every reason why the kettle trembled and the lid of it rose and fell.

Now, was the kettle really an evil one? It is just as you look at it. The crotchety old gentleman on Wall Street would probably have said "Yes" a thousand times over, and would have much preferred to go by coach, however long it took to travel a hundred miles! But the world would never have advanced, peoples would never have known as much of each other as they do, had Watt's pathetic cry to his mother been heeded. And there never would have been Kipling's rattling, throbbing story, "007." Think of that! Or his poem :

From aloe to rose-oak, from rose-oak to fir,
    From level to upland, from upland to crest,
From rice-field to rock-ridge, from rock-ridge to spur,
    Fly the soft-sandalled feet, strains the brawny, brown chest.
From rail to ravine — to the peak from the vale —
Up, up through the night goes the Overland Mail.

Maybe there are other plays written by Lord Dunsany which would be good reading for young folks — those plays of his, like "The Gods of the Mountains", which are as though some Oriental fairy tale had come to life. But I have chosen for inclusion here "The Evil Kettle" because it deals with Youth and the things Youth most dreams about. For long stretches of time I have stood with a certain small Boy before an early engine model and its coachlike railway carriages, and we have wondered much how this gentle little outfit ever made speed. Yet it went too fast for long ago. And here we are dreaming of the time when the distance between New York and Chicago will be a hop and a skip; and from New York to San Francisco, three hops and no skip. Perhaps little Jamie of Scotland was fearful of that. He was a dear boy for thinking of us so. And maybe he was right.

THE EVIL KETTLE

A ONE–ACT PLAY

By LORD DUNSANY

CHARACTERS

Mrs. Watt
James Watt
Satan

THE EVIL KETTLE

SCENE. *The House of Mrs. Watt.*

TIME. *Tea time.*

A room in a cottage. Window in center of back, looking out upon pleasant hills. Cupboard at right of back. Door right, near back. Table in center. Fireplace left. Couch or sofa along wall left, with head touching back. This is as I see it, but all details are unimportant except the hills, and should not fetter the initiative or fancy of a producer. James Watt, a lad of fifteen or sixteen, is leaning with folded arms on the window sill, looking at the hills. It is what is called a "costume play", period about one hundred and fifty years ago.

Mrs. Watt is laying the table-cloth.

MRS. WATT. Tea time.

JAMES WATT (*glancing over his shoulder and back again to window*). Yes, Mother.

[*He goes on looking at the hills.*

MRS. WATT (*going on smoothing out the table-cloth*). Come on.

JAMES WATT. How lovely the hills are, Mother.

MRS. WATT. The hills? Of course they are.

JAMES WATT. There's such a golden light on them.

MRS. WATT. Come and watch the kettle.

JAMES WATT. All right, Mother; in a moment. I do so want to look at the hills. They are so lovely.

MRS. WATT. It's past five.

JAMES WATT. And the woods along the top. All the beech came out yesterday. The woods are like brass. Aren't they lovely, Mother?

MRS. WATT. Of course they are. All God's work is lovely. Come and watch the kettle, dearie.

JAMES WATT. What is God's work, Mother?

MRS. WATT. All the things what was intended, of course.

JAMES WATT. Didn't He make everything?

MRS. WATT. Not the ugly things. Satan makes the ugly things.

JAMES WATT. What are the things that were intended, Mother?

MRS. WATT. Oh, questions, questions. What a boy it is to ask questions. I wonder if you'll be very wise when you grow up, for all the questions you've asked, or if you'll still be asking questions about everything. Deary me, I wonder.

JAMES WATT. Perhaps I'll be very wise, Mother, and still not know much.

MRS. WATT. I don't see as how that could be.

JAMES WATT. But what are the things that were intended, Mother?

MRS. WATT. Oh, well: woods and hills and flowers and butter-flies, and the wind and the rain and the crops, and birds and young girls and all that kind of thing. Satan just makes the ugly things. Come on, now.

JAMES WATT. But look at the hills, Mother, with that light on them.

[*She goes to the window.*

MRS. WATT. Yes, there they are. I remember them hills before you were born or thought of.

JAMES WATT (*meditatively*). And they're still just the same.

MRS. WATT. Well, I wouldn't say just the same. They seem a little smaller like.

JAMES WATT. But they couldn't be smaller, Mother.

MRS. WATT. Oh, I don't know. The hills are so old they might have shrunk a little.

JAMES WATT. But they couldn't do that, Mother.

MRS. WATT. And they seemed to be brighter, somehow. The summers was warmer when I was young.

JAMES WATT. What would have caused that, Mother?

MRS. WATT. Oh, bless the boy! How can I tell? It was a long time ago and the days just used to be brighter. Come and watch the kettle. Make the tea the moment it boils.

JAMES WATT. Very well, Mother.

[*She prepares teapot. He sits before the fire. She puts bread, plates, etc., on table. The kettle boils. Watt stretches out his*

THE EVIL KETTLE

James Watt. — "The lid is lifting up and down. There must be great force in it, Mother, to lift the lid like that."

hand to take it, then he draws it back. He clasps his hands round his knees and sits watching the kettle intently.

JAMES WATT. Mother.

MRS. WATT. Well, child, what is it now?

JAMES WATT. There must be great force in a kettle, Mother.

MRS. WATT. In a kettle, child? What ever do you mean?

JAMES WATT. The lid is lifting up and down.

MRS. WATT. Then it's boiling. Make the tea quick.

JAMES WATT. There must be a great force in it, Mother, to lift the lid like that.

MRS. WATT. Bless the child. That's only steam.

JAMES WATT. Mother. I've been thinking that if steam can do that, it might move a rod, mightn't it? And the rod might move a wheel.

MRS. WATT. Move a wheel, child?

JAMES WATT. Yes, Mother. And if we could set wheels moving, we could do all the work men have to do without ever using horses.

MRS. WATT. Stands to reason you couldn't do it without horses, whatever steam could do.

JAMES WATT. Why, Mother?

MRS. WATT. Why? Always asking why. Well, where does steam mostly come from? It goes up from the horses ploughing when they get hot. So where would you get your steam without them horses? You'd never get enough from them little kettles.

JAMES WATT. But Mother, I'll make big kettles.

MRS. WATT. Go on and make the tea. (*He pours water into the teapot*) You'll never get a cup of tea to do the work of a horse.

JAMES WATT (*puts teapot on fire while Mrs. Watt cuts bread, etc.*). I'll make big kettles when I grow up. (*He gazes at the kettle again*) Whenever the lids move, great iron bars will move with them. I'll fasten the bars to wheels, Mother, and I'll make steam do everything. All the work of the world would be done in the morning, and men could walk about the beautiful hills all the rest of the day.

[*Enters Satan right. He crosses the room and taps James Watt on his left shoulder. Stretching out his left arm, he beckons to the window and goes there, James Watt following, gazing dumbly. Satan is invisible to Mrs. Watt. She cannot see him, though looking straight at him. At the window Satan waves his left hand a few times upwards. Smoke as of factories rises up, covering the entire landscape. The noise and clangour are heard of the twentieth century. The smoke lifts and a factory city appears in all its devilish ugliness, with an unsightly yellow poster in the foreground, on which is written:* TAKE MEDICO. THE CURE FOR ALL AILMENTS. SO NICE. *The smoke thickens again and the city is covered. Again it lifts and shows the city: and so on.*

[*Satan points at it. The boy stares speechless. Satan slaps him on the back with cheerful encouragement. James Watt turns and stares at Satan with wide eyes and open mouth, motionless in horror at the idea that Satan's thanks were due to him for this. Satan nods to him.*

JAMES WATT (*in horror*). Oh!

[*Satan passes his hand backwards and forwards before the window as one rubbing out a blackboard. The city and smoke disappear, the hills come back and the noise of the twentieth century ceases.*

[*When Mrs. Watt hears James Watt say "Oh" she looks up.*

MRS. WATT. Why, Jimmy, what ever is the matter?

JAMES WATT. Oh, Mother, he wants me to do a dreadful thing.

MRS. WATT. Why, who wants you, child?

JAMES WATT. But I won't do it, Mother. I won't do it. (*To Satan*) I won't — I tell you I won't.

[*Satan smiles with scornful assurance.*

MRS. WATT. You won't what, child? You won't what? What ever is it?

JAMES WATT. I won't, I won't.

[*James Watt flies at Satan and beats him with his fists upon his bare black folded arms, not easily reaching higher. Satan goes on smiling with scornful assurance.*

MRS. WATT. Child, child, what has come over you? What ever are you doing?

[*She goes towards him anxiously. Satan steps back and bows gracefully to James Watt. Exit Satan.*

JAMES WATT. I won't. I won't.

MRS. WATT. Jimmy, Jimmy, what ever is the matter?

JAMES WATT. He wants me to invent a bad thing, Mother! He wants me to spoil our hills. He wants me to do it, Mother. He wants to cover our hills with dreadful things.

MRS. WATT. Who, child? Who? What ever is come over you?

JAMES WATT. He! He!

MRS. WATT. Where?

JAMES WATT. He is gone now.

MRS. WATT. Come to bed, Jimmy. Come and lie down.

JAMES WATT. He sha'n't spoil our hills.

MRS. WATT. Come along. Come and lie down, now.

JAMES WATT. He sha'n't spoil our lovely hills.

MRS. WATT. No, no. No one will hurt the hills. That's right, lie down, now. I'll look after the hills.

[*She takes his jacket off.*

JAMES WATT. I won't invent it. I won't.

MRS. WATT. No, and you sha'n't. Now your boots.

[*She takes his boots off.*

JAMES WATT. I'll never invent it.

MRS. WATT. No, of course you won't, dearie. Now you lie there while I get you something nice. (*He sits up*) Now lie still, dearie. Lie still. Do as Mother says.

JAMES WATT. But, Mother, I want to lock the door for fear he comes again.

MRS. WATT. Lie still, Jimmy.

JAMES WATT. But, Mother, I must lock the door.

MRS. WATT. I'll lock the door. No one shall come.

[*She locks the door. He lies down. She goes to cupboard. She takes out a bundle of weeds and selects three different varieties, three or four of each. She puts them together in a bunch and wrings the juice out of the stalks into a saucer. She pours the saucer into a cup and fills it with milk. James Watt all the*

while is stirring restlessly. She gives him the cup to drink and pulls the blind down and sits beside his bed.
There is now no light in the room but the red light of the fire, and it turns the steam from the kettle into a dull red glow.

JAMES WATT. You locked the door, Mother? You did lock the door?

MRS. WATT. Yes, dear, the door's locked. Go to sleep. Nobody shall disturb you.

[*James Watt is soothed and lays his head down.*

JAMES WATT (*quietly*). They sha'n't take our hills.

MRS. WATT. No, no, dearie. Go to sleep now.

[*He lies quiet. Reënter Satan through the solid middle of the locked door.*

JAMES WATT. Mother! Mother! He's come again. He's come again! Don't you see him? He's after our hills, Mother!

MRS. WATT. No one can come, child. I've locked the door. Go to sleep. Go to sleep.

JAMES WATT. He's squatting before the fire, Mother.

[*Satan has crossed the room and squatted down by the fire in front of the kettle.*

MRS. WATT. No, no, Jimmy. Go to sleep. It's only the steam from the kettle. I'm here; no one shall hurt you.

[*James Watt is silent but stares at Satan.*

SATAN. Oh, dear kettle. Evil kettle. Beloved evil kettle. Most dear, most evil kettle. Speak to him again, dear evil kettle. (*The kettle puffs out steam into Satan's face; its lid lifts up and down*) Yes, speak to him again. He has my work to do. Speak to him. Speak to him. We shall conquer the world, dear kettle, you and I. You are cold, poor kettle, poor evil kettle. But see; you shall be warm as never before. (*He puts his hand into the fire just underneath the kettle. Steam rushes from its spout, the lid shakes*) There, poor evil kettle, you are warm now. You are warm now, dear kettle.

[*He pats the kettle. Steam bursts up from under the devil's hand where he touches it.*

JAMES WATT. I won't. I won't. I won't invent it. I won't spoil our hills.

MRS. WATT. Invent what, child? Nothing can spoil our hills. Nothing can spoil them. Invent what?

JAMES WATT. Never mind what, Mother. It shall never be told. I'll never do it, Mother.

SATAN. Speak to him once again, beloved evil kettle. (*The kettle puffs out steam*) Speak to him, evil kettle. [*He goes over to the window and raises a corner of the blind and calls up black factory smoke outside with his left hand. He smiles, and waves it away with his right hand with the same motion as before.*

JAMES WATT. He wants to spoil our hills.

MRS. WATT. Go to sleep now, dearie, go to sleep. There's a good little boy. The herbs will do you a world of good if only you'll go to sleep.

JAMES WATT. But he'll spoil our hills if I don't watch him. (*Satan approaches the bed. He stretches out his right hand. He begins to move it before James Watt's face as if rubbing out a slate*) Mother! He's trying to make me forget! I won't forget. I won't forget. I'll remember. Mother! Help me, Mother. Mother! Never let me go near the kettle, Mother. Don't let me talk of the kettle. It's steam, Mother. Steam and the devil will spoil our hills. Oh, Mother, don't let me, don't let me. Tell me never to invent anything with steam. (*He grips her arm*) Promise me, Mother! Promise.

MRS. WATT. Yes, yes, dear, I promise.

JAMES WATT. Never with steam, Mother. I *won't* forget. They sha'n't spoil our hills. I — Oh, Mother.

MRS. WATT. Yes, dearie.

JAMES WATT. I'm sleepy, Mother.

[*Satan tiptoes out. James Watt sleeps. For a while Mrs. Watt sits quietly by the bed. Then she looks attentively at the boy's sleeping face and is satisfied.*

MRS. WATT. Ah, it's those good herbs.

[*She draws up the blind, revealing the cheerful hills, and goes on preparing the table for tea. She makes the tea and puts it on the table. Presently James Watt awakes.*

JAMES WATT. Hullo, Mother. What am I doing here?

MRS. WATT. You was took over queer, Jimmy. Are you all right now?

JAMES WATT. Yes, Mother, I'm all right now. What was the matter with me?

MRS. WATT. Took over queer you was. But I gave you those good herbs what I got from the hills, and they cured you, thank God. That's what He puts them on the hills for, Jimmy, among all the other flowers. They cures folk wonderful.

JAMES WATT. I'm all right now, Mother.

MRS. WATT. Could you fancy a cup of tea?

JAMES WATT. Yes, Mother. Proper, I could. (*He gets up and comes to the table. The kettle spouts noisily. James Watt sits down. The kettle splutters louder. James Watt takes up his cup of tea*) Thank you, Mother.

[*The kettle makes a still noisier outburst. Watt looks round. He rises and goes over to look at the kettle. He sits in the chair before the fire and looks at it. The kettle steams and the lid lifts: James Watt gazes at it.*

MRS. WATT. Come away from that kettle, Jimmy.

JAMES WATT. The kettle can't hurt me, Mother.

MRS. WATT. Come away from the kettle.

JAMES WATT. But I want to watch it, Mother. I want to watch the lid lifting.

MRS. WATT. Jimmy. When you was ill, you made me promise you something.

JAMES WATT. Did I, Mother? What was it?

MRS. WATT. Not to let you go near the kettle, Jimmy, nor to let you talk of steam. There didn't seem any sense in it; but there, I gave you my promise.

JAMES WATT. Did I, Mother? But Mother, I've been thinking while I was watching the lid lifting. I've been thinking that, if steam can do that, it might move a rod, mightn't it? And the rod might move a wheel.

MRS. WATT. Move a wheel, child? That's what you said before.

JAMES WATT. Yes, Mother. And if we could set wheels moving we could do all the work men have to do without ever —

MRS. WATT. Now come away, Jimmy, and stop thinking that nonsense. You made me promise, you know; and it didn't do you no good last time. You was took queer like. (*James Watt still gazes at the kettle*) Go and look at the hills, Jimmy, there's a good boy. There's good in the hills. (*He goes*) That's right, Jimmy. There's enough good in the hills to keep a body right, whatever trouble of mind he had. Go now and look at the hills. When you was quite a little boy, I used to leave you where you could look at them, and I'd go and get on with my work. I knew no harm could come to you from the hills.

[*James Watt stops halfway, pondering.*

JAMES WATT. Yes, Mother, they're wonderful; but Mother, I can't have made you promise not to let me talk of steam, I've thought of such a great invention with steam, Mother.

MRS. WATT. You made me promise and I promised you, Jimmy.

JAMES WATT. I can't have known what I was saying.

MRS. WATT. Well, anyway, keep away from the kettle, Jimmy. If I can't stop you talking, I promised you that. (*The kettle spouts away*) I don't like the looks of the kettle neither, now I come to notice. He seems to — it seems — but that's all nonsense. But anyway, keep away from it, same as I promised you. Look at the lovely hills, Jimmy.

JAMES WATT. But, Mother, I want to think. It's such a wonderful scheme I've thought of, Mother. It's to make steam do all the work that men have to do. The whole day's work, Mother, would be done in an hour, and every one would be free all the rest of the day.

MRS. WATT. Well, dearie, if you must have steam, get it from the plough horses when they're hot. Good honest beasts. But leave the kettle alone.

JAMES WATT. But, Mother, the kind of steam I want must come from kettles.

MRS. WATT (*giving way*). Oh, well. After all, bless the boy, what harm can he ever do with a cup of tea?
[*She looks at the hills. The sun sets.*
James Watt sits gazing at the kettle. The hills darken. The fire glows. And the kettle appears more evil.

CURTAIN

MISS EDGEWORTH'S LITTLE HEROES
AND HEROINES

MARIA EDGEWORTH (1767–1849) lived in a time when manners were very prim and staid. She had a father who was strict in the way he educated his household, and, while there was happiness in his family, there was also much severe discipline. The reading of children was so carefully supervised that, if a story contained passages not thought good for them, these same passages were either cut out of the book with scissors, or blotted out with a pen. The young in those days were to be seen and not heard: they stood whenever their elders came into a room; they never turned their backs to any one, but disappeared curtseying. Miss Edgeworth and her father believed that the best reading for girls and boys was to be found in Mrs. Barbauld's "Lessons." It was the age of the moral story, and if a fairy tripped into the pages of a book, her wings were clipped and she was promptly sent to her fairy bed.

Yet, notwithstanding the fact that the girls and boys of Miss Edgeworth's generation were staid and prim, they had their amusements. For instance, in the Edgeworth family, they gave private theatricals which afforded much exciting preparation. Birthdays, holidays were very festive with homemade performances. And it is a play written for one of these occasions that I have selected for inclusion in this "Treasury." There is a certain gentleness of manner in the good heroes and heroines of these dramas, contained in the volume of "The Parents' Assistant" entitled "Little Plays for Children" (London, 1827); there is an unmistakable sourness of manner in the characters of evil thought. "The Dame School Holiday" gives us both.

What quaint little misses and quaint little men
There lived in those quaint little days;
 How terribly prim they were,
 Prettily slim they were,
 Nattily trim they were,
Once when Miss Edgeworth wrote plays.

What precious behaviour and dutiful manner
They had in those excellent years;
 When boastful and vicious,
 The least avaricious,
 How deeply contritious
They grew to be, sweet little dears.

What mean little brothers and mean little sisters
There lived in those old-fashioned days:
 How shockingly bold they were,
 Awfully old they were,
 Sneeringly cold they were,
Once when Miss Edgeworth wrote plays.

How greedy those children when greedy they happened,
How terribly solemn in prayer;
 How old was the youth of them,
 Strict was the truth of them,
 Painful the ruth of them,
Once when Miss Edgeworth was there.

What quaint little dresses and quaint little tippets
They wore in those quaint little years;
 How sacred the deed to them,
 Awful the creed to them,
 Dutiful speed to them,
When they were good, little dears.

How horrid they were, when once they were naughty,
How wicked they were to the blind;
    How luckless the name of them,
    Hapless the shame of them,
    Lazy the aim of them,
When they were proud and unkind!

How tender the Dame with her little dame-scholars,
How kind to the children was she, —
    How sweet to each "ma-am" of them,
    Every pet lamb of them,
    Every soft tam of them,
Once when Miss Edgeworth drank tea.

What grace in their skipping, how charming their patter,
What questions they asked in their walk, —
    The quiety way of them,
    Piety way of them,
    Society way of them, —
Ancient in manner and talk.

What quaint little misses and quaint little men
There lived in those quaint little days:
    The ribbons and curls of them,
    The boys and the girls of them,
    Even the churls of them,
Once when Miss Edgeworth wrote plays!

THE DAME SCHOOL HOLIDAY

By MARIA EDGEWORTH

From "Little Plays for Children"
(London, 1827)

DRAMATIS PERSONÆ

DAME, an old village schoolmistress.
MISS BABBERLY
JENNY PARROT, her maid
ROSE . . . .
MARY . . . .
HANNAH . . . . } Children at the Dame's School
NANCY . . . .
WILLY . . . .
CHERRY . . . .
EDWIN . . . . } Children of the village
PHILIP . . . .   clergyman
FELIX, brother of Miss Babberly
A PEDLAR

THE DAME SCHOOL HOLIDAY

ACT I

Scene I

A new mown field. — Enter Cherry and Philip, carrying a large basket of green boughs and flowers.

CHERRY.   Here, Philip, let us set it down here, for I am quite tired.

PHILIP.   Tired! But you must not be tired, Cherry, consider that this is my father's birth-day, and we have a great, great deal to do! to make his room into a bower with these green branches and honeysuckles. Oh, it will be beautiful, with roses here and there, in garlands; and then we must make nosegays for papa and mamma, and aunts, and have a green bough for every house in the village. Oh! Cherry, indeed you must not say you are tired.

CHERRY.   Well, I will not: but I may say I am hot, may I not?

PHILIP.   Hot, are you? well, so I am, I must confess, hot enough, if that's all: but push your hat back as I do — off with this frillikin ruff that you have about your neck. There, now, sit down comfortably, and I will fan you with this great green fan. (*Fans her with a green bough*) Is not that pleasant, Cherry?

CHERRY.   Very pleasant, only I think it makes me hotter afterwards; besides, it must make you all the time so very hot doing it. Now, Philip, let us make our nosegays; that will cool us best. Here, this moss-rose bud I'll have for mamma.

PHILIP.   But it is not her birth-day.

CHERRY.   But she may have a rose for all that, may not she? Here, Philip, is a beautiful blush-rose for papa.

PHILIP.   Mamma should have the blush-rose, because she is a woman, and blushes. But I will tell you what, Cherry, it will not be right to give papa a red, and mamma a white rose.

CHERRY. Why?

PHILIP. Because it would seem as if they had quarrelled.

CHERRY (*laughing*). Quarrelled!

PHILIP (*gravely*). I assure you it is no laughing matter, as you would know if you had read the history of England, as I have. A great while ago, in the dark ages, the houses of York and Lancaster — but you are not old enough to understand me.

CHERRY. But I know *what* I am old enough to understand, and something that you don't know, Philip.

PHILIP. What?

CHERRY. Oh! that is a secret.

PHILIP. A secret! and you will not tell it to Philip!

CHERRY. No, not to Philip, or any body; for I was desired not.

PHILIP. By whom?

CHERRY. Oh! by somebody: but that's a secret too, and I have promised not to tell till the time comes, and the time will come this evening, this very evening — after dinner — after tea, you will see! — you will be very much surprised; and you will be very happy; and you will then know all.

PHILIP. I know all now, Cherry.

CHERRY. Oh! no, indeed, Philip, you do not know about Edwin.

PHILIP. Yes, but I do.

CHERRY. And about the play?

PHILIP. Oh! hush! take care — you promised not to tell.

CHERRY. But since you know it —

PHILIP. But how do you know that I know it?

CHERRY. My dear! did not you say so?

PHILIP. But you might tell me by accident more than I know; and I should be very sorry for that, because it would not be right.

CHERRY. Then the best way is for you to tell me, Philip, all that you know.

PHILIP. All that I know is, that my brother Edwin has written a little play, for my father's birth-day.

CHERRY. Ah! but I know the name.

PHILIP. So do I.

CHERRY. What is it?

[Enter Felix.

PHILIP. Oh! here's Felix come home at last — how do you do, Felix?

CHERRY. How do you do, Felix?

FELIX. Felix! Mr. Felix, I think you might say, children.

CHERRY. You are grown very tall, indeed, since you have been in London; you are quite a grown-up person now, I think.

FELIX. A grown-up person! yes, to be sure I am, Little-one.

PHILIP. But he is not as tall as our brother Edwin tho' — are you, Felix?

FELIX. How can I tell, I have not measured myself since I came from Lon'on.

PHILIP. Come, come then, and see Edwin directly, he will be so glad to see you!

CHERRY. And then you can measure yourself with him too.

FELIX. I have no desire to measure myself with him, I can assure you. To be in such a hurry to measure oneself is so childish.

PHILIP. Well, but it is not childish to be in a hurry to see one's friends, is it?

FELIX. That depends upon what sort of friends they are.

PHILIP. Sort of friends! what do you mean? I know of but one sort of friends — good friends.

FELIX. But I know several sorts of friends; and so will you when you have been in Lon'on. For instance, there are town friends and country friends.

CHERRY. And country mice and city mice. Do you remember fable, Felix?

FELIX. Not I; I have so many other things in my head now, ve no room for fables, I promise you.

PHILIP. Cherry, let us go on with our business.

FELIX. And what is your mighty business, pray? what's all this trumpery?

CHERRY. Trumpery! — Oh! Felix, don't kick my nosegays, they are for my father and mother, and this is my father's birth-day.

FELIX. What is your father's birth-day to me?

CHERRY. Nothing, perhaps; but do, pray then, if you *ple-a-se*, stand a little farther off.

FELIX. I won't stir.

PHILIP (*pushing*). You shall though! — for you have no right to trample on my sister's nosegays.

FELIX. Don't push me, or I'll make you repent.

PHILIP. You cannot make me repent it, for I know it is right to defend my sister, when she is trampled upon; and if you had been in London a hundred times, and a hundred million of times, you could not make me believe it to be wrong; and if you beat me to a jelly, you could never make me repent of it.

CHERRY (*putting herself between them*). Oh! don't quarrel, don't fight. Felix, here's a rose for you. Philip, he did not mean to do me any harm, I'm sure. Come, we had better go home and dress up my father's room — come, *dear* Philip, help me to carry this great basket; you see I cannot carry it by myself, and we shall be late, indeed we shall.

PHILIP. Well, I'll go with *you*, Cherry; but mind, I don't run, at least I don't run away from you, Mr. Felix; you may come after me and beat me, if you like it — and if you can.
[*Exeunt Cherry and Philip.*

FELIX. *Can!* you pigmy, you are beneath my notice. What a little savage it is! I expected to be treated with rather more respect at my return to the country; but these children have no manners — how should they indeed! And they don't know the difference between one person and another, they did not even take notice of my new coat.
[*Enter Edwin.*

EDWIN. Fe — (*aside*) no, it cannot be Felix. I beg pardon, sir, but I took you for a friend of mine.

FELIX. Very likely, sir.

EDWIN. It is Felix! I cannot be mistaken in his voice.

FELIX. Really — that's odd.

EDWIN. Come, come, Felix, shake hands, and don't play the fool; I am sure you must know me.

FELIX. Cannot you imagine it possible to forget you?

EDWIN. Not possible *for a friend* — what! forget your old play-fellow, Edwin — oh, you are only joking, you want to see how I shall take it.

FELIX. You don't *take* me, I find — did you never hear of *cutting* a man — of *dropping a fellow* — of *shirking a bore?*

EDWIN. Shirking a bore!

FELIX. You don't seem to see what I would be at: in plain English, you do not understand me.

EDWIN. No, indeed, I do not; but shake hands at any rate.

FELIX. Don't shake my arm off, like a country clown — look, this is the way to shake hands genteelly — "I am very glad to see you, Mr. Edwin Spencer — *d'y'do, d'y'do?* — hope I have the pleasure to see you in good health? and all your house, I hope, 'scaped the influenza? Do me the honour to remember my compliments to them; and do me the favour to tell me where you are, that I may leave my card the first opportunity." — Then bow or nod your head so, and pass on directly — that's *the thing.*

EDWIN. You are not serious? This is just like characters I have read of in plays. Well, I must *pass on*, as you call it, now, for I really am in a great hurry.

FELIX. In a hurry, in the country — what *can* you have to do?

EDWIN. That's a secret.

FELIX. A secret worth knowing, hey? but you don't understand me. "*Secrets worth knowing*" is the title of a play I saw when I was in Lon'on.

EDWIN. Would you like to see a play to-night? No — you would rather, I dare say, stay at home with your own father and mother, now you are just come back to them.

FELIX. As to that, I don't care; but what sort of a play, I wonder, can you possibly get up in this place; and what sort of a theater can you have — where on earth do you act?

EDWIN. At the bowling-green. You must not expect fine things; but as it is summer time, the audience can all sit out of doors; and we have carried the benches from the school-house — dear good Dame Deborah lent them to us; and she has worked so hard to make our dresses for us! and Mr. Hampden has lent us, not only the bowling-green, but the two summer-houses, and the alcove: that alcove makes the prettiest theatre!

FELIX. The prettiest theatre! it is a sign you have never seen a real theatre. Oh! if you had seen a real theatre, as I have!

EDWIN. I am glad I have not, because I should then perhaps be discontented with ours; and now, we all like it very much: and I do so hope my father will be pleased! Which way are you going now? If you pass by the school-house, do peep in, and you'll see them rehearsing "*The Sailor's Return*", that is the name of our little play. Willy Grant, whom you may remember, is to act the sailor, and he has a good notion of it, and he teaches the rest: come, do come! won't you? [*Exeunt.*

Scene II

A Dame School. — Dame Deborah in an arm-chair, knitting. — Children standing on each side of her, some with papers, as if getting by heart, some looking over the shoulders of their companions.

WILLY. Look, dear Dame, how well your Johnny's trowsers fit me! and see my sailor's jacket! now, don't I look like a sailor, just come home from sea? and hear how well I can whistle — (*whistles the tune of "'Twas in the good ship Rover"*) That was not quite the tune; if you would but sing it once for me, good Dame Deborah.

DAME. Ah! my dear boy, my singing days are over.

WILLY. Oh! no, no, that they are not; and I hope they never will be, whilst I am alive.

DAME. How the youngster talks! (*Stroking his head*) I shall be laid in my grave, long and long before you're a man.

WILLY (*stopping her mouth*). Don't talk of that, or you'll stop my whistling. (*Trying again to whistle*) I can't do it now.

DAME. Well, I must sing for you, I see.
(*Dame Deborah sings in a tremulous voice*)

> "'Twas in the good ship Rover,
>   I sailed the world around;
> And for three years and over,
>   I ne'er touch'd British ground.
> At length in England landed,
>   I left the roaring main;
> Found all relations stranded,
>   And put to sea again."

DAME. I forget the next verses, till we come to

"My precious limb was lopped off."

ROSE (*interrupting*). Oh! that about your precious limb, Willy, must be left out; for your leg must not be lopped off, because you are to dance a hornpipe.

WILLY. That's true; and I'll dance it this minute, that I may be quite perfect.
[*He dances a hornpipe.*

DAME. Very well! — very well done, my Willy! but you should have a little stick under your arm — that was the fashion, at least, in my days.

WILLY. I have one here, and I'll peel it quite white in a minute.
[*Sits down to peel the stick.*

ROSE. Dame, I have my part quite perfect now — don't you think so?

DAME. As to that, you will do well enough; only, my Rosy, take care not to speak so fast — and make your voice shake a little.

NANCY. Mine is a very, *very* long part, and I have a very, *very*, short memory; dear Dame, will you prompt me exceedingly loud — as loud as this? [*Bawling.*

DAME. The company, love, would hear that. Do not be frightened, and I dare say your memory will serve you very well.

NANCY. But how can I help being frightened before so many

people? Now, I am not the least bit afraid, when I am saying anything to you, Dame.

MARY. No, to be sure; who could be afraid of our Dame — except naughty children. Dame Deborah, will you lend me one of your nice plaited caps for this evening?

NANCY. And your black mittens and best shoes to me?

ROSE. And your nice silk handkerchief to me?

NANCY. And a white apron for me?

DAME. Aye, aye, dears — only patience — till I can find my keys.

NANCY. But, Dame Deborah, I have a great favour to ask — I am almost afraid.

DAME. Out with it! — you know, none are afraid of me but naughty children.

NANCY. Will you be so *very* good as to lend me your velvet hood? because I am to be a very old woman.

ROSE. Not at all, you are only to be a middle-aged sort of woman. Dame Deborah's black bonnet would just do for you, and the velvet hood for me, because I am to be a *really* old woman; a grandmother with a stick — this way.

NANCY. Very true; but Dame Deborah's Sunday bonnet! her best black bonnet! oh! I could not think of that, it's a great deal too good for me.

OMNES. Oh, yes, it is a great deal too good for us to meddle with.

DAME. My dear children, I do not think anything I have in this world is too good for you. To be sure, that's little enough, but such as it is, you are heartily welcome, for you are good children, and I love you, one and all. It is the greatest pleasure I have on earth to see you happy, dears, and in your own innocent plays to help you all I can. Here, Rose, love, take this key, for you understand a lock, and unlock yonder press, and there you may suit yourselves to your fancies; only don't lose my black silk mittens; and leave me one clean cap for this evening, dears. (*The children go to rummage — Dame Deborah, aside*) They are as good children, I will say *that* for them, though I should not praise 'em, being all, I may say, my own, as much as if they were all born my own; they are as good children as any on the face of this earth — always speaking the truth; and honest, so that I could trust them anywhere, and with anything, or anybody; — then so dutiful, so willing and obedient, so sweet-tempered, and so grateful for the little one does for them! Expert enough at their needles too, and for their ages no ways backward at their books! — but these are not the first things with me. Their duty to their God and their neighbour, first and foremost, I have taught them, to the best of my ability; and if I die to-morrow, I shall die with a clear conscience on that score. But this is no time to talk of dying. — Well, dears, have you found all you want?

ROSE. Oh, yes, yes; thank you, thank you, Dame. Look how well the velvet hood suits me; and though your shoes have high heels, and are rather too large, Dame, see, I can walk in them exceedingly well.

WILLY. Girls, never mind your heels, and hoods, and caps, and bonnets, but let us try and do better that part of my coming home. Here, Rose, you are to be my grandmother — here's your stick, and here's your spectacles; sit you down in the great chair, reading of your book. Now, grandmother, remember, you must not know me too soon, or you spoil all. I seem, you know, only a strange gentleman as it were; and what's that to you? So you keep on minding your book, you know, natural like; and you must not stare at the passenger; and do remember that you are very, *very* old.

ROSE. Aye, sure; have not I a velvet hood, see, tied under my chin.

WILLY. But that won't do quite of itself. It won't do if you jump about so nimbly, and turn your head so quick and smart. You must keep in mind that your eyes be dim, and that you can't see without your spectacles; and you must stick 'em on your nose without laughing — this way — natural-like; and take 'em off, and wipe 'em slow, with your apron, as our Dame does; and then put your finger in your book, to keep your place; and hold the spectacles, so — do try to look like a real old woman.

ROSE (*sits in the attitude of an old woman*). Is that it? I hope I am old enough now to please you, and slow enough too: I cannot, for the life of me, be slower than this; and Master Edwin himself said I was slow enough last time; but you are more particular, by a great deal, than he; howsomever, I'll not be cross. Am I cross, Dame Deborah?

DAME. Not more than an old woman may be — an old woman may be cross sometimes.

ROSE. But you are never cross; and I will be such an old woman as you are.

WILLY. That will do bravely, Rosy. (*Fixes her hand in the proper position*) Now, all I ask of you, Rosy, is to take heed not to know me, till the old dog jumps up and licks my hand. First, when he comes up smelling, you are to call him away, and bid him not to be troublesome to the gentleman — you must call out, "Keeper! Keeper! come hither! come hither, sir!" But the dog knows better; he keeps wagging his tail, and won't go back to you; then he jumps up, and puts his paws on my breast; and you cry, "Down! down!" in a fuss, because of his dirty paws: then he licks my hand.

ROSE. And then I may speak, sure? And then I may throw down my spinning-wheel, and cry, "My boy, Willy! my own good grandson, Willy!"

WILLY. But stay; we are not come to that yet. Where's the real dog — Keeper! Keeper! Keeper! He'd come to my whistle if he was at the land's end. (*Whistles*) Keeper! Keeper! Keeper! I'll have him here in a trice. (*Exit whistling*) Sit still, Rosy — stock still.

DAME. But I be sadly afraid, when Willy has him, Keeper will never do his part right.

ROSE. Oh! dear Dame, if you'd teach him your own self, he could not but learn.

DAME (*shaking her head*). Ah! my child, he's too old to learn; and I do not know how to teach dogs; I had rather teach you ten hundred — that is to say, one thousand times over.

ROSE. Oh! I wish Willy and his dog would make haste, for I'm tired sitting stock still, waiting for him; and my hand

has the cramp, so it has. I wish he would come — do look out for him. Daisy! What have we here?
[*Enter Jenny Parrot, with band-boxes.*

JENNY. Dear heart! pity me! Such a load — so hot up the hill; and such rough road! Haven't walked so much this twel'month, except in Lon'on streets, which is as smooth as my hand.

DAME (*aside*). Rosy, my spectacles, dear; they're on your nose. Who is it? (*Aloud*) Jenny Parrot! welcome, welcome, Jenny — sit ye down.

JENNY (*throws herself into the Dame's chair*). I ha'n't a leg to stand upon, I vow and purtest.

DAME. Tired after your journey? 'Tis a long journey enough — when did you get home?

JENNY. Last night *at* tea.

DAME. And we not know till now! Well! if your mother had been alive, she'd have been here to tell me, if it were ten o'clock at night even, that she had come. But I won't scold; you are very good to come at all; for, may be, you are wanted at home.

JENNY. No, no; my young lady sent me here this minute. Besides, as to being wanted, I'm my own mistress for else I shouldn't condescend to stay with her for I could have got places enough and with the quality in Lon'on. Oh! Lon'on is a fine place! 'Tis a pity you were never there, Mistress Deborah.

DAME. Call me Dame, if you be pleased, Jenny Parrot.

JENNY (*speaking very quickly*). Well, Dame Deborah, as I was saying, you've no notion of all the fine things I've *seed* since I *seed* you, such loads of fine ladies and fine gentlemen and *milliners* and mantua-makers and lace and ribbons and coaches and fans and di'monds and feathers and flowers and farces and balls and Sadler's Wells and lions and bears and and the *Tow'r* and St. Paul's and bonnets and caps and the king and the queen and the princesses and the wax-work.

DAME. Take breath, Jenny.

JENNY. Breath, forsooth! d'ye think I'm in an asthma? Why,

I could talk ten times as much without ever taking breath except you put me out.   Where was I?   Oh!   *Mrs. Jane*, says my young lady to me (for nobody, Dame, ever calls me any thing but *Mrs. Jane*), we must see everything, Mrs. Jane — says she.   Says I, To be sure ma'am 'tis so fitting for a young lady like you to see everything that is to be seen.   So hurry skurry went we, dress dress dress; rattle rattle rattle.   Lord! you'll not know my young lady again; every tittle *on* her spick and span new from the top *on* her head to the sole *on* her foot, silk stockings and all flesh coloured!   Miss Babberly was always tasty.   But how now, children! for your life don't lay your dirty fingers on that there band-box.

DAME.   Their fingers be seldom or never dirty, I will say that for them.   But stand back, dears, for you have nothing to do with band-boxes, and I am not sorry for it — no offence.

JENNY.   But if you *knewed* what was in that band-box — but I'm to be mumchance — my young lady's to tell all.   Good-bye to you, Dame.   I've not had time to say a word yet but some other day — some other time — not a *syllabil* am I to say till Miss Babberly comes.

DAME.   Miss Babberly!   Is she coming here?

JENNY.   Aye is she — will be here by and by — didn't I tell you so? that was what I came to say.   Miss Babberly sent me on to give ye notice and wouldn't let me stay to finish dressing *on* her out.

DAME.   *Dressing her out!*   To come here!

JENNY.   No, no; but to go through the village.   Folks would stare indeed if she *wa'n't* dressed *somew'at* extr'ordinary, just come from Lon'on.   Well I'm glad she didn't come along with me for when she's by there's no getting in a word endways or edgeways or anyways; she likes to have all the talk to herself, that's the plague of it.   Now I must be going to the bowling-green to tell the Lon'on news, and then to Squire Strut's, for his nurse's maid's my foster brother's sister, so for old relation's sake must give her a call, and then to Mrs. Blair's, for her housekeeper's brother's son's married to my cousin-german Peggy Patten, you know, so she must have a

call. Lord! when one comes from Lon'on one has so many friends to call upon and so much to do and so much to say one ha' need have a *hundered* heads and a thousand legs and a *hundered* thousand tongues, so good-morrow to you, Dame — I ha'n't had time to say a word to you but will presently. Children, not a finger on the band-boxes on your peril!
[*Exit Jenny Parrot.*

DAME. Well, if her poor tongue be not tired before night, it will be a wonderful tongue. But I loved talking once upon a time myself, I remember; and we must not expect to find gray heads upon green shoulders, especially when just come from London. Children, dears, let us carry these band-boxes; they will be safer there —

ROSE. But you know we must not lay a finger upon them for our lives, Dame.

DAME. Then open the door for me, and I will carry them myself; though, to my knowledge, I never carried a band-box in my life before.
[*Exit Dame, carrying a band-box. Rose, Mary, and children follow.*

ROSE. Oh! if the band-box should open!

MARY. Oh! if it should fall!

ROSE. I'm glad I'm not to carry it. I wonder what's in it!
[*Exeunt.*

ACT II

SCENE I

Edwin, Philip, and Cherry — Edwin writing at a small table.

CHERRY. Make haste! make haste! write very fast, as papa does.

EDWIN. When I have finished all these notes, you will fold them up, Cherry; and Philip will seal them.

CHERRY. But let me seal some, Philip — only let me press the seal down, will you? I am old enough for that.

PHILIP. We shall see. Have you written to invite everybody in the village, Edwin?

CHERRY. Let us count how many notes are there — one, two, three.

[*Enter Felix. — Edwin rises and comes forward. — Philip and Cherry remain at the table folding notes.*

FELIX. Well, I've called, as you desired, to see the children's theatre.

EDWIN. Thank you; and do you think it will do?

FELIX (*whips his boots, and sneers*). Why, as to that, if you ask my opinion, as a friend, candidly, I think the thing will be a horrid bore: it will never do, even for the country — take my advice, and give it up.

PHILIP AND CHERRY. Give it up! give it up! Oh, no, Edwin, don't give it up.

CHERRY. I am sure papa and mamma will like it.

PHILIP. And all the poor children, and Dame Deborah, and everybody would be so much disappointed. Oh! don't give it up.

EDWIN. Perhaps, Felix, you could show me some of the faults, that I might mend them.

FELIX (*sarcastically*). 'Pon my honour, I see no faults *that can be mended*. But why did not you take some real play; some of the new plays that have been acted in Lon'on? then we might have had a chance of some fun, instead of all this stupid stuff, about children and grandmothers and old nurses.

EDWIN. I never saw any of the new plays.

FELIX. Never! then how could you, my dear fellow, possibly think of writing anything in the dramatic line, as they call it?

EDWIN. You know, mine is only a little play for children.

PHILIP. But will you, Felix, who have seen so many of these grand plays that have been acted in London, tell us what sort of things they are?

FELIX. Oh, I could not make such children as you understand anything about them.

EDWIN. But perhaps I could understand them. Try, will you?

FELIX. Really I don't remember exactly: I've seen so many, they are jumbled together in my head; and they are so like

one another, there's no telling 'em asunder.   There's a ******
good character in one — I forget which.

CHERRY (*aside to Philip*).   Did you hear the word Felix said
before *good character?*

FELIX.   A ****** good character, upon my honour.   There's
a man that's a buck, and has been a tailor; and he's always
saying, *Push on! keep moving! push on! keep moving!*

EDWIN.   But is that all he says?

FELIX.   All that I remember.   You know, one only remembers
the good things.

EDWIN.   Well, but I suppose he does something very divert-
ing.

FELIX.   Yes, that he does.   He tears his coat; and his father
takes it off to mend it.

EDWIN.   Upon the stage?

FELIX.   Yes, upon the stage: for the father was a tailor too,
therefore it was quite *in character* — quite natural.   So the
son stands without his coat; and whilst he is standing in that
condition, a fine lady with a great fortune, whom he is court-
ing, comes pop in upon them; and then he scrambles and
shuffles himself into his coat, this way (*imitates*); and he,
or the father tailor, I forget which, sits down upon the
needle, and pricks himself; and then all the house clap, and
cry, encore! encore!

EDWIN.   But this is a farce, is not it?

FELIX.   No, no, it's a comedy: surely I must know, that have
been in Lon'on, and have read the play-bill.   The farce
always comes after the play — do you understand?   First
there is a tragedy, or else a comedy, do ye see; and afterwards, a farce.   Now this did not come afterwards, so it
could not be a farce, you know; and it could not be a
tragedy, because there was no killing, and it ended happily;
so it must be a comedy.

EDWIN.   But are all things that are neither tragedies nor farces,
comedies?

FELIX.   To be sure, what else can they be, unless they are
operas; and those are all singing almost.

EDWIN. But *all* the new comedies cannot be like this, Felix?
What other characters do you remember?

FELIX. I don't recollect any in particular; but I know in
general, there is always a dasher, a buck, a dandy; and he
must walk *this way*, and stand *this way*, and lounge *this way;*
and he must swear and slash about; and he must have a whip,
or a little stick; and his neck must be made as thick as his
body with cravats over his chin — that's his character.

EDWIN. His dress, you mean.

FELIX. Well; but I tell you, the dress makes the character.

EDWIN. Oh, I did not know that.

FELIX. For sometimes a man that's dressed in character, makes
the house roar before he has said a word. Then there must
be a fine lady, a flirt, a coquette; and she must be dressed too,
in the tip, tip, top of the fashion; and she must stare *this
way*, or put up her glass so; and everybody, squires, and
baronets, and lords, and all, must be in love with her; I mean
if she has a large fortune; and if she has nothing, then some
ridiculous old, old man, hobbling *this way*, must be in love
with her, and she must *quiz* him.

PHILIP. *Quiz* him! what's that?

FELIX. Pshaw! I can't explain it — but everybody knows —
those that aren't in the fashion are *quizzes;* and all poor
people, and old people, uncles and aunts, mothers and fathers
in wigs, are quizzes, and always are quizzed in the new plays;
without them, there could be no fun. Why do you look
so stupid, child? [*To Philip.*

PHILIP. Because I do not understand what you mean by quizzing, and quizzed, and quiz.

CHERRY. Look in the dictionary, cannot you, Philip?

EDWIN. You will not find it in the dictionary, my dear.

FELIX. No, no, because it is a fashionable word. How can
you be so stupid, child! it means taking a person in — making
them look like fools — making a joke of them.

PHILIP. But then, what did you mean by quizzing fathers, and
mothers, and uncles, and aunts, and poor people, and old
people?

FELIX (*with infinite contempt*). Child! I wish you would not pester me with such foolish questions: what can you know of the world, and how can I explain these things to *you?*

CHERRY. Come away, Philip, let us mind our business, and seal the notes — I'll light the candle. [*Exit Cherry.*

FELIX. Where was I? Oh, besides a fine dashing gentleman, and a fine dashing lady, and some quizzical old people, there must be attorneys and apothecaries that are always ridiculous; and there must be an Irishman to make blunders, and talk with the brogue; and there must be a Frenchman to talk broken English, and say *dis* and *dat*, and a few words of French — *comme il faut* — *je ne sais quoi* — *pardonnez-moi* — *tout au contraire;* and then the scenes must change very often; and there must be some good songs — nonsense-songs.

EDWIN. What do you mean by nonsense-songs?

FELIX. Oh, anything will do, if you sing it well; for instance (*sings*) —

> With a wig-wig-wag;
> With a jig-jig-jag;
> With a crick-crick-crack;
> With a nick-nick-nack;
> With a whack-whack-whack,
> On the back-back-back.

PHILIP. Oh, Felix! but *really!* it is like a little child's song.

FELIX. No matter what it is like, it is very much admired — quite the rage. (*Reënter Cherry with a candle*) But this is nothing to "*The Little Farthing Rushlight.*" Give me that candle, Cherry, and you shall hear it.

[*Felix sings "The Little Farthing Rushlight."*

PHILIP AND CHERRY (*laugh*). Oh, Felix! it is impossible that grown up people can be so very silly.

FELIX. Silly! nothing's silly that's the fashion.

[*Enter a servant.*

SERVANT. Mr. Edwin, there's a pedlar below; he has a load of fine things: toothpick-cases, and pins, and broaches, and watches.

FELIX. Who would look at such travelling fellow's trumpery, that has been in Lon'on?

EDWIN. We do not want anything — don't keep the poor man waiting.

CHERRY. But, Edwin, let us look at the pretty boxes and things.

PHILIP. And the watches! Oh, Edwin! let us look at the watches.

EDWIN. As we do not intend to buy anything from this man, we should not give him the trouble of opening his pack.

PHILIP. No; to be sure we should not.

EDWIN. Tell him that he need not wait.

SERVANT. Sir, the poor man fell against a stone, and has cut his leg sadly.

EDWIN. Cut his leg! Let us go and see him, perhaps we can do some good.

[*Edwin going.*

CHERRY. Oh! I know an excellent thing — lint! Dame Deborah said so — Dame Deborah is the best person in the world for lint, when I cut my hand. Oh, Philip! stay for me.

PHILIP. Come along then, quick.

[*Exeunt Philip and Cherry.*

FELIX. Lord! what a fuss about a cut on a pedlar's shin: why, if it was the king, or my lord mayor himself, they could not run faster. But poor children, they know nothing of the world — how should they? (*Goes to the table and looks at the notes*) Heyday! what a parcel of notes — invitations to the world and his wife, to see this foolish play. Edwin thinks to have all the village at his beck, I see; and to be lord of the manor, and king over us all! But it sha'n't do — it sha'n't do. He may invite as many people as he pleases; but I'm too sharp for him. His play shall not be acted to-night, that I'm resolved upon. I'll outwit him yet, or my name's not Felix.

[*Exit.*

Scene II

*The Dame School — Dame Deborah in her great chair, knitting.
— Enter Miss Babberly.*

MISS BABBERLY. So, Dame Deborah, are you alive still?
Looking, for all the world, just as you used to do, before I
went to Lon'on.

DAME. Aye, Miss, just as I used to do; and I hope, Miss,
you are the same.

MISS BABBERLY (*aside*). *The same!* Has the old trowdledum
no eyes? (*Aloud*) Why, Dame Deborah, you must be as
old as Paul's ; or the Monument, at least; I remember you
sitting in that very chair, knitting, ever since I was born.
La! how tired you must be; and every one of the old things,
and the Bible and all, just the same as before I went to
Lon'on. La! how dull you must be; and have you only
the old little corner of a garden (*looking out*), that you used
to have?

DAME. No more, Miss; but I be happy — at your service.

MISS BABBERLY. Why, how can you be happy with such a little
bit of a thing? Our town garden is twenty times as big; and
I and papa are always fretting because it is not bigger.

DAME. Ah, Miss! a little thing will make a person happy, if
they be so inclinable; and all the great things in this mortal
world will not do as much, if they be not so inclined.

MISS BABBERLY. Very true, very likely; but I did not come
here to be preached to. Pray, did not my maid, Jane, leave
a band-box here?

DAME. Aye, she did (*going for the band-box, and bringing it out*);
and here it is safe, Miss. What would you be pleased to
have done with it?

MISS BABBERLY (*opening it*). In the first and foremost place,
Dame, you must do something for me.

DAME. Any service in my power, and in reason, and right,
you may be sure of from me, Miss Babberly; for I loved your
mother from the time she was this high, learning her criss-

cross row at my knee; she was as sweet a child, God bless her, as —

MISS BABBERLY (*interrupting*). Aye, I dare say she was. I wonder they did not send her to a Lon'on school; but that's over now. Look here, Dame Deborah (*opening the band-box*), look at this elegant silk shawl handkerchief, as good as new; I never wore it, but at my Lady Grimdrum's one night, and once at Vauxhall, and once at Ranelagh, and twice at the play. I don't know what my maid, Mrs. Jane, will say to my giving away so good a thing, which, by right, ought to be hers; but here, Dame, take it, and now —

DAME. I ask your pardon, Miss, I cannot take it. It would not become me to wear such a fine thing; but I am as much beholden to you as if I took it; and glad, moreover, I am, to see you have so much of your mother's heart, to think when far away of a poor old woman.

MISS BABBERLY (*aside*). La! how she mistakes; I'm sure I never thought of her when I was away. (*Aloud*) Come, come, take this shawl, without more parading or palaver; and throw away this horrid dowdy thing that looks as if you had worn it these hundred years.

DAME. No, Miss, no: with your good leave, I value this, plain serge though it be, above all the shawls, silk or other, that ever can be; for it was made of the spinnings of my dear children, two generations of them; and your own sweet mother had her hand in it. I think I see her now, a-turning that very wheel yonder, under my own eye, for the first time. Pretty soul! God bless her little fingers!

MISS BABBERLY (*aside*). She's doting, certainly. She'd talk for ever, if I'd let her, I believe.

DAME (*after wiping her eyes*). Well, Miss Babberly, pray be pleased to tell me what I can do to serve you; for 'twill be a satisfaction to me to do anything, be it ever so little, for your mother's daughter.

MISS BABBERLY. What I want, in truth, is little enough — only your old school-benches for to-night.

DAME. Ah! you should be heartily welcome to them, Miss,

only that I have promised them to Master Edwin for to-night;
'tis his father's birth-day, and he has made a little play for
our young folks to act; and all the village, and even old I,
reckon to be at the bowling-green this night, by six o'clock.

MISS BABBERLY. Well, well, I know all that; but my brother
Felix and I have a scheme of our own, and we must have
the benches, do you understand; and we'll show your young
folks how to do something better worth seeing by all the
village, than this nonsensical play of Master Edwin's, as you
call him. What can he know of plays — he that has never
been in Lon'on?

DAME. Indeed, Miss Babberly, I cannot say as to that: but
this I know, that I have promised him my benches.

MISS BABBERLY. Pooh! what signifies your promise?

DAME. *My promise!* what signifies it, Miss! Poor as I am,
my promise is as much to me — as much, aye, as mountains
of shawls would be to you, Miss Babberly.

MISS BABBERLY. La! how the woman talks.

DAME. Though I be *nobody*, I would not break my promise,
look you, for anybody upon earth, Miss: not for the queen's
majesty, if so be she were to come down from her throne in
her royal robes, and crown upon her head, to this poor cottage,
and say to me, "Dame Deborah, break your word for me, and
I'll make you a duchess": I would make answer — "No,
please your queenship, I have a soul to be saved as well as
your majesty's ladyship; and as to being a duchess here
upon earth, I reckon to be soon an angel in heaven."

MISS BABBERLY. You an angel! you look wondrous like one,
indeed! you must alter greatly before you are an angel.

DAME. True, Miss Babberly; and great alterations do come
to pass in a short time, as we see in people even here upon
earth.

MISS BABBERLY. So the short and the long of it is, that you
won't lend us your old benches.

DAME. I cannot, Miss, having promised to lend them to another.

MISS BABBERLY. La! you could make an excuse, if you had

but a mind. Could not you say that you did not know we was to come home; and that you'd promised them first, long ago, to me?

DAME. Would not that be a lie, Miss?

MISS BABBERLY. Dear me, no; that's only called an excuse in Lon'on.

DAME. I never was in Lon'on, Miss; (*aside*) and wish you had never been there neither, if this is all the good you've learnt by it.

MISS BABBERLY. Keep your old benches to yourself then; I'll be bound we'll do as well without them; and I'll answer for it, I'll get your *little dears* to do what we want in spite of you.

DAME. It will not be in spite of me, Miss, if it be anything right that you want of them; and in spite of you — no offence meant, Miss Babberly — they will not do anything that's wrong.

MISS BABBERLY. Right or wrong, I'll make them do whatever I choose. (*Dame shakes her head*) That is, when you are not by to shake your head at them, and frighten them out of their wits.

DAME. As to that, they ben't a bit afraid of *me*, Miss; 'tis only of doing wrong they be taught to be afraid; I will not say a word to them, one way or other, but just stand by, this way; and do you ask them, Miss Babberly, what you please: if it be right, they'll say, yes; if wrong (*striking her stick on the ground*), they'll say, no!

MISS BABBERLY (*softening her voice*). Oh, come, come, Dame Deborah, don't be so stiff and cross, but do you get them to do what I want. I only just want these children to give up acting this foolish play of Edwin's; and my brother and I will show them how to act a much better.

DAME. Oh! surely, Miss Babberly, you would not ask them to do such an ill-natured thing by poor Mr. Edwin, when he has taken such pains to get this little play ready for his father's birth-day.

MISS BABBERLY. He was very ill-natured to me; he did not

dance with me this time last year at the ball; and one bad turn deserves another.

DAME. And can you, Miss Babberly, remember to bear malice a whole year? No, no, take my advice.

MISS BABBERLY. I don't want any advice — I hate advice — all I ask of you is to let me see the children — where are they?

DAME. They be out in the field hard by; but if I ring this little bell, they will be here in a trice.

MISS BABBERLY. Ring it then — ring it directly.

DAME. Ah! my dear Miss Babberly, *do-ye'* think a bit, and you'll not go to do a spiteful thing, and you'll not go to spoil all the sport of these innocent little ones, and breed ill-will, especially on this happy day. (*Dame Deborah lays her hand affectionately on Miss Babberly's arm*) Ah! my dear Miss, think a bit, think a bit, *do-ye'!* pray!

MISS BABBERLY (*shaking her off*). I have thought long enough, and I hate thinking. Ring! ring! that's all I want of you: ring, ring, and no more preaching — if you won't ring, *I* will. [*The Dame sighs, and leans on her stick. — Miss Babberly snatches the bell and rings.*

Scene III

Enter the children. — Miss Babberly, taking artificial flowers out of a bandbox.

MISS BABBERLY. Come, children! I want you to do something for me. Look at these beautiful things, just fresh from Lon'on. I'll give you these, if you'll do what I want. [*All the children exclaim:* "How pretty! how pretty!"

NANCY. How like a real lilac! — I should like to have that pretty bunch of laburnums.

MARY. And these roses — oh! how pretty they are; but they have no smell. I would much rather have the real sweet roses in our Dame's garden.

MISS BABBERLY. But real roses wither in a minute. Now, you may stick these artificial flowers in your bonnet, and they will last for ever. Don't they look pretty this way? [*Placing them in Mary's hat.*

HANNAH (*laughing*). They look very odd, Mary, in your old hat. I don't think they are suited to us poor children.

MISS BABBERLY. Very likely — yet they are quite the fashion, I assure you.

ROSE. But we know nothing of fashion — we care nothing for fashion!

MISS BABBERLY (*aside*). They are the most stupid, countrified creatures I ever saw. (*Aloud*) But only consider, Mary, how this becomes you!

MARY. Indeed, Miss, I thank you kindly, but I do not think it would become me at all to wear such things — would it, Dame?

[*Dame Deborah puts her finger on her lips, and is silent.*

MISS BABBERLY. But, Hannah, this necklace; would not you like to have this?

HANNAH. No, Miss, I am obliged to you, I have no wish for it; I have no use for it.

ROSE. Would you be pleased to tell us at once, Miss, what it is that you want us to do for you? because if we can do it we will, without any presents.

MISS BABBERLY. Why! I only want you to give up acting this foolish thing for Mr. Edwin, and my brother Felix and I will show you how to do an *impromptu* of our own invention: then you will have nothing to get by heart, and will have an elegant supper ready for you after it's over; and sweetmeats of all sorts; and *everybody*, that is, all the company we have in our house from Lon'on, will admire you.

MARY (*to Rose, aside*). Sweetmeats of all sorts! do you hear that?

HANNAH (*aside*). Oh! I should like sweetmeats very much.

MISS BABBERLY (*aside*). Ha! ha! I see the sweetmeats will do the business.

ROSE (*aside to Mary*). But then, I would not break my word for sweetmeats — would you, Mary?

MARY (*aside to Rose*). No, to be sure.

HANNAH (*aside to Mary and Rose*). No, no, we must not do that.

ROSE (*aside to Mary and Hannah*). Beside, Mr. Edwin is always so good to us.

MISS BABBERLY. Well, children, do you intend to keep me here all day — yes, or no?

ROSE. No, thank you, Miss; we are much obliged to you; but we cannot break our promise, you know, with Mr. Edwin.

MISS BABBERLY. Speak for yourself only, if you please, Miss Pert; do not say *we*, for I dare say there are many here who are not of your mind. [*The children all exclaim:* "No! not one! not one! Rose has said what we all thought."

DAME. This is just what I expected from you, my dear children. (*She goes to kiss them*) I told Miss Babberly so: I advised her —

MISS BABBERLY. Don't talk of advising me, you preaching old woman!
[*Pushes the crutch from under Dame Deborah, as she stoops, and throws her down.*

CHILDREN (*exclaiming*). She pushed our Dame down!
[*Some of them help the Dame up, while Mary catches hold of Miss Babberly's hands, and Rose throws Miss Babberly's shawl over the young lady, and winds it round her whilst she struggles and screams.*

DAME. My dears, what are you about? she could not mean to do me any harm.

ROSE. Oh, yes she did, she did; and now we have her hands safe.

MISS BABBERLY. Impertinence! Insolence! Children! Brats! Let me go! You shall be all put in jail — papa will put you all in the pillory for this — if you don't let me loose this minute.

ROSE. Not till you have asked our Dame's pardon.

MISS BABBERLY (*struggles in vain, crying loudly*). Let me loose! — let me loose, children!

DAME. My dears, this must not be. I will let you loose, Miss, if you will only be still. (*She unwinds the shawl, and sets Miss Babberly at liberty*) You know, my dear children, we should return good for evil.

MISS BABBERLY. You shall all suffer for this, I promise you.
[*Exit Miss Babberly.*

ROSE. Miss Babberly, you have left your band-box.

DAME. Run after her with it, Rosy, and carry it to her house.
Pray be civil, my child. You will find me, when you come
back, sitting out under the great tree in the meadow, hearing
these little ones their parts; and do you come and say yours,
do you mind me, Rose?
[*Exeunt.*

SCENE IV

*A room, ornamented with boughs, and garlands, and flowers —
Edwin, Philip, and Cherry.*

PHILIP (*on the top of a step-ladder*). Oh! I am very glad Edwin
likes our work.

CHERRY (*clapping her hands*). So am I! so am I!

PHILIP. Edwin, will you be so kind as to hang up these garlands for me, for I cannot reach quite high enough. Edwin,
do you think my father will like it?

CHERRY. Edwin, do you think mamma will like it? and shall
we bring papa in before dinner, or wait till tea-time? Do
you think the smell of the flowers is too strong? — I don't
know what people mean by the smell of flowers being too
strong for them — Edwin, do you? — Edwin, do you like
the smell of honey-suckles, or roses, best? and do you like
these dog-roses?

EDWIN. Which of the six questions that you have asked me,
Cherry, shall I answer first?
[*Edwin is busy putting up the garlands.*

PHILIP. My dear Cherry, six questions! that is really too much.
Now, Edwin, don't you think we had better ask mamma to
have the tea-table here, that we may drink tea before we go
to the play? Oh! my dear Edwin, have the children their
parts quite perfect? Do you think Rosy will act the old
grandmother well? Does Dame Deborah come? I hope
she will — I love Dame Deborah. Does not Willy play the
sailor admirably well? and do not the trowsers fit him very
well?

The Dame School Holiday

Act II. Scene iv

Willy.—" 'Give up this here nonsensical play,' says he, 'and I'll
show you how to do something better.' "

off your wet clothes; and all I ask of you is that you will forgive Felix, and let us have no quarrels in our village.

WILLY. I'll forgive him, and I'll never say a word more about it. [*Exit Edwin.*

WILLY (*solus*). Well! I am very, very much obliged to Master Edwin for putting off the play till my poor dog's leg is well; more obliged than if he had given me ever so many coats and hats. *That* is really good-natured of him, and I love him for it : but he is always so — he never thinks of himself when he can do a kind thing by another.

[*Enter Cherry and Philip, with a plate of meat for the dog.*

PHILIP. So the play is put off!

CHERRY. So the play is put off!

PHILIP. Let us give poor Keeper the meat at any rate — it is not his fault.

CHERRY. No, it is Felix's fault. Here, Keeper! Keeper!

[*They feed the dog.*

PHILIP. Willy, you must go home directly, and take off your wet clothes; Edwin bid me not let you stay. It is not very civil, I know, to turn you out of the house; but it is for your good.

WILLY. That I am sure it is, when Master Edwin desired it — a good morning to you! and thank you for being so kind to Keeper. Come along, poor fellow! poor fellow! come along; I won't walk too fast for you.

[*Exit Willy.*

CHERRY. Oh! my dear Philip, are not you sorry that poor Edwin's play is not to be acted to-night?

PHILIP. Very, *very* sorry, indeed! but as soon as Keeper gets well, it will be acted. I will tell you what, Cherry, as my father's birth-day is to be put off, we should take down all these flowers, and wait till the day when Edwin's play is to be acted, before we show my father our bower.

CHERRY. What! pull down all our work — all our beautiful garlands — all we have been doing since five o'clock this morning — all our bower — all!

PHILIP.   Yes, all! because it would be good-natured to Edwin to keep it all for the day when he has his play.   Oh, Cherry, my dear!   Let us be good-natured to Edwin, who is so good to us, and to everybody.

CHERRY.   Well, do — pull it all down then; and when you have done, tell me, and — I will look up.

[*Cherry sits down and hides her face with her hands. — Philip tears down the branches and flowers.*

PHILIP.   Look up, Cherry; it is all down.

CHERRY.   All down!   (*After a pause*) I will help you to carry the flowers away.   It is a great pity!

PHILIP.   But we can make it as pretty again, another day. Come, help me to drag these great boughs.

[*Exeunt, dragging off the boughs.*

ACT III

SCENE I

Felix and Miss Babberly.

MISS BABBERLY.   To be insulted in this manner by a parcel of beggarly brats and an obstinate old woman!

FELIX.   But what provokes me is that this Edwin has become quite king of the village; and nothing is to be done contrary to his will and pleasure: and what a rout about *his* father's birth-day, and his own nonsensical play.   I gave a little rascal and his dog one good ducking, however, for talking to me about it.   Edwin is so cursedly conceited too; for I was giving him an account of the Lon'on plays, and he did not seem to admire them at all.

MISS BABBERLY.   Admire them! no; he admires nothing but himself.   He told somebody, who told Jenny Parrot, who told me, that he did not see anything to be admired in *me* — the quiz!

FELIX.   Quiz, indeed! you'll see how finely I'll quiz him, before this day's over.   This foolish play of his shall not be acted,

I promise him : and all the people whom he has invited shall stand staring at one another, like a parcel of fools; and he, fool in the middle.

MISS BABBERLY. But how? how?

FELIX. Oh, leave that to me — I have contrived it all. Look at this key — this is the key of the summer-house in the bowling-green, where they have their famous theatre. It was lying on the table at the porter's lodge just now, when I was there; and a bright thought came into my head at the moment; so I put an old key, which is just the same size, in its place, and no one will perceive the difference till night; and then, just when the company, and the actors, and actresses, and Mr. Manager, and all, want the key, they will stand staring at one another, and at last will be forced to go home like fools as they are, for not one of 'em would have the spirit to break open a gentleman's door. Oh! they'll be finely quizzed.

MISS BABBERLY. Excellent! excellent! and those impertinent children will be punished just as they ought for their insolence to me. Did you ever, in all your life, hear of anything so impertinent as their tying me up in my own scarf?

FELIX. What! did they tie you up quite tight, Bab?

MISS BABBERLY. Quite tight.

FELIX. With your arms *in*, close to your sides.

MISS BABBERLY. Yes, just so.

FELIX. Capital! you must have looked exactly like a mummy, Bab; I wish I'd seen you.
[*Laughs loud.*

MISS BABBERLY. Mummy! indeed! Brother, I wish you wouldn't laugh so, like a horse.

FELIX. Horse! indeed, Miss Bab. Let me tell you, Miss —
[*Enter Edwin.*

EDWIN. I hope I don't interrupt you.

FELIX. No; we were only — only —

MISS BABBERLY. Not at all, sir; we were only —
[*Miss Babberly makes him a scornful awkward half-curtesy, half-bow.*

EDWIN. I am come to tell you, Felix, that we have given up all intention of acting my play to-night.

FELIX. Really! (*Aside*) Then I can't quiz him; how provoking.

MISS BABBERLY. Then I suppose we can have Dame Deborah's benches.

EDWIN. Not to-night. Miss Babberly will not ask for them, I am sure, because the children and the people of the village will want them; for instead of the play, they are to have a little dance.

MISS BABBERLY. Dance! and where will you get beaux?

EDWIN. We shall not want beaux, for we shall have no belles. Felix told me that all your family have company at home.

FELIX. But, pray, how *could* you give up your play?

EDWIN. Very easily; I would give up anything to avoid disputes.

FELIX. Disputes! why, I thought you had everything your own way in this place. I thought you were Lord Paramount here.

MISS BABBERLY. Yes; I thought you had partisans enough here, sir.

EDWIN. Far from wishing to have partisans, or to be the cause of quarrel, I am ready to give up my own schemes, you see. We are all very happy in this village, and do let us continue to be so; let us all be good friends.

FELIX. To be sure — certainly — I have no objection. But I really do not see exactly what you would be at: disputes! quarrels! What do you mean?

EDWIN. What do I mean, Felix? You cannot have forgotten poor little Willy and his dog.

FELIX (*embarrassed*). As to that, I remember the little scoundrel was impertinent to me, and I gave him and his dog a ducking, that's all.

EDWIN. And nearly broke the dog's leg. Was Willy impertinent? I did not understand that.

FELIX. Well, no matter how it was; if he put me in a passion, he must take the consequences. Mr. Edwin, you always

take the part of every vulgar fellow against me; and let me
tell you, sir, I do not think this very genteel conduct.

MISS BABBERLY. And I assure you, sir, if you expect me to be
at your dance this evening, I have the pleasure to assure you
that you will be disappointed.

[*Exit Miss Babberly, tossing her head.*

FELIX. That's right, sister; there's a girl of spirit!

EDWIN. I shall never think you a boy of spirit, after what I
have now heard and seen.

[*Exit Edwin.*

FELIX (*going out at the opposite door*). I'll make you repent
of this before the sun goes down.

[*Exit.*

SCENE II

*Philip and Cherry at their own house, with a large basket of
strawberries and a bowl of cream.*

CHERRY. After joy comes sorrow; after sorrow comes joy.
Though we did pull down our garlands, and though we did
give up Edwin's play, we shall be very happy to-night; and
we shall make all the children at the Dame's so happy with
these strawberries and cream! Was not mamma very good
to let us gather so many, and to give us such a great quantity
of nice cream?

PHILIP. Yes; but I am thinking how we shall carry it without
spilling it, as far as the Dame School.

CHERRY. As the milk-maids do: put it on my head, and you
shall see how well I can carry it.

PHILIP. No, no, I will carry it; for I am better able than you,
and stronger, and wiser.

[*He tries to carry the bowl on his head.*

CHERRY. My dear! my dear! it is spilling in spite of all your
strength and wisdom: besides, boys are never milk-maids.

PHILIP. But you know it is the part of a woman not to dispute about trifles with a man.

CHERRY. Well, I will not dispute: now give it me. (*Meekly,
and putting her hands before her*) Pray!

PHILIP. So I will, because you are so gentle and good-humoured : besides, I know it is the part of a man to give up to
a woman, if she does not dispute. (*Places the bowl on her
head*) Only don't tumble down, that's all I ask of you.

CHERRY. Tumble, my dear! look how steadily I carry it.

[*Exeunt.*

SCENE III

Mr. Babberly's House — Miss Babberly and Felix.

MISS BABBERLY. Do you know, I've been explaining to papa
all about the behaviour of Dame Deborah, and her rudeness
about the benches; and telling him what a party there is
made against us here in the village : and he says he can punish that old beldam, and have her benches in spite of her, and
this very night too.

FELIX. This night, can he? I'm glad of that, for it will
humble Edwin's pride. She and all those stupid children
are his partisans, and under his protection, I see; and he is
always doing things to make himself popular. You see that
though the play is given up, he will give them a dance to-
night. The pedlar who cut his leg, and who stays at their
house, can play on the fiddle, and he will be their music.
And I saw the children carrying such baskets of strawberries,
and bowls of cream. They are determined to keep their
father's birth-day, it seems, to provoke us; but maybe we
shall be too many for them yet.

MISS BABBERLY. My father will manage that for you.

FELIX. Manage that! How! how! Oh, tell me how!

MISS BABBERLY. I will tell you how he will manage it : Dame
Deborah is *his* tenant — she forgets *that;* and she forgets
that she hasn't paid her rent, nor can't, he says, for her cow
has just died; and so he'll send Bateman, the bailiff, down to
seize all she has, this very evening, and the benches first
and foremost.

FELIX. Joe, triumph! Joe, triumph!

MISS BABBERLY. Come, you'll hear him giving orders this
minute.

[*Exeunt.*

SCENE IV

A Meadow near Dame Deborah's cottage. — Dame Deborah setting out a table with a large bowl of cream, and children with baskets of strawberries. — Cherry and Philip distributing the strawberries. — Edwin sets the benches to the table. — The pedlar tuning his fiddle.

PHILIP.   Now everybody has strawberries.

CHERRY.   And let everybody pick for themselves.

[The children begin eating.

EDWIN.   But, Philip, you have forgot your poor fiddler here; is not he to have any?

PHILIP.   He shall have half of mine.

CHERRY.   And half of mine.

[They give him a plate of strawberries.

PHILIP.   I will put your fiddle out of your way, for we shall be an hour before we are ready for it.   Picking strawberries is a serious affair.

EDWIN.   But then consider that Dame Deborah came out on purpose to see you all dance; and if you are so long before you begin, the sun will set, and it will be too late for her to stay out.

DAME.   Never mind me, dears — please yourselves, and never mind *me.*

ROSE.   Oh, yes, but we *will* mind you; we can't please ourselves without minding you.   Let us dance before we eat our strawberries, that we may not keep our Dame out in the night dew.

OMNES.   Yes, yes, yes.

[They push away their strawberries, and all rise and get ready to dance.

PEDLAR.   What tune shall I play, Master?   *[To Edwin.*

EDWIN.   "Rural Felicity."

[He plays "Rural Felicity", and the children dance. — Whilst they are dancing, enter Felix with the bailiff. — Miss Babberly follows.

DAME.   What comes here?   what is all this?

MISS BABBERLY. All this is what you've brought on yourself, old woman, by your stubbornness.

FELIX. Bateman, do your duty — there are the benches.

MISS BABBERLY. Aye; if you had lent them to us by fair means, it would have been better for you.

BATEMAN (*pushing by Edwin*). By your leave, sir! By your leave, Dame! (*Takes hold of the end of the bench on which Dame Deborah is sitting*) My orders be to seize all this household furniture here, for rent and arrears, due to J. Babberly, Esq.

DAME. What, all my little goods! all! — and all on such a night as this!

[*She clasps her hands in an agony — the children gather round her in consternation.*

PHILIP (*to Felix*). You cruel creature!

CHERRY. Poor Dame Deborah! — poor good Dame Deborah!

ROSE. Oh! what *can* we do for her?

NANCY. Oh! is there anything *we* can do for her?

MARY. I never saw her cry before.

[*Dame wipes her eyes.*

DAME. God's will be done! — God's will be done! He has left me these. (*She stoops and kisses the children*) Don't cry, dears — don't *you* cry, or I can't help it. Well, sir (*to the bailiff*), as Mr. Felix says, do your duty.

EDWIN (*springing forward*). Stop, stop! — how much is the debt?

BATEMAN. Seven guineas.

EDWIN. I have only four: but here is my watch, it is worth —

FELIX (*interrupting*). No matter what it is worth, it won't do; the rent is to be paid in money; I heard my father read the lease; and *ready-money* is the words mentioned in the lease. Bateman, carry off the benches.

THE PEDLAR (*coming forward*). Master Edwin, if you want ready-money, if you be pleased, I can let you have it.

[*Gives guineas.*

EDWIN. Thank you, my good friend. Take my watch.

PEDLAR. No, Master, no; I'll not take the watch — I'll take your word — that is enough.

EDWIN. Mr. Felix Babberly, here is the whole of what is due to you, or to your father, in *ready-money*. Now, let go this bench, if you please.

FELIX. Very well, sir; vastly well, sir; I will be revenged some time or other, you'll see.

MISS BABBERLY. Yes, yes, you have not done with us yet, I promise you. But go on with your vulgar diversions, and welcome; and be assured, we don't want to be of the party. It is not such dancing as this, and such parties as these, we have been used to in Lon'on, I can tell you; and I will make papa live in Lon'on. Come away, brother Felix.
[*Exit Miss Babberly.*

FELIX (*aside*). So! they will have their dance, and be happy in spite of us! How provoking!
[*Exit Felix.*

CHERRY. How excessively ugly he looked!

PHILIP. Yes; people always look ugly when they are in a passion.

DAME. Handsome is, that handsome does. (*Turning to Edwin*) Mr. Edwin, how shall I thank you? — But your own good heart thanks you enough.

WILLY. Yes, that it does, I'll answer for it. See how happy he looks!

EDWIN. What a pity that Felix cannot be as happy —

DAME. As good, you mean?

PHILIP. Oh, let us think no more of Felix. It is very disagreeable to think of bad people.

CHERRY. Especially on papa's birth-day: so let us go on dancing. (*Cherry and the rest of the children join hands; and she sings as they dance*)

> Come, follow, follow me,
> Ye fairy elves that be;
> Light tripping o'er the green,
> Come, follow Mab your queen.
>   &c., &c.

[*Exeunt.*

THE END

JOHN DRINKWATER'S ABRAHAM LINCOLN

STRANGE that so far no American dramatist has written a real play about Abraham Lincoln. Strange that an English poet, John Drinkwater, should have been the one to place the great American President in a simple stage story, full of dignity, and warm with true humanity. This drama was first given in Birmingham, England, — and, after a while, it came to London. The King and Queen went to see it twice; so did the Prince of Wales. The London County Council arranged that English school children should see it. The clergy flocked to it. Then it crossed the ocean, and swept New York. Why was it?

I remember once hearing a minister deliver before children a sermon on Abraham Lincoln; the first two rows of pews were lined with bobbing heads and growing bodies. In front of the pulpit was hung one of the most ungainly likenesses of the martyred President. In the ordinary sense no one could call Lincoln handsome. "You all think this is a picture of a very ugly man?" questioned the minister. There was a roar of affirmation. "Well, now — look at his eyes — have they not compassion in them? See his mouth — is there not gentleness in the sensitive lines of the lips? Watch the eyes closely — are not kindness and humor there?" Thus he described for those girls and boys the essential humanity of Lincoln. Then he asked the question again, "Do you still think this is the picture of an ugly man?" And again the answer was, "Yes."

What this minister was attempting to say was that history is a matter of character, not of facts: that the ugliness of Lincoln's face was almost hidden for him by the imprint of character upon feature and expression: the man's spirit breathed beauty in his eyes.

Mr. John Drinkwater, having all his life held Lincoln to his heart as a hero, wrote a play which, in substance, is little more than a series of events contained in almost every school history, and yet which, in its effect, makes us see Lincoln as that minister would have had his children see him. This has been done by the simple use of simple speech, and with no effort to put more drama into the play than the events themselves actually held. Having seen or read Mr. Drinkwater's drama, "Abraham Lincoln", you have a living figure of Lincoln in your mind forever — a man of destiny amidst moving, crushing events — a man whose homely face showed in every line the shaping of a soul which was helping to shape a nation; upon whose bent shoulders rested the weight of the Union.

Mr. Drinkwater has modelled his Lincoln in this play as a sculptor — as Gutzon Borglum actually did, when he made his head of Lincoln, now in the retunda of the Capitol at Washington — would carve him out of stone, — conscious of how Lincoln felt at every hour he was called to act. What makes the scenes in this play so effective is that *we* are made to feel exactly what is stirring in Lincoln's mind : when the Committee calls on him to accept the nomination for the presidency; when, in his first Cabinet meeting, he sees what opposition he has to face among his "official family"; when, at the supreme height of determination, he announces his Emancipation Proclamation; and when, as a visitor to Grant on the battlefield, he pardons the sentry — a mere boy — found asleep at his post.

These commonplaces of school history are the beacon lights of character in Lincoln. By word and phrase, Mr. Drinkwater colors them with the spirit of the Great Man, and he gives us a figure which both London and New York loved, when it came upon the stage.

I recall going to see "Abraham Lincoln" with the sculptor, Mr. Borglum. We sat through the evening enthralled; each had witnessed it before. I never had seen at the theater a man more completely fascinated than my companion. For he knew Lincoln, after a long study of every photograph of the President he could lay his hands on ; after visiting all the scenes with which he was identified. How he chuckled over the way Lincoln handled his Cabinet, as the different members connived against him. "Lincoln had the keenness of a horse trader," Mr. Borglum said under his breath, as the Great Leader in one scene faced Seward and forced him to own up to his double-dealing. "They couldn't put anything over on him!" Then he sat up with the eagerness of a boy, as Lincoln, entering the fateful Cabinet meeting with his Emancipation Proclamation, paused a moment to read aloud one of the latest anecdotes of Artemus Ward.

"There's the supreme moment. Lincoln is applying the acid test. It's a joy!" So interpolated the sculptor.

Here was one — Mr. Borglum — steeped in Lincoln lore, and thrilling over the simple narrative of events he knew by heart. "Watch Grant," he exclaimed, "it was just in that way he used to throw his cigar into his mouth, and wipe the ash end of it on the lapel of his coat." When, in the play, Lincoln with Hay visits Grant in camp, he stays the night, eager to learn if General Meade will bring news of Lee's willingness to surrender. Propped up in a chair the Great Leader falls asleep. Grant passes, gets his army coat, and tenderly covers the President with it. Before going out, he looks into Lincoln's face. Tears were in Mr. Borglum's eyes. "I know nothing greater," he said, "than to see two great men together."

Thus the evening passed for us — and for many like us — moved by the stupendous sweep of history and the greatness of one of the world's great characters.

Mr. Drinkwater has told us that, as a student in England, at the Birmingham University, he first came to know and to love Lincoln. He read Lord Charnwood's "Life of Lincoln," and, as he modestly declared, his play was well-nigh written. He has quoted freely from the President's letters and speeches; he has written with no effort for effect. It is because of this that the play is so easily understood, so forcible in all its scenes.

I am glad to be able to put this play in a volume intended for young readers. They will see for themselves how simple greatness is, how easily understood is simple speech. Mr. Drinkwater must have been under the spell of Lincoln's Bible English. If some of my readers, whose age has not yet passed into two numbers, fail to reach the full meaning of the poetic interludes (printed in different types from the play itself) they need only know that these chronicles are of events that have happened between scenes — events that helped to bow in agony the head of Lincoln, who took upon himself the whole outcome of the Civil War. These interludes are not wholly essential for an understanding of the play.

The writing of a history of fact is one thing, and it is necessary. The writing of history in terms of Great Souls is another. And it is equally as important. Mr. Drinkwater has not always adhered to the facts of history — you will, for example, never find a Mr. Hook among Lincoln's Cabinet members. But if Hook is not a real character, at least he is a symbolic one : he is used for the purpose of concentrating in one person the virulent opposition to Lincoln's policies which was to be found in the many. He may not be accurate, this Hook, but he stands for Opposition — and Lincoln had much of it.

When you have read "Abraham Lincoln," you have come very near a great man, and, if Mr. Drinkwater has made you feel that, he has fulfilled his object successfully. Strange that an Englishman should have been the first so to succeed.

ABRAHAM LINCOLN

By JOHN DRINKWATER

"Abraham Lincoln" was presented at the Birmingham Repertory Theatre, in England, on October 12, 1918, before it was brought to the Lyric Theatre, Hammersmith. Under the direction of William Harris, Jr., it was given its first New York production, at the Cort Theatre, December 15, 1919, and Mr. Frank McGlynn assumed the rôle of *Lincoln*. The London program is reproduced from "The Story of the Lyric Theatre, Hammersmith", by Nigel Playfair. London: Chatto and Windus. 1925.

To THE LORD CHARNWOOD

ABRAHAM LINCOLN

By JOHN DRINKWATER

As Produced at the Lyric Theatre
Hammersmith, London, England
February 19, 1919
The Play produced by the Author
Stage Decorations designed by Barry V. Jackson

CAST

FIRST CHRONICLER		Margaret Chatwin
SECOND CHRONICLER		Dorothy Massingham
MR. CUFFNEY } *neighbours of Lincoln*		J. Adrian Byrne
MR. STONE } *at Springfield*		Joseph A. Dodd
SUSAN DEDDINGTON (*a maidservant*) .		Cathleen Orford
MRS. LINCOLN		Mary Raby
ABRAHAM LINCOLN		William J. Rea
WILLIAM TUCKER }		Gerald Jerome
HENRY HIND } *deputation from the*		Peter Creswell
ELIAS PRICE } *Republican Convention*		William Dexter
JAMES MACINTOSH }		Frank Milray
JOHNSON WHITE } *emissaries from the*		Herbert Marshall
CALEB JENNINGS } *Southern States*		Ernest Warburton
WILLIAM SEWARD (*of Lincoln's Cabinet*)		Noel Shammon
HAWKINS (*a clerk*)		Reginald Denham
SECOND CLERK		Arnold Pilbeam
THIRD CLERK		Percy Robinson
MR. SLANEY (*Lincoln's Secretary*) . .		A. E. Filmer
MESSENGER (*from Fort Sumter*) . . .		H. Victor Tandy

SALMON CHASE		Edwin Greenwood
MONTGOMERY BLAIR		J. Adrian Byrne
SIMON CAMERON		Arthur Ewart
CALEB SMITH	*of Lincoln's Cabinet*	Richard Coke
BURNET HOOK		John Darnley
GIDEON WELLES		William Dexter
EDWIN STANTON		Herbert Marshall
MRS. GOLIATH BLOW		Isabel Thornton
MRS. OTHERLEY		Maud Gill
FREDERICK DOUGLASS (*a negro*) . .		Joseph A. Dodd
GENERAL GRANT (*commanding the Northern armies*)		H. Victor Tandy
CAPTAIN MALINS (*his aide-de-camp*) .		Ernest Warburton
DENNIS (*his orderly*)		Frank Milray
AN OFFICER		Arnold Pilbeam
WILLIAM SCOTT (*a Northern soldier*) .		E. Stewart Linder
FIRST SOLDIER		Reginald Denham
SECOND SOLDIER		Percy Robinson
GENERAL MEADE (*of the North*) . . .		J. Adrian Byrne
CAPTAIN SONE (*his aide-de-camp*) . .		Gerald Jerome
GENERAL LEE (*commanding the armies of the South*)		E. Harcourt Williams
AN OFFICER OF HIS STAFF		Edwin Greenwood
JOHN WILKES BOOTH (*Lincoln's assassin*)		Arthur Ewart
A DOCTOR		Joseph A. Dodd
FIRST GENTLEMAN		Peter Creswell
SECOND GENTLEMAN		William Dexter
THIRD GENTLEMAN		Percy Robinson
AN OLD GENTLEMAN		Richard Coke
A YOUNG MAN	*of the audience at Ford's Theatre*	Noel Shammon
FIRST LADY		Alma Broadbridge
SECOND LADY		Dorothy Taylor
THIRD LADY		Maud Gill
FOURTH LADY		Nancy Byrne
FIFTH LADY		Mona Glynne
A GIRL		Beatrice Filmer
ATTENDANT (*of Ford's Theatre*) . . .		Arnold Pilbeam

ABRAHAM LINCOLN

TWO CHRONICLERS (the two speaking together).

> *Kinsmen, you shall behold*
> *Our stage, in mimic action, mould*
> *A man's character.*
>
> *This is the wonder, always, everywhere —*
> *Not that vast mutability which is event,*
> *The pits and pinnacles of change,*
> *But man's desire and valiance that range*
> *All circumstance, and come to port unspent.*
>
> *Agents are these events, these ecstasies,*
> *And tribulations, to prove the purities*
> *Of poor oblivions that are our being.   When*
> *Beauty and peace possess us, they are none*
> *But as they touch the beauty and peace of men,*
> *Nor, when our days are done,*
> *And the last utterance of doom must fall,*
> *Is the doom anything*
> *Memorable for its apparelling;*
> *The bearing of man facing it is all.*
>
> *So, kinsmen, we present*
> *This for no loud event*
> *That is but fugitive,*
> *But that you may behold*
> *Our mimic action mould*
> *The spirit of man immortally to live.*

FIRST CHRONICLER.

> *Once when a peril touched the days*
> *Of freedom in our English ways,*
> *And none renowned in government*
> *Was equal found,*

Came to the steadfast heart of one,
Who watched in lonely Huntingdon,
A summons, and he went,
And tyranny was bound,
And Cromwell was the lord of his event.

SECOND CHRONICLER.

And in that land where voyaging
The pilgrim Mayflower came to rest,
Among the chosen, counselling,
Once, when bewilderment possessed
A people, none there was might draw
To fold the wandering thoughts of men,
And make as one the names again
Of liberty and law.

And then, from fifty fameless years
In quiet Illinois was sent
A word that still the Atlantic hears,
And Lincoln was the lord of his event.

THE TWO (speaking together).

So the uncounted spirit wakes
To the birth
Of uncounted circumstance.
And time in a generation makes
Portents majestic a little story of earth
To be remembered by chance
At a fireside.
But the ardours that they bear,
The proud and invincible motions of character —
These — these abide.

SCENE I

The parlour of Abraham Lincoln's House at Springfield, Illinois, early in 1860. Mr. Stone, a farmer, and Mr. Cuffney, a store-keeper, both men of between fifty and sixty, are sitting before an early spring fire. It is dusk, but the curtains are not drawn. The men are smoking silently.

MR. STONE (*after a pause*). Abraham. It's a good name for a man to bear, anyway.

MR. CUFFNEY. Yes. That's right.

MR. STONE (*after another pause*). Abraham Lincoln. I've known him forty years. Never crooked once. Well.

[*He taps his pipe reflectively on the grate. There is another pause. Susan, a servant-maid, comes in, and busies herself lighting candles and drawing the curtains to.*

SUSAN. Mrs. Lincoln has just come in. She says she'll be here directly.

MR. CUFFNEY. Thank you.

MR. STONE. Mr. Lincoln isn't home yet, I dare say?

SUSAN. No, Mr. Stone. He won't be long, with all the gentlemen coming.

MR. STONE. How would you like your master to be President of the United States, Susan?

SUSAN. I'm sure he'd do it very nicely, sir.

MR. CUFFNEY. He would have to leave Springfield, Susan, and go to live in Washington.

SUSAN. I dare say we should take to Washington very well, sir.

MR. CUFFNEY. Ah! I'm glad to hear that.

SUSAN. Mrs. Lincoln's rather particular about the tobacco smoke.

MR. STONE. To be sure, yes, thank you, Susan.

SUSAN. The master doesn't smoke, you know. And Mrs. Lincoln's specially particular about this room.

MR. CUFFNEY. Quite so. That's very considerate of you, Susan.

[*They knock out their pipes.*

SUSAN. Though some people might not hold with a gentleman not doing as he'd a mind in his own house, as you might say.

[*She goes out.*

MR. CUFFNEY (*after a further pause, stroking his pipe*). I suppose there's no doubt about the message they'll bring?

MR. STONE. No, that's settled right enough. It'll be an invitation. That's as sure as John Brown's dead.

MR. CUFFNEY. I could never make Abraham out rightly

about old John. One couldn't stomach slaving more than the other, yet Abraham didn't hold with the old chap standing up against it with the sword. Bad philosophy, or something, he called it. Talked about fanatics who do nothing but get themselves at a rope's end.

MR. STONE. Abraham's all for the Constitution. He wants the Constitution to be an honest master. There's nothing he wants like that, and he'll stand for that, firm as a Samson of the spirit, if he goes to Washington. He'd give his life to persuade the state against slaving, but until it is persuaded and makes its laws against it, he'll have nothing to do with violence in the name of laws that aren't made. That's why old John's raiding affair stuck in his gullet.

MR. CUFFNEY. He was a brave man, going like that, with a few zealous like himself, and a handful of niggers, to free thousands.

MR. STONE. He was. And those were brave words when they took him out to hang him. "I think, my friends, you are guilty of a great wrong against God and humanity. You may dispose of me very easily. I am nearly disposed of now. But this question is still to be settled — this negro question, I mean. The end of that is not yet." I was there that day. Stonewall Jackson was there. He turned away. There was a colonel there giving orders. When it was over, "So perish all foes of the human race," he called out. But only those that were afraid of losing their slaves believed it.

MR. CUFFNEY (*after a pause*). It was a bad thing to hang a man like that. . . . There's a song that they've made about him. (*He sings quietly*)

John Brown's body lies a mould'ring in the grave,
But his soul goes marching on. . . .

MR. STONE. I know.

THE TWO TOGETHER (*singing quietly*).

The stars of heaven are looking kindly down
On the grave of old John Brown. . . .

[*After a moment Mrs. Lincoln comes in. The men rise.*

MRS. LINCOLN. Good-evening, Mr. Stone. Good-evening, Mr. Cuffney.

MR. STONE AND MR. CUFFNEY. Good-evening, ma'am.

MRS. LINCOLN. Sit down, if you please.

[*They all sit.*

MR. STONE. This is a great evening for you, ma'am.

MRS. LINCOLN. It is.

MR. CUFFNEY. What time do you expect the deputation, ma'am?

MRS. LINCOLN. They should be here at seven o'clock. (*With an inquisitive nose*) Surely, Abraham hasn't been smoking.

MR. STONE (*rising*). Shall I open the window, ma'am? It gets close of an evening.

MRS. LINCOLN. Naturally, in March. You may leave the window, Samuel Stone. We do not smoke in the parlour.

MR. STONE (*resuming his seat*). By no means, ma'am.

MRS. LINCOLN. I shall be obliged to you.

MR. CUFFNEY. Has Abraham decided what he will say to the invitation?

MRS. LINCOLN. He will accept it.

MR. STONE. A very right decision, if I may say so.

MRS. LINCOLN. It is.

MR. CUFFNEY. And you, ma'am, have advised him that way, I'll be bound.

MRS. LINCOLN. You said this was a great evening for me. It is, and I'll say more than I mostly do, because it is. I'm likely to go into history now with a great man. For I know better than any how great he is. I'm plain looking and I've a sharp tongue, and I've a mind that doesn't always go in his easy, high way. And that's what history will see, and it will laugh a little, and say, "Poor Abraham Lincoln." That's all right, but it's not all. I've always known when he should go forward, and when he should hold back. I've watched, and watched, and what I've learnt America will profit by. There are women like that, lots of them. But I'm lucky. My work's going farther than Illinois — it's going farther than any of us can tell. I made things easy for him to think and think when we were poor, and now his thinking has brought him to this. They wanted to make him Governor of Oregon, and he would have gone and have come to nothing there. I stopped him. Now they're coming to ask him to be President, and I've told him to go.

MR. STONE. If you please, ma'am, I should like to apologise for smoking in here.

MRS. LINCOLN. That's no matter, Samuel Stone. Only, don't do it again.

MR. CUFFNEY. It's a great place for a man to fill. Do you know how Seward takes Abraham's nomination by the Republicans?

MRS. LINCOLN. Seward is ambitious. He expected the nomination. Abraham will know how to use him.

MR. STONE. The split among the Democrats makes the election of the Republican choice a certainty, I suppose?

MRS. LINCOLN. Abraham says so.

MR. CUFFNEY. You know, it's hard to believe. When I think of the times I've sat in this room of an evening, and seen your husband come in, ma'am, with his battered hat nigh falling off the back of his head, and stuffed with papers that won't go into his pockets, and god-darning some rascal who'd done him about an assignment or a trespass, I can't think he's going up there into the eyes of the world.

MRS. LINCOLN. I've tried for years to make him buy a new hat.

MR. CUFFNEY. I have a very large selection just in from New York. Perhaps Abraham might allow me to offer him one for his departure.

MRS. LINCOLN. He might. But he'll wear the old one.

MR. STONE. Slavery and the South. They're big things he'll have to deal with. "The end of that is not yet." That's what old John Brown said, "the end of that is not yet."

[*Abraham Lincoln comes in, a greenish and crumpled top hat leaving his forehead well uncovered, his wide pockets brimming over with documents. He is fifty, and he still preserves his clean-shaven state. He kisses his wife and shakes hands with his friends.*

LINCOLN. Well, Mary. How d'ye do, Samuel. How d'ye do, Timothy.

MR. STONE AND MR. CUFFNEY. Good-evening, Abraham.

LINCOLN (*while he takes off his hat and shakes out sundry papers from the lining into a drawer*). John Brown, did you say? Aye, John Brown. But that's not the way it's to be done. And you can't do the right thing the wrong way. That's as bad as the wrong thing, if you're going to keep the state together.

MR. CUFFNEY. Well, we'll be going. We only came in to give you good-faring, so to say, in the great word you've got to speak this evening.

MR. STONE. It makes a humble body almost afraid of himself, Abraham, to know his friend is to be one of the great ones of the earth, with his yes and no law for these many, many thousands of folk.

LINCOLN. It makes a man humble to be chosen so, Samuel. So humble that no man but would say "No" to such bidding if he dare. To be President of this people, and trouble gathering everywhere in men's hearts. That's a searching thing. Bitterness, and scorn, and wrestling often with men I shall despise, and perhaps nothing truly done at the end. But I must go. Yes. Thank you, Samuel; thank you, Timothy. Just a glass of that cordial, Mary, before they leave. (*He goes to a cupboard*) May the devil smudge that girl! (*Calling at the door*) Susan! Susan Deddington! Where's that darnation cordial?

MRS. LINCOLN. It's all right, Abraham. I told the girl to keep it out. The cupboard's choked with papers.

SUSAN (*coming in with bottle and glasses*). I'm sure I'm sorry. I was told —

LINCOLN. All right, all right, Susan. Get along with you.

SUSAN. Thank you, sir.

[*She goes.*

LINCOLN (*pouring out drink*). Poor hospitality for whiskey-drinking rascals like yourselves. But the thought's good.

MR. STONE. Don't mention it, Abraham.

MR. CUFFNEY. We wish you well, Abraham. Our compliments, ma'am. And God bless America! Samuel, I give you the United States, and Abraham Lincoln.

[*Mr. Cuffney and Mr. Stone drink.*

MRS. LINCOLN. Thank you.

LINCOLN. Samuel, Timothy — I drink to the hope of honest friends. Mary, to friendship. I'll need that always, for I've a queer, anxious heart. And, God bless America!

[*He and Mrs. Lincoln drink.*

MR. STONE. Well, good-night, Abraham. Good-night, ma'am.

MR. CUFFNEY. Good-night, good-night.

MRS. LINCOLN. Good-night, Mr. Stone. Good-night, Mr. Cuffney.

LINCOLN. Good-night, Samuel. Good-night, Timothy. And thank you for coming.

[*Mr. Stone and Mr. Cuffney go out.*

MRS. LINCOLN. You'd better see them in here.

LINCOLN. Good. Five minutes to seven. You're sure about it, Mary?

MRS. LINCOLN. Yes. Aren't you?

LINCOLN. We mean to set bounds to slavery. The South will resist. They may try to break away from the Union. That cannot be allowed. If the Union is set aside America will crumble. The saving of it may mean blood.

MRS. LINCOLN. Who is to shape it all if you don't?

LINCOLN. There's nobody. I know it.

MRS. LINCOLN. Then go.

LINCOLN. Go.

MRS. LINCOLN (*after a moment*). This hat is a disgrace to you, Abraham. You pay no heed to what I say, and you think it doesn't matter. A man like you ought to think a little about gentility.

LINCOLN. To be sure. I forget.

MRS. LINCOLN. You don't. You just don't heed. Samuel Stone's been smoking in here.

LINCOLN. He's a careless, poor fellow.

MRS. LINCOLN. He is, and a fine example you set him. You

don't care whether he makes my parlour smell poison or not.

LINCOLN. Of course I do —

MRS. LINCOLN. You don't. Your head is too stuffed with things to think about my ways. I've got neighbours if you haven't.

LINCOLN. Well, now, your neighbours are mine, I suppose.

MRS. LINCOLN. Then why won't you consider appearances a little?

LINCOLN. Certainly. I must.

MRS. LINCOLN. Will you get a new hat?

LINCOLN. Yes, I must see about it.

MRS. LINCOLN. When?

LINCOLN. In a day or two. Before long.

MRS. LINCOLN. Abraham, I've got a better temper than anybody will ever guess.

LINCOLN. You have, my dear. And you need it, I confess.

[*Susan comes in.*

SUSAN. The gentlemen have come.

LINCOLN. I'll come to them.

SUSAN. Does the master want a handkerchief, ma'am? He didn't take one this morning.

LINCOLN. It's no matter now, Susan.

SUSAN. If you please, I've brought you one, sir.

[*She gives it to him, and goes.*

MRS. LINCOLN. I'll send them in. Abraham, I believe in you.

LINCOLN. I know, I know.

[*Mrs. Lincoln goes out. Lincoln moves to a map of the United States that is hanging on the wall, and stands silently looking at it. After a few moments Susan comes to the door.*

SUSAN. This way, please.

[*She shows in William Tucker, a florid, prosperous merchant; Henry Hind, an alert little attorney; Elias Price, a lean lay preacher; and James Macintosh, the editor of a Republican journal. Susan goes.*

TUCKER. Mr. Lincoln. Tucker my name is — William Tucker. (*He presents his companions*) Mr. Henry Hind — follows your profession, Mr. Lincoln. Leader of the bar in Ohio.

Mr. Elias Price, of Pennsylvania. You've heard him preach, maybe. James Macintosh you know. I come from Chicago.

LINCOLN. Gentlemen, at your service. How d'ye do, James. Will you be seated?

[*They sit round the table.*

TUCKER. I have the honour to be chairman of this delegation. We are sent from Chicago by the Republican Convention, to enquire whether you will accept their invitation to become the Republican candidate for the office of President of the United States.

PRICE. The Convention is aware, Mr. Lincoln, that under the circumstances, seeing that the Democrats have split, this is more than an invitation to candidature. Their nominee is almost certain to be elected.

LINCOLN. Gentlemen, I am known to one of you only. Do you know my many disqualifications for this work?

HIND. It's only fair to say that they have been discussed freely.

LINCOLN. There are some, shall we say graces, that I lack. Washington does not altogether neglect these.

TUCKER. They have been spoken of. But these are days, Mr. Lincoln, if I may say so, too difficult, too dangerous, for these to weigh at the expense of other qualities that you were considered to possess.

LINCOLN. Seward and Hook have both had great experience.

MACINTOSH. Hook had no strong support. For Seward, there are doubts as to his discretion.

LINCOLN. Do not be under any misunderstanding, I beg you. I aim at moderation so far as it is honest. But I am a very stubborn man, gentlemen. If the South insists upon the extension of slavery, and claims the right to secede, as you know it very well may do, and the decision lies with me, it will mean resistance, inexorable, with blood if needs be. I would have everybody's mind clear as to that.

PRICE. It will be for you to decide, and we believe you to be an upright man, Mr. Lincoln.

LINCOLN. Seward and Hook would be difficult to carry as subordinates.

TUCKER. But they will have to be carried so, and there's none likelier for the job than you.

LINCOLN. Will your Republican Press stand by me for a principle, James, whatever comes?

MACINTOSH. There's no other man we would follow so readily.

LINCOLN. If you send me, the South will have little but derision for your choice.

HIND. We believe that you'll last out their laughter.

LINCOLN. I can take any man's ridicule — I'm trained to it by a . . . somewhat odd figure that it pleased God to give me, if I may so far be pleasant with you. But this slavery business will be long, and deep, and bitter. I know it. If you do me this honour, gentlemen, you must look to me for no compromise in this matter. If abolition comes in due time by constitutional means, good. I want it. But, while we will not force abolition, we will give slavery no approval, and we will not allow it to extend its boundaries by one yard. The determination is in my blood. When I was a boy I made a trip to New Orleans, and there I saw them, chained, beaten, kicked as a man would be ashamed to kick a thieving dog. And I saw a young girl driven up and down the room that the bidders might satisfy themselves. And I said then, "If ever I get a chance to hit that thing, I'll hit it hard." (*A pause*) You have no conditions to make?

TUCKER. None.

LINCOLN (*rising*). Mrs. Lincoln and I would wish you to take supper with us.

TUCKER. That's very kind, I'm sure. And your answer, Mr. Lincoln?

LINCOLN. When you came, you did not know me, Mr. Tucker. You may have something to say now not for my ears.

TUCKER. Nothing in the world, I assure —

LINCOLN. I will prepare Mrs. Lincoln. You will excuse me for no more than a minute.

[*He goes out.*

TUCKER. Well, we might have chosen a handsomer article, but I doubt whether we could have chosen a better.

HIND. He would make a great judge — if you weren't prosecuting.

PRICE. I'd tell most people, but I'd ask that man.

TUCKER. He hasn't given us yes or no yet. Why should he leave us like that, as though plain wasn't plain?

HIND. Perhaps he wanted a thought by himself first.

MACINTOSH. It wasn't that. But he was right. Abraham Lincoln sees deeper into men's hearts than most. He knows this day will be a memory to us all our lives. Under his eye, which of you could have given play to any untoward thought that had started in you against him since you came into this room? But, leaving you, he knew you could test yourselves to your own ease, and speak the more confident for it, and, if you found yourselves clean of doubt, carry it all the happier in your minds after. Is there a doubt among us?

TUCKER.
HIND. } No, none.
PRICE.

MACINTOSH. Then, Mr. Tucker, ask him again when he comes back.

TUCKER. I will.

[*They sit in silence for a moment, and Lincoln comes in again, back to his place at the table.*

LINCOLN. I wouldn't have you think it graceless of me to be slow in my answer. But once given, it's for the deep good or the deep ill of all this country. In the face of that a man may well ask himself twenty times, when he's twenty times sure. You make no qualification, any one among you?

TUCKER. None. The invitation is as I put it when we sat down. And I would add that we are, all of us, proud to bear it to a man as to whom we feel there is none so fitted to receive it.

LINCOLN. I thank you. I accept. (*He rises, the others with him. He goes to the door and calls*) Susan.

[*There is silence. Susan comes in.*

SUSAN. Yes, Mr. Lincoln.

LINCOLN.   Take these gentlemen to Mrs. Lincoln.   I will follow
at once.

[*The four men go with Susan.   Lincoln stands silently for a moment.   He goes again to the map and looks at it.   He then turns
to the table again, and kneels beside it, possessed and deliberate,
burying his face in his hands.*

THE CURTAIN FALLS

THE TWO CHRONICLERS.

> *Lonely is the man who understands.*
> *Lonely is vision that leads a man away*
> *From the pasture-lands,*
> *From the furrows of corn and the brown loads of hay,*
> *To the mountain-side,*
> *To the high places where contemplation brings*
> *All his adventurings*
> *Among the sowers and the tillers in the wide*
> *Valleys to one fused experience,*
> *That shall control*
> *The courses of his soul,*
> *And give his hand*
> *Courage and continence.*

THE FIRST CHRONICLER.

> *Shall a man understand,*
> *He shall know bitterness because his kind,*
> *Being perplexed of mind,*
> *Hold issues even that are nothing mated.*
> *And he shall give*
> *Counsel out of his wisdom that none shall hear;*
> *And steadfast in vain persuasion must he live,*
> *And unabated*
> *Shall his temptation be.*

SECOND CHRONICLER.

> *Coveting the little, the instant gain,*
> *The brief security,*
> *And easy-tongued renown,*

> *Many will mock the vision that his brain*
> *Builds to a far, unmeasured monument,*
> *And many bid his resolutions down*
> *To the wages of content.*

FIRST CHRONICLER.

> *A year goes by.*

THE TWO TOGETHER.

> *Here contemplate*
> *A heart, undaunted to possess*
> *Itself among the glooms of fate,*
> *In vision and in loneliness.*

SCENE II

Ten months later. Seward's room at Washington. William H. Seward, Secretary of State, is seated at his table with Johnson White and Caleb Jennings, representing the Commissioners of the Confederate States.

WHITE. It's the common feeling in the South, Mr. Seward, that you're the one man at Washington to see this thing with large imagination. I say this with no disrespect to the President.

SEWARD. I appreciate your kindness, Mr. White. But the Union is the Union — you can't get over that. We are faced with a plain fact. Seven of the Southern States have already declared for secession. The President feels — and I may say that I and my colleagues are with him — that to break up the country like that means the decline of America.

JENNINGS. But everything might be done by compromise, Mr. Seward. Withdraw your garrison from Fort Sumter, Beauregard will be instructed to take no further action, South Carolina will be satisfied with the recognition of her authority, and, as likely as not, be willing to give the lead to the other states in reconsidering secession.

SEWARD. It is certainly a very attractive and, I conceive, a humane proposal.

WHITE. By furthering it you might be the saviour of the country from civil war, Mr. Seward.

SEWARD. The President dwelt on his resolution to hold Fort Sumter in his inaugural address. It will be difficult to persuade him to go back on that. He's firm in his decisions.

WHITE. There are people who would call him stubborn. Surely if it were put to him tactfully that so simple a course might avert incalculable disaster, no man would nurse his dignity to the point of not yielding. I speak plainly, but it's a time for plain speaking. Mr. Lincoln is doubtless a man of remarkable qualities : on the two occasions when I have spoken to him I have not been unimpressed. That is so, Mr. Jennings?

JENNINGS. Certainly.

WHITE. But what does his experience of great affairs of state amount to beside yours, Mr. Seward? He must know how much he depends on certain members of his Cabinet, I might say upon a certain member, for advice.

SEWARD. We have to move warily.

JENNINGS. Naturally. A man is sensitive, doubtless, in his first taste of office.

SEWARD. My support of the President is, of course, unquestionable.

WHITE. Oh, entirely. But how can your support be more valuable than in lending him your unequalled understanding?

SEWARD. The whole thing is coloured in his mind by the question of slavery.

JENNINGS. Disabuse his mind. Slavery is nothing. Persuade him to withdraw from Fort Sumter, and slavery can be settled round a table. You know there's a considerable support even for abolition in the South itself. If the trade has to be allowed in some districts, what is that compared to the disaster of civil war?

WHITE. We do not believe that the Southern States wish with any enthusiasm to secede. They merely wish to establish their right to do so. Acknowledge that by evacuating Fort Sumter, and nothing will come of it but a perfectly proper concession to an independence of spirit that is not disloyal to the Union at heart.

SEWARD. You understand, of course, that I can say nothing officially.

JENNINGS. These are nothing but informal suggestions.

SEWARD. But I may tell you that I am not unsympathetic.

WHITE. We were sure that that would be so.

SEWARD. And my word is not without influence.

JENNINGS. It can be used to bring you very great credit, Mr. Seward.

SEWARD. In the mean time, you will say nothing of this interview, beyond making your reports, which should be confidential.

WHITE. You may rely upon us.

SEWARD (*rising with the others*). Then I will bid you good-morning.

WHITE. We are profoundly sensible of the magnanimous temper in which we are convinced you will conduct this grave business. Good-morning, Mr. Seward.

JENNINGS. And I —

[*There is a knock at the door.*

SEWARD. Yes — come in.

[*A Clerk comes in.*

CLERK. The President is coming up the stairs, sir.

SEWARD. Thank you. (*The Clerk goes*) This is unfortunate. Say nothing, and go at once.

[*Lincoln comes in, now whiskered and bearded.*

LINCOLN. Good-morning, Mr. Seward. Good-morning, gentlemen.

SEWARD. Good-morning, Mr. President. And I am obliged to you for calling, gentlemen. Good-morning.

[*He moves towards the door.*

LINCOLN. Perhaps these gentlemen could spare me ten minutes.

WHITE. It might not —

LINCOLN. Say five minutes.

JENNINGS. Perhaps you would —

LINCOLN. I am anxious always for any opportunity to exchange

views with our friends of the South. Much enlightenment
may be gained in five minutes. Be seated, I beg you — if
Mr. Seward will allow us.

SEWARD. By all means. Shall I leave you?

LINCOLN. Leave us — but why? I may want your support,
Mr. Secretary, if we should not wholly agree. Be seated,
gentlemen.

[*Seward places a chair for Lincoln, and they sit at the table.*

You have messages for us?

WHITE. Well, no, we can't say that.

LINCOLN. No messages? Perhaps I am inquisitive?

SEWARD. These gentlemen are anxious to sound any moderating influences.

LINCOLN. I trust they bring moderating influences with them.
You will find me a ready listener, gentlemen.

JENNINGS. It's a delicate matter, Mr. Lincoln. Ours is just
an informal visit.

LINCOLN. Quite, quite. But we shall lose nothing by knowing
each other's minds.

WHITE. Shall we tell the President what we came to say, Mr.
Seward?

LINCOLN. I shall be grateful. If I should fail to understand,
Mr. Seward, no doubt, will enlighten me.

JENNINGS. We thought it hardly worth while to trouble you
at so early a stage.

LINCOLN. So early a stage of what?

JENNINGS. I mean —

SEWARD. These gentlemen, in a common anxiety for peace,
were merely seeking the best channel through which suggestions could be made.

LINCOLN. To whom?

SEWARD. To the government.

LINCOLN. The head of the government is here.

WHITE. But —

LINCOLN. Come, gentlemen. What is it?

JENNINGS. It's this matter of Fort Sumter, Mr. President.
If you withdraw your garrison from Fort Sumter it won't be

looked upon as weakness in you. It will merely be looked upon as a concession to a natural prejudice. We believe that the South at heart does not want secession. It wants to establish the right to decide for itself.

LINCOLN. The South wants the stamp of national approval upon slavery. It can't have it.

WHITE. Surely that's not the point. There's no law in the South against slavery.

LINCOLN. Laws come from opinion, Mr. White. The South knows it.

JENNINGS. Mr. President, if I may say so, you don't quite understand.

LINCOLN. Does Mr. Seward understand?

WHITE. We believe so.

LINCOLN. You are wrong. He doesn't understand, because you didn't mean him to. I don't blame you. You think you are acting for the best. You think you've got an honest case. But I'll put your case for you, and I'll put it naked. Many people in this country want abolition; many don't. I'll say nothing for the moment as to the rights and wrongs of it. But every man, whether he wants it or not, knows it may come. Why does the South propose secession? Because it knows abolition may come, and it wants to avoid it. It wants more : it wants the right to extend the slave foundation. We've all been to blame for slavery, but we in the North have been willing to mend our ways. You have not. So you'll secede, and make your own laws. But you weren't prepared for resistance ; you don't want resistance. And you hope that if you can tide over the first crisis and make us give way, opinion will prevent us from opposing you with force again, and you'll be able to get your own way about the slave business by threats. That's your case. You didn't say so to Mr. Seward, but it is. Now, I'll give you my answer. Gentlemen, it's no good hiding this thing in a corner. It's got to be settled. I said the other day that Fort Sumter would be held as long as we could hold it. I said it because I know exactly what it means. Why are you investing it? Say, if you like, it's to establish your right of secession with no purpose of exercising it. Why do you want to establish that right? Because now we will allow no extension of slavery, and because some day we may abolish it. You can't deny it; there's no other answer.

JENNINGS. I see how it is. You may force freedom as much as you like, but we are to beware how we force slavery.

LINCOLN. It couldn't be put better, Mr. Jennings. That's what the Union means. It is a Union that stands for common right. That is its foundation — that is why it is for every honest man to preserve it. Be clear about this issue. If there is war, it will not be on the slave question. If the South is loyal to the Union, it can fight slave legislation by constitutional means, and win its way if it can. If it claims the right to secede, then to preserve this country from disruption, to maintain that right to which every state pledged itself when the Union was won for us by our fathers, war may be the only way. We won't break up the Union, and you sha'n't. In your hands, and not in mine, is the momentous issue of civil war. You can have no conflict without yourselves being the aggressors. I am loath to close. We are not enemies, but friends. We must not be enemies. Though passion may have strained, do not allow it to break our bonds of affection. That is our answer. Tell them that. Will you tell them that?

WHITE. You are determined?

LINCOLN. I beg you to tell them.

JENNINGS. It shall be as you wish.

LINCOLN. Implore them to order Beauregard's return. You can telegraph it now, from here. Will you do that?

WHITE. If you wish it.

LINCOLN. Earnestly. Mr. Seward, will you please place a clerk at their service. Ask for an answer.

[*Seward rings a bell. A Clerk comes in.*

SEWARD. Give these gentlemen a private wire. Place yourself at their disposal.

CLERK. Yes, sir.

[White and Jennings go out with the Clerk. For a moment Lincoln and Seward are silent, Lincoln pacing the room, Seward standing at the table.

LINCOLN. Seward, this won't do.

SEWARD. You don't suspect —

LINCOLN. I do not. But let us be plain. No man can say how wisely, but Providence has brought me to the leadership of this country, with a task before me greater than that which rested on Washington himself. When I made my Cabinet, you were the first man I chose. I do not regret it. I think I never shall. But remember, faith earns faith. What is it? Why didn't those men come to see me?

SEWARD. They thought my word might bear more weight with you than theirs.

LINCOLN. Your word for what?

SEWARD. Discretion about Fort Sumter.

LINCOLN. Discretion?

SEWARD. It's devastating, this thought of war.

LINCOLN. It is. Do you think I'm less sensible of that than you? War should be impossible. But you can only make it impossible by destroying its causes. Don't you see that to withdraw from Fort Sumter is to do nothing of the kind? If one half of this country claims the right to disown the Union, the claim in the eyes of every true guardian among us must be a cause for war, unless we hold the Union to be a false thing instead of the public consent to decent principles of life that it is. If we withdraw from Fort Sumter, we do nothing to destroy that cause. We can only destroy it by convincing them that secession is a betrayal of their trust. Please God we may do so.

SEWARD. Has there, perhaps, been some timidity in making all this clear to the country?

LINCOLN. Timidity? And you were talking of discretion.

SEWARD. I mean that perhaps our policy has not been sufficiently defined.

LINCOLN. And have you not concurred in all our decisions? Do not deceive yourself. You urge me to discretion in one breath and tax me with timidity in the next. While there was hope that they might call Beauregard back out of their own good sense, I was determined to say nothing to inflame them. Do you call that timidity? Now their intention is clear, and you've heard me speak this morning clearly also. And now you talk about discretion — you, who call what was discretion at the right time, timidity, now counsel timidity at the wrong time, and call it discretion. Seward, you may think I'm simple, but I can see your mind working as plainly as you might see the innards of a clock. You can bring great gifts to this government, with your zeal, and your administrative experience, and your love of men. Don't spoil it by thinking I've got a dull brain.

SEWARD (*slowly*). Yes, I see. I've not been thinking quite clearly about it all.

LINCOLN (*taking a paper from his pocket*). Here's the paper you sent me. "Some Thoughts for the President's Consideration. Great Britain . . . Russia . . . Mexico . . . policy. Either the President must control this himself, or devolve it on some member of his Cabinet. It is not in my especial province, but I neither seek to evade nor assume responsibility."

[*There is a pause, the two men looking at each other without speaking. Lincoln hands the paper to Seward, who holds it for a moment, tears it up, and throws it into his basket.*

SEWARD. I beg your pardon.

LINCOLN (*taking his hand*). That's brave of you.

[*John Hay, a Secretary, comes in.*

HAY. There's a messenger from Major Anderson, sir. He's ridden straight from Fort Sumter.

LINCOLN. Take him to my room. No, bring him here.

[*Hay goes.*

SEWARD. What does it mean?

LINCOLN. I don't like the sound of it. (*He rings a bell. A Clerk comes in*) Are there any gentlemen of the Cabinet in the house?

CLERK. Mr. Chase and Mr. Blair, I believe, sir.

LINCOLN. My compliments to them, and will they be prepared to see me here at once if necessary. Send the same message to any other ministers you can find.

CLERK. Yes, sir.

[*He goes.*

LINCOLN. We may have to decide now — now. (*Hay shows in a perspiring and dust-covered Messenger, and retires*) From Major Anderson?

THE MESSENGER. Yes, sir. Word of mouth, sir.

LINCOLN. Your credentials?

THE MESSENGER (*giving Lincoln a paper*). Here, sir.

LINCOLN (*glancing at it*). Well?

THE MESSENGER. Major Anderson presents his duty to the government. He can hold the Fort three days more without provisions and reinforcements.

[*Lincoln rings the bell, and waits until a third Clerk comes in.*

LINCOLN. See if Mr. White and Mr. Jennings have had any answer yet. Mr. — what's his name?

SEWARD. Hawkins.

LINCOLN. Mr. Hawkins is attending to them. And ask Mr. Hay to come here.

CLERK. Yes, sir.

[*He goes. Lincoln sits at the table and writes. Hay comes in.*

LINCOLN (*writing*). Mr. Hay, do you know where General Scott is?

HAY. At headquarters, I think, sir.

LINCOLN. Take this to him yourself and bring an answer back.

HAY. Yes, sir.

[*He takes the note, and goes.*

LINCOLN. Are things very bad at the Fort?

THE MESSENGER. The major says three days, sir. Most of us would have said twenty-four hours.

[*A knock at the door.*

SEWARD. Yes.

[*Hawkins comes in.*

HAWKINS. Mr. White is just receiving a message across the wire, sir.

LINCOLN. Ask him to come here directly he's finished.

HAWKINS. Yes, sir.

[*He goes. Lincoln goes to a far door and opens it. He speaks to the Messenger.*

LINCOLN. Will you wait in here?

[*The Messenger goes through.*

SEWARD. Do you mind if I smoke?

LINCOLN. Not at all, not at all. (*Seward lights a cigar*) Three days. If White's message doesn't help us — three days.

SEWARD. But surely we must withdraw as a matter of military necessity now.

LINCOLN. Why doesn't White come? (*Seward goes to the window and throws it up. He stands looking down into the street. Lincoln stands at the table looking fixedly at the door. After a moment or two there is a knock*) Come in. (*Hawkins shows in White and Jennings, and goes out. Seward closes the window*) Well?

WHITE. I'm sorry. They won't give way.

LINCOLN. You told them all I said?

JENNINGS. Everything.

LINCOLN. It's critical.

WHITE. They are definite.

[*Lincoln paces once or twice up and down the room, standing again at his place at the table.*

LINCOLN. They leave no opening?

WHITE. I regret to say, none.

LINCOLN. It's a grave decision. Terribly grave. Thank you, gentlemen. Good-morning.

WHITE AND JENNINGS. Good-morning, gentlemen.

[*They go out.*

LINCOLN. My God! Seward, we need great courage, great faith. (*He rings the bell. The second Clerk comes in*) Did you take my messages?

THE CLERK. Yes, sir. Mr. Chase and Mr. Blair are here. The other ministers are coming immediately.

LINCOLN. Ask them to come here at once. And send Mr. Hay in directly he returns.

THE CLERK. Yes, sir.

[*He goes.*

LINCOLN (*after a pause*). "There is a tide in the affairs of men
. . ." Do you read Shakespeare, Seward?

SEWARD. Shakespeare? No.

LINCOLN. Ah! (*Salmon P. Chase, Secretary of the Treasury,
and Montgomery Blair, Postmaster-General, come in*) Good-
morning, Mr. Chase, Mr. Blair.

SEWARD. Good-morning, gentlemen.

BLAIR. Good-morning, Mr. President. How d'ye do, Mr.
Seward.

CHASE. Good-morning, Mr. President. Something urgent?

LINCOLN. Let us be seated. (*As they draw chairs up to the table,
the other members of the Cabinet, Simon Cameron, Caleb Smith,
Burnet Hook, and Gideon Welles, come in. There is an exchange of greetings, while they arrange themselves round the table*)
Gentlemen, we meet in a crisis, the most fateful, perhaps, that
has ever faced any government in this country. It can be
stated briefly. A message has just come from Anderson.
He can hold Fort Sumter three days at most unless we send
men and provisions.

CAMERON. How many men?

LINCOLN. I shall know from Scott in a few minutes how many
are necessary.

WELLES. Suppose we haven't as many.

LINCOLN. Then it's a question of provisioning. We may not
be able to do enough to be effective. The question is whether
we shall do as much as we can.

HOOK. If we withdrew altogether, wouldn't it give the South
a lead towards compromise, as being an acknowledgment of
their authority, while leaving us free to plead military necessity if we found public opinion dangerous?

LINCOLN. My mind is clear. To do less than we can do, whatever that may be, will be fundamentally to allow the South's
claim to right of secession. That is my opinion. If you evade
the question now, you will have to answer it to-morrow.

BLAIR. I agree with the President.

HOOK. We ought to defer action as long as possible. I consider that we should withdraw.

LINCOLN. Don't you see that to withdraw may postpone war, but that it will make it inevitable in the end?

SMITH. It is inevitable if we resist.

LINCOLN. I fear it will be so. But in that case we shall enter it with uncompromised principles. Mr. Chase?

CHASE. It is difficult. But, on the whole, my opinion is with yours, Mr. President.

LINCOLN. And you, Seward?

SEWARD. I respect your opinion, but I must differ.

[*A knock at the door.*

LINCOLN. Come in. (*Hay comes in. He gives a letter to Lincoln and goes. Reading*) Scott says twenty thousand men.

SEWARD. We haven't ten thousand ready.

LINCOLN. It remains a question of sending provisions. I charge you, all of you, to weigh this thing with all your understanding. To temporise now, cannot, in my opinion, avert war. To speak plainly to the world in standing by our resolution to hold Fort Sumter with all our means, and in a plain declaration that the Union must be preserved, will leave us with a clean cause, simply and loyally supported. I tremble at the thought of war. But we have in our hands a sacred trust. It is threatened. We have had no thought of aggression. We have been the aggressed. Persuasion has failed, and I conceive it to be our duty to resist. To withhold supplies from Anderson would be to deny that duty. Gentlemen, the matter is before you. (*A pause*) For provisioning the fort? (*Lincoln, Chase, and Blair hold up their hands*) For immediate withdrawal? (*Seward, Cameron, Smith, Hook, and Welles hold up their hands. There is a pause of some moments*) Gentlemen, I may have to take upon myself the responsibility of over-riding your vote. It will be for me to satisfy Congress and public opinion. Should I receive any resignations? (*There is silence*) I thank you for your consideration, gentlemen. That is all. (*They rise, and the Min-*

isters, with the exception of Seward, go out, talking as they pass beyond the door)   You are wrong, Seward, wrong.

SEWARD.   I believe you.   I respect your judgment even as far as that.   But I must speak as I feel.

LINCOLN.   May I speak to this man alone?

SEWARD.   Certainly.

[*He goes out.   Lincoln stands motionless for a moment.   Then he moves to a map of the United States, much larger than the one in his Illinois home, and looks at it as he did there.   He goes to the far door and opens it.*

LINCOLN.   Will you come in?   (*The Messenger comes)*   Can you ride back to Major Anderson at once?

THE MESSENGER.   Yes, sir.

LINCOLN.   Tell him that we cannot reinforce him immediately. We haven't the men.

THE MESSENGER.   Yes, sir.

LINCOLN.   And say that the first convoy of supplies will leave Washington this evening.

THE MESSENGER.   Yes, sir.

LINCOLN.   Thank you.   (*The Messenger goes.   Lincoln stands at the table for a moment; he rings the bell.   Hawkins comes in)* Mr. Hay, please.

HAWKINS.   Yes, sir.

[*He goes, and a moment later Hay comes in.*

LINCOLN.   Go to General Scott.   Ask him to come to me at once.

HAY.   Yes, sir.

[*He goes.*

THE CURTAIN FALLS

THE TWO CHRONICLERS.

> *You who have gone gathering*
> *Cornflowers and meadowsweet,*
> *Heard the hazels glancing down*
> *On September eves,*
> *Seen the homeward rooks on wing*
> *Over fields of golden wheat,*

And the silver cups that crown
  Water lily leaves;

You who know the tenderness
  Of old men at eve-tide,
Coming from the hedgerows,
  Coming from the plough,
And the wandering caress
  Of winds upon the woodside,
When the crying yaffle goes
  Underneath the bough;

FIRST CHRONICLER.

You who mark the flowing
  Of sap upon the May-time,
And the waters welling
  From the watershed,
You who count the growing
  Of harvest and hay-time,
Knowing these the telling
  Of your daily bread;

SECOND CHRONICLER.

You who cherish courtesy
  With your fellows at your gate,
And about your hearthstone sit
  Under love's decrees,
You who know that death will be
  Speaking with you soon or late,

THE TWO TOGETHER.

Kinsmen, what is mother-wit
  But the light of these?
Knowing these, what is there more
  For learning in your little years?
Are not these all gospels bright
  Shining on your day?
How then shall your hearts be sore
  With envy and her brood of fears,
How forget the words of light
  From the mountain-way? . . .

> *Blessed are the merciful. . . .*
> > *Does not every threshold seek*
> *Meadows and the flight of birds*
> > *For compassion still?*
> *Blessed are the merciful. . . .*
> > *Are we pilgrims yet to speak*
> *Out of Olivet the words*
> > *Of knowledge and good-will?*

FIRST CHRONICLER.

> *Two years of darkness, and this man but grows*
> *Greater in resolution, more constant in compassion.*
> *He goes*
> *The way of dominion in pitiful, high-hearted fashion.*

Scene III

Nearly two years later.

A small reception room at the White House. Mrs. Lincoln, dressed in a fashion perhaps a little too considered, despairing as she now does of any sartorial grace in her husband, and acutely conscious that she must meet this necessity of office alone, is writing. She rings the bell, and Susan, who has taken her promotion more philosophically, comes in.

MRS. LINCOLN. Admit any one who calls, Susan. And enquire whether the President will be in to tea.

SUSAN. Mr. Lincoln has just sent word that he will be in.

MRS. LINCOLN. Very well. (*Susan is going*) Susan.

SUSAN. Yes, ma'am.

MRS. LINCOLN. You still say Mr. Lincoln. You should say the President.

SUSAN. Yes, ma'am. But you see, ma'am, it's difficult after calling him Mr. Lincoln for fifteen years.

MRS. LINCOLN. But you must remember. Everybody calls him the President now.

SUSAN. No, ma'am. There's a good many people call him Father Abraham now. And there's some that like him even better than that. Only to-day Mr. Coldpenny, at the stores, said, "Well, Susan, and how's old Abe this morning?"

MRS. LINCOLN. I hope you don't encourage them.

SUSAN. Oh, no, ma'am. I always refer to him as Mr. Lincoln.

MRS. LINCOLN. Yes, but, you must say the President.

SUSAN. I'm afraid I sha'n't ever learn, ma'am.

MRS. LINCOLN. You must try.

SUSAN. Yes, of course, ma'am.

MRS. LINCOLN. And bring any visitors up.

SUSAN. Yes, ma'am. There's a lady waiting now.

MRS. LINCOLN. Then why didn't you say so?

SUSAN. That's what I was going to, ma'am, when you began to talk about Mr. — I mean the President, ma'am.

MRS. LINCOLN. Well, show her up.

[*Susan goes. Mrs. Lincoln closes her writing desk. Susan returns, showing in Mrs. Goliath Blow.*

SUSAN. Mrs. Goliath Blow.

[*She goes.*

MRS. BLOW. Good-afternoon, Mrs. Lincoln.

MRS. LINCOLN. Good-afternoon, Mrs. Blow. Sit down, please.

[*They sit.*

MRS. BLOW. And is the dear President well?

MRS. LINCOLN. Yes. He's rather tired.

MRS. BLOW. Of course, to be sure. This dreadful war. But I hope he's not getting tired of the war.

MRS. LINCOLN. It's a constant anxiety for him. He feels his responsibility very deeply.

MRS. BLOW. To be sure. But you mustn't let him get war-weary. These monsters in the South have got to be stamped out.

MRS. LINCOLN. I don't think you need be afraid of the President's firmness.

MRS. BLOW. Oh, of course not. I was only saying to Goliath yesterday, "The President will never give way till he has the South squealing," and Goliath agreed.

[*Susan comes in.*

SUSAN. Mrs. Otherly, ma'am.

MRS. LINCOLN. Show Mrs. Otherly in.

[*Susan goes.*

MRS. BLOW. Oh, that dreadful woman! I believe she wants the war to stop.

SUSAN (*at the door*). Mrs. Otherly.

[*Mrs. Otherly comes in and Susan goes.*

MRS. LINCOLN. Good-afternoon, Mrs. Otherly. You know Mrs. Goliath Blow?

MRS. OTHERLY. Yes. Good-afternoon.

[*She sits.*

MRS. BLOW. Goliath says the war will go on for another three years at least.

MRS. OTHERLY. Three years? That would be terrible, wouldn't it?

MRS. BLOW. We must be prepared to make sacrifices.

MRS. OTHERLY. Yes.

MRS. BLOW. It makes my blood boil to think of those people.

MRS. OTHERLY. I used to know a lot of them. Some of them were very kind and nice.

MRS. BLOW. That was just their cunning, depend on it. I'm afraid there's a good deal of disloyalty among us. Shall we see the dear President this afternoon, Mrs. Lincoln?

MRS. LINCOLN. He will be here directly, I think.

MRS. BLOW. You're looking wonderfully well, with all the hard work that you have to do. I've really had to drop some of mine. And with expenses going up, it's all very lowering, don't you think? Goliath and I have had to reduce several of our subscriptions. But, of course, we all have to deny ourselves something. Ah, good-afternoon, dear Mr. President.

[*Lincoln comes in. The ladies rise and shake hands with him.*

LINCOLN. Good-afternoon, ladies.

MRS. OTHERLY. Good-afternoon, Mr. President.

[*They all sit.*

MRS. BLOW. And is there any startling news, Mr. President?

LINCOLN. Madam, every morning when I wake up, and say to myself, a hundred, or two hundred, or a thousand of my countrymen will be killed to-day, I find it startling.

MRS. BLOW. Oh, yes, of course, to be sure. But I mean, is there any good news.

LINCOLN. Yes. There is news of a victory. They lost twenty-seven hundred men — we lost eight hundred.

MRS. BLOW. How splendid!

LINCOLN. Thirty-five hundred.

MRS. BLOW. Oh, but you mustn't talk like that, Mr. President. There were only eight hundred that mattered.

LINCOLN. The world is larger than your heart, madam.

MRS. BLOW. Now the dear President is becoming whimsical, Mrs. Lincoln.

[*Susan brings in tea-tray, and hands tea round. Lincoln takes none. Susan goes.*

MRS. OTHERLY. Mr. President.

LINCOLN. Yes, ma'am.

MRS. OTHERLY. I don't like to impose upon your hospitality. I know how difficult everything is for you. But one has to take one's opportunities. May I ask you a question?

LINCOLN. Certainly, ma'am.

MRS. OTHERLY. Isn't it possible for you to stop this war? In the name of a suffering country, I ask you that.

MRS. BLOW. I'm sure such a question would never have entered my head.

LINCOLN. It is a perfectly right question. Ma'am, I have but one thought always — how can this thing be stopped? But we must ensure the integrity of the Union. In two years war has become an hourly bitterness to me. I believe I suffer no less than any man. But it must be endured. The cause was a right one two years ago. It is unchanged.

MRS. OTHERLY. I know you are noble and generous. But I believe that war must be wrong under any circumstances, for any cause.

MRS. BLOW. I'm afraid the President would have but little encouragement if he listened often to this kind of talk.

LINCOLN. I beg you not to harass yourself, madam. Ma'am, I too believe war to be wrong. It is the weakness and the jealousy and the folly of men that make a thing so wrong possible. But we are all weak, and jealous, and foolish. That's how the world is, ma'am, and we cannot outstrip the world. Some of the worst of us are sullen, aggressive still — just clumsy, greedy pirates. Some of us have grown out of that. But the best of us have an instinct to resist aggression if it won't listen to persuasion. You may say it's a wrong instinct. I don't know. But it's there, and it's there in millions of good men. I don't believe it's a wrong instinct. I believe that the world must come to wisdom slowly. It is for us who hate aggression to persuade men always and earnestly against it, and hope that, little by little, they will hear us. But in the mean time there will come moments when the aggressors will force the instinct to resistance to act. Then we must act earnestly, praying always in our courage that never again will this thing happen. And then we must turn again, and again, and again to persuasion. This appeal to force is the misdeed of an imperfect world. But we are imperfect. We must strive to purify the world, but we must not think ourselves pure above the world. When I had this thing to decide, it would have been easy to say, "No, I will have none of it; it is evil, and I will not touch it." But that would have decided nothing, and I saw what I believed to be the truth as I now put it to you, ma'am. It's a forlorn thing for any man to have this responsibility in his heart. I may see wrongly, but that's how I see.

MRS. BLOW. I quite agree with you, Mr. President. These brutes in the South must be taught, though I doubt whether you can teach them anything except by destroying them. That's what Goliath says.

LINCOLN. Goliath must be getting quite an old man.

MRS. BLOW. Indeed, he's not, Mr. President. Goliath is only thirty-eight.

LINCOLN. Really, now? Perhaps I might be able to get him a commission.

MRS. BLOW. Oh, no. Goliath couldn't be spared. He's doing contracts for the government, you know. Goliath couldn't possibly go. I'm sure he will be very pleased when I tell him what you say about these people who want to stop the war, Mr. President. I hope Mrs. Otherly is satisfied. Of course, we could all complain. We all have to make sacrifices, as I told Mrs. Otherly.

MRS. OTHERLY. Thank you, Mr. President, for what you've said. I must try to think about it. But I always believed war to be wrong. I didn't want my boy to go because I believed it to be wrong. But he would. That came to me last week.

[*She hands a paper to Lincoln.*

LINCOLN (*looks at it, rises, and hands it back to her*). Ma'am, there are times when no man may speak. I grieve for you, I grieve for you.

MRS. OTHERLY (*rising*). I think I will go. You don't mind my saying what I did?

LINCOLN. We are all poor creatures, ma'am. Think kindly of me. (*He takes her hand*). Mary.

[*Mrs. Lincoln goes out with Mrs. Otherly.*

MRS. BLOW. Of course it's very sad for her, poor woman. But she makes her trouble worse by these perverted views, doesn't she? And, I hope you will show no signs of weakening, Mr. President, till it has been made impossible for those shameful rebels to hold up their heads again. Goliath says you ought to make a proclamation that no mercy will be shown to them afterwards. I'm sure I shall never speak to one of them again. (*Rising*) Well, I must be going. I'll see Mrs. Lincoln as I go out. Good-afternoon, Mr. President.

[*She turns at the door, and offers Lincoln her hand, which he does not take.*

LINCOLN. Good-afternoon, madam. And I'd like to offer ye a word of advice. That poor mother told me what she thought. I don't agree with her, but I honour her. She's wrong, but she is noble. You've told me what you think. I don't agree with you, and I'm ashamed of you and your like. You, who have sacrificed nothing, babble about destroying the South while other people conquer it. I accepted this war with a sick heart, and I've a heart that's near to breaking every day. I accepted it in the name of humanity, and just and merciful dealing, and the hope of love and charity on earth.   And you come to me, talking of revenge and destruction, and malice, and enduring hate.   These gentle people are mistaken, but they are mistaken cleanly, and in a great name.   It is you that dishonour the cause for which we stand — it is you who would make it a mean and little thing.   Good-afternoon.   (*He opens the door and Mrs. Blow, finding words inadequate, goes.   Lincoln moves across the room and rings a bell.   After a moment, Susan comes in*) Susan, if that lady comes here again she may meet with an accident.

SUSAN.   Yes, sir.   Is that all, sir?

LINCOLN.   No, sir, it is not all, sir.   I don't like this coat.   I am going to change it.   I shall be back in a minute or two, and if a gentleman named Mr. William Custis calls, ask him to wait in here.

[*He goes out.   Susan collects the teacups.   As she is going to the door a quiet, grave, white-haired negro appears, facing her.   Susan starts violently.*

THE NEGRO (*he talks slowly and very quietly*).   It is all right.

SUSAN.   And who in the name of night might you be?

THE NEGRO.   Mista William Custis.   Mista Lincoln tell me to come here.   Nobody stop me, so I come to look for him.

SUSAN.   Are you Mr. William Custis?

CUSTIS.   Yes.

SUSAN.   Mr. Lincoln will be here directly.   He's gone to change his coat.   You'd better sit down.

CUSTIS.   Yes.   (*He does so, looking about him with a certain pathetic inquisitiveness*)   Mista Lincoln live here?   You his servant?   A very fine thing for young girl to be servant to Mista Lincoln.

SUSAN.   Well, we get on very well together.

CUSTIS.   A very bad thing to be slave in South.

SUSAN.   Look here, you Mr. Custis, don't you go mixing me up with slaves.

CUSTIS.   No, you not slave.   You servant, but you free body.   That very mighty thing.   A poor servant, born free.

SUSAN.   Yes, but look here, are you pitying me, with your poor servant?

CUSTIS. Pity? No. I think you very mighty.

SUSAN. Well, I don't know so much about mighty. But I expect you're right. It isn't every one that rises to the White House.

CUSTIS. It not every one that is free body. That is why you mighty.

SUSAN. I've never thought much about it.

CUSTIS. I think always about it.

SUSAN. I suppose you're free, aren't you?

CUSTIS. Yes. Not born free. I was beaten when I a little nigger. I saw my mother — I will not remember what I saw.

SUSAN. I'm sorry, Mr. Custis. That was wrong.

CUSTIS. Yes. Wrong.

SUSAN. Are all nig — I mean are all black gentlemen like you?

CUSTIS. No. I have advantages. They not many have advantages.

SUSAN. No, I suppose not. Here's Mr. Lincoln coming. (*Lincoln, coated after his heart's desire, comes to the door. Custis rises*) This is the gentleman you said, sir. [*She goes out with the tray.*

LINCOLN. Mr. Custis, I'm very glad to see you. (*He offers his hand. Custis takes it, and is about to kiss it. Lincoln stops him gently. Sitting*) Sit down, will you?

CUSTIS (*still standing, keeping his hat in his hand*). It very kind of Mista Lincoln ask me to come to see him.

LINCOLN. I was afraid you might refuse.

CUSTIS. A little shy? Yes. But so much to ask. Glad to come.

LINCOLN. Please sit down.

CUSTIS. Polite?

LINCOLN. Please. I can't sit myself, you see, if you don't.

CUSTIS. Black, black. White, white.

LINCOLN. Nonsense. Just two old men, sitting together (*Custis sits to Lincoln's gesture*) — and talking.

CUSTIS. I think I older man than Mista Lincoln.

LINCOLN. Yes, I expect you are. I'm fifty-four.

CUSTIS. I seventy-two.

LINCOLN.　I hope I shall look as young when I'm seventy-two.

CUSTIS.　Cold water.　Much walk.　Believe in Lord Jesus Christ.　Have always little herbs learnt when a little nigger. Mista Lincoln try.　Very good.

[*He hands a small twist of paper to Lincoln.*

LINCOLN.　Now, that's uncommon kind of you.　Thank you. I've heard much about your preaching, Mr. Custis.

CUSTIS.　Yes.

LINCOLN.　I should like to hear you.

CUSTIS.　Mista Lincoln great friend of my people.

LINCOLN.　I have come at length to a decision.

CUSTIS.　A decision?

LINCOLN.　Slavery is going.　We have been resolved always to confine it.　Now it shall be abolished.

CUSTIS.　You sure?

LINCOLN.　Sure.

[*Custis slowly stands up, bows his head, and sits again.*

CUSTIS.　My people much to learn.　Years, and years, and years.　Ignorant, frightened, suspicious people.　It will be difficult, very slow.　(*With growing passion*) But born free bodies.　Free.　I born slave, Mista Lincoln.　No man understand who not born slave.

LINCOLN.　Yes, yes.　I understand.

CUSTIS (*with his normal regularity*).　I think so.　Yes.

LINCOLN.　I should like you to ask me any question you wish.

CUSTIS.　I have some complaint.　Perhaps I not understand.

LINCOLN.　Tell me.

CUSTIS.　Southern soldiers take some black men prisoner. Black men in your uniform.　Take them prisoner.　Then murder them.

LINCOLN.　I know.

CUSTIS.　What you do?

LINCOLN.　We have sent a protest.

CUSTIS.　No good.　Must do more.

LINCOLN.　What more can we do?

CUSTIS.　You know.

LINCOLN.　Yes; but don't ask me for reprisals.

CUSTIS (*gleaming*).   Eye for an eye, tooth for a tooth.

LINCOLN.   No, no.   You must think.   Think what you are saying.

CUSTIS.   I think of murdered black men.

LINCOLN.   You would not ask me to murder?

CUSTIS.   Punish — not murder.

LINCOLN.   Yes, murder.   How can I kill men in cold blood for what has been done by others?   Think what would follow. It is for us to set a great example, not to follow a wicked one.   You do believe that, don't you?

CUSTIS (*after a pause*).   I know.   Yes.   Let your light so shine before men.   I trust Mista Lincoln.   Will trust.   I was wrong.   I was too sorry for my people.

LINCOLN.   Will you remember this?   For more than two years I have thought of you every day.   I have grown a weary man with thinking.   But I shall not forget.   I promise that.

CUSTIS.   You great, kind friend.   I will love you.

[*A knock at the door.*

LINCOLN.   Yes.

[*Susan comes in.*

SUSAN.   An officer gentleman.   He says it's very important.

LINCOLN.   I'll come.   (*He and Custis rise*) Wait, will you, Mr. Custis?   I want to ask you some questions.

[*He goes out.   It is getting dark, and Susan lights a lamp and draws the curtains.   Custis stands by the door looking after Lincoln.*

CUSTIS.   He very good man.

SUSAN.   You've found that out, have you?

CUSTIS.   Do you love him, you white girl?

SUSAN.   Of course I do.

CUSTIS.   Yes, you must.

SUSAN.   He's a real white man.   No offence, of course.

CUSTIS.   Not offend.   He talk to me as if black no difference.

SUSAN.   But I tell you what, Mr. Custis.   He'll kill himself over this war, his heart's that kind — like a shorn lamb, as they say.

CUSTIS.   Very unhappy war.

SUSAN.   But I suppose he's right.   It's got to go on till it's settled.

[*In the street below a body of people is heard approaching, singing " John Brown's Body."   Custis and Susan stand listening, Susan joining in the song as it passes and fades away.*

THE CURTAIN FALLS

FIRST CHRONICLER.

> Unchanged our time.   And further yet
> In loneliness must be the way,
> And difficult and deep the debt
> Of constancy to pay.

SECOND CHRONICLER.

> And one denies, and one forsakes.
> And still unquestioning he goes,
> Who has his lonely thoughts, and makes
> A world of those.

THE TWO TOGETHER.

> When the high heart we magnify,
> And the sure vision celebrate,
> And worship greatness passing by,
> Ourselves are great.

SCENE IV

About the same date.   A meeting of the Cabinet at Washington. Smith has gone and Cameron has been replaced by Edwin M. Stanton, Secretary of War.   Otherwise the ministry, completed by Seward, Chase, Hook, Blair, and Welles, is as before.   They are now arranging themselves at the table, leaving Lincoln's place empty.

SEWARD (*coming in*).   I've just had my summons.   Is there some special news?

STANTON.   Yes.   McClellan has defeated Lee at Antietam. It's our greatest success.   They ought not to recover from it.   The tide is turning.

BLAIR. Have you seen the President?

STANTON. I've just been with him.

WELLES. What does he say?

STANTON. He only said, "At last." He's coming directly.

HOOK. He will bring up his proclamation again. In my opinion it is inopportune.

SEWARD. Well, we've learnt by now that the President is the best man among us.

HOOK. There's a good deal of feeling against him everywhere, I find.

BLAIR. He's the one man with character enough for this business.

HOOK. There are other opinions.

SEWARD. Yes, but not here, surely.

HOOK. It's not for me to say. But I ask you, what does he mean about emancipation? I've always understood that it was the Union we were fighting for, and that abolition was to be kept in our minds for legislation at the right moment. And now one day he talks as though emancipation were his only concern, and the next as though he would throw up the whole idea, if by doing it he could secure peace with the establishment of the Union. Where are we?

SEWARD. No, you're wrong. It's the Union first now with him, but there's no question about his views on slavery. You know that perfectly well. But he has always kept his policy about slavery free in his mind, to be directed as he thought best for the sake of the Union. You remember his words: "If I could save the Union without freeing any slaves, I would do it; and if I could save it by freeing all the slaves, I would do it; and if I could save it by freeing some and leaving others alone, I would also do that. My paramount object in this struggle is to save the Union." Nothing could be plainer than that, just as nothing could be plainer than his determination to free the slaves when he can.

HOOK. Well, there are some who would have acted differently.

BLAIR. And you may depend upon it they would not have acted so wisely.

STANTON. I don't altogether agree with the President. But he's the only man I should agree with at all.

HOOK. To issue the proclamation now, and that's what he will propose, mark my words, will be to confuse the public mind just when we want to keep it clear.

WELLES. Are you sure he will propose to issue it now?

HOOK. You see if he doesn't.

WELLES. If he does I shall support him.

SEWARD. Is Lee's army broken?

STANTON. Not yet — but it is in grave danger.

HOOK. Why doesn't the President come? One would think this news was nothing.

CHASE. I must say I'm anxious to know what he has to say about it all.

[*A Clerk comes in.*

CLERK. The President's compliments, and he will be here in a moment.

[*He goes.*

HOOK. I shall oppose it if it comes up.

CHASE. He may say nothing about it.

SEWARD. I think he will.

STANTON. Anyhow, it's the critical moment.

BLAIR. Here he comes.

[*Lincoln comes in carrying a small book.*

LINCOLN. Good-morning, gentlemen.

[*He takes his place.*

THE MINISTERS. Good-morning, Mr. President.

SEWARD. Great news, we hear.

HOOK. If we leave things with the army to take their course for a little now, we ought to see through our difficulties.

LINCOLN. It's an exciting morning, gentlemen. I feel rather excited myself. I find my mind not at its best in excitement. Will you allow me? (*Opening his book*) It may compose us all. It is Mr. Artemus Ward's latest. (*The Ministers, with the exception of Hook, who makes no attempt to hide his irritation, and Stanton, who would do the same but for his dis-approval of Hook, listen with good-humoured patience and amuse-*

ment while he reads the following passage from Artemus Ward)
"High Handed Outrage at Utica."

"In the Faul of 1856, I showed my show in Utiky, a trooly grate city in the State of New York. The people gave me a cordyal recepshun. The press was loud in her prases. 1 day as I was givin a descripshun of my Beests and Snaiks in my usual flowry stile what was my skorn and disgust to see a big burly feller walk up to the cage containin my wax figgers of the Lord's last Supper, and cease Judas Iscarrot by the feet and drag him out on the ground. He then commenced fur to pound him as hard as he cood.

"'What under the son are you abowt,' cried I.

"Sez he, 'What did you bring this pussylanermus cuss here fur?' and he hit the wax figger another tremenjis blow on the hed.

"Sez I, 'You egrejus ass, that airs a wax figger — a representashun of the false 'Postle.'

"Sez he, 'That's all very well fur you to say; but I tell you, old man, that Judas Iscarrot can't show himself in Utiky with impunerty by a darn site,' with which observashun he kaved in Judassis hed. The young man belonged to 1 of the first famerlies in Utiky. I sood him, and the Joory brawt in a verdick of Arson in the 3d degree."

STANTON. May we now consider affairs of state?

HOOK. Yes, we may.

LINCOLN. Mr. Hook says, yes, we may.

STANTON. Thank you.

LINCOLN. Oh, no. Thank Mr. Hook.

SEWARD. McClellan is in pursuit of Lee, I suppose.

LINCOLN. You suppose a good deal. But for the first time McClellan has the chance of being in pursuit of Lee, and that's the first sign of their end. If McClellan doesn't take his chance, we'll move Grant down to the job. That will mean delay, but no matter. The mastery has changed hands.

BLAIR. Grant drinks.

LINCOLN. Then tell me the name of his brand. I'll send some barrels to the others. He wins victories.

HOOK. Is there other business?

LINCOLN. There is. Some weeks ago I showed you a draft I made proclaiming freedom for all slaves.

HOOK (*aside to Welles*). I told you so.

LINCOLN. You thought then it was not the time to issue it. I agreed. I think the moment has come. May I read it to you again? "It is proclaimed that on the first day of January in the year of our Lord one thousand eight hundred and sixty-three, all persons held as slaves within any state, the people whereof shall then be in rebellion against the United States, shall be then, thenceforward, and forever free." That allows three months from to-day. There are clauses dealing with compensation in a separate draft.

HOOK. I must oppose the issue of such a proclamation at this moment in the most unqualified terms. This question should be left until our victory is complete. To thrust it forward now would be to invite dissension when we most need unity.

WELLES. I do not quite understand, Mr. President, why you think this the precise moment.

LINCOLN. Believe me, gentlemen, I have considered this matter with all the earnestness and understanding of which I am capable.

HOOK. But when the "New York Tribune" urged you to come forward with a clear declaration six months ago, you rebuked them.

LINCOLN. Because I thought the occasion not the right one. It was useless to issue a proclamation that might be as inoperative as the Pope's bull against the comet. My duty, it has seemed to me, has been to be loyal to a principle, and not to betray it by expressing it in action at the wrong time. That is what I conceive statesmanship to be. For long now I have had two fixed resolves. To preserve the Union, and to abolish slavery. How to preserve the Union I was always clear, and more than two years of bitterness have not dulled my vision. We have fought for the Union, and we are now winning for the Union. When and how to proclaim abolition I have all this time been uncertain. I am uncertain no longer. A few weeks ago I saw that, too, clearly. So soon, I said to myself, as the rebel army shall be driven out of Maryland, and it becomes plain to the world that victory is assured to us in the end, the time will have come to announce that with that victory and a vindicated Union will come abolition. I made the promise to myself — and to my Maker. The rebel army is now driven out, and I am going to fulfil that promise. I do not wish your advice about the main matter, for that I have determined for myself. This I say without intending anything but respect for any one of you. But I beg you to stand with me in this thing.

HOOK. In my opinion, it's altogether too impetuous.

LINCOLN. One other observation I will make. I know very well that others might in this matter, as in others, do better than I can, and if I was satisfied that the public confidence was more fully possessed by any one of them than by me, and knew of any constitutional way in which he could be put in my place, he should have it. I would gladly yield it to him. But, though I cannot claim undivided confidence, I do not know that, all things considered, any other person has more; and, however this may be, there is no way in which I can have any other man put where I am. I am here; I must do the best I can, and bear the responsibility of taking the course which I feel I ought to take.

STANTON. Could this be left over a short time for consideration?

CHASE. I feel that we should remember that our only public cause at the moment is the preservation of the Union.

HOOK. I entirely agree.

LINCOLN. Gentlemen, we cannot escape history. We of this administration will be remembered in spite of ourselves. No personal significance or insignificance can spare one or another of us. In giving freedom to the slave we assure freedom to the free. We shall nobly save or meanly lose the last, best hope on earth. (*He places the proclamation in front of him*) "Shall be thenceforward and forever free." Gentlemen, I pray for your support.

[*He signs it.*

[The Ministers rise. Seward, Welles, and Blair shake Lincoln's hand and go out. Stanton and Chase bow to him, and follow. Hook, the last to rise, moves away, making no sign.

LINCOLN. Hook.

HOOK. Yes, Mr. President.

LINCOLN. Hook, one cannot help hearing things.

HOOK. I beg your pardon?

LINCOLN. Hook, there's a way some people have, when a man says a disagreeable thing, of asking him to repeat it, hoping to embarrass him. It's often effective. But I'm not easily embarrassed. I said one cannot help hearing things.

HOOK. And I do not understand what you mean, Mr. President.

LINCOLN. Come, Hook, we're alone. Lincoln is a good enough name. And I think you understand.

HOOK. How should I?

LINCOLN. Then, plainly, there are intrigues going on.

HOOK. Against the government?

LINCOLN. No. In it. Against me.

HOOK. Criticism, perhaps.

LINCOLN. To what end? To better my ways?

HOOK. I presume that might be the purpose.

LINCOLN. Then, why am I not told what it is?

HOOK. I imagine it's a natural compunction.

LINCOLN. Or ambition?

HOOK. What do you mean?

LINCOLN. You think you ought to be in my place.

HOOK. You are well informed.

LINCOLN. You cannot imagine why every one does not see that you ought to be in my place.

HOOK. By what right do you say that?

LINCOLN. Is it not true?

HOOK. You take me unprepared. You have me at a disadvantage.

LINCOLN. You speak as a very scrupulous man, Hook.

HOOK. Do you question my honour?

LINCOLN. As you will.

HOOK. Then I resign.

LINCOLN. As a protest against . . . ?

HOOK. Your suspicion.

LINCOLN. It is false?

HOOK. Very well, I will be frank. I mistrust your judgment.

LINCOLN. In what?

HOOK. Generally. You over-emphasize abolition.

LINCOLN. You don't mean that. You mean that you fear possible public feeling against abolition.

HOOK. It must be persuaded, not forced.

LINCOLN. All the most worthy elements in it are persuaded. But the ungenerous elements make the most noise, and you hear them only. You will run from the terrible name of Abolitionist even when it is pronounced by worthless creatures whom you know you have every reason to despise.

HOOK. You have, in my opinion, failed in necessary firmness in saying what will be the individual penalties of rebellion.

LINCOLN. This is a war. I will not allow it to become a blood-feud.

HOOK. We are fighting treason. We must meet it with severity.

LINCOLN. We will defeat treason. And I will meet it with conciliation.

HOOK. It is a policy of weakness.

LINCOLN. It is a policy of faith — it is a policy of compassion. (*Warmly*) Hook, why do you plague me with these jealousies? Once before I found a member of my Cabinet working behind my back. But he was disinterested, and he made amends nobly. But, Hook, you have allowed the burden of these days to sour you. I know it all. I've watched you plotting and plotting for authority. And I, who am a lonely man, have been sick at heart. So great is the task God has given to my hand, and so few are my days, and my deepest hunger is always for loyalty in my own house. You have withheld it from me. You have done great service in your office, but you have grown envious. Now you resign, as you did once before when I came openly to you in friendship. And you think that again I shall flatter you and coax you to stay. I don't think

I ought to do it.   I will not do it.   I must take you at your word.

HOOK.   I am content.

[*He turns to go.*

LINCOLN.   Will you shake hands?

HOOK.   I beg you will excuse me.

[*He goes. Lincoln stands silently for a moment, a travelled, lonely captain.   He rings a bell, and a Clerk comes in.*

LINCOLN.   Ask Mr. Hay to come in.

CLERK.   Yes, sir.

[*He goes. Lincoln, from the folds of his pockets, produces another book, and holds it unopened. Hay comes in.*

LINCOLN.   I'm rather tired to-day, Hay.   Read to me a little. (*He hands him the book*)   "The Tempest" — you know the passage.

HAY (*reading*).

> Our revels now are ended; these our actors,
> As I foretold you, were all spirits, and
> Are melted into air, into thin air;
> And, like the baseless fabric of this vision,
> The cloud-capp'd towers, the gorgeous palaces,
> The solemn temples, the great globe itself,
> Yea, all which it inherit, shall dissolve
> And, like this insubstantial pageant faded,
> Leave not a rack behind.   We are such stuff
> As dreams are made on, and our little life
> Is rounded with a sleep.

LINCOLN.

>   We are such stuff
> As dreams are made on, and our little life . . .

THE CURTAIN FALLS

FIRST CHRONICLER.

> *Two years again.*
> *Desolation of battle, and long debate,*
> *Counsels and prayers of men,*
> *And bitterness of destruction and witless hate,*

And the shame of lie contending with lie,
Are spending themselves, and the brain
That set its lonely chart four years gone by,
Knowing the word fulfilled,
Comes with charity and communion to bring
To reckoning,
To reconcile and build.

THE TWO TOGETHER.

What victor coming from the field
   Leaving the victim desolate,
But has a vulnerable shield
   Against the substances of fate?
That battle's won that leads in chains
   But retribution and despite,
And bids misfortune count her gains
   Not stricken in a penal night.

His triumph is but bitterness
   Who looks not to the starry doom
When proud and humble but possess
   The little kingdom of the tomb.
Who, striking home, shall not forgive,
   Strikes with a weak returning rod,
Claiming a fond prerogative
   Against the armoury of God.

Who knows, and for his knowledge stands
   Against the darkness in dispute,
And dedicates industrious hands,
   And keeps a spirit resolute,
Prevailing in the battle, then
   A steward of his word is made,
To bring it honour among men,
   Or know his captaincy betrayed.

Scene V

An April evening in 1865. A farmhouse near Appomattox. General Grant, Commander-in-Chief, under Lincoln, of the Northern armies, is seated at a table with Captain Malins, an aide-de-

camp. He is smoking a cigar, and at intervals he replenishes his glass of whiskey. Dennis, an orderly, sits at a table in the corner, writing.

GRANT (*consulting a large watch lying in front of him*). An hour and a half. There ought to be something more from Meade by now. Dennis.

DENNIS (*coming to the table*). Yes, sir.

GRANT. Take these papers to Captain Templeman, and ask Colonel West if the twenty-third are in action yet. Tell the cook to send some soup at ten o'clock. Say it was cold yesterday.

DENNIS. Yes, sir.

[*He goes.*

GRANT. Give me that map, Malins. (*Malins hands him the map at which he is working. After studying it in silence*) Yes. There's no doubt about it. Unless Meade goes to sleep it can only be a question of hours. Lee's a great man, but he can't get out of that.

[*Making a ring on the map with his finger.*

MALINS (*taking the map again*). This ought to be the end, sir.

GRANT. Yes. If Lee surrenders, we can all pack up for home.

MALINS. By God, sir, it will be splendid, won't it, to be back again?

GRANT. By God, sir, it will.

MALINS. I beg your pardon, sir.

GRANT. You're quite right, Malins. My boy goes to school next week. My word, I may be able to go down with him and see him settled in.

[*Dennis comes back.*

DENNIS. Colonel West says, yes, sir, for the last half-hour. The cook says he's sorry, sir. It was a mistake.

GRANT. Tell him to keep his mistakes in the kitchen.

DENNIS. I will, sir.

[*He goes back to his place.*

GRANT (*at his papers*). Those rifles went up this afternoon?

MALINS. Yes, sir.

[*Another Orderly comes in.*

ORDERLY. Mr. Lincoln has just arrived, sir. He's in the yard now.

GRANT. All right, I'll come.

[*The Orderly goes. Grant rises and crosses to the door, but is met there by Lincoln and Hay. Lincoln, in top boots and tall hat that has seen many campaigns, shakes hands with Grant and takes Malins's salute.*

GRANT. I wasn't expecting you, sir.

LINCOLN. No; but I couldn't keep away. How's it going?

[*They sit.*

GRANT. Meade sent word an hour and a half ago that Lee was surrounded all but two miles, which was closing in.

LINCOLN. That ought about to settle it, eh?

GRANT. Unless anything goes wrong in those two miles, sir. I'm expecting a further report from Meade every minute.

LINCOLN. Would there be more fighting?

GRANT. It will probably mean fighting through the night, more or less. But Lee must realise it's hopeless by the morning.

AN ORDERLY (*entering*). A despatch, sir.

GRANT. Yes.

[*The Orderly goes, and a young Officer comes in from the field. He salutes and hands a despatch to Grant.*

OFFICER. From General Meade, sir.

GRANT (*taking it*). Thank you. (*He opens it and reads*) You needn't wait. (*The Officer salutes and goes*) Yes, they've closed the ring. Meade gives them ten hours. It's timed at eight. That's six o'clock in the morning.

[*He hands the despatch to Lincoln.*

LINCOLN. We must be merciful. Bob Lee has been a gallant fellow.

GRANT (*taking a paper*). Perhaps you'll look through this list, sir. I hope it's the last we shall have.

LINCOLN (*taking the paper*). It's a horrible part of the business, Grant. Any shootings?

GRANT. One.

LINCOLN. Damn it, Grant, why can't you do without it? No, no, of course not? Who is it?

GRANT. Malins.

MALINS (*opening a book*). William Scott, sir. It's rather a hard case.

LINCOLN. What is it?

MALINS. He had just done a heavy march, sir, and volunteered for double guard duty to relieve a sick friend. He was found asleep at his post.

[*He shuts the book.*

GRANT. I was anxious to spare him. But it couldn't be done. It was a critical place, at a gravely critical time.

LINCOLN. When is it to be?

MALINS. To-morrow, at daybreak, sir.

LINCOLN. I don't see that it will do him any good to be shot. Where is he?

MALINS. Here, sir.

LINCOLN. Can I go and see him?

GRANT. Where is he?

MALINS. In the barn, I believe, sir.

GRANT. Dennis.

DENNIS (*coming from his table*). Yes, sir.

GRANT. Ask them to bring Scott in here. (*Dennis goes*) I want to see Colonel West. Malins, ask Templeman if those figures are ready yet.

[*He goes, and Malins follows.*

LINCOLN. Will you, Hay?

[*Hay goes. After a moment, during which Lincoln takes the book that Malins has been reading from, and looks into it, William Scott is brought in under guard. He is a boy of twenty.*

LINCOLN (*to the Guard*). Thank you. Wait outside, will you? (*The men salute and withdraw*) Are you William Scott?

SCOTT. Yes, sir.

LINCOLN. You know who I am?

SCOTT. Yes, sir.

LINCOLN. The General tells me you've been court-martialled.

SCOTT. Yes, sir.

LINCOLN. Asleep on guard?

SCOTT. Yes, sir.

LINCOLN. It's a very serious offence.

SCOTT. I know, sir.

LINCOLN. What was it?

SCOTT (*a pause*). I couldn't keep awake, sir.

LINCOLN. You'd had a long march?

SCOTT. Twenty-three miles, sir.

LINCOLN. You were doing double guard?

SCOTT. Yes, sir.

LINCOLN. Who ordered you?

SCOTT. Well, sir, I offered.

LINCOLN. Why?

SCOTT. Enoch White — he was sick, sir. We come from the same place.

LINCOLN. Where's that?

SCOTT. Vermont, sir.

LINCOLN. You live there?

SCOTT. Yes, sir. My — we've got a farm down there, sir.

LINCOLN. Who has?

SCOTT. My mother, sir. I've got her photograph, sir.
[*He takes it from his pocket.*

LINCOLN (*taking it*). Does she know about this?

SCOTT. For God's sake, don't, sir.

LINCOLN. There, there, my boy. You're not going to be shot.

SCOTT (*after a pause*). Not going to be shot, sir?

LINCOLN. No, no.

SCOTT. Not — going — to — be — shot.
[*He breaks down, sobbing.*

LINCOLN (*rising and going to him*). There, there. I believe you when you tell me that you couldn't keep awake. I'm going to trust you, and send you back to your regiment.
[*He goes back to his seat.*

SCOTT. When may I go back, sir?

LINCOLN. You can go back to-morrow. I expect the fighting will be over, though.

SCOTT. Is it over yet, sir?

LINCOLN. Not quite.

SCOTT. Please, sir, let me go back to-night — let me go back to-night.

LINCOLN. Very well. (*He writes*) Do you know where General Meade is?

SCOTT. No, sir.

LINCOLN. Ask one of those men to come here.

[*Scott calls one of his guards in.*

LINCOLN. Your prisoner is discharged. Take him at once to General Meade with this.

[*He hands a note to the man.*

THE SOLDIER. Yes, sir.

SCOTT. Thank you, sir.

[*He salutes and goes out with the soldier.*

LINCOLN. Hay.

HAY (*outside*). Yes, sir.

[*He comes in.*

LINCOLN. What's the time?

HAY (*looking at the watch on the table*). Just on half-past nine, sir.

LINCOLN. I shall sleep here for a little. You'd better shake down too. They'll wake us if there's any news.

[*Lincoln wraps himself up on two chairs. Hay follows suit on a bench. After a few moments Grant comes to the door, sees what has happened, blows out the candles quietly, and goes away.*

THE CURTAIN FALLS

THE FIRST CHRONICLER.

> *Under the stars an end is made,*
> *And on the field the Southern blade*
> *Lies broken,*
> *And, where strife was, shall union be,*
> *And, where was bondage, liberty.*
> *The word is spoken. . . .*
> *Night passes.*

The Curtain rises on the same scene, Lincoln and Hay still lying asleep. The light of dawn fills the room. The Orderly comes in with two smoking cups of coffee and some biscuits. Lincoln wakes.

LINCOLN. Good-morning.

ORDERLY. Good-morning, sir.

LINCOLN (*taking coffee and biscuits*). Thank you.

[*The Orderly turns to Hay, who sleeps on, and he hesitates.*

LINCOLN. Hay. (*Shouting*) Hay.

HAY (*starting up*). Hullo! What the devil is it? I beg your pardon, sir.

LINCOLN. Not at all. Take a little coffee.

HAY. Thank you, sir.

[*He takes coffee and biscuits. The Orderly goes.*

LINCOLN. Slept well, Hay?

HAY. I feel a little crumpled, sir. I think I fell off once.

LINCOLN. What's the time?

HAY (*looking at the watch*). Six o'clock, sir.

[*Grant comes in.*

GRANT. Good-morning, sir; good-morning, Hay.

LINCOLN. Good-morning, general.

HAY. Good-morning, sir.

GRANT. I didn't disturb you last night. A message has just come from Meade. Lee asked for an armistice at four o'clock.

LINCOLN (*after a silence*). For four years life has been but the hope of this moment. It is strange how simple it is when it comes. Grant, you've served the country very truly. And you've made my work possible. (*He takes his hand*) Thank you.

GRANT. Had I failed, the fault would not have been yours, sir. I succeeded because you believed in me.

LINCOLN. Where is Lee?

GRANT. He's coming here. Meade should arrive directly.

LINCOLN. Where will Lee wait?

GRANT. There's a room ready for him. Will you receive him, sir?

LINCOLN. No, no, Grant. That's your affair. You are to mention no political matters. Be generous. But I needn't say that.

GRANT (*taking a paper from his pocket*). Those are the terms I suggest.

LINCOLN (*reading*). Yes, yes. They do you honour.

[*He places the paper on the table. An Orderly comes in.*

ORDERLY. General Meade is here, sir.

GRANT. Ask him to come here.

ORDERLY. Yes, sir.

[*He goes.*

GRANT. I learnt a good deal from Robert Lee in early days. He's a better man than most of us. This business will go pretty near the heart, sir.

LINCOLN. I'm glad it's to be done by a brave gentleman, Grant. (*General Meade and Captain Sone, his aide-de-camp, come in. Meade salutes*) Congratulations, Meade. You've done well.

MEADE. Thank you, sir.

GRANT. Was there much more fighting?

MEADE. Pretty hot for an hour or two.

GRANT. How long will Lee be?

MEADE. Only a few minutes, I should say, sir.

GRANT. You said nothing about terms?

MEADE. No, sir.

LINCOLN. Did a boy Scott come to you?

MEADE. Yes, sir. He went into action at once. He was killed, wasn't he, Sone?

SONE. Yes, sir.

LINCOLN. Killed? It's a queer world, Grant.

MEADE. Is there any proclamation to be made, sir, about the rebels?

GRANT. I —

LINCOLN. No, no. I'll have nothing of hanging or shooting these men, even the worst of them. Frighten them out of the country, open the gates, let down the bars, scare them off. Shoo! (*He flings out his arms*)
Good-bye, Grant. Report at Washington as soon as you can. (*He shakes hands with him*) Good-bye, gentlemen. Come along, Hay.

[*Meade salutes and Lincoln goes, followed by Hay.*

GRANT. Who is with Lee?

MEADE. Only one of his staff, sir.

GRANT. You might see Malins, will you, Sone, and let us know directly General Lee comes.

SONE. Yes, sir.

[*He goes out.*

GRANT. Well, Meade, it's been a big job.

MEADE. Yes, sir.

GRANT. We've had courage and determination. And we've had wits, to beat a great soldier. I'd say that to any man. But it's Abraham Lincoln, Meade, who has kept us a great cause clean to fight for. It does a man's heart good to know he's given victory to such a man to handle. A glass, Meade? (*Pouring out whiskey*) No? (*Drinking*) Do you know, Meade, there were fools who wanted me to oppose Lincoln for the next Presidency. I've got my vanities, but I know better than that.

[*Malins comes in.*

MALINS. General Lee is here, sir.

GRANT. Meade, will General Lee do me the honour of meeting me here? (*Meade salutes and goes*) Where the deuce is my hat, Malins? And sword.

MALINS. Here, sir.

[*Malins gets them for him. Meade and Sone come in, and stand by the door at attention. Robert Lee, General-in-Chief of the Confederate forces, comes in, followed by one of his staff. The days of critical anxiety through which he has just lived have marked themselves on Lee's face, but his groomed and punctilious toilet contrasts pointedly with Grant's unconsidered appearance. The two commanders face each other. Grant salutes and Lee replies.*

GRANT. Sir, you have given me occasion to be proud of my opponent.

LEE. I have not spared my strength. I acknowledge its defeat.

GRANT. You have come —

LEE. To ask upon what terms you will accept surrender. Yes.

GRANT (*taking the paper from the table and handing it to Lee*). They are simple. I hope you will not find them ungenerous.

LEE (*having read the terms*).   You are magnanimous, sir.   May I make one submission?

GRANT.   It would be a privilege if I could consider it.

LEE.   You allow our officers to keep their horses.   That is gracious.   Our cavalry troopers' horses also are their own.

GRANT.   I understand.   They will be needed on the farms. It shall be done.

LEE.   I thank you.   It will do much towards conciliating our people.   I accept your terms.

[*Lee unbuckles his sword, and offers it to Grant.*

GRANT.   No, no.   I should have included that.   It has but one rightful place.   I beg you.

[*Lee replaces his sword.   Grant offers his hand and Lee takes it.   They salute, and Lee turns to go.*

THE CURTAIN FALLS

THE TWO CHRONICLERS.

> *A wind blows in the night,*
> *And the pride of the rose is gone.*
> *It laboured, and was delight,*
> *And rains fell, and shone*
> *Suns of the summer days,*
> *And dews washed the bud,*
> *And thanksgiving and praise*
> *Was the rose in our blood.*
>
> *And out of the night it came,*
> *A wind, and the rose fell,*
> *Shattered its heart of flame,*
> *And how shall June tell*
> *The glory that went with May?*
> *How shall the full year keep*
> *The beauty that ere its day*
> *Was blasted into sleep?*
>
> *Roses.   Oh, heart of man:*
> *Courage, that in the prime*
> *Looked on truth, and began*
> *Conspiracies with time*

To flower upon the pain
Of dark and envious earth. . . .
A wind blows, and the brain
Is the dust that was its birth.

What shall the witness cry,
He who has seen alone
With imagination's eye
The darkness overthrown?
Hark: from the long eclipse
The wise words come —
A wind blows, and the lips
Of prophecy are dumb.

SCENE VI

*The evening of April 14, 1865. The small lounge of a theatre.
On the far side are the doors of three private boxes. There is silence
for a few moments. Then the sound of applause comes from the
auditorium beyond. The box doors are opened. In the centre box
can be seen Lincoln and Stanton, Mrs. Lincoln, another lady, and
an Officer, talking together.*

*The occupants come out from the other boxes into the lounge,
where small knots of people have gathered from different directions,
and stand or sit talking busily.*

A LADY. Very amusing, don't you think?

HER COMPANION. Oh, yes. But it's hardly true to life, is it?

ANOTHER LADY. Isn't that dark girl clever? What's her name?

A GENTLEMAN (*consulting his programme*). Eleanor Crowne.

ANOTHER GENTLEMAN. There's a terrible draught, isn't there?
I shall have a stiff neck.

HIS WIFE. You should keep your scarf on.

THE GENTLEMAN. It looks so odd.

ANOTHER LADY. The President looks very happy this evening,
doesn't he?

ANOTHER. No wonder, is it? He must be a proud man.

[*A young man, dressed in black, passes among the people, glancing furtively into Lincoln's box, and disappears. It is John
Wilkes Booth.*

A LADY (*greeting another*). Ah, Mrs. Bennington. When do you expect your husband back?

[*They drift away. Susan, carrying cloaks and wraps, comes in. She goes to the box, and speaks to Mrs. Lincoln. Then she comes away, and sits down apart from the crowd to wait.*

A YOUNG MAN. I rather think of going on the stage myself. My friends tell me I'm uncommon good. Only I don't think my health would stand it.

A GIRL. Oh, it must be a very easy life. Just acting — that's easy enough.

[*A cry of "Lincoln" comes through the auditorium. It is taken up, with shouts of "The President," "Speech," "Abraham Lincoln," "Father Abraham," and so on. The conversation in the lounge stops as the talkers turn to listen. After a few moments, Lincoln is seen to rise. There is a burst of cheering. The people in the lounge stand round the box door. Lincoln holds up his hand, and there is a sudden silence.*

LINCOLN. My friends, I am touched, deeply touched, by this mark of your good-will. After four dark and difficult years, we have achieved the great purpose for which we set out. General Lee's surrender to General Grant leaves but one Confederate force in the field, and the end is immediate and certain. (*Cheers*) I have but little to say at this moment. I claim not to have controlled events, but confess plainly that events have controlled me. But as events have come before me, I have seen them always with one faith. We have preserved the American Union, and we have abolished a great wrong. (*Cheers*) The task of reconciliation, of setting order where there is now confusion, of bringing about a settlement at once just and merciful, and of directing the life of a reunited country into prosperous channels of good-will and generosity, will demand all our wisdom, all our loyalty. It is the proudest hope of my life that I may be of some service in this work. (*Cheers*) Whatever it may be, it can be but little in return for all the kindness and forbearance that I have received. With malice toward none, with charity for all, it is for us to resolve that this nation, under God, shall have a new birth of freedom; and that government of the people, by the people, for the people, shall not perish from the earth.

[*There is a great sound of cheering. It dies down, and a boy passes through the lounge and calls out* "Last act, ladies and gentlemen." *The people disperse, and the box doors are closed. Susan is left alone and there is silence.*

[*After a few moments, Booth appears. He watches Susan and sees that her gaze is fixed away from him. He creeps along to the centre box and disengages a hand from under his cloak. It holds a revolver. Poising himself, he opens the door with a swift movement, fires, flings the door to again, and rushes away. The door is thrown open again, and the Officer follows in pursuit. Inside the box, Mrs. Lincoln is kneeling by her husband, who is supported by Stanton. A doctor runs across the lounge and goes into the box. There is complete silence in the theatre. The door closes again.*

SUSAN (*who has run to the box door, and is kneeling there, sobbing*). Master, master! No, no, not my master!

[*The other box doors have opened, and the occupants with others have collected in little terror-struck groups in the lounge. Then the centre door opens, and Stanton comes out, closing it behind him.*

STANTON.   Now he belongs to the ages.

THE CHRONICLERS speak.

FIRST CHRONICLER.

> Events go by. And upon circumstance
> Disaster strikes with the blind sweep of chance,
> And this our mimic action was a theme,
> Kinsmen, as life is, clouded as a dream.

SECOND CHRONICLER.

> But, as we spoke, presiding everywhere
> Upon event was one man's character.
> And that endures; it is the token sent
> Always to man for man's own government.

THE CURTAIN FALLS

THE END

THE BIRTHDAY OF THE INFANTA

MR. STUART WALKER has made a very charming dramatization of Oscar Wilde's story of this name. He made it for his Portmanteau Theater which was described in the first "Treasury of Plays for Children." This traveling playhouse, which was so small that it could be crammed into a few suit-cases and taken anywhere, is one of the present Editor's pleasant recollections in the theater. Here was an idea which, seemingly abandoned by Mr. Walker, should not be allowed to die, for it is so practical, so easily within the reach of the farthest removed little village. If there is a desire to establish a Children's Theater, here is the way to start one, with the smallest outlay of expense. It is not necessary to have a theater building; the most essential requirements are a pair of graceful curtains, warm in color; against these curtains almost any simple scene may be enacted. In "The Birthday of the Infanta", the situation that is described would be very beautiful indeed; in fact, Mr. Walker's production gave to the eye many of the details in the stage directions. But to me everything could very well be dispensed with except the curtains, a draped mirror, and a few formal chairs. With these, in whatever room of the house you cared to use, this little play could be "set up" with ease.

It is to be hoped that most young readers are familiar with all of Oscar Wilde's "Fairy Tales." If they are, they can read the story of "The Birthday of the Infanta", and then Mr. Walker's version of it, and they will understand what is meant by the dramatization of a story. While a play is "dialogue" or "conversation", it is something more than that. And while the dresses of the actors will suggest to you much of the Spanish color, so too must the dialogue give you an idea of the terrific dignity of an Infanta's life and the awful sedateness of her birthday. If young actors are going to play in this piece, I should strongly advise first reading the story. For there is much color in the descriptions which Mr. Walker, being a dramatist, could only suggest. A play cannot stop long to describe things. Yet it is surprising how much Mr. Walker has put into the small compass of his play.

Listen to how Oscar Wilde starts the adventures of the *Infanta's* birthday. It will give you some idea of the manner in which Court children were dressed, and, maybe in some old trunks or among some discarded finery of the elders, you will find a few things approaching all this richness.

It was the birthday of the Infanta. She was just twelve years of age, and the sun was shining brightly in the gardens of the palace.

Although she was a real Princess and the Infanta of Spain, she had only one birthday every year, just like the children of quite poor people, so it was naturally a matter of great importance to the whole country that she should have a really fine day for the occasion. And a really fine day it certainly was. The tall striped tulips stood straight up upon their stalks, like long rows of soldiers, and looked defiantly across the grass at the roses and said : "We are quite as splendid as you are now." The purple butterflies fluttered about with gold-dust on their wings, visiting each flower in turn ; the little lizards crept out of the crevices of the wall, and lay basking in the white glare ; and the pomegranates split and cracked with the heat, and showed their bleeding red hearts. Even the pale yellow lemons, that hung in such profusion from the mouldering trellis and along the dim arcades, seemed to have caught a richer colour from the wonderful sunlight, and the magnolia trees opened their great globe-like blossoms of folded ivory, and filled the air with a sweet heavy perfume.

The little Princess herself walked up and down the terrace with her companions, and played at hide and seek round the stone vases and the old moss-grown statues. On ordinary days she was only allowed to play with children of her own rank, so she had always to play alone, but her birthday was an exception and the King had given orders that she was to invite any of her young friends whom she liked to come and amuse themselves with her. There was a stately grace about these slim Spanish children as they glided about, the boys with their large-plumed

hats and short fluttering cloaks, the girls holding up the trains
of their long brocaded gowns, and shielding the sun from their
eyes with huge fans of black and silver.   But the Infanta was
the most graceful of all, and the most tastefully attired, after
the somewhat cumbrous fashion of the day.   Her robe was of
grey satin, the skirt and the wide puffed sleeves heavily embroidered with silver, and the stiff corset studded with rows of
fine pearls.   Two tiny slippers with big pink rosettes peeped
out beneath her dress as she walked.   Pink and pearl was her
great gauze fan, and in her hair, which like an aureole of faded
gold stood out stiffly round her pale little face, she had a beautiful white rose.

Thus the story begins, and thus do we get a portrait of the
Infanta, which is only lacking a gold frame to hang in a portrait
gallery.   Could one ask for a better costume design?

All the stately entertainments that this little Infanta witnessed on her birthday are described by Oscar Wilde very
carefully and at length.   But Mr. Walker, the dramatist, is
only interested in one : it is that one upon which the whole
beauty of his play depends, and he can waste no time in doing
anything more than to lead up to it.   The *Dwarf* is the real
tragic hero of the piece.   Thus does Oscar Wilde describe him :

But the funniest part of the whole morning's entertainment
was undoubtedly the dancing of the little Dwarf.   When he
stumbled into the arena, waddling on his crooked legs and
wagging his huge misshapen head from side to side, the children
went off into a loud shout of delight, and the Infanta herself
laughed so much that the Camerera was obliged to remind her
that although there were many precedents in Spain for a King's
daughter weeping before her equals, there were none for a
Princess of the blood royal making so merry before those who
were her inferiors in birth.   The Dwarf, however, was really
quite irresistible, and even at the Spanish Court, always noted
for its cultivated passion for the horrible, so fantastic a little
monster had never been seen.   It was his first appearance, too.
He had been discovered only the day before, running wild
through the forest, by two of the nobles who happened to have
been hunting in a remote part of the great cork wood that surrounded the town, and had been carried off by them to the
palace as a surprise for the Infanta ; his father, who was a poor

charcoal-burner, being but too well pleased to get rid of so ugly and useless a child.   Perhaps the most amusing thing about him was his complete unconsciousness of his own grotesque appearance.   Indeed he seemed quite happy and full of the highest spirits.   When the children laughed, he laughed as freely and as joyously as any of them, and at the close of each dance he made them each the funniest of bows, smiling and nodding at them just as if he was really one of themselves, and not a little misshapen thing that Nature, in some humourous mood, had fashioned for others to mock at.   As for the Infanta, she absolutely fascinated him.   He could not keep his eyes off her, and seemed to dance for her alone, and when, at the close of the performance, remembering how she had seen the great ladies of the Court throw bouquets at Caffarelli, the famous Italian treble, whom the Pope had sent from his own chapel to Madrid that he might cure the King's melancholy by the sweetness of his voice, she took out of her hair the beautiful white rose, and partly for a jest, and partly to tease the Camerera, threw it to him across the arena with her sweetest smile, he took the whole matter quite seriously, and pressing the flower to his rough coarse lips, he put his hand upon his heart, and sank on one knee before her, grinning from ear to ear, and with his little bright eyes sparkling with pleasure.

One could go on and print the entire story by Oscar Wilde, and there would be great entertainment in it, for it contains so much of the rich life of the Spanish Court.   Mr. Walker takes what he needs for his purpose.   He makes us love the little Dwarf, though he does not dwell as much as Oscar Wilde does on the beautiful simplicity of his character, his great love for Nature, his worship of the little Infanta and his dreams about her. What he is intent on reaching is the pathetic climax of the play and of the story too — the climax being the highest point of interest, and the point where our sympathy is roused to its greatest tension.

In a Southern town a little Boy from the West came to visit. He had been living all his small life on the plains, away from civilization; and while he had seen his face in a small piece of glass which had served his mother when she fixed her hair, and while he knew what it was to gaze at himself in a stream of water, he had never seen what he was like in all the height of his six years. He visited the Southern relatives, and found himself in a beautiful room alone. There were very sedate pictures on the wall, there were terribly heavy chairs, oaken and carved, in the corners; there were tables with heavy books upon them, and there was a bear's rug near the huge fireplace. His feet sank in plushy carpets, and the cold quiet of the room — for it was seldom used, and the windows never seemed to be opened — gave him a peculiar feeling that he was very tiny indeed. Suddenly he saw a boy on the opposite side of the room; when he moved the little lad moved too; like him, the other had a broad linen collar and cuffs and curls. He went closer; the boy opposite faced him and walked directly toward him; he waved his hand, so did the boy. Then fright took hold of the little lad and he rushed from the room screaming. For the first time he had seen a long bevel mirror and himself in it.

So you can understand, the situation in this play is not impossible. But — well, never mind the rest; let's ring up the curtain.

As a matter of record, the following needs to be noted. The first performance of "The Birthday of the Infanta", as dramatized by Mr. Walker, was in Binghamton, New York, November 4, 1916; the first time in New York City at the Princess Theater, December 11, 1916. The cast of characters was as follows:

A Page	Edgar Stehli
The Infanta of Spain	Nancy Winston
The Duchess of Albuquerque . . .	Judith Lowry
An Attendant	Edmond Crenshaw
The Fantastic	Gregory Kelly
The Chamberlain	McKay Morris
The Count of Tierra-Nueva . . .	Robert Cook

Scenery designed by Frank J. Zimmerer. Costumes and properties by Mrs. John W. Alexander, executed by the Arden Galleries. Music by Harry Gilbert. It is to be noted that Alfred Noyes's poem, "The Dwarf's Tragedy", is also based on the Oscar Wilde story.

THE BIRTHDAY OF THE INFANTA
BASED ON A STORY BY OSCAR WILDE

By STUART WALKER

THE BIRTHDAY OF THE INFANTA

(Founded on Oscar Wilde's Story)

CHARACTERS

THE INFANTA OF SPAIN
THE DUCHESS OF ALBUQUERQUE
THE COUNT OF TIERRA-NUEVA
THE CHAMBERLAIN
THE FANTASTIC
A MOORISH PAGE
ANOTHER PAGE

The scene is the royal balcony overlooking a garden.
The time is the sixteenth century.

THE BIRTHDAY OF THE INFANTA

The opening of the curtains discloses a balcony overlooking a garden. The grim stone arch frames a brilliant sky. Gay flowers and a few white roses cover the railing. A bit of gaudy awning which can be lowered over the arch flutters in the breeze. At the right is a large mirror so draped that the dull, black hangings can be lowered to cover the mirror entirely. The hangings are of velvet, powdered with suns and stars. At the left similar hangings adorn a doorway. There are rich floor coverings and several formal chairs.

A Moorish attendant in black and yellow livery enters and arranges the chairs, and stands at attention.

The Infanta enters, followed by the Duchess of Albuquerque. The Infanta is dressed in gray brocade, very, very stiff and stately. She is small, with reddish hair and a settled air of self-possession and formality. Occasionally her eyes twinkle and her feet suggest her childishness, but she soon recovers herself under the watchful eye of the Camerera, and she never really forgets that she is the Infanta of Spain.

The Infanta bows, if the slight inclination of her head can be called bowing, to the Moorish attendant. The Duchess also inclines her head and stands in the doorway.

INFANTA. I would be alone.

DUCHESS. Your Highness —

INFANTA. I would be alone.

[*The Duchess turns in the doorway and speaks to those behind her.*

DUCHESS. Her Highness would be alone. (*Then to the Infanta*) This is unheard of.

INFANTA. My birthday is rare enough to be almost unheard of, your Grace of Albuquerque. I would be alone on my birthday

— and I'm going to be alone! (*Then to the attendant*) You may go! . . . But wait. . . . (*She stands admiringly before the mirror*) Hold back the curtain. (*The attendant lifts the curtain. She preens herself*) Why do I not look so well in my own suite? See how wonderful this is here. Look at the gold in my hair.

DUCHESS. That is vanity, your Highness.

INFANTA. Can I not admire myself on my birthday? Have I so many birthdays that I must live them as I live every other day?

DUCHESS. What is wickedness on other days is also wickedness on your birthday.

INFANTA (*taking a white rose from the balustrade and trying it in her hair and at her waist*). See — see — I like it here.

[*The Duchess, outraged, speaks to the attendant.*

DUCHESS. You may go.

INFANTA. No, no — stay — draw the curtains across the mirror!

DUCHESS. What will your father say?

[*The Infanta is quite beside her little self.*

INFANTA. Draw the curtains across the mirror and hide me from myself as those curtains hide my dead mother's room!

DUCHESS. Please —

INFANTA. I have spoken, your Grace. The curtains are to be drawn. We shall have no mirror to-day.

[*The attendant closes the curtain.*

INFANTA. You may go!

[*The attendant exits.*

The Infanta goes to the balustrade and looks into the gardens below.

The Duchess, quite at a loss what to do, finally crosses to the Infanta.

DUCHESS. Your Highness, I am compelled to remonstrate with you. What will his Majesty, your father, say?

INFANTA. My father will say nothing. He does not seem to care.

DUCHESS. Oh — Oh — Oh —

INFANTA. And my uncle wishes that I were dead. . . . No

one cares. I have to be a queen all the time, and I can never be a little girl like the little girl I saw in Valladolid. She just played . . . and no one corrected her every moment.

DUCHESS. You play with the finest dolls in the world.

INFANTA. But I do not have mud like hers!

DUCHESS. Mud!

INFANTA. I'd like to smear my face!

DUCHESS. Oh!

INFANTA. And I'd like to climb a tree!

DUCHESS. Oh, your Highness, you fill me with horror! You forget that you are the daughter of a king!

INFANTA. Well, it's my birthday — and I'm tired of being a wooden body.

[*She seats herself most unmajestically on the footstool.*

DUCHESS. Such wickedness! I shall have to call the Grand Inquisitor. There is a devil in you!

INFANTA. Call him! I'll rumple my hair at him.

DUCHESS. He'll forbid you to enjoy your birthday.

INFANTA. What is it for my birthday — the same old story.

DUCHESS (*mysteriously*). Who knows?

INFANTA (*not so surely*). When I was ten, they had dancing in the garden, but I could not go amongst the little girls. They played and I looked on.

DUCHESS. An Infanta of the house of Aragon must not play with children.

INFANTA. And when I was eleven they had dancing in the garden and a shaggy bear and some Barbary apes; but I could only sit here. I couldn't touch the bear, even when he smiled at me. And when one of the apes climbed to this balustrade, you drew me away.

DUCHESS. Such animals are very dangerous, your Highness.

INFANTA. And here I am — twelve years old to-day — and still I must stay up here like a prisoner.

DUCHESS. Your Highness is very ill-tempered to-day.

INFANTA. I do not care. I do not want to be an Infanta.

DUCHESS. You are the daughter of Ferdinand, by grace of God, King of Spain!

INFANTA. Will my father come to me to-day? And will he smile?

DUCHESS. This is all for you alone.

INFANTA. Will not my sad father then come to me to-day? And will he not smile?

DUCHESS. He will see you after the surprise.

INFANTA. A surprise?

DUCHESS. Yes, your Highness.

INFANTA. What is it?

DUCHESS. I cannot tell.

INFANTA. If I guess?

DUCHESS. Perhaps.

INFANTA. It's hobby-horses!

DUCHESS. No.

[*They almost forget their royalty.*

INFANTA. It's an African juggler with two green and gold snakes in a red basket.

DUCHESS. No.

INFANTA. In a blue basket?

DUCHESS. No.

INFANTA (*ecstatically*). Three snakes?

DUCHESS. Not at all.

INFANTA (*dully*). Is it a sermon by the Grand Inquisitor?

DUCHESS. No.

INFANTA (*with new hope*). Is it a troupe of Egyptians with tambourines and zithers?

DUCHESS. No.

INFANTA. Is it something I've never seen before?

DUCHESS. Never in the palace.

INFANTA (*screaming*). It's a fantastic!

DUCHESS. Who knows?

INFANTA. Oh, it's a fantastic. It's a fantastic!

[*She dances about.*

DUCHESS. Your Highness forgets herself.

INFANTA. It's a fantastic! It's a fantastic! (*She suddenly regains her poise*) Where is my cousin, the Count of Tierra-Nueva? I shall tell him that I am to be entertained on my birthday by a fantastic. And I shall let him come here to see it.

[The Moorish attendant steps inside the door and holds the curtain aside.

INFANTA. Your Grace, inform the Chamberlain that I shall have the fantastic dance for me in my balcony. The sun in the garden hurts my eyes. Besides, I want to touch his back. *[She goes out, every inch a queen.*

DUCHESS. She has guessed. Tell the Chamberlain to send the fantastic here.

ATTENDANT. The fantastic is waiting in the ante-chamber, your Grace.

[The Duchess exits after the Infanta.
The Attendant crosses to ante-chamber.

ATTENDANT. Her Grace, the Duchess of Albuquerque, bids you enter. Inform the Chamberlain that her Highness, the Infanta, is ready for the dance.

[The Fantastic and an Attendant enter. The Fantastic is a hunchback, with a huge mane of black hair and a bright face that shows no trace of beauty, but great light and wonder.
The Fantastic looks about the balcony. It is all so strange to him. As he goes about touching the things in the place the Attendant follows him closely, watching him with eagle eyes. As the boy nears the mirror and lays his hand upon the black velvet hangings the Attendant steps in front of him and prevents his opening the curtains. The little boy then sits — a very small, misshapen little creature — on the steps of the balcony. The Chamberlain enters. He is a middle-aged man, with some tenderness left in his somewhat immobile face, and when he addresses the little boy there is a note of pathos that is almost indefinable.

CHAMBERLAIN. Little grotesque, you are to see the King's daughter!

FANTASTIC *(almost overcome)*. Where is she?

CHAMBERLAIN. Come now, you must not be afraid.

FANTASTIC. I have never seen a king's daughter.

CHAMBERLAIN. You must smile.

FANTASTIC.   Is she very big — and all bright and shiny?

CHAMBERLAIN.   Smile! You did not have such a long face yesterday. That is why we bought you.

FANTASTIC.   Will she smile upon me?

CHAMBERLAIN.   You must make her smile.

FANTASTIC.   Will she beat me if I do not make her smile?

CHAMBERLAIN.   You shall be beaten if you displease her. This is her Highness's birthday. And you are to dance for her to make her happy.

FANTASTIC.   I have never danced for a king's daughter before.

CHAMBERLAIN.   You must dance bravely before her as you danced when we found you in the woods yesterday.

FANTASTIC.   I am afraid of the King's daughter.

CHAMBERLAIN.   We cannot have fear on the Infanta's birthday. We must have happiness.

FANTASTIC.   I wish my father had not sold me.

CHAMBERLAIN.   Your father was very poor, and he wanted you to make the Infanta happy.

FANTASTIC.   My father did not care for me.

CHAMBERLAIN.   You shall make the Infanta happy.

FANTASTIC.   If you had a son would you sell him?

CHAMBERLAIN.   You were sold to the Infanta.

FANTASTIC.   Have you a son?

CHAMBERLAIN.   No.

FANTASTIC.   My father had seven sons.

CHAMBERLAIN.   I had a little boy once.

FANTASTIC.   And did you sell him?

CHAMBERLAIN.   No. He went away. . . . He died.

FANTASTIC.   Could he make the Infanta smile?

CHAMBERLAIN.   I think he could.

FANTASTIC.   Did he dance for her?

CHAMBERLAIN.   No, he rode a hobby-horse in the mock bull fight.

FANTASTIC.   What is a hobby-horse?

CHAMBERLAIN.   A hobby-horse is a make-believe horse — like the stick that you ride through the woods.

FANTASTIC.   Oh, can't I ride a hobby-horse in a bull fight?

CHAMBERLAIN. Some time. . . . If you make the Infanta happy on her birthday I'll give you a hobby-horse.

FANTASTIC. Can I ride it to-day — for her?

CHAMBERLAIN. No. You'll have to dance for her.

FANTASTIC. Is she terrible?

CHAMBERLAIN. Not if you are good.

FANTASTIC. I think — I'm afraid.

CHAMBERLAIN. Afraid? You were not afraid of the woods.

FANTASTIC. They would not hurt me. I did not have to make them smile.

CHAMBERLAIN. What will you do when you see the Infanta?

FANTASTIC. I don't know. That man who dressed me up said I must smile and bow. My smile was very funny, he said, and my bow was funnier. I didn't try to be funny.

CHAMBERLAIN. Some boys are funny even when they don't try to be.

FANTASTIC. I don't feel funny. I just feel happy, and when I am happy people laugh. . . . Did she smile upon your son when he rode the hobby-horse?

CHAMBERLAIN. She threw a rose to him.

FANTASTIC. Do you think she'll throw a rose to me? I like roses. . . . Am I like your son?

CHAMBERLAIN. My son was tall.

FANTASTIC. I would be tall and strong, too; but I broke my back, and my brothers say I am very crooked. . . . I do not know. . . . I am not as strong as they are, but I can dance and sometimes I sing, too. . . . I make up my songs as I go along. And they are good songs, too, I know, because I've heard them.

CHAMBERLAIN. How did you hear them, Señor Merry-Face?

FANTASTIC. Some one sang them back to me.

CHAMBERLAIN. A little girl, perhaps?

FANTASTIC. Some one. . . . When I sang in the valley she would mock me.

CHAMBERLAIN. Who was it? . . . Tell me.

FANTASTIC. It was Echo.

CHAMBERLAIN. Echo? And does she live near your house?

FANTASTIC.   She lives in the hills — and sometimes she used to come into the woods when it was very still.

CHAMBERLAIN.   Did you ever see Echo?

FANTASTIC.   No. You can't see her. . . . You can only hear her.

CHAMBERLAIN.   Would you like to see her?

FANTASTIC.   I always wonder if Echo might not mock my face as she mocks my voice?

CHAMBERLAIN.   Who knows?

FANTASTIC.   I go into the hills and I sing a song and then Echo sings back to me — just as I sing. . . . But when I go into the woods Echo doesn't stand in front of me — just as I look.

CHAMBERLAIN.   Haven't you ever seen yourself?

FANTASTIC.   No, but I would like to. I always make people happy when they look at me. They always laugh. Would I laugh if Echo mocked my face?

CHAMBERLAIN.   I do not know.

FANTASTIC.   Am I really happy looking?

CHAMBERLAIN.   You are a fantastic.

FANTASTIC.   That sounds happy.

CHAMBERLAIN.   I hope it always will be.

FANTASTIC.   Have you ever seen yourself?

CHAMBERLAIN.   Yes.

FANTASTIC.   Did your son see himself?

CHAMBERLAIN.   Yes.

FANTASTIC.   Where?

CHAMBERLAIN.   In a mirror.

FANTASTIC.   Is that Echo's other name?

CHAMBERLAIN.   Yes.

FANTASTIC.   Can I see myself sometime?

CHAMBERLAIN.   Yes.

FANTASTIC.   I'll sing, too.

[*The Attendant enters.*

ATTENDANT.   Her Royal Highness, the Infanta of Spain!

[*The Fantastic is very much frightened.*

CHAMBERLAIN.   Go behind the door there. . . . Wait. . . .

Be brave. . . . Smile. . . . And do not speak until you are asked to.

[*The Infanta enters sedately, followed by the Duchess and the Count of Tierra-Nueva, an unpleasant-looking boy of sixteen.*

The Chamberlain bows very low and kisses the Infanta's stiffly proffered hand.

INFANTA (*regally*). My lord Chamberlain, this is our royal birthday, and in accord with the wish of our father, the King of Spain, we are to be entertained with some mirthful sport (*suddenly a little girl*) — and I know what it is. It's a fantastic.

CHAMBERLAIN. Your Highness, it is the pleasure of the Chamberlain to His Majesty, your father, the King of Spain, to offer my felicitations this day on which God has deigned to send happiness and good fortune to Spain in your royal person. His Majesty the King through me desired to surprise you with mirth this day.

INFANTA. Is our royal father well? And does he smile to-day?

CHAMBERLAIN. His Majesty does not smile, your Highness. He cannot smile in his great grief.

INFANTA. Let the surprise be brought to us. But I guessed what it was! . . . It must be very ugly and very crooked and very, very funny to look at — or we shall be highly displeased.

[*She settles into her royal place and takes on a manner.*

The Fantastic, having been summoned by the page, barely enters the door.

The Infanta, looking royally straight before her, does not turn her head.

After a moment.

INFANTA. Well?

CHAMBERLAIN. Here is the surprise, your Highness.

[*The Fantastic is the picture of grotesque misery. He looks first at the Chamberlain and then at the Infanta. Finally she turns to him, and he tries a timid smile and an awkward bow.*

The Infanta claps her little hands and laughs in sheer delight.

The Fantastic looks desperately at the Chamberlain.

INFANTA.　Go on. . . . Isn't he funny!

CHAMBERLAIN (*to Fantastic*).　Bow again and then begin to dance.

FANTASTIC (*joyfully*).　She is only a little girl, and I've made her happy!

CHAMBERLAIN.　What will you dance, Señor Merry-Face?

FANTASTIC.　I'll dance the one I made up and no one ever saw or heard it except Echo. It's the dance of the autumn leaf. I'll show you what the autumn leaves do and I'll tell you what they say.

INFANTA.　How do you know, you comic little beast?

FANTASTIC.　I know because I live in the woods, up in the hills, and I dance with the leaves — and I have two pet wood-pigeons.

INFANTA.　Where is the music?

FANTASTIC.　I sing — it's happier that way.

INFANTA.　Dance! Dance!

[*The Fantastic bows in an absurdly grotesque way — his idea of stateliness and grace.*

INFANTA.　I've never seen such a monstrous fantastic.

COUNT.　We must touch his back before he goes — for good luck.

[*The Fantastic begins to sing and dance The Song of the Autumn Leaf.*

FANTASTIC (*singing*).

> All summer long
> I cling to the tree,
> Merrily, merrily!
> The winds play and play,
> But I cling to the tree,
> Merrily, merrily!
> The summer sun
> Is hot and gold,
> Cheerily, cheerily.
> But I hang on
> In the August heat,
> Wearily, wearily!

THE BIRTHDAY OF THE INFANTA

Infanta. — "Dance! Dance!"

I am not free,
For I have to hang
Wearily, wearily !
Until autumn frosts
Release my grasp,
Cheerily, cheerily !
Then I'm free,
All crumpled and brown
Merrily, merrily !
I roll and I blow
Up and around,
Merrily, merrily !
All crumpled and brown
In my autumn coat,
I dance in the wind,
I hide in the rain,
Dancing and blowing
And waiting for winter,
Cheerily, cheerily,
Merrily, merrily,
Wearily, wearily.

[*He falls like a dead leaf on to the floor.*
The Infanta is delighted.

INFANTA. I'm going to throw him a rose !

DUCHESS. Your Highness !

INFANTA. See — like the Court ladies to Caffarelli, the treble.
[*The Fantastic has risen and bowed in his grotesque way.*
The Infanta tosses the rose to him.
He takes it up and, bowing absurdly, presses it to his lips.

DUCHESS (*who has never smiled*). Your Highness, you must prepare for your birthday feast.

INFANTA. Oh, let him dance again ! The same dance !

DUCHESS. Think of the birthday feast, your Highness. Your father, the King of Spain ; your uncle, the Grand Inquisitor ; the noble children.

INFANTA. Once more !

DUCHESS.   Your Highness, you must see the huge birthday cake with your initials on it in painted sugar — and a silver flag. . . .

INFANTA.   Very well.   He can dance again after my siesta. . . . My cousin, I trust that you will see the next dance.

COUNT.   I'll ride a hobby-horse and he'll be the bull.   It will be very funny with such a funny bull.

[*He kisses her hand and exits the opposite way.*

The Infanta, followed by the Duchess, exits, and as she goes she looks once more at the Fantastic and breaks into a laugh.

The Fantastic is delighted and stands looking after her.

CHAMBERLAIN.   Come !

FANTASTIC (*putting out his hand*).   I think she liked me.

CHAMBERLAIN.   The Infanta of Spain is the daughter of the King of Spain.   You have made her smile.   Come !

[*They go out.*

The Attendant crosses and closes the awning.   He draws the curtains from the mirror and preens himself a bit, looking now and then until he disappears.

A sunbeam coming through the fluttering awning, strikes the mirror, and reflects on to the tesselated floor.

There is a short intermezzo.   Far-a-way harps and violins echo the Fantastic's little song.

The Fantastic enters furtively, looking about.   He takes the rose from his bosom.

FANTASTIC.   I think I'll ask her to come away with me when I've finished my dance.

[*He crosses to her door and listens.   Then smiles and skips a step or two.   He sees the sunbeam through the awning and goes to it.   He again takes the rose from his coat and holds it in the sunlight.   Again he dances to the door and listens, then he turns facing the mirror for the first time.   He breaks into a smile, but first hides the rose hastily.   He waves his hand.*

FANTASTIC.   Good morrow ! . . .   You are very funny ! . . . You are very crooked ! . . .   Don't look that way ! . . . Why do you frown at me ? . . .   Can't you talk ? . . .   You only move your lips. . . .   Oh, you funny little boy !

[*He puts his hands on his sides and breaks into a great laugh.*

FANTASTIC. If you could see yourself, you'd laugh still more.

[*He makes a mocking bow and breaks into shouts. He plays before the mirror. The mockery is too clever.*

FANTASTIC. You mock me, you little beast! . . . Stop it! Speak to me. . . . You make me afraid. . . . Like night in the forest.

[*He has never known anything like this. He is in turn enraged, terrified.*

He runs forward and puts out his hand. He rubs his hand over the face of the mirror and the cold, hard surface mystifies him. He brushes the hair from his eyes. He makes faces. He retreats. He looks about the room. He sees everything repeated in the mirror — the awning, the chairs, the sunbeam on the floor.

FANTASTIC (*calling*). Echo!

[*He strains for an answer. He hides behind a chair. He makes a plan.*

FANTASTIC. I know, miserable little monster. You sha'n't mock me.

[*He takes the rose from his coat.*

FANTASTIC. She gave me this rose. It is the only one in the world. . . . She gave it to me — to me.

[*He emerges from behind the chair and holds out the rose. With a dry sob he shrinks away and, fascinated, stares at the mirror. He compares the rose, petal by petal, terror and rage rising in him. He kisses it and presses it to his heart. Suddenly he rushes to the mirror with a cry. He touches the glass again, then with a cry of despair he hurls himself sobbing on the floor. Once more he looks upon the picture and then, covering his face with his hands, he crawls away like a wounded animal, lies moaning in the shadow and beating the ground with his impotent hands.*

The Infanta enters, followed by the Count. At the sight of the Fantastic the Infanta stops and breaks into a laugh.

INFANTA. His dancing was funny, but his acting is funnier still. Indeed he is almost as good as the puppets.

[*His sobs grow fainter and fainter. He drags himself toward the door, trying to hide his face. Then with a sudden gasp he*

clutches his side and falls back across the step and lies quite still.
The Infanta waits a moment.

INFANTA.   That is capital; it would make even my father,
the King of Spain, smile. . . .   But now you must dance for
me:

> Cheerily, cheerily!
> Merrily, merrily!
> Wearily, wearily!

COUNT.   Yes, you must get up and dance and then we'll have a
bull fight and I'll kill you.

[*The Fantastic does not answer.*

INFANTA (*stamping her foot*).   My funny little fantastic is sulk-
ing.   You must wake him up and tell him to dance for me.

COUNT.   You must dance, little monster, you must dance.   The
Infanta of Spain and the Indies wishes to be amused (*Then
to a page*)   A whipping master should be sent for.

[*The page goes out.*

COUNT.   Let's touch his back (*as the children touch his hump*)
and make a wish.

INFANTA.   I *wish* he would dance.

[*Enter the Chamberlain and the Duchess.*

DUCHESS.   Your Highness!

INFANTA.   Make him dance or I shall have him flogged.

[*The Chamberlain rushes to the body.   He kneels.   Feels the
heart — sees the sunbeam and the exposed mirror — shrugs his
shoulders — rises.*

CHAMBERLAIN.   Mi bella Princess, your funny little fantastic
will never dance again.

INFANTA (*laughing*).   But why will he not dance again?

CHAMBERLAIN.   Because his heart is broken.

INFANTA (*thinks a moment, then frowns*).   For the future let those
who come to play with me have no hearts.

[*She passes out, not deigning to look back, every inch the queen
— the disappointed, lonely, shut-in little queen.*
*The others follow her properly according to rank; but the Cham-
berlain, remembering a little boy who would ride hobby-horses*

no more in mock bull fights, returns and throws the Infanta's mantilla over the little warped body. It is a moment of glory. The Chamberlain again starts to follow his Mistress; but memory is stronger than etiquette. He goes to the Fantastic and takes up the little hand which clutches something precious. He opens the fingers and finds the rose. He holds it out and lets the petals flutter to the floor. That is all.

THE CURTAINS CLOSE

THE JOY OF GILBERT AND SULLIVAN

GILBERT and Sullivan comic operas are great fun. So thoroughly was a certain Boy I know brought up on them that he could sing most of the tunes in them long before he was ten. There was so much lilt to the lyrics, whether you understood the satire of them or not; there was so much real humor to the pictures they conjured up in one's mind; there were so many tricks to the lines — words rattled off at great speed, melodies raced to a finish without a pause; there were so many beautiful costumes to be imagined — Admirals, Heavy Dragoons, Members of Parliament, fairies, policemen and pirates — indeed an agreeable company always sure of finding sanctuary in the Nursery! Games, or if you will, "stunts", were to be had in a Gilbert and Sullivan opera: for instance, can you, without once taking breath during the test, recite (much less sing) the following, one of the verses from a song in "The Yeoman of the Guard; or, The Merryman and his Maid"?

I have a song to sing, O!

Sing me a song, O!

It was sung to the moon
By a love-lorn loon,
Who fled from the mocking throng, O!
It's the song of a merryman, moping mum,
Whose soul was sad, and whose glance was glum,
Who sipped no sup, and who craved no crumb,
As he sighed for the love of a ladye.
Heighdy! heighdy!
Misery me, lackadaydee!
He sipped no sup, and he craved no crumb,
As he sighed for the love of a ladye.

Have you ever thought of reciting at school the excellent romance of the Magnet and the Silver Churn?   You'll find it in "Patience; or Bunthorne's Bride", a jolly opera, as full of sparkling melodies as the sky is of glittering stars on an August night.   Hark you, are not the very lines singing ones to the listening ear?

A magnet hung in a hardware shop,
And all around was a loving crop
Of scissors and needles, nails and knives,
Offering love for all their lives;
But for iron the magnet felt no whim,
Though he charmed iron, it charmed not him,
From needles and nails and knives he'd turn,
For he'd set his love on a Silver Churn!
        A Silver Churn?
        A Silver Churn!
            His most æsthetic,
            Very magnetic
            Fancy took this turn —
            "If I can wheedle
            A knife or a needle,
        Why not a Silver Churn?"

And Iron and Steel expressed surprise,
The needles opened their well-drilled eyes,
The penknives felt "shut up," no doubt,
The scissors declared themselves "cut out,"
The kettles, they boiled with rage, 'tis said,
While every nail went off its head,
And hither and thither began to roam,
Till a hammer came up — and drove them home.
        It drove them home?
        It drove them home!
            While this magnetic,
            Peripatetic

Lover he lived to learn,
By no endeavour
Can a magnet ever
Attract a Silver Churn !

It is on such topsy-turvy lyrics that this little Boy I have in
mind once feasted. He didn't have any radio to bring him the
melodies straight from the stage; there were no victrolas in
those days upon which he might hear the songs whenever he
cared to turn a crank. His was a much closer connection with
the Gilbert and Sullivan operas. Around a fire in the winter
evening, on the porch in the balmy summer twilight, with the
scent of honeysuckle and cape jasmine, and always — hot or
cold, indoors or out — the guitar, he would hear these tickling,
trickling tunes. What tests the memory was put to ! Even now
whenever I listen to the *Lord Chancellor* rattling off some of his
symptoms, in "Iolanthe ; or, The Peer and the Peri", I ache at
the very twistings of the tongue called forth by Gilbert's skilful
jumble of rhyme, rhythm and reason. Listen to this verse from
the *Major-General's* song in "The Pirates of Penzance" :

I am the very pattern of a modern major-gineral,
I've information vegetable, animal, and mineral ;
I know the kings of England, and I quote the fights historical
From Marathon to Waterloo, in order categorical ;
I'm very well acquainted too with matters mathematical ;
I understand equations, both the simple and quadratical ;
About binomial theorem I'm teeming with a lot o' news —
(*Bothered for next rhyme*) — Lot o' news — lot o' news —
    (*struck with an idea*)
With many cheerful facts about the square of the hypothenuse.

In those days, the household which harbored that little Boy
was glib with Gilbert and Sullivan. The Doctor — handsome
and Southern in manner, with a high chuckle that showed his
pleasure, and a funny habit, whenever he was pleased, of pinch-
ing his well-shaped nose several times in rapid succession —
used to call regularly for these tunes and lyrics, every time he

came to the house. Against the wall the Girl would stand, flashing forth verse after verse:

> If you want a receipt for that popular mystery,
>   Known to the world as a Heavy Dragoon,
> Take all the remarkable people in history,
>   Rattle them off to a popular tune —

and . . .

But this is not an anthology of Gilbert and Sullivan; it is merely a statement of the fact that when the Boy grew up, he never forgot those times; he never lost zest for the comic operas; he made it his duty, as well as his pleasure, to go to every Gilbert and Sullivan performance he had a chance to see, whenever or wherever the time struck. They never grow stale and weary — these operas — though they flourished about the time Oscar Wilde lived, he who wrote that charming story, "The Birthday of the Infanta", upon which Mr. Stuart Walker based his equally charming play. And all of this was in the reign of Queen Victoria.

Never were two men more suited to work together than W. S. Gilbert and his musical collaborator, Arthur Sullivan. To mention one is to think of the other: their names are as necessarily linked together as the words *either, or* — *neither, nor.* The one would write the libretto, or story of the opera; and would bear in mind those twists and variations which would allow the other to compose his most effective music. The history of how these various comic operas came to be written reads in itself like a romance. As one listens to the gay, sparkling music, which seems to be twin sister to the gay, sparkling lyrics, one hardly suspects that the Sullivan who composed it was the same Sullivan who wrote "Onward, Christian Soldiers", "Nearer, My God, to Thee" and "The Lost Chord."

It is a strange thing about some of the books we like best in literature, how by chance they come into being. The writer's mind is set in motion by the slightest happening. For instance, this operetta, "The Mikado" — we wonder would it ever have been written at the moment, if at all, had not an accident occurred in Gilbert's study. On the wall there hung a beautiful old Japanese sword, suspended by a silken cord. Suddenly one day the weapon crashed to the floor and this shock started "The Mikado" on its successful journey. Other incidents may have added to the fire of Gilbert's imagination and hastened the development of the idea. Japan in those times was little known to the Western Nations: she was not then open to the new ideas which later turned her into the most progressive of Eastern States. She had only reticently shown friendly feeling to England and America, and, for her overtures of friendship, Queen Victoria had presented her with a battleship. Most likely to follow up the *entente cordiale*, Japan had reproduced for the English people a Japanese village, perfect to the smallest detail, somewhere in Knightsbridge. These events were grist to Gilbert's creative mill; but the immediate urge was the sword in his study. Surely in this case one might say that the sword was as mighty as the pen.

This is not a learned essay on Gilbert and Sullivan: it is merely salt or sugar for a dish which I verily believe needs no added salt or sugar for its relish. The Editor is merely the introducer: Reader, allow me to make known to you "The Mikado." I'm going to leave you two together, but may I, before I go, say one word more? When Gilbert in later life became Sir William — through the gracious touching of his shoulder by the sword of knighthood (his collaborator was so honored too), he and Sir Arthur no longer wrote together, which was unfortunate for both, since either was one-handed without the other. But ever the mind of Sir William dwelt tenderly on these operas which had won him fame and fortune. He was persuaded to turn "The Mikado" into a story for young people, and, when it appeared, it was illustrated by Alice B. Woodward in such manner as excellently to suggest the costumes. In this retelling, many of his lyrics were retouched, and a new version given of one of the best of the old songs. I reproduce it here as an indication that Sir William, born in 1836, never grew old. "The Mikado" was first given at the Savoy Theatre, March 14,

1885. This new "little list" song was among the very last pieces of work done by him.   He died in 1911.

KOKO'S SONG

(As used in "The Story of the Mikado."   Told by Sir W. S.
Gilbert.   New York: Alfred A. Knopf.)

As some day it may happen that a victim must be found,
    I've made a little list — I've made a little list —
Of inconvenient people who might well be underground,
        For they never would be missed — they never would be
        missed.
The donkey who of nine-times-six and eight-times-seven prates,
And stumps you with enquiries on geography and dates,
And asks for your ideas on spelling "parallelogram,"
All narrow-minded people who are stingy with their jam,
And the torture-dealing dentist, with the forceps in his fist —
They'd none of them be missed — they'd none of them be
        missed.

There's the nursemaid who each evening in curl-papers does
        your hair
    With an aggravating twist — *she* never would be missed —
And tells you that you mustn't cough or sneeze or yawn or
        stare —
    She never would be missed — I'm sure she'd not be missed.
All those who hold that children shouldn't have too much to eat,
And think cold suet pudding a delicious birthday treat,
Who say that little girls to bed at seven should be sent,
And consider pocket money isn't given to be spent,
And doctors who on giving you unpleasant draughts insist —
They never would be missed, they'd none of them be missed.

Then the teacher who for hours keeps you practising your scales
    With an ever-aching wrist — *she* never would be missed —
And children, too, who out of school are fond of telling tales —
    They never would be missed — I'm sure they'd not be
        missed.

All people who maintain (in solemn earnest — not in joke)
That quantities of sugar-plums are bad for little folk,
And those who hold the principle, unalterably fixed,
That instruction with amusement should most carefully be
      mixed;
All these (and many others) I have placed upon the list,
For they never would be missed — never, never would be missed!

There is much in "The Mikado" to remind one of the cherry blossoms in spring — the color is alluring, the fragrance is refreshing, and, to the eye, the blossoms, with fluttering petals, are grace itself. One hears the flicking of fans like bird wings; one listens to the shuffle of tiny feet, as sashes dart hither and thither like butterflies. This is such a comic opera as pleases the young. At least, so thinks the Boy who is now Grown Up.

THE MIKADO;

OR

THE TOWN OF TITIPU

A JAPANESE OPERA

By W. S. GILBERT

Produced at the Savoy Theatre, London, on Saturday, March 14th, 1885, under the management of Mr. R. D'Oyly Carte

DRAMATIS PERSONÆ

The Mikado of Japan . . .	Mr. R. Temple
Nanki-Poo, *his Son, disguised as a wandering minstrel, and in love with* Yum-Yum	Mr. Durward Lely
Ko-Ko, *Lord High Executioner of Titipu*	Mr. George Grossmith
Pooh-Bah, *Lord High Everything Else*	Mr. Rutland Barrington
Pish-Tush, *a Noble Lord* . . .	Mr. Frederick Bovill

Yum-Yum ⎫
Pitti-Sing ⎬ *Three Sisters — Wards of* Ko-Ko
Peep-Bo ⎭

⎧ Miss Leonora Braham
⎨ Miss Jessie Bond
⎩ Miss Sybil Grey

Katisha, *an elderly Lady, in love with* Nanki-Poo . . . . . Miss Rosina Brandram

Chorus of School Girls, Nobles, Guards, and Coolies

ACT I
Courtyard of Ko-Ko's official residence

ACT II
Ko-Ko's garden

THE MIKADO

ACT I

SCENE.   *Courtyard of Ko-Ko's Palace in Titipu.   Japanese Nobles discovered standing and sitting in attitudes suggested by native drawings.*

CHORUS.   If you want to know who we are,
    We are gentlemen of Japan:
  On many a vase and jar —
    On many a screen and fan,
     We figure in lively paint:
     Our attitudes queer and quaint —
    You're wrong if you think it ain't.

  If you think we are worked by strings,
    Like a Japanese marionette,
  You don't understand these things:
    It is simply Court etiquette.
     Perhaps you suppose this throng
     Can't keep it up all day long?
    If that's your idea, you're wrong.

[*Enter Nanki-Poo in great excitement.   He carries a native guitar on his back, and a bundle of ballads in his hand.*

NANKI-POO.   RECITATIVE

  Gentlemen, I pray you tell me,
  Where a lovely maiden dwelleth,
  Named Yum-Yum, the ward of Ko-Ko,
  In pity speak — oh, speak, I pray you!
A NOBLE. Why, who are you who ask this question?
NANKI-POO. Come, gather round me, and I'll tell you.

SONG

A wandering minstrel I —
  A thing of shreds and patches,
  Of ballads, songs, and snatches,
A dreamy lullaby!

My catalogue is long,
  Through every passion ranging,
  And to your humours changing
I tune my supple song!

  Are you in sentimental mood?
    I'll sigh with you,
      Oh, willow, willow!
  On maiden's coldness do you brood?
    I'll do so too —
      Oh, willow, willow!
  I'll charm your willing ears
  With songs of lover's fears,
  While sympathetic tears
    My cheeks bedew —
      Oh, willow, willow!

But if patriotic sentiment is wanted,
  I've patriotic ballads cut and dried;
For where'er our country's banner may be planted
  All other local banners are defied!
Our warriors, in serried ranks assembled,
  Never quail — or they conceal it if they do —
And I shouldn't be surprised if nations trembled
  Before the mighty troops of Titipu!

And if you call for a song of the sea,
  We'll heave the capstan round,
With a yeo heave ho, for the wind is free,
Her anchor's a-trip and her helm's a-lee,
  Hurrah for the homeward bound!
    Yeo-ho — heave ho —
  Hurrah for the homeward bound!

To lay aloft in a howling breeze
    May tickle a landsman's taste,
But the happiest hours a sailor sees
      Is when he's down
      At an inland town,
With his Nancy on his knees, yeo ho!
    And his arm around her waist!

    Then man the capstan — off we go,
      As the fiddler swings us round,
      With a yeo heave ho,
      And a rumbelow.
      Hurrah for the homeward bound!

    A wandering minstrel I, etc.

[*Enter Pish-Tush.*

PISH-TUSH. And what may be your business with Yum-Yum?

NANKI-POO. I'll tell you. A year ago I was a member of the Titipu town band. It was my duty to take the cap round for contributions. While discharging this delicate office, I saw Yum-Yum. We loved each other at once, but she was betrothed to her guardian, Ko-Ko, a cheap tailor, and I saw that my suit was hopeless. Overwhelmed with despair, I quitted the town. Judge of my delight when I heard, a month ago, that Ko-Ko had been condemned to death for flirting! I hurried back at once, in the hope of finding Yum-Yum at liberty to listen to my protestations.

PISH-TUSH. It is true that Ko-Ko was condemned to death for flirting; but he was reprieved at the last moment, and raised to the exalted rank of Lord High Executioner under the following remarkable circumstances:

SONG

Our great Mikado, virtuous man,
When he to rule our land began,
    Resolved to try
    A plan whereby
Young men might best be steadied.

So he decreed, in words succinct,
That all who flirted, leered, or winked
(Unless connubially linked),
　　Should forthwith be beheaded.

　　And I expect you'll all agree
　　That he was right to so decree.
　　　　And I am right,
　　　　And you are right,
　　And all is right as right can be!

CHORUS.　　　　And I expect, etc.

PISH-TUSH.　This stern decree, you'll understand,
Caused great dismay throughout the land;
　　　　For young and old
　　　　And shy and bold
　　Were equally affected.
The youth who winked a roving eye,
Or breathed a non-connubial sigh,
Was thereupon condemned to die —
　　He usually objected.

　　And you'll allow, as I expect,
　　That he was right to so object.
　　　　And I am right,
　　　　And you are right,
　　And everything is quite correct!

CHORUS.　　　　And you'll allow, as I expect, etc.

PISH-TUSH.　And so we straight let out on bail
A convict from the county jail,
　　　　Whose head was next,
　　　　On some pretext,
　　Condemnéd to be mown off,
And made *him* Headsman, for we said,
"Who's next to be decapited
Cannot cut off another's head
　　Until he's cut his own off."

And we are right, I think you'll say,
To argue in this kind of way,
And I am right,
And you are right,
And all is right — too-looral-lay!

CHORUS.   And they were right, etc.

[*Exeunt Chorus.*
[*Enter Pooh-Bah.*

NANKI-POO. Ko-Ko, the cheap tailor, Lord High Executioner of Titipu! Why, that's the highest rank a citizen can attain!

POOH-BAH. It is. Our logical Mikado, seeing no moral difference between the dignified judge, who condemns a criminal to die, and the industrious mechanic who carries out the sentence, has rolled the two offices into one, and every judge is now his own executioner.

NANKI-POO. But how good of you (for I see that you are a nobleman of the highest rank) to condescend to tell all this to me, a mere strolling minstrel!

POOH-BAH. Don't mention it. I am, in point of fact, a particularly haughty and exclusive person, of pre-Adamite ancestral descent. You will understand this when I tell you that I can trace my ancestry back to a protoplasmal primordial atomic globule. Consequently, my family pride is something inconceivable. I can't help it. I was born sneering. But I struggle hard to overcome this defect. I mortify my pride continually. When all the great officers of State resigned in a body, because they were too proud to serve under an ex-tailor, did I not unhesitatingly accept all their posts at once?

PISH-TUSH. And the salaries attached to them? You did.

POOH-BAH. It is consequently my degrading duty to serve this upstart as First Lord of the Treasury, Lord Chief Justice, Commander-in-Chief, Lord High Admiral, Master of the Buckhounds, Groom of the Back Stairs, Archbishop of Titipu, and Lord Mayor, both acting and elect, all rolled into one. And at a salary! A Pooh-Bah paid for his services! I a salaried minion! But I do it! It revolts me, but I do it.

NANKI-POO. And it does you credit.

POOH-BAH. But I don't stop at that. I go and dine with middle-class people on reasonable terms. I dance at cheap suburban parties for a moderate fee. I accept refreshment at any hands, however lowly. I also retail State secrets at a very low figure. For instance, any further information about Yum-Yum would come under the head of a State secret. (*Nanki-Poo takes the hint, and gives him money. Aside*) Another insult, and, I think, a light one!

SONG

Young man, despair,
Likewise go to,
Yum-Yum the fair
You must not woo.
It will not do:
I'm sorry for you,
You very imperfect ablutioner!
This very day
From school Yum-Yum
Will wend her way,
And homeward come
With beat of drum,
And a rum-tum-tum,
To wed the Lord High Executioner!
And the brass will crash,
And the trumpets bray,
And they'll cut a dash
On their wedding-day.
From what I say, you may infer
It's as good as a play for him and her,
She'll toddle away, as all aver,
With the Lord High Executioner!

It's a hopeless case
As you may see,
And in your place
Away I'd flee;
But don't blame me —
I'm sorry to be
Of your pleasure a diminutioner.
They'll vow their pact
Extremely soon,
In point of fact
This afternoon
Her honeymoon,
With that buffoon,
At seven, commences, so *you* shun her :

ALL.   The brass will crash, etc.

RECITATIVE

NANKI-POO.   And have I journeyed for a month, or nearly,
To learn that Yum-Yum, whom I love so dearly
This day to Ko-Ko is to be united !

POOH-BAH.   The fact appears to be as you've recited :
But here he comes, equipped as suits his station :
He'll give you any further information.

[*Enter Ko-Ko, attended.*

CHORUS.   Behold the Lord High Executioner !
A personage of noble rank and title —
A dignified and potent officer,
Whose functions are particularly vital.
Defer, defer,
To the noble Lord High Executioner !

SOLO

KO-KO.   Taken from the county jail
By a set of curious chances;
Liberated then on bail,
On my own recognizances;

> Wafted by a favouring gale,
>   As one sometimes is in trances,
> To a height that few can scale,
>   Save by long and weary dances;
> Surely, never had a male
>   Under such like circumstances
> So adventurous a tale,
>   Which may rank with most romances.

CHORUS.   Behold the Lord High Executioner, etc.

KO-KO.   Gentlemen, I'm much touched by this reception. I can only trust that by strict attention to duty I shall ensure a continuance of those favours which it will ever be my study to deserve. Gentlemen, I expect my three beautiful wards, Yum-Yum, Peep-Bo, and Pitti-Sing, in a few minutes. If you will kindly receive them with a show of abject deference, I shall feel obliged to you. I know how painful it must be to noblemen of your rank to have to humilate yourselves before a person of my antecedents, but discipline must be observed. (*Chorus bow and exeunt*)* Pooh-Bah, it seems that the

---

* In other editions, the Lord High Executioner suggests that he is "happy to think that" (should he ever be called upon to act professionally) "there will be no difficulty in finding plenty of people whose loss will be a distinct gain to society." With Chorus he sings:

SONG

KO-KO.   As some day it may happen that a victim must be found,
        I've got a little list — I've got a little list
    Of social offenders who might well be underground,
        And who never would be missed — who never would be missed!
    There's the pestilential nuisances who write for autographs —
        All people who have flabby hands and irritating laughs —
        All children who are up in dates, and floor you with 'em flat —
        All persons who in shaking hands, shake hands with you like *that* —
        And all third persons who on spoiling *tête-à-têtes* insist —
        They'd none of 'em be missed — they'd none of 'em be missed!

CHORUS.   He's got 'em on the list — he's got 'em on the list;
        And they'll none of 'em be missed — they'll none of 'em be missed!

KO-KO.   There's the nigger serenader, and the others of his race,
        And the piano-organist — I've got him on the list!

festivities in connection with my approaching marriage must last a week. I should like to do it handsomely, and I want to consult you as to the amount I ought to spend upon them.

POOH-BAH. Certainly. In which of my capacities? As First Lord of the Treasury, Lord Chamberlain, Attorney-General, Chancellor of the Exchequer, Privy Purse, or Private Secretary?

KO-KO. Suppose we say as Private Secretary.

POOH-BAH. Speaking as your Private Secretary, I should say that, as the city will have to pay for it, don't stint yourself, do it well.

KO-KO. Exactly — as the city will have to pay for it. That is your advice.

POOH-BAH. As Private Secretary. Of course you will understand that, as Chancellor of the Exchequer, I am bound to see that due economy is observed.

KO-KO. Oh. But you said just now, "Don't stint yourself, do it well."

And the people who eat peppermint and puff it in your face,
   They never would be missed — they never would be missed!
Then the idiot who praises, with enthusiastic tone,
All centuries but this, and every country but his own;
And the lady from the provinces, who dresses like a guy,
And "who doesn't think she waltzes, but would rather like to try!"
And that singular anomaly, the lady novelist —
   I don't think she'd be missed — I'm *sure* she'd not be missed!

CHORUS. He's got her on the list — he's got her on the list;
   And I don't think she'll be missed — I'm *sure* she'll not be missed!

KO-KO. And that *Nisi Prius* nuisance, who just now is rather rife,
   The Judicial humorist — I've got *him* on the list!
All funny fellows, comic men, and clowns of private life —
   They'd none of 'em be missed — they'd none of 'em be missed!
And apologetic statesmen of a compromising kind,
Such as — What d'ye call him — Thing'em bob, and likewise
   Never Mind,
And 'St—'st—'st— and What's-his-name, and also You-know-who —
The task of filling up the blanks I'd rather leave to *you*.
But it really doesn't matter whom you put upon the list,
   For they'd none of 'em be missed — they'd none of 'em be missed!

CHORUS. You may put 'em on the list — you may put 'em on the list;
   And they'll none of 'em be missed — they'll none of 'em be missed!

POOH-BAH. As Private Secretary.

KO-KO. And now you say that due economy must be observed.

POOH-BAH. As Chancellor of the Exchequer.

KO-KO. I see. Come over here, where the Chancellor can't hear us. (*They cross stage*) Now, as my Solicitor, how do you advise me to deal with this difficulty?

POOH-BAH. Oh, as your Solicitor, I should have no hesitation in saying, "Chance it —"

KO-KO. Thank you. (*Shaking his hand*) I will.

POOH-BAH. If it were not that, as Lord Chief Justice, I am bound to see that the law isn't violated.

KO-KO. I see. Come over here where the Chief Justice can't hear us. (*They cross the stage*) Now, then, as First Lord of the Treasury?

POOH-BAH. Of course, as First Lord of the Treasury, I could propose a special vote that would cover all expenses, if it were not that, as leader of the Opposition, it would be my duty to resist it, tooth and nail. Or, as Paymaster-General, I could so cook the accounts, that as Lord High Auditor I should never discover the fraud. But then, as Archbishop of Titipu, it would be my duty to denounce my dishonesty and give myself into my own custody as First Commissioner of Police.

KO-KO. That's extremely awkward.

POOH-BAH. I don't say that all these people couldn't be squared; but it is right to tell you that I shouldn't be sufficiently degraded in my own estimation unless I was insulted with a very considerable bribe.

KO-KO. The matter shall have my careful consideration. But my bride and her sisters approach, and any little compliment on your part, such as an abject grovel in a characteristic Japanese attitude, would be esteemed a favour.

[*Enter procession of Yum-Yum's schoolfellows, heralding Yum-Yum, Peep-Bo, and Pitti-Sing.*

CHORUS.   Comes a train of little ladies
    From scholastic trammels free,
    Each a little bit afraid is,
    Wondering what the world can be!

Is it but a world of trouble —
Sadness set to song?
Is its beauty but a bubble
Bound to break ere long?

Are its palaces and pleasures
Fantasies that fade?
And the glory of its treasures
Shadow of a shade?

Schoolgirls we, eighteen and under,
From scholastic trammels free,
And we wonder — how we wonder! —
What on earth the world can be!

TRIO

YUM-YUM, PEEP-BO, AND PITTI-SING.
Three little maids from school are we,
Pert as a schoolgirl well can be,
Filled to the brim with girlish glee,
Three little maids from school!

YUM-YUM.   Everything is a source of fun.   (*Chuckle*)
PEEP-BO.   Nobody's safe, for we care for none! (*Chuckle*)
PITTI-SING.   Life is a joke that's just begun!   (*Chuckle*)
THE THREE.   Three little maids from school!

ALL (*dancing*).   Three little maids who, all unwary,
Come from a ladies' seminary,
Freed from its genius tutelary —
THE THREE (*suddenly demure*).   Three little maids from school!

YUM-YUM.   One little maid is a bride, Yum-Yum —
PEEP-BO.   Two little maids in attendance come —
PITTI-SING.   Three little maids is the total sum.
THE THREE.   Three little maids from school!

YUM-YUM.   From three little maids take one away —
PEEP-BO.   Two little maids remain, and they —
PITTI-SING.   Won't have to wait very long, they say —
THE THREE.   Three little maids from school!

ALL (*dancing*).   Three little maids who, all unwary,
                     Come from a ladies' seminary,
                     Freed from its genius tutelary —
THE THREE (*suddenly demure*).   Three little maids from school!

KO-KO.   At last, my bride that is to be!
  [*About to embrace her.*
YUM-YUM.   You're not going to kiss me before all these people?
KO-KO.   Well, that was the idea.
YUM-YUM (*aside to Peep-Bo*).   It seems odd, don't it?
PEEP-BO.   It's rather peculiar.
PITTI-SING.   Oh, I expect it's all right.   Must have a beginning,
  you know.
YUM-YUM.   Well, of course I know nothing about these things;
  but I've no objection if it's usual.
KO-KO.   Oh, it's quite usual, I think.   Eh, Lord Chamberlain?
  [*Appealing to Pooh-Bah.*
POOH-BAH.   I have known it done.
  [*Ko-Ko embraces her.*
YUM-YUM.   That's over!   (*Sees Nanki-Poo, and rushes to him*)
  Why, that's never you?
  [*The Three Girls rush to him and shake his hands, all speaking
  at once.*

  YUM-YUM.   Oh, I'm so glad!   I haven't seen you for ever so
    long, and I'm right at the top of the school, and I've got
    three prizes, and I've come home for good, and I'm not
    going back any more!
  PEEP-BO.   And have you got an engagement? — Yum-Yum's
    got one, but she don't like it, and she'd ever so much rather
    it was you.   I've come home for good, and I'm not going
    back any more!
  PITTI-SING.   Now tell us all the news, because you go about
    everywhere, and we've been at school; but, thank good-
    ness, that's all over now, and we've come home for good,
    and we're not going back any more!

  [*These three speeches are spoken together in one breath.*
KO-KO.   I beg your pardon.   Will you present me?

YUM-YUM. ⎰ Oh, this is the musician who used —
PEEP-BO. ⎱ Oh, this is the gentleman who used —
PITTI-SING. ⎰ Oh, it is only Nanki-Poo who used —

KO-KO. One at a time, if you please.

YUM-YUM. He's the gentleman who used to play so beautifully on the — on the —

PITTI-SING. On the Marine Parade.

YUM-YUM. Yes, I think that was the name of the instrument.

NANKI-POO. Sir, I have the misfortune to love your ward, Yum-Yum — oh, I know I deserve your anger!

KO-KO. Anger! Not a bit, my boy. Why, I love her myself. Charming little girl, isn't she? Pretty eyes, nice hair. Taking little thing, altogether. Very glad to hear my opinion backed by a competent authority. Thank you very much. Good-bye. (*To Pish-Tush*) Take him away.

[*Pish-Tush removes him.*

PITTI-SING (*who has been examining Pooh-Bah*). I beg your pardon, but what is this? Customer come to try on?

KO-KO. That is a Tremendous Swell.

[*She starts back in alarm.*

POOH-BAH. Go away, little girls. Can't talk to little girls like you. Go away, there's dears.

KO-KO. Allow me to present you, Pooh-Bah. These are my three wards. The one in the middle is my bride elect.

POOH-BAH. What do you want me to do to them? Mind, I *will not* kiss them.

KO-KO. No, no, you sha'n't kiss them : a little bow — a mere nothing — you needn't mean it, you know.

POOH-BAH. It goes against the grain. They are not young ladies, they are young persons.

KO-KO. Come, come, make an effort, there's a good nobleman.

POOH-BAH (*aside to Ko-Ko*). Well, I sha'n't mean it. (*With a great effort*) How de do, how de do, little girls! (*Aside*) Oh, my protoplasmal ancestor!

KO-KO. That's very good.

[*Girls indulge in suppressed laughter.*

POOH-BAH. I see nothing to laugh at. It is very painful to me to have to say, "How de do, how de do, little girls" to young persons. I'm not in the habit of saying "How de do, how de do, little girls" to anybody under the rank of a Stockbroker.

KO-KO (*aside to Girls*). Don't laugh at him — he's under treatment for it. (*Aside to Pooh-Bah*) Never mind them, they don't understand the delicacy of your position.

POOH-BAH. We know how delicate it is, don't we?

KO-KO. I should think we did! How a nobleman of your importance can do it at all is a thing I never can, never shall understand.

[*Ko-Ko retires up and goes off.*

QUARTETTE AND CHORUS

YUM-YUM, PEEP-BO, AND PITTI-SING.

> So please you, sir, we much regret
> If we have failed in etiquette
> Towards a man of rank so high —
> We shall know better by-and-by.
> But youth, of course, must have its fling,
> > So pardon us,
> > So pardon us,
> And don't in girlhood's happy spring,
> > Be hard on us,
> > Be hard on us,
> If we're disposed to dance and sing,
> > Tra la la, etc.

[*Dancing.*

CHORUS OF GIRLS. But youth of course, etc.

POOH-BAH.

> I think you ought to recollect
> You cannot show too much respect
> Towards the highly-titled few;
> But nobody does, and why should you?
> That youth at us should have its fling,
> > Is hard on us,
> > Is hard on us;

To our prerogative we cling —
So pardon us,
So pardon us,
If we decline to dance and sing —
Tra la la, etc.

[*Dancing.*

CHORUS OF GIRLS. But youth, of course, must have its fling, etc.

[*Exeunt all but Yum-Yum.*

YUM-YUM. How pitiable is the condition of a young and innocent child brought from the gloom of a ladies' academy into the full-blown blaze of her own marriage ceremony; and with a man for whom I care nothing! True, he loves me; but everybody does that.

[*Enter Nanki-Poo.*

NANKI-POO. Yum-Yum, at last we are alone! I have sought you night and day for three weeks, in the belief that your guardian was beheaded, and I find that you are about to be married to him this afternoon!

YUM-YUM. Alas, yes!

NANKI-POO. But you do not love him?

YUM-YUM. Alas, no!

NANKI-POO. Modified rapture! But why do you not refuse him?

YUM-YUM. What good would that do? He's my guardian, and he wouldn't let me marry you!

NANKI-POO. But I would wait until you were of age!

YUM-YUM. You forget that in Japan girls do not arrive at years of discretion until they are fifty.

NANKI-POO. True; from seventeen to forty-nine are considered years of indiscretion.

YUM-YUM. Besides, a wandering minstrel, who plays a wind instrument outside tea-houses, is hardly a fitting husband for the ward of a Lord High Executioner.

NANKI-POO. But — (*Aside*) Shall I tell her? Yes! She will not betray me! (*Aloud*) What if it should prove that, after all, I am no musician!

YUM-YUM. There! I was certain of it, directly I heard you play!

NANKI-POO. What if it should prove that I am no other than the son of his Majesty the Mikado?

YUM-YUM. The son of the Mikado! But why is your Highness disguised? And what has your Highness done? And will your Highness promise never to do it again?

NANKI-POO. Some years ago I had the misfortune to captivate Katisha, an elderly lady of my father's court. She misconstrued my customary affability into expressions of affection, and claimed me in marriage, under my father's law. My father, the Lucius Junius Brutus of his race, ordered me to marry her within a week, or perish ignominiously on the scaffold. That night I fled his court, and, assuming the disguise of a Second Trombone, I joined the band in which you found me when I had the happiness of seeing you!
[*Approaching her.*

YUM-YUM (*retreating*). If you please, I think your Highness had better not come too near. The laws against flirting are excessively severe.

NANKI-POO. But we are quite alone, and nobody can see us.

YUM-YUM. Still that don't make it right. To flirt is illegal, and we must obey the law.

NANKI-POO. Deuce take the law!

YUM-YUM. I wish it would, but it won't!

NANKI-POO. If it were not for that, how happy we might be!

YUM-YUM. Happy indeed!

NANKI-POO. If it were not for the law, we should now be sitting side by side, like that.
[*Sits by her.*

YUM-YUM. Instead of being obliged to sit half a mile off, like that.
[*Crosses and sits at other side of stage.*

NANKI-POO. We should be gazing into each other's eyes, like that.
[*Approaching and gazing at her sentimentally.*

YUM-YUM. Breathing vows of unutterable love — like that.
[*Sighing and gazing lovingly at him.*

NANKI-POO.   With our arms around each other's waists like that.
[*Embracing her.*

YUM-YUM.   Yes, if it wasn't for the law.

NANKI-POO.   If it wasn't for the law.

YUM-YUM.   As it is, of course, we couldn't do anything of the
kind.

NANKI-POO.   Not for worlds!

YUM-YUM.   Being engaged to Ko-Ko, you know!

NANKI-POO.   Being engaged to Ko-Ko!

NANKI-POO.*   So, in spite of all temptation,
   Such a theme I'll not discuss,
  And on no consideration
   Will I kiss you fondly thus — (*kissing her*)
  Let me make it clear to you,
   This, oh, this, oh, this, oh, this — (*kissing her*)
  This is what I'll never do!

[*Exeunt in opposite directions.*
[*Enter Ko-Ko.*

---

* In other editions, one finds:

DUET — YUM-YUM AND NANKI-POO

NANKI-POO.   Were you not to Ko-Ko plighted,
  I would say in tender tone,
 "Loved one, let us be united —
  Let us be each other's own!"
 I would merge all rank and station,
  Worldly sneers are nought to us,
 And, to mark my admiration,
  I would kiss you fondly thus — (*kisses her*)

BOTH. $\left\{ \begin{array}{c} \text{I} \\ \text{He} \end{array} \right\}$ would kiss $\left\{ \begin{array}{c} \text{you} \\ \text{me} \end{array} \right\}$ fondly thus — (*kiss*)

YUM-YUM.   But as I'm engaged to Ko-Ko,
  To embrace you thus, *con fuoco*,
  Would distinctly be no *gioco*,
  And for jam I should get toco —

BOTH.   Toco, toco, toco, toco.

NANKI-POO.   So, in spite of all temptation,
  Such a theme I'll not discuss,

KO-KO (*looking after Yum-Yum*). There she goes! To think how entirely my future happiness is wrapped up in that little parcel! Really, it hardly seems worth while! Oh, matrimony!

[*Enter Pooh-Bah and Pish-Tush.*

Now then, what is it? Can't you see I'm soliloquizing? You have interrupted an apostrophe, sir!

PISH-TUSH. I am the bearer of a letter from His Majesty the Mikado.

KO-KO (*taking it from him reverentially*). A letter from the Mikado! What in the world can he have to say to me? (*Reads letter*) Ah, here it is at last! I thought it would come! The Mikado is struck by the fact that no executions have taken place in Titipu for a year, and decrees that, unless someone is beheaded within one month, the post of Lord High Executioner shall be abolished, and the city reduced to the rank of a village!

PISH-TUSH. But that will involve us all in irretrievable ruin!

KO-KO. Yes. There's no help for it, I shall have to execute somebody. The only question is, who shall it be?

POOH-BAH. Well, it seems unkind to say so, but as you're already under sentence of death for flirting, everything seems to point to *you*.

KO-KO. To me? What are you talking about? I can't execute myself, Recorder!

POOH-BAH. Why not?

KO-KO. Why not? Because, in the first place, self-decapitation is an extremely difficult, not to say dangerous, thing to attempt; and, in the second, it's suicide, and suicide is a capital offense.

POOH-BAH. That is so, no doubt.

> And on no consideration
> Will I kiss you fondly thus — (*kissing her*)
> Let me make it clear to you,
> This, oh this, oh this, oh this (*kissing her*)
> This is what I'll never do!

[*Exeunt in opposite directions.*

PISH-TUSH. We might reserve that point.

POOH-BAH. True, it could be argued six months hence, before the full Court.

KO-KO. Besides, I don't see how a man *can* cut off his own head.

POOH-BAH. A man might try.

PISH-TUSH. Even if you only succeeded in cutting it half off, that would be something.

POOH-BAH. It would be taken as an earnest of your desire to comply with the Imperial will.

KO-KO. No. Pardon me, but there I am adamant. As official Headsman, my reputation is at stake, and I can't consent to embark on a professional operation unless I see my way to a successful result.

POOH-BAH. This professional conscientiousness is highly creditable to *you*, but it places us in a very awkward position.

KO-KO. My good sir, the awkwardness of your position is grace itself compared with that of a man engaged in the act of cutting off his own head.

PISH-TUSH. I am afraid that, unless you can obtain a substitute —

KO-KO. A substitute? Oh, certainly — nothing easier. (*To Pooh-Bah*) Pooh-Bah, I appoint you my substitute.

POOH-BAH. I should like it above all things. Such an appointment would realize my fondest dreams. But no, at any sacrifice, I must set bounds to my insatiable ambition!

TRIO

KO-KO	POOH-BAH	PISH-TUSH
My brain it teems	I am so proud,	I heard one day,
With endless schemes,	If I allowed	A gentleman say
Both good and new	My family pride	That criminals who
For Titipu;	To be my guide,	Are cut in two
But if I flit,	I'd volunteer	Can hardly feel
The benefit	To quit this sphere	The fatal steel,
That I'd diffuse	Instead of you,	And so are slain
The town would lose!	In a minute or two,	Without much pain.
Now every man	But family pride	If this is true
To aid his clan	Must be denied,	It's jolly for you;

TRIO (*continued*)

KO-KO	POOH-BAH	PISH-TUSH
Should plot and plan	And set aside,	Your courage screw
As well as he can,	And mortified,	To bid us adieu,
And so,	And so,	And go
Although	Although	And show
I'm ready to go,	I wish to go,	Both friend and foe
Yet recollect	And greatly pine	How much you dare,
'Twere disrespect	To brightly shine,	I'm quite aware
Did I neglect	And take the line	It's your affair,
To thus effect	Of a hero fine,	Yet I declare
This aim direct,	With grief condign	I'd take your share,
So I object —	I must decline —	But I don't much care —
So I object —	I must decline —	I don't much care —
So I object —	I must decline —	I don't much care —

All. To sit in solemn silence in a dull, dark dock,
In a pestilential prison, with a life-long lock,
Awaiting the sensation of a short, sharp shock,
From a cheap and chippy chopper on a big black block!

[*Exeunt all but Ko-Ko.*

KO-KO. This is simply appalling! I, who allowed myself to be respited at the last moment, simply in order to benefit my native town, am now required to die within a month, and that by a man whom I have loaded with honours! Is this public gratitude? Is this — (*Enter Nanki-Poo, with a rope in his hands*) Go away, sir! How dare you? Am I never to be permitted to soliloquize?

NANKI-POO. Oh, go on — don't mind me.

KO-KO. What are you going to do with that rope?

NANKI-POO. I am about to terminate an unendurable existence.

KO-KO. Terminate your existence? Oh, nonsense! What for?

NANKI-POO. Because you are going to marry the girl I adore.

KO-KO. Nonsense, sir. I won't permit it. I am a humane man, and if you attempt anything of the kind I shall order your instant arrest. Come, sir, desist at once, or I summon my guard.

NANKI-POO. That's absurd. If you attempt to raise an alarm, I instantly perform the Happy Despatch with this dagger.

KO-KO. No, no, don't do that. This is horrible! (*Suddenly*) Why, you cold-blooded scoundrel, are you aware that, in taking your life, you are committing a crime which — which — which is — Oh!
[*Struck by an idea.*

NANKI-POO. What's the matter?

KO-KO. Is it *absolutely certain* that you are resolved to die?

NANKI-POO. Absolutely!

KO-KO. Will *nothing* shake your resolution?

NANKI-POO. Nothing.

KO-KO. Threats, entreaties, prayers — all useless?

NANKI-POO. All! My mind is made up.

KO-KO. Then, if you really mean what you say, and if you are absolutely resolved to die, and if nothing whatever will shake your determination — don't spoil yourself by committing suicide, but be beheaded handsomely at the hands of the Public Executioner!

NANKI-POO. I don't see how that would benefit me.

KO-KO. You don't? Observe: you'll have a month to live, and you'll live like a fighting-cock at my expense. When the day comes, there'll be a grand public ceremonial — you'll be the central figure — no one will attempt to deprive you of that distinction. There'll be a procession — bands — dead march — bells tolling — all the girls in tears — Yum-Yum distracted — then, when it's all over, general rejoicings, and a display of fireworks in the evening. *You* won't see them, but they'll be there all the same.

NANKI-POO. Do you think Yum-Yum would really be distracted at my death?

KO-KO. I am convinced of it. Bless you, she's the most tender-hearted little creature alive.

NANKI-POO. I should be sorry to cause her pain. Perhaps, after all, if I were to withdraw from Japan, and travel in Europe for a couple of years, I might contrive to forget her.

KO-KO. Oh, I don't think you could forget Yum-Yum so easily, and, after all, what is more miserable than a love-blighted life?

NANKI-POO. True.

KO-KO. Life without Yum-Yum — why, it seems absurd!

NANKI-POO. And yet there are a good many people in the world who have to endure it.

KO-KO. Poor devils, yes! You are quite right not to be of their number.

NANKI-POO (*suddenly*). I *won't* be of their number!

KO-KO. Noble fellow!

NANKI-POO. I'll tell you how we'll manage it. Let me marry Yum-Yum to-morrow, and in a month you may behead me.

KO-KO. No, no. I draw the line at Yum-Yum.

NANKI-POO. Very good. If you can draw the line, so can I. [*Preparing rope.*

KO-KO. Stop, stop — listen one moment — be reasonable. How can I consent to your marrying Yum-Yum, if I'm going to marry her myself?

NANKI-POO. My good friend, she'll be a widow in a month, and you can marry her then.

KO-KO. That's true, of course. I quite see that, but, dear me, my position during the next month will be most unpleasant — most unpleasant!

NANKI-POO. Not half so unpleasant as my position at the end of it.

KO-KO. But — dear me — well — I agree. After all, it's only putting off my wedding for a month. But you won't prejudice her against me, will you? You see, I've educated her to be my wife; she's been taught to regard me as a wise and good man. Now, I shouldn't like her views on that point disturbed.

NANKI-POO. Trust me, she shall never learn the truth from me.

[*Enter Chorus, Pooh-Bah, and Pish-Tush.*

CHORUS.   With aspect stern
                And gloomy stride,
              We come to learn
                How you decide.

                Don't hesitate
                    Your choice to name,
                A dreadful fate
                    You'll suffer all the same.

POOH-BAH.   To ask you what you mean to do we punctually
                appear.

KO-KO.   Congratulate me, gentlemen, I've found a Vol-
                unteer!

ALL.   The Japanese equivalent for Hear, Hear, Hear!

KO-KO (*presenting him*).   'Tis Nanki-Poo!

ALL.   Hail, Nanki-Poo!

KO-KO.   I think he'll do?

ALL.   Yes, yes, he'll do!

KO-KO.   He yields his life if I'll Yum-Yum surrender;
                Now, I adore that girl with passion tender,
                And could not yield her with a ready will,
                    Or her allot,
                    If I did not
                Adore myself with passion tenderer still!

ALL.   Ah, yes!
            He loves himself with passion tenderer still!

KO-KO (*to Nanki-Poo*).   Take her — she's yours!

[*Enter Yum-Yum, Peep-Bo, and Pitti-Sing.*

NANKI-POO AND YUM-YUM.   Oh, rapture!

                        ENSEMBLE

YUM-YUM AND NANKI-POO. The threatened cloud has passed
                    away,
            And brightly shines the dawning day;
            What though the night may come too soon,
            There's yet a month of afternoon!
                    Then let the throng
                        Our joy advance,
                    With laughing song,
                        And merry dance,
            With joyous shout and ringing cheer,
            Inaugurate our brief career!

CHORUS.   Then let the throng, etc.

PITTI-SING.   A day, a week, a month, a year —
                    Or be it far, or be it near,
                    Life's eventime comes much too soon,
                    You'll live at least a honeymoon!

ALL.   Then let the throng, etc.

SOLO

POOH-BAH.   As in three weeks you've got to die,
                    If Ko-Ko tells us true,
                    'Twere empty compliment to cry
                    Long life to Nanki-Poo!
                    But as you've got three weeks to live
                    As fellow citizen,
                    This toast with three times three we'll give —
                    "Long life to you — till then!"

CHORUS.   May all good fortune prosper you,
                    May you have health and riches too,
                    May you succeed in all you do —
                    Long life to you — till then!

[*Dance.*
[*Enter Katisha, melodramatically.*

KATISHA.   Your revels cease — assist me, all of you!

CHORUS.   Why, who is this whose evil eyes
                    Rain blight on our festivities?

KATISHA.   I claim my perjured lover, Nanki-Poo!
                    Oh, fool! to shun delights that never cloy!
                    Come back, oh, shallow fool! Come back to joy!

CHORUS.   Go, leave thy deadly work undone;
                    Away, away! ill-favoured one!

NANKI-POO (*aside to Yum-Yum*). Ah!
                    'Tis Katisha!
                    The maid of whom I told you.
                              [*About to go.*

KATISHA (*detaining him*). No !
You shall not go,
These arms shall thus enfold you !

SONG

KATISHA (*addressing* NANKI-POO). Oh fool, that fleest
My hallowed joys !
Oh blind, that seest
No equipoise !
Oh rash, that judgest
From half, the whole !
Oh base, that grudgest
Love's lightest dole !
Thy heart unbind,
Oh fool, oh blind !
Give me my place,
Oh rash, oh base !

CHORUS. If she's thy bride, restore her place,
Oh fool, oh blind, oh rash, oh base !

KATISHA (*addressing Yum-Yum*). Pink cheek, that rulest
Where wisdom serves !
Bright eye, that foolest
Steel-tempered nerves ;
Rose-lip, that scornest
Lore-laden years —
Sweet tongue, that warnest
Who rightly hears —
Thy doom is nigh,
Pink cheek, bright eye !
Thy knell is rung,
Rose-lip, sweet tongue.

CHORUS. If true her tale, thy knell is rung,
Pink cheek, bright eye, rose-lip, sweet tongue !

PITTI-SING. Away, nor prosecute your quest —
From our intention well expressed,
You cannot turn us !

The state of your connubial views
Towards the person you accuse
Does not concern us!
For he's going to marry Yum-Yum —

ALL.   Yum-Yum!

PITTI-SING.   Your anger pray bury,
For all will be merry,
I think you had better succumb —

ALL.   Cumb — cumb.

PITTI-SING.   And join our expressions of glee,
On this subject I pray you be dumb —

ALL.   Dumb — dumb.

PITTI-SING.   You'll find there are many
Who'll wed for a penny —
The word for your guidance is, "Mum" —

ALL.   Mum — mum!

PITTI-SING. There's lots of good fish in the sea!

ALL.   There's lots of good fish in the sea!
And you'll find there are many, etc.

Solo

KATISHA.   The hour of gladness
Is dead and gone;
In silent sadness
I live alone!
The hope I cherished
All lifeless lies,
And all has perished
Save love, which never dies!
Oh, faithless one, this insult you shall rue!
In vain for mercy on your knees you'll sue.
I'll tear the mask from you disguising!

NANKI-POO (*aside*).   Now comes the blow!

KATISHA.   Prepare yourself for news surprising!

NANKI-POO (*aside*).   How foil my foe?

KATISHA. No minstrel he, despite bravado!

YUM-YUM (*aside, struck by an idea*).   Ha! ha! I know!

KATISHA.   He is the son of your —

[*Nanki-Poo and Yum-Yum, interrupting, sing Japanese words to drown her voice.*

> O ni! bikkuri shakkuri to!
> O sa! bikkuri shakkuri to!

KATISHA.   In vain you interrupt with this tornado:
          He is the only son of your —

ALL.   *O ni! bikkuri shakkuri to!*

KATISHA.   I'll spoil —

ALL.   *O ni! bikkuri shakkuri to!*

KATISHA.   Your gay gambado!

          He is the son —

ALL.   *O ni! bikkuri shakkuri to!*

KATISHA.   Of your —

ALL.   *O ni! bikkuri shakkuri to!*

ENSEMBLE

KATISHA	THE OTHERS
Ye torrents roar!	We'll hear no more,
Ye tempests howl!	Ill-omened owl,
Your wrath outpour	To joy we soar,
With angry growl!	Despite your scowl!
Do ye your worst, my vengeance call	The echoes of our festival
Shall rise triumphant over all!	Shall rise triumphant over all!
Prepare for woe,	Away you go,
Ye haughty lords,	Collect your hordes;
At once I go	Proclaim your woe
Mikado-wards,	In dismal chords;
And when he learns his son is found,	We do not heed their dismal sound,
My wrongs with vengeance will be crowned!	For joy reigns everywhere around!

[*Katisha rushes furiously up stage, clearing the crowd away right and left, finishing on steps at the back of stage.*

ACT II

SCENE. *Ko-Ko's Garden. Yum-Yum discovered seated at her bridal toilet, surrounded by Maidens, who are dressing her hair and painting her face and lips, as she judges of the effect in a mirror.*

CHORUS.
    Braid the raven hair —
       Weave the supple tress —
    Deck the maiden fair
       In her loveliness —
    Paint the pretty face —
       Dye the coral lip —
    Emphasize the grace
       Of her ladyship !
    Art and nature, thus allied,
    Go to make a pretty bride !

SOLO

PITTI-SING.
    Sit with downcast eye —
       Let it brim with dew —
    Try if you can cry —
       We will do so, too.
    When you're summoned, start,
       Like a frightened roe —
    Flutter, little heart,
       Colour, come and go !
    Modesty at marriage-tide
    Well becomes a pretty bride !

CHORUS.   Braid the raven hair, etc.
[*Exeunt Chorus.*

YUM-YUM (*looking at herself in glass*). Yes, I am indeed beautiful ! Sometimes I sit and wonder, in my artless Japanese way, why it is that I am so much more attractive than anybody else in the whole world ? Can this be vanity ? No ! Nature is lovely and rejoices in her loveliness. I am a child of Nature, and take after my mother.

Song

The sun, whose rays
Are all ablaze
   With every living glory,
Does not deny
His majesty —
   He scorns to tell a story!
He don't exclaim,
"I blush for shame,
   So kindly be indulgent."
But, fierce and bold,
In fiery gold,
   He glories all effulgent!

     I mean to rule the earth,
       As he the sky —
     We really know our worth,
       The sun and I!

Observe his flame,
That placid dame,
   The moon's Celestial Highness;
There's not a trace
Upon her face
   Of diffidence or shyness:
She borrows light
That, through the night,
   Mankind may all acclaim her!
And, truth to tell,
She lights up well,
   So I, for one, don't blame her!

     Ah, pray make no mistake,
       We are not shy;
     We're very wide awake,
       The moon and I!

Yes, everything seems to smile upon me.   I am to be married to-day to the man I love best, and I believe I am the very happiest girl in Japan!

PEEP-BO. The happiest girl indeed, for she is indeed to be envied who has attained happiness in all but perfection.

YUM-YUM. In "all but" perfection?

PEEP-BO. Well, dear, it can't be denied that the fact that your husband is to be beheaded in a month is, in its way, a drawback.

PITTI-SING. I don't know about that. It all depends!

PEEP-BO. At all events, *he* will find it a drawback.

PITTI-SING. Not necessarily. Bless you, it all depends!

YUM-YUM (*in tears*). I think it very indelicate of you to refer to such a subject on such a day. If my married happiness *is* to be — to be —

PEEP-BO. Cut short.

YUM-YUM. Well, cut short — in a month, can't you let me forget it?
[*Weeping.*
[*Enter Nanki-Poo, followed by Pish-Tush.*

NANKI-POO. Yum-Yum in tears — and on her wedding morn!

YUM-YUM (*sobbing*). They've been reminding me that in a month you're to be beheaded!
[*Bursts into tears.*

PITTI-SING. Yes, we've been reminding her that you're to be beheaded.
[*Bursts into tears.*

PEEP-BO. It's quite true, you know, you *are* to be beheaded!
[*Bursts into tears.*

NANKI-POO (*aside*). Humph! How some bridegrooms would be depressed by this sort of thing! (*Aloud*) A month? Well, what's a month? Bah! These divisions of time are purely arbitrary. Who says twenty-four hours make a day?

PITTI-SING. There's a popular impression to that effect.

NANKI-POO. Then we'll efface it. We'll call each second a minute — each minute an hour — each hour a day — and each day a year. At that rate we've about thirty years of married happiness before us!

PEEP-BO.   And at that rate, this interview has already lasted four hours and three-quarters!
[*Exit Peep-Bo.*

YUM-YUM (*still sobbing*).   Yes.   How time flies when one is thoroughly enjoying one's self!

NANKI-POO.   That's the way to look at it!   Don't let's be downhearted!   There's a silver lining to every cloud.

YUM-YUM.   Certainly.   Let's — let's be perfectly happy!
[*Almost in tears.*

PISH-TUSH.   By all means.   Let's — let's thoroughly enjoy ourselves.

PITTI-SING.   It's — it's absurd to cry!
[*Trying to force a laugh.*

YUM-YUM.   Quite ridiculous!
[*Trying to laugh.*
[*All break into a forced and melancholy laugh.*

QUARTETTE

YUM-YUM, PITTI-SING, NANKI-POO, AND PISH-TUSH

Brightly dawns our wedding-day;
    Joyous hour, we give thee greeting!
    Whither, whither art thou fleeting?
Fickle moment, prithee stay!
    What though mortal joys be hollow?
    Pleasures come, if sorrows follow:
Though the tocsin sound, ere long,
    Ding dong!   Ding dong!
Yet until the shadows fall
Over one and over all,
Sing a merry madrigal —
            A madrigal!
    Fal-la — fal-la!   etc.   (*Ending in tears*)

Let us dry the ready tear,
    Though the hours are surely creeping,
    Little need for woeful weeping,
Till the sad sundown is near.

> All must sip the cup of sorrow —
> I to-day and thou to-morrow:
> This the close of every song —
> Ding dong! Ding dong!
> What, though solemn shadows fall,
> Sooner, later, over all?
> Sing a merry madrigal —
> A madrigal!
> Fal-la — fal-la! etc. (*Ending in tears*)

[*Exeunt Pitti-Sing and Pish-Tush.*

[*Nanki-Poo embraces Yum-Yum. Enter Ko-Ko. Nanki-Poo releases Yum-Yum.*

KO-KO. Go on — don't mind me.

NANKI-POO. I'm afraid we're distressing you.

KO-KO. Never mind, I must get used to it. Only please do it by degrees. Begin by putting your arm round her waist. (*Nanki-Poo does so*) There; let me get used to that first.

YUM-YUM. Oh, wouldn't you like to retire? It must pain you to see us so affectionate together!

KO-KO. No, I must learn to bear it! Now oblige me by allowing her head to rest on your shoulder. (*He does so — Ko-Ko much affected*). I am much obliged to you. Now — kiss her! (*He does so — Ko-Ko writhes with anguish*) Thank you — it's simple torture!

YUM-YUM. Come, come, bear up. After all, it's only for a month.

KO-KO. No. It's no use deluding one's self with false hopes.

NANKI-POO AND YUM-YUM (*together*). What do you mean?

KO-KO (*to Yum-Yum*). My child — my poor child. (*Aside*) How shall I break it to her? (*Aloud*) My little bride that was to have been.

YUM-YUM (*delighted*). *Was* to have been!

KO-KO. Yes; you never can be mine!

YUM-YUM (*in ecstasy*). What! ! !

KO-KO. I've just ascertained that, by the Mikado's law, when a married man is beheaded his wife is buried alive.

NANKI-POO AND YUM-YUM (*together*). Buried alive!

KO-KO. Buried alive. It's a most unpleasant death.

NANKI-POO. But whom did you get that from?

KO-KO. Oh, from Pooh-Bah. He's my solicitor.

YUM-YUM. But he may be mistaken!

KO-KO. So I thought, so I consulted the Attorney-General, the Lord Chief Justice, the Master of the Rolls, the Judge Ordinary, and the Lord Chancellor. They're all of the same opinion. Never knew such unanimity on a point of law in my life!

NANKI-POO. But, stop a bit! This law has never been put in force?

KO-KO. Not yet. You see, flirting is the only crime punishable with decapitation, and married men never flirt.

NANKI-POO. Of course they don't. I quite forget that! Well, I suppose I may take it that my dream of happiness is at an end!

YUM-YUM. Darling, I don't want to appear selfish, and I love you with all my heart — I don't suppose I shall ever love anybody else half as much — but when I agreed to marry you, my own, I had no idea, pet, that I should have to be buried alive in a month!

NANKI-POO. Nor I! It's the very first I've heard of it!

YUM-YUM. It — it makes a difference, doesn't it?

NANKI-POO. It *does* make a difference, of course!

YUM-YUM. You see — burial alive — it's such a stuffy death! You see my difficulty, don't you?

NANKI-POO. Yes; and I see my own. If I insist on your carrying out your promise, I doom you to a hideous death; if I release you, you marry Ko-Ko at once!

TRIO

YUM-YUM, NANKI-POO, AND KO-KO.

YUM-YUM. Here's a how-de-do!
If I marry you,
When your time has come to perish,
Then the maiden whom you cherish
Must be slaughtered too!
Here's a how-de-do!

NANKI-POO. Here's a pretty mess!
In a month, or less,
I must die without a wedding!
Let the bitter tears I'm shedding
Witness my distress,
Here's a pretty mess!

KO-KO. Here's a state of things!
To her life she clings!
Matrimonial devotion
Doesn't seem to suit her notion —
Burial it brings!
Here's a state of things!

YUM-YUM AND NANKI-POO	KO-KO
With a passion that's intense	With a passion that's intense
I worship and adore,	You worship and adore,
But the laws of common sense	But the laws of common sense
We oughtn't to ignore.	You oughtn't to ignore.
If what he says is true,	If what I say is true,
It is death to marry you!	It is death to marry you!
Here's a pretty state of things!	Here's a pretty state of things!
Here's a pretty how-de-do!	Here's a pretty how-de-do!

[*Exit Yum-Yum.*

KO-KO (*going up to Nanki-Poo*). My poor boy, I'm really very sorry for you.

NANKI-POO. Thanks, old fellow. I'm sure you are.

KO-KO. You see I'm quite helpless.

NANKI-POO. I quite see that.

KO-KO. I can't conceive anything more distressing than to have one's marriage broken off at the last moment. But you sha'n't be disappointed of a wedding — you shall come to mine.

NANKI-POO. It's awfully kind of you, but that's impossible.

KO-KO. Why so?

NANKI-POO. To-day I die.

KO-KO. What do you mean?

NANKI-POO. I can't live without Yum-Yum. This afternoon I perform the Happy Despatch.

KO-KO. No, no — pardon me — I can't allow that.

NANKI-POO. Why not?

KO-KO. Why, hang it.all, you're under contract to die by the hand of the Public Executioner in a month's time! If you kill yourself, what's to become of me? Why, I shall have to be executed in your place!

NANKI-POO. It would certainly seem so!
[*Enter Pooh-Bah.*

KO-KO. Now then, Lord Mayor, what is it?

POOH-BAH. The Mikado and his suite are approaching the city, and will be here in ten minutes.

KO-KO. The Mikado! He's coming to see whether his orders have been carried out! (*To Nanki-Poo*) Now, look here, you know — this is getting serious — a bargain's a bargain, and you really mustn't frustrate the ends of justice by committing suicide. As a man of honour and a gentleman, you are bound to die ignominiously by the hands of the Public Executioner.

NANKI-POO. Very well, then — behead me.

KO-KO. What, now?

NANKI-POO. Certainly; at once.

KO-KO. My good sir, I don't go about prepared to execute gentlemen at a moment's notice. Why, I never even killed a blue-bottle!

POOH-BAH. Still, as Lord High Executioner —

KO-KO. My good sir, as Lord High Executioner I've got to behead him in a month. I'm not ready yet. I don't know how it's done. I'm going to take lessons. I mean to begin with a guinea-pig, and work my way through the animal kingdom till I come to a second trombone. Why, you don't suppose that, as a humane man, I'd have accepted the post of Lord High Executioner if I hadn't thought the duties were purely nominal? I *can't* kill you — I can't kill anything!
[*Weeps.*

NANKI-POO. Come, my poor fellow, your feelings do you credit; but you must nerve yourself to this — you must, indeed. We all have unpleasant duties to discharge at times; and when these duties present themselves we must nerve ourselves to an effort. Come, now — after all, what is it? If I don't mind, why should you? Remember, sooner or later it must be done.

KO-KO (*springing up suddenly*). *Must it?* I'm not so sure about that!

NANKI-POO. What do you mean?

KO-KO. Why should I kill you when making an affidavit that you've been executed will do just as well? Here are plenty of witnesses — the Lord Chief Justice, and Lord High Admiral, Commander-in-Chief, Secretary of State for the Home Department, First Lord of the Treasury, and Chief Commissioner of Police. They'll all swear to it — won't you? [*To Pooh-Bah.*

POOH-BAH. Am I to understand that all of us high Officers of State are required to perjure ourselves to ensure your safety?

KO-KO. Why not? You'll be grossly insulted as usual.

POOH-BAH. Will the insult be cash down, or at a date?

KO-KO. It will be a ready-money transaction.

POOH-BAH (*aside*). Well, it will be a useful discipline. (*Aloud*) Very good. Choose your fiction, and I'll endorse it! (*Aside*) Ha! ha! Family Pride, how do you like *that*, my buck?

NANKI-POO. But I tell you that life without Yum-Yum —

KO-KO. Oh, Yum-Yum, Yum-Yum! Bother Yum-Yum! Here, Commissionaire (*to Pooh-Bah*), go and fetch Yum-Yum. (*Exit Pooh-Bah*) Take Yum-Yum and marry Yum-Yum, only go away and never come back again. (*Enter Pooh-Bah with Yum-Yum and Pitti-Sing*) Here she is. Yum-Yum, are you particularly busy?

YUM-YUM. Not particularly.

KO-KO. You've five minutes to spare?

YUM-YUM. Yes.

KO-KO. Then go along with his Grace the Archbishop of Titipu; he'll marry you at once.

YUM-YUM. But if I'm to be buried alive?

KO-KO. Now don't ask any questions, but do as I tell you, and Nanki-Poo will explain all.

NANKI-POO. But one moment —

KO-KO. Not for worlds. Here comes the Mikado, no doubt to ascertain whether I've obeyed his decree, and if he finds you alive, I shall have the greatest difficulty in persuading him that I've beheaded you. (*Exeunt Nanki-Poo and Yum-Yum, followed by Pooh-Bah*). Close thing that, for here he comes!

[*March. Enter procession, heralding Mikado, with Katisha.*

CHORUS. *"March of the Mikado's Troops."*

> Miya sama, miya sama,
> On ma no mayé ni
> Pira-Pira suru no wa
> Nan gia na
> Toké tonyaré tonyaré na!

DUET

MIKADO AND KATISHA.

MIKADO.
> From every kind of man
> Obedience I expect;
> I'm the Emperor of Japan.

KATISHA.
> And I'm his daughter-in-law elect!
> He'll marry his son
> (He has only got one)
> To his daughter-in-law elect.

MIKADO.
> My morals have been declared
> Particularly correct;

KATISHA.
> But they're nothing at all, compared
> With those of his daughter-in-law elect!
> Bow! Bow!
> To his daughter-in-law elect!

ALL.
> Bow! Bow!
> To his daughter-in-law elect.

MIKADO.
> In a fatherly kind of way
> I govern each tribe and sect,
> All cheerfully own my sway —

KATISHA.   Except his daughter-in-law elect!
     As tough as a bone,
     With a will of her own,
Is his daughter-in-law elect!

MIKADO.   My nature is love and light —
     My freedom from all defect —

KATISHA.   Is insignificant quite,
     Compared with his daughter-in-law elect!
       Bow! Bow!
     To his daughter-in-law elect!

ALL.   Bow! Bow!
     To his daughter-in-law elect.

Song

MIKADO.   A more humane Mikado never
     Did in Japan exist,
       To nobody second,
       I'm certainly reckoned
     A true philanthropist.
It is my very humane endeavour
     To make, to some extent,
       Each evil liver
       A running river
Of harmless merriment.

     My object all sublime
     I shall achieve in time —
To let the punishment fit the crime —
     The punishment fit the crime;
     And make each prisoner pent
     Unwillingly represent
     A source of innocent merriment,
       Of innocent merriment!

All prosy dull society sinners,
     Who chatter and bleat and bore,

Are sent to hear sermons
From mystical Germans
Who preach from ten to four.
The amateur tenor, whose vocal villainies
All desire to shirk,
Shall, during off-hours,
Exhibit his powers
To Madame Tussaud's waxwork.

My object all sublime, etc.

The lady who dies a chemical yellow,
Or stains her grey hair puce,
Or pinches her figger,
Is blacked like a nigger
With permanent walnut juice.
The idiot who, in railway carriages,
Scribbles on window-panes,
We only suffer
To ride on a buffer
In parliamentary trains.

My object all sublime, etc.

The advertising quack who wearies
With tales of countless cures,
His teeth, I've enacted,
Shall all be extracted
By terrified amateurs.
The music-hall singer attends a series
Of masses and fugues and "ops"
By Bach, interwoven
With Spohr and Beethoven,
At classical Monday Pops.

My object all sublime, etc.

> The billiard sharp whom any one catches,
> His doom's extremely hard —
>   He's made to dwell —
>   In a dungeon cell
> On a spot that's always barred.
> And there he plays extravagant matches
> In fitless finger-stalls,
>   On a cloth untrue
>   With a twisted cue,
> And elliptical billiard balls!

My object all sublime, etc.

[*Enter Pooh-Bah, who hands a paper to Ko-Ko.*

KO-KO.   I am honoured in being permitted to welcome your Majesty.   I guess the object of your Majesty's visit — your wishes have been attended to.   The execution has taken place.

MIKADO.   Oh, you've had an execution, have you?

KO-KO.   Yes.   The Coroner has just handed me his certificate.

POOH-BAH.   I am the Coroner.

[*Ko-Ko hands certificate to Mikado.*

MIKADO (*reads*).   "At Titipu, in the presence of the Lord Chancellor, Lord Chief Justice, Attorney-General, Secretary of State for the Home Department, Lord Mayor, and Groom of the Second Floor Front."

POOH-BAH.   They were all present, your Majesty.   I counted them myself.

MIKADO.   Very good house.   I wish I'd been in time for the performance.

KO-KO.   A tough fellow he was, too — a man of gigantic strength.   His struggles were terrific.   It was really a remarkable scene.

TRIO

KO-KO, PITTI-SING, AND POOH-BAH.

KO-KO.

    The criminal cried, as he dropped him down,
        In a state of wild alarm —
    With a frightful, frantic, fearful frown
        I bared my big right arm.
    I seized him by his little pig-tail,
        And on his knees fell he;
            As he squirmed and struggled
            And gurgled and guggled,
        I drew my snickersnee!
           Oh, never shall I
           Forget the cry,
    Or the shriek that shriekèd he;
           As I gnashed my teeth,
           When from its sheath
        I drew my snickersnee!

CHORUS.

        We know him well,
        He cannot tell
    Untrue or groundless tales —
        He always tries
        To utter lies,
    And every time he fails.

PITTI-SING.

    He shivered and shook as he gave the sign
        For the stroke he didn't deserve;
    When all of a sudden his eye met mine,
        And it seemed to brace his nerve,
    For he nodded his head and kissed his hand,
        And he whistled an air, did he,
           As the sabre true
           Cut cleanly through
        His cervical vertebræ!
           When a man's afraid,
           A beautiful maid
    Is a cheering sight to see,

     And it's oh, I'm glad
     That moment sad
    Was soothed by sight of me!

CHORUS.   Her terrible tale
     You can't assail,
    With truth it quite agrees;
     Her taste exact
     For faultless fact
    Amounts to a disease.

POOH-BAH. Now though you'd have said that head was dead
    (For its owner dead was he),
   It stood on its neck with a smile well bred,
    And bowed three times to me!
  It was none of your impudent off-hand nods,
    But as humble as could be;
     For it clearly knew
     The deference due
    To a man of pedigree!
     And it's oh, I vow,
     This deathly bow
    Was a touching sight to see;
     Though trunkless, yet
     It couldn't forget
   The deference due to me!

CHORUS.   This haughty youth
     He speaks the truth
    Wherever he finds it pays,
     And in this case
     It all took place
    Exactly as he says!

[*Exeunt Chorus.*

MIKADO. All this is very interesting, and I should like to have
seen it. But we came about a totally different matter. A

year ago my son, the heir to the throne of Japan, bolted from our Imperial Court.

KO-KO. Indeed? Had he any reason to be dissatisfied with his position?

KATISHA. None whatever. On the contrary, I was going to marry him — yet he fled!

POOH-BAH. I am surprised that he should have fled from one so lovely!

KATISHA. That's not true. You hold that I am not beautiful because my face is plain. But you know nothing; you are still unenlightened. Learn, then, that it is not in the face alone that beauty is to be sought. But I have a left shoulder blade that is a miracle of loveliness. People come miles to see it. My right elbow has a fascination that few can resist. It is on view Tuesdays and Fridays, on presentation of visiting-card. As for my circulation, it is the largest in the world. Observe this ear.

KO-KO. Large.

KATISHA. Large? Enormous! But think of its delicate internal mechanism. It is fraught with beauty! As for this tooth, it almost stands alone. Many have tried to draw it, but in vain.

KO-KO. And yet he fled!

MIKADO. And is now masquerading in this town, disguised as a second trombone.

KO-KO, POOH-BAH, AND PITTI-SING (*together*). A second trombone!

MIKADO. Yes; would it be troubling you too much if I asked you to produce him? He goes by the name of Nanki-Poo.

KO-KO. Oh, no; not at all — only —

MIKADO. Yes?

KO-KO. It's rather awkward; but, in point of fact, he's gone abroad!

MIKADO. Gone abroad? His address!

KO-KO. Knightsbridge!

KATISHA (*who is reading certificate of death*). Ha!

MIKADO. What's the matter?

KATISHA. See here — his name — Nanki-Poo — beheaded this morning! Oh, where shall I find another! Where shall I find another!

[*Ko-Ko, Pooh-Bah, and Pitti-Sing fall on their knees.*

MIKADO (*looking at paper*). Dear, dear, dear; this is very tiresome. (*To Ko-Ko*) My poor fellow, in your anxiety to carry out my wishes, you have beheaded the heir to the throne of Japan!

KO-KO. ⎫ But I assure you we had no idea —
POOH-BAH. ⎬ (*Together*) But, indeed, we didn't know —
PITTI-SING. ⎭ We really hadn't the least notion —

MIKADO. Of course you hadn't. How could you? Come, come, my good fellow, don't distress yourself — it was no fault of yours. If a man of exalted rank chooses to disguise himself as a second trombone, he must take the consequences. It really distresses me to see you take on so. I've no doubt he thoroughly deserved all he got.

[*They rise.*

KO-KO. We are infinitely obliged to your Majesty.

MIKADO. Obliged? Not a bit. Don't mention it. How *could* you tell?

POOH-BAH. No, of course we couldn't know that he was the Heir Apparent.

PITTI-SING. It wasn't written on his forehead, you know.

KO-KO. It might have been on his pocket-handkerchief, but Japanese don't use pocket-handkerchiefs! Ha! ha! ha!

MIKADO. Ha! ha! ha! (*To Katisha*) I forget the punishment for compassing the death of the Heir Apparent.

KO-KO, POOH-BAH, AND PITTI-SING (*together*). Punishment!

[*They drop down on their knees again.*

MIKADO. Yes. Something lingering, with boiling oil in it, I fancy. Something of that sort. I think boiling oil occurs in it, but I'm not sure. I know it's something humorous, but lingering, with either boiling oil or melted lead. Come, come, don't fret — I'm not a bit angry.

KO-KO (*in abject terror*). If your Majesty will accept our assurance, we had no idea —

MIKADO. **Of** course you hadn't. That's the pathetic part of it. Unfortunately the fool of an Act says "compassing the death of the Heir Apparent." There's not a word about a mistake, or not knowing, or having no notion. There should be, of course, but there isn't. That's the slovenly way in which these Acts are drawn. However, cheer up, it'll be all right. I'll have it altered next session.

KO-KO. What's the good of that?

MIKADO. Now, let's see — will after luncheon suit you? Can you wait till then?

KO-KO, PITTI-SING, AND POOH-BAH. Oh, yes — we can wait till then!

MIKADO. Then we'll make it after luncheon. I'm really very sorry for you all, but it's an unjust world, and virtue is triumphant only in theatrical performances.

GLEE

MIKADO, KATISHA, KO-KO, POOH-BAH, AND PITTI-SING.

MIKADO AND KATISHA.   See how the Fates their gifts allot,
For A is happy — B is not.
Yet B is worthy, I dare say,
Of more prosperity than A!

KO-KO, POOH-BAH, AND PITTI-SING.
       Is B more worthy?

MIKADO AND KATISHA.   I should say
He's worth a great deal more than **A.**

ENSEMBLE

Yet A is happy!
Oh, so happy!
Laughing, Ha! ha!
Chaffing, Ha! ha!
Nectar quaffing, Ha! ha! ha! ha!
Ever joyous, ever gay,
Happy, undeserving A!

KO-KO, POOH-BAH, AND PITTI-SING.

> If I were fortune — which I'm not —
> B should enjoy A's happy lot,
> And A should die in miserie,
> That is, assuming I am B.

MIKADO AND KATISHA.   But *should* A perish?

KO-KO, POOH-BAH, AND PITTI-SING.   That should he,

> (Of course assuming I am B).
> B should be happy!
> Oh, so happy!
> Laughing, Ha! ha!
> Chaffing, Ha! ha!
> Nectar quaffing, Ha! ha! ha! ha!
> But condemned to die is he,
> Wretched, meritorious B!

[*Exeunt Mikado and Katisha.*

KO-KO.   Well! a nice mess you've got us into, with your nodding head and the deference due to a man of pedigree!

POOH-BAH.   Merely corroborative detail, intended to give artistic verisimilitude to a bold and unconvincing narrative.

PITTI-SING.   Corroborative detail indeed! Corroborative fiddlestick!

KO-KO.   And you're just as bad as he is, with your cock-and-a-bull stories about catching his eye, and his whistling an air. But that's so like you! You must put in your oar!

POOH-BAH.   But how about your big right arm?

PITTI-SING.   Yes, and your snickersnee!

KO-KO.   Well, well, never mind that now. There's only one thing to be done. Nanki-Poo hasn't started yet — he must come to life again at once. (*Enter Nanki-Poo and Yum-Yum prepared for journey*) Here he comes. Here, Nanki-Poo, I've good news for you — you're reprieved.

NANKI-POO.   Oh, but it's too late. I'm a dead man, and I'm off for my honeymoon.

KO-KO.   Nonsense. A terrible thing has just happened. It seems you're the son of the Mikado.

NANKI-POO. Yes; but that happened some time ago.

KO-KO. Is this a time for airy persiflage? Your father is here, and with Katisha.

NANKI-POO. My father! And with Katisha!

KO-KO. Yes; he wants you particularly.

POOH-BAH. So does she.

YUM-YUM. Oh, but he's married now.

KO-KO. But, bless my heart, what has that to do with it?

NANKI-POO. Katisha claims me in marriage, but I can't marry her because I'm married already — consequently she will insist on my execution, and if I'm executed, my wife will have to be buried alive.

YUM-YUM. You see our difficulty.

KO-KO. Yes. I don't know what's to be done.

NANKI-POO. There's one chance for you. If you could persuade Katisha to marry you, she would have no further claim on me, and in that case I could come to life without any fear of being put to death.

KO-KO. I marry Katisha!

YUM-YUM. I really think it's the only course.

KO-KO. But, my good girl, have you seen her? She's something appalling!

PITTI-SING. Ah, that's only her face. She has a left elbow which people come miles to see!

POOH-BAH. I am told that her right heel is much admired by connoisseurs.

KO-KO. My good sir, I decline to pin my heart upon any lady's right heel.

NANKI-POO. It comes to this: while Katisha is single, I prefer to be a disembodied spirit. When Katisha is married, existence will be as welcome as the flowers in spring.

DUET

NANKI-POO AND KO-KO.

NANKI-POO. The flowers that bloom in the spring,
Tra la,
Breathe promise of merry sunshine —
As we merrily dance and we sing,
Tra la,

We welcome the hope that they bring,
    Tra, la,
Of a summer of roses and wine;
And that's what we mean when we say that a thing
Is welcome as flowers that bloom in the spring.
    Tra la la la la la, etc.

ALL.   And that's what we mean, etc.

KO-KO.   The flowers that bloom in the spring,
    Tra la,
Have nothing to do with the case.
I've got to take under my wing,
    Tra, la,
A most unattractive old thing,
    Tra la,
With a caricature of a face;
And that's what I mean when I say, or I sing,
"Oh bother the flowers that bloom in the spring!"
    Tra la la la la la, etc.

ALL.   And that's what he means when he ventures to sing, etc.

[*Dance and exeunt Nanki-Poo, Yum-Yum, Pooh-Bah, and Pitti-Sing.*
[*Enter Katisha.*

RECITATIVE

KATISHA.   Alone, and yet alive! Oh sepulchre!
My soul is still my body's prisoner!
Remote the peace that Death alone can give —
My doom to wait! my punishment to live!

SONG

Hearts do not break!
They sting and ache
For old sake's sake,
    But do not die!

THE MIKADO

Act II

Ko-Ko. — "Katisha—behold a suppliant at your feet! Katisha
—mercy!"

Though with each breath
They long for death,
As witnesseth
The living I!
Oh living I!
Come, tell me why,
When hope is gone
Dost thou stay on?
Why linger here,
Where all is drear?
May not a cheated maiden die?

KO-KO (*approaching her timidly*). Katisha!

KATISHA. The miscreant who robbed me of my love! But vengeance pursues — they are heating the cauldron!

KO-KO. Katisha — behold a suppliant at your feet! Katisha — mercy!

KATISHA. Mercy? Had you mercy on him? See here, you! You have slain my love. He did not love *me*, but he would have loved me in time. I am an acquired taste — only the educated palate can appreciate *me*. I was educating *his* palate when he left me. Well, he is dead, and where shall I find another? It takes years to train a man to love me — am I to go through the weary round again, and, at the same time, implore mercy for you who robbed me of my prey — I mean my pupil — just as his education was on the point of completion? Oh, where shall I find another!

KO-KO (*suddenly, and with great vehemence*). Here! — Here!

KATISHA. What! ! !

KO-KO (*with intense passion*). Katisha, for years I have loved you with a white-hot passion that is slowly but surely consuming my very vitals! Ah, shrink not from me! If there is aught of woman's mercy in your heart, turn not away from a love-sick suppliant whose every fibre thrills at your tiniest touch! True it is that, under a poor mask of disgust, I have endeavoured to conceal a passion whose inner fires are broiling the soul within me. But the fire will not be smothered — it defies all attempts at extinction, and, breaking forth, all the more eagerly for its long restraint, it declares itself in words that will not be weighed — that cannot be schooled — that should not be too severely criticized. Katisha, I dare not hope for your love — but I will not live without it!

KATISHA.   You, whose hands still reek with the blood of my betrothed, dare to address words of passion to the woman you have so foully wronged!

KO-KO.   I do — accept my love, or I perish on the spot!

KATISHA.   Go to! Who knows so well as I that no one ever yet died of a broken heart!

KO-KO.   You know not what you say.   Listen!

SONG

On a tree by a river a little tom-tit
    Sang, "Willow, titwillow, titwillow!"
And I said to him, "Dicky-bird, why do you sit
    Singing 'Willow, titwillow, titwillow'?"
"Is it weakness of intellect, birdie?" I cried,
"Or a rather tough worm in your little inside?"
With a shake of his poor little head he replied,
    "Oh, willow, titwillow, titwillow!"

He slapped at his chest, as he sat on that bough,
    Singing, "Willow, titwillow, titwillow!"
And a cold perspiration bespangled his brow,
    Oh, willow, titwillow, titwillow!
He sobbed and he sighed, and a gurgle he gave,
Then he threw himself into the billowy wave,
And an echo arose from the suicide's grave —
    "Oh, willow, titwillow, titwillow!"

Now, I feel just as sure as I'm sure that my name
    Isn't willow, titwillow, titwillow,
That 'twas blighted affection that made him exclaim,
    "Oh, willow, titwillow, titwillow!"
And if you remain callous and obdurate, I

Shall perish as he did, and you will know why,
Though I probably shall not exclaim as I die,
"Oh, willow, titwillow, titwillow!"

[*During this song Katisha has been greatly affected, and at the end is almost in tears.*

KATISHA (*whimpering*). Did he really die of love?

KO-KO. He really did.

KATISHA. All on account of a cruel little hen?

KO-KO. Yes.

KATISHA. Poor little chap!

KO-KO. It's an affecting tale, and quite true. I knew the bird intimately.

KATISHA. Did you? He must have been very fond of her!

KO-KO. His devotion was something extraordinary.

KATISHA (*still whimpering*). Poor little chap! And — and if I refuse you, will you go and do the same?

KO-KO. At once.

KATISHA. No, no — you mustn't! Anything but that! (*Falls on his breast*) Oh, I'm a silly little goose!

KO-KO (*making a wry face*). You are!

KATISHA. And you won't hate me because I'm just a little teeny weeny wee bit blood-thirsty, will you?

KO-KO. Hate you? Oh, Katisha! is there not beauty even in blood-thirstiness?

KATISHA. My idea exactly!

DUET

KO-KO AND KATISHA.

KATISHA. There is beauty in the bellow of the blast,
There is grandeur in the growing of the gale,
There is eloquent out-pouring
When the lion is a-roaring,
And the tiger is a-lashing of his tail!

KO-KO. Yes, I like to see a tiger
From the Congo or the Niger,
And especially when lashing of his tail!

KATISHA.   Volcanoes have a splendour that is grim,
      And earthquakes only terrify the dolts,
        But to him who's scientific
        There's nothing that's terrific
      In the falling of a flight of thunderbolts!

KO-KO.   Yes, in spite of all my meekness,
          If I have a little weakness,
      It's a passion for a flight of thunderbolts.

BOTH.   If that is so,
          Sing derry down derry!
        It's evident, very,
           Our tastes are one.
       Away we'll go,
          And merrily marry,
        Nor tardily tarry
           Till day is done!

KO-KO.   There is beauty in extreme old age —
      Do you fancy you are elderly enough?
        Information I'm requesting
        On a subject interesting:
      Is a maiden all the better when she's tough?

KATISHA.   Throughout this wide dominion
        It's the general opinion
      That she'll last a good deal longer when she's tough.

KO-KO.   Are you old enough to marry, do you think?
      Won't you wait till you are "eighty in the shade"?
        There's a fascination frantic
        In a ruin that's romantic;
      Do you think you are sufficiently decayed?

KATISHA.   To the matter that you mention
        I have given some attention,
      And I think I am sufficiently decayed.

BOTH. If that is so,
    Sing derry down derry!
    It's evident, very,
    Our tastes are one!
   Away we'll go,
    And merrily marry,
    Nor tardily tarry
    Till day is done!

[Exeunt together.
Flourish. Enter the Mikado, attended by Pish-Tush, and Court.

MIKADO. Now then, we've had a capital lunch, and we're quite ready. Have all the painful preparations been made?

PISH-TUSH. Your Majesty, all is prepared.

MIKADO. Then produce the unfortunate gentleman and his two well-meaning but misguided accomplices.
[Enter Ko-Ko, Katisha, Pooh-Bah, and Pitti-Sing. They throw themselves at the Mikado's feet.

KATISHA. Mercy! Mercy for Ko-Ko! Mercy for Pitti-Sing! Mercy even for Pooh-Bah!

MIKADO. I beg your pardon, I don't think I quite caught that remark.

KATISHA. Mercy! My husband that was to have been is dead, and I have just married this miserable object.

MIKADO. Oh! You've not been long about it!

KO-KO. We were married before the Registrar.

POOH-BAH. *I* am the Registrar.

MIKADO. I see. But my difficulty is that, as you have slain the Heir Apparent —
[Enter Nanki-Poo and Yum-Yum. They kneel.

NANKI-POO. The Heir Apparent is *not* slain.

MIKADO. Bless my heart, my son!

YUM-YUM. And your daughter-in-law elected!

KATISHA (*seizing Ko-Ko*). Traitor, you have deceived me!

MIKADO. Yes, you are entitled to a little explanation, but I think he will give it better whole than in pieces.

KO-KO. Your Majesty, it's like this. It is true that I stated that I had killed Nanki-Poo —

MIKADO. Yes, with most affecting particulars.

POOH-BAH. Merely corroborative detail intended to give verisimilitude to a bald and —

KO-KO. *Will* you refrain from putting in your oar? (*To Mikado*) It's like this: when your Majesty says, "Let a thing be done," it's as good as done — practically, it *is* done — because your Majesty's will is law. Your Majesty says, "Kill a gentleman," and a gentleman is told off to be killed. Consequently that gentleman is as good as dead — practically he *is* dead — and if he is dead, why not say so?

MIKADO. I see. Nothing could possibly be more satisfactory.

FINALE

YUM-YUM AND NANKI-POO.

The threatened cloud has passed away,
And brightly shines the dawning day;
What though the night may come too soon,
We've years and years of afternoon!
    Then let the throng
        Our joy advance,
    With laughing song
        And merry dance,
With joyous shout and ringing cheer,
Inaugurate our new career!
    Then let the throng, etc.

CURTAIN

[This text, from an English edition of the operetta, varies in some respects from the text as reproduced in the excellent edition of "The Savoy Operas", published by The Macmillan Company. The indication is that Gilbert from year to year touched up his scripts, even as in late life he wrote new lyrics for one or two of his favorite songs.]

FAIRY TALES, ESPECIALLY SNOW WHITE

THERE is very little to be said in explanation of a fairy tale, unless we write a learned essay on folklore. One either likes fairy tales or one doesn't; one either believes in them or one doesn't. If Queen Mab hath been with you, then the world is yours to dream on. Have you ever imagined a fairy queen? Go into the corner, away from the roar of trams and motor cars, and think of one, or, if you know your Shakespeare, recall *Mercutio's* description of one in "Romeo and Juliet."

> . . . she comes
> In shape no bigger than an agate-stone
> On the forefinger of an alderman,
> Drawn with a team of little atomies
> Athwart men's noses as they lie asleep:
> Her waggon-spokes made of long spinners' legs,
> The cover of the wings of grasshoppers,
> The traces of the smallest spider's web,
> The collars of the moonshine's watery beams,
> Her whip, of cricket's bone, the lash, of film,
> Her waggoner, a small grey-coated gnat,
> Not half so big as a round little worm
> Prick'd from the lazy finger of a maid;
> Her chariot is an empty hazel-nut,
> Made by the joiner squirrel or old grub,
> Time out o' mind the fairies' coachmakers.
> And in this state she gallops night by night. . . .

Is not that as authentic a picture as though the Little Lady had sat for her portrait? I remember once talking to an artist who makes scenery in the theater. He was telling me of an ideal production of "Jack and the Beanstalk" he wanted to see. His idea of a Giant was just the picture of what we all imagine a real giant to be. He was joyfully wondering how splendid the big boots would be, what a noise they would make if one of them was dropped on the stage, how stupendous the thumb of a Giant must be, and what mechanical cleverness it would take to work the joints of the Giant's hand; how exciting a beanstalk would be which could grow faster than an elevator moves. So his imagination worked, and so he pictured for me a performance of delight.

Now, there is this much to be said about a fairy tale, if it is made into a play, or if an artist illustrates it: everything the children love about it must be put in. To leave any details out would be a misfit indeed. Mr. Ames' beautiful entertainment, "Snow White and the Seven Dwarfs", was a revel of delicate colors, of dainty dances, of lyrical song. *He* never missed any of the fine points of the fairy tale; for Mr. Ames has proven more than once — his recent exquisite Gilbert and Sullivan opera, "Iolanthe" assures us this once more — that Queen Mab was at his christening.

Do you remember the "Just So Stories" of Kipling? He himself drew the pictures for them: and in one, that which illustrated "How the Rhino Got His Rumpled Skin", he wrote: "The skin of the Rhino is buttoned on. The buttons are underneath the Rhino's tummy, and that's why you can't see them." These are not the exact words but they are the meaning of them. Now, Mr. Kipling left out a detail in his drawing: the buttons. When I talked with Mr. Sarg about the picture for "Snow White", he said: "Well, there's one thing I daren't omit, — the Seven Dwarfs!" He had the right point of view: he understood he couldn't draw five, and say the other two were hidden behind chairs or screens, as Kipling said the buttons were hidden beneath the Rhino's tummy. In fairy tales you can't do such things, especially if the fairy tales are plays.

SNOW WHITE AND THE SEVEN DWARFS

A FAIRY TALE PLAY

BASED ON THE STORY OF THE BROTHERS GRIMM

By JESSIE BRAHAM WHITE

Copyright, 1916, by Jessie Braham White

All rights reserved

Warning.—This play is fully protected and copyrighted. Applications for the right of performance or adaptation made in America or elsewhere through 25 West 45th Street, New York, must be for permission of the publishers, Doubleday, Page and Company, New York City.

CAST

"Snow White and the Seven Dwarfs" was first produced by Winthrop Ames at The Little Theatre, New York, October 31, 1921, with the following Cast:

Princess Snow White		Marguerite Clark
Queen Brangomar		Elaine Inescort
Rosalys		Madeline Fairbanks
Amelotte		Harriett Ingalls
Ermengarde	*Maids of*	Jeannette Dix
Guinivere	*Honor to*	Dorothy Preyer
Christabel	*Snow*	Marion Fairbanks
Astolaine	*White*	Madeline Chieffo
Ursula		Alison Coe
Lynette		Phyllis Anderson
Sir Dandiprat Bombas, *the Court Chamberlain*		Frank McCormack
Berthold, *the Chief Huntsman*		Arthur Barry
Prince Florimond of Calydon		Donald Gallaher
Valentine	*Pages to*	Peter Miller
Vivian	*the Prince*	Royal Herring
Blick		Edward See
Flick		Harry Burnham
Glick	*The*	Marie Cullen
Snick	*Seven*	Emmet Hampton
Plick	*Dwarfs*	Charles Everett
Whick		John Davis
Quee		Dorothy Farrier
Witch Hex		Ada Boshell

LONG TAIL ⎫
SHORT TAIL ⎬ *Witch Hex's Cats*
LACK TAIL ⎭

William Grey
Patrick Driscoll
Arthur Simpson

DUKES, DUCHESSES *and* FLUNKIES

THE SCENES OF THE PLAY

I. *The Throne Room in Queen Brangomar's Palace.*

II. *In the Forest.*

III. *The House of the Seven Dwarfs.*

IV. *Where the Witch Lives.*

V. *The House of the Seven Dwarfs.*

VI. *The Throne Room.*

SNOW WHITE AND THE SEVEN DWARFS

Scene I

The Throne Room in Queen Brangomar's Palace

The Throne Room is a fine apartment, hung with blue damask embroidered with silver peacocks, birds of which Queen Brangomar is very fond. At the back wide steps lead to a terrace of white marble. Beyond shines the sea. On one side stands the great Throne, inlaid with colored mosaics. Opposite is an entrance to the other rooms of the Palace.

When the play begins the Seven Maids of Honor are playing a game with colored balls. They are little girls about twelve years old; and their names are Rosalys, Amelotte, Ermengarde, Guinivere, Christabel, Ursula and Lynette. As they play they sing:

GAME OF BALL [1]

High and low,
High and low,
Round about and 'cross they go.
Blue and green,
Gold and white,
Toss them true and hold them tight.
Miss a ball,
Let it fall,
Make the least mistake at all —
One, two, three,
Out goes she !
One, two, three, *and* out goes she !

[Just here Rosalys does miss, and the others rush to "tag" her, crying, "Rosalys is out! Rosalys is out!"

[1] The music and stage directions to accompany this play may be found in the edition printed by Samuel French, New York.

CHRISTABEL. Play again?

GUINIVERE. I will.

[*But just as they are about to begin again, Sir Dandiprat Bombas, the Court Chamberlain, appears on the terrace. He is a fat, puffy little man with an enormous wig, and a great sense of his own importance.*

SIR DANDIPRAT. Ah, young ladies . . . What! playing in the Throne Room? Tut, tut! Tut, tut!

THE MAIDS OF HONOR. Oh, please don't tell. . . . Don't tell the Queen. . . . We didn't break anything.

SIR DANDIPRAT. No, on the whole, I won't tell her Majesty. She *might* blame me. As I was going to say, I have an important announcement to make. Since Lady Cecily was sent home with the mumps your usual number, eight, has been reduced to seven. Am I right? One from eight leaves seven, I think.

[*He tries to do the sum on his fingers.*

ROSALYS. Yes, it is seven.

SIR DANDIPRAT. I *am* right. The Queen wishes your number kept complete, so I have brought another young lady to take the vacant place. (*He leads on little Lady Astolaine and presents her*) The Lady Astolaine. These are the Maids of Honor to the Princess Snow White. (*Lady Astolaine curtsies to the Maids of Honor and they to her. Sir Dandiprat goes on*) You must teach Lady Astolaine all she ought to know. How to dance your minuet, for instance. (*And the little man dances a few steps, puffing out the tune meantime*) "Tum, tum, tum, ti; dum, tum, tum, ti!" And how to make a proper curtsey — so — (*And he tries to make one*) And how to retire backwards gracefully — so! (*But as he retires backwards he stumbles against the terrace steps and falls flat. He is so embarrassed by this mishap that he scrambles out of the room as fast as he can, puffing*) Gracefully, young ladies! Gracefully! [*Till he is out of sight.*

ASTOLAINE (*laughing*). Who's that old thing?

ROSALYS (*mimicking Sir Dandiprat's voice and strut*). That's Sir Dandiprat Bombas, Court Chamberlain to the Queen.

CHRISTABEL. He gives us our "instructions."

ERMENGARDE. But we don't mind *him*.

ASTOLAINE. Do you have good times here?

ROSALYS. Splendid. Except — (*confidentially*) — when the Queen is especially cross.

CHRISTABEL. And then, oh, my, we have to be careful!

ASTOLAINE. I don't think I shall like the Queen!

MAIDS OF HONOR (*hastily*). Ssh!

ASTOLAINE. Why, ssh?

ROSALYS (*whispering*). Never say anything uncomplimentary about the Queen!

MAIDS OF HONOR (*loudly, intending to be overheard*). We all *adore* the Queen!
[*But they shake their heads, and make little faces to show Astolaine that they don't mean it.*

ASTOLAINE (*whispering*). I shall *hate* the Queen!

MAIDS OF HONOR (*also whispering*). *We* all do!

ASTOLAINE. But I'm to be Maid of Honor to the Princess Snow White, so I'll take my orders from her.

ROSALYS. Oh, Snow White never gives orders.

ASTOLAINE. I shall like *her*. When shall I see her?

CHRISTABEL. Sometimes every day, and then again not for ever so long. It just depends on the Queen's temper.

ERMENGARDE. And how much Snow White has to do.

ASTOLAINE. I thought a Princess never had anything to do.

CHRISTABEL (*confidentially*). Well, you see, Snow White isn't exactly a regular Princess.

ROSALYS. Oh, Christabel! Of course she's a regular Princess, but . . .

ASTOLAINE. But what? (*Wonderingly*) You don't hate Snow White, too?

MAIDS OF HONOR (*in indignant chorus*). Hate Snow White! . . . The idea! . . . She's the dearest — loveliest — kindest . . . We just adore her!

ROSALYS (*to the others*). Oh, do you think we could get Snow White to come and see Astolaine now while we're all alone?

CHRISTABEL. Oh, let's try!

[*And they all hop up and down and clap their hands at the idea.*

ROSALYS. Where is she?

CHRISTABEL. Kitchen, I think. She said she had to bake some bread, and ——

ROSALYS. Bread isn't important. Anyway, it can't do any harm to ask her.

AMELOTTE. I'll go! I'll go!

[*And off she darts to the kitchen.*

ASTOLAINE (*wonderingly*). But what is the Princess doing in the kitchen?

ROSALYS. Of course you don't understand about Snow White yet. It's a Court secret. (*To the others*) But I think we ought to tell her right away, don't you? — before she sees Snow White, or she might think . . .

[*They evidently agree, for they all rush at Astolaine and begin to speak at once.*

MAIDS OF HONOR. I'll tell her! . . . No, let me. I know! . . . Snow White was born . . . This Queen isn't her real mother. . . . It's like a fairy-tale!

ASTOLAINE (*stopping her ears*). I can't *possibly* understand if you all talk at once. I choose — (*she hesitates, and then points to Rosalys*) — *her* to tell.

ROSALYS. Gracious, I was so afraid it wouldn't be me! I tell it so much the best. Come over here where we can talk quietly. (*She runs to the throne and climbs into the big seat, while the others cuddle close beside her*) Now, nobody must interrupt, except by 'spress permission. Button mouths! First, Queen Brangomar isn't Snow White's real mother.

ASTOLAINE. Oh, I know *that*!

CHRISTABEL. But my father says that her real father and mother were the best King and Queen —

ROSALYS (*glaring at Christabel*). What about interrupting?

CHRISTABEL. I forgot. 'Scuse me!

[*And she "buttons" her mouth again.*

ROSALYS (*continuing*). One day in winter, before Snow White was born, her real mother was sitting by the window, embroidering at an ebony frame.   And she pricked her finger, so she opened the window and shook the drop of blood on the snow outside.   And it looked so beautiful that she said, "Oh, how I wish I had a little daughter with hair as black as ebony, skin as white as snow, and lips as red as blood!"   She'd never had a baby before; but a little while after that a baby daughter was born with . . .

MAIDS OF HONOR (*chanting impressively*).   Hair as black as ebony, skin as white as snow, and lips as red as blood.

ASTOLAINE.   So *that's* why they named her Snow White.

ROSALYS.   But then Snow White's mother died, and I suppose the King thought there ought to be *somebody* to mind the baby, for he married Queen Brangomar, and she's Queen now.

ASTOLAINE.   Oh, I see!

ROSALYS.   As long as the King lived, Queen Brangomar was as sweet as sugar to Snow White.

CHRISTABEL (*interrupting in a whisper*).   I am glad she was ever nice to somebody.

ROSALYS.   But after he died, then ——
[*She pauses impressively.*

ASTOLAINE.   Then what?

ROSALYS.   Then — she grew awfully jealous of Snow White.

ASTOLAINE.   Not really?

ERMENGARDE.   Of course everybody loved the Princess best.

CHRISTABEL.   And Brangomar really is the horridest woman!

ROSALYS.   Ssh!   First, she pretended that Snow White might grow up vain, so she took away all her princessy clothes and made her wear old, rag-baggety things.

CHRISTABEL.   Then she pretended that she might grow up lazy, so she made her sweep and dust the Palace.

ROSALYS.   And now Snow White is really almost like a kitchen-maid, and sleeps in the little closet under the stairs where we keep the umbrellas and overshoes.

ASTOLAINE (*springing up*).   I think it's outrageous!   **Why does** Princess Snow White endure it?   I wouldn't!

MAIDS OF HONOR (*apprehensively*).   Oh, ssh!

ASTOLAINE.　Why "ssh?"　I never heard anything so "sshy" as this palace.

ROSALYS (*whispering*).　But what can she do?　The Queen . . .

ASTOLAINE.　Oh, I don't want to hear any more about that hateful Queen.

ROSALYS.　But you must.　It isn't safe that you shouldn't. We'll *have* to tell her.　(*Turning to Christabel*)　*You* tell.

CHRISTABEL.　No, you.　It makes me feel all creepy.

ROSALYS (*to Ermengarde*).　Well, *you!*

ERMENGARDE.　No!　You told us not to interrupt.

ROSALYS.　Oh, dear!　(*She goes on in a hushed whisper*)　The reason it's not safe to do or say anything against the Queen is — that she might *magic* you.

ASTOLAINE.　What do you mean?

ROSALYS.　Enchant you, bewitch you — do some terrible magic thing to you!

ASTOLAINE.　You don't mean that she's a — Witch!

[*The others nod silently, and snuggle closer together.*

ROSALYS.　If she isn't a Witch herself, she is friends with one. You see, she must really be very old.

CHRISTABEL.　She's thirty if she's a minute!

ROSALYS.　And she's still the most beautiful woman in the Seven Kingdoms.

CHRISTABEL.　And once a chamber-maid found a broomstick, the kind that witches ride on, under her bed.

ROSALYS.　So you see, if you did anything against her, she might magic you, and turn you into a toad.

ERMENGARDE.　Or a caterpillar.

CHRISTABEL.　Or something worse.

ASTOLAINE.　There isn't anything worse than a caterpillar! Oh, I want to go home!　I am afraid!

[*And she bursts into tears.　The others gather about her to comfort her.*

MAIDS OF HONOR.　Please, Astolaine, there's nothing really to be afraid of. . . .　It's all right, honestly. . . .　The Queen hardly ever notices us! . . .　And we all want you to stay, for we like you ever so much.

ROSALYS (*in despair*).   Oh, if Snow White would only come now ! Then she wouldn't want to go home.

[*Just at this moment* AMELOTTE *reappears in the doorway.*

AMELOTTE.   Princess Snow White says she'll come if nobody's here.

GUINIVERE.   There isn't anybody.

AMELOTTE.   She'll come !   She'll come !   She's right here !

[*And she darts out of sight again.*

ROSALYS.   Oh, she's coming !   Snow White's coming !   Now you'll see !

[*In joyous excitement, the Maids of Honor join hands and dance a "ring-around", and then wind up into a little squirming knot, hugging each other and dancing up and down.*

AMELOTTE (*re-entering, announces*).   The Princess Snow White !

[*Instantly the Maids of Honor separate, and kneel to receive their little Princess.   Snow White appears in the doorway.   She is dressed in a frock of ragged black, and she has on neither shoes nor stockings.*

SNOW WHITE.   Is this my new playmate, Lady Astolaine ?   I hope you'll like me.

ASTOLAINE (*kissing the hand which Snow White holds out to her*). I love you already, dear Princess.

[*Like a flight of birds, the Maids of Honor run to surround Snow White.*

MAIDS OF HONOR.   We all love you, dear Princess.

SNOW WHITE (*laughing down at them*).   Did you want anything particular ?   I've left hundreds of buns in my oven.

ROSALYS.   Can't you stay just a moment and teach Astolaine our minuet ?   Sir Dandiprat said she must learn it, and you do it so much the best.

SNOW WHITE.   Do you think I have time ?

MAIDS OF HONOR.   Oh, yes, yes !

ROSALYS (*running on to the terrace*).   I'll watch and tell you if anybody's coming.

SNOW WHITE (*to Astolaine*).   Well, Astolaine, you'd better be my partner.   It's very simple.   Are you ready ?   Now !

*[The Maids of Honor take positions for the Dance; and, as
Snow White teaches Astolaine the steps, they sing.*

MAIDS OF HONOR DANCE.

SNOW WHITE.

Turn to me and curtsey low.

THE MAIDS.

One, two, three,
One, two, three.

SNOW WHITE.

Turn away and point your toe.

THE MAIDS.

One and two and three.

SNOW WHITE.

Turn again, and hand in hand,

THE MAIDS.

Hand in hand,
Hand in hand,

SNOW WHITE.

Turn your partner where you stand.

THE MAIDS.

One and two and three,
One and two . . .

[But here Rosalys comes running in from the terrace.

ROSALYS.   Look out ! Old Dandiprat's coming !

SNOW WHITE.   Oh, dear, I must run . . .

ROSALYS (*catching her*).   No, don't ! He won't stay a minute.
Hide behind the throne till he's gone.

MAIDS OF HONOR.   Yes, yes ! Quick ! Get behind the throne !
*[Snow White runs behind the throne, and the Maids of Honor
spread themselves out before it so that she is quite hidden.   But
they are not a moment too soon, for Sir Dandiprat waddles in,
followed by two Flunkies in gorgeous liveries.*

SIR DANDIPRAT.   Ah, young ladies ! I am fortunate to have
found you all together.   I have a most important announcement to make.   I composed it myself.   (*He unrolls an impos-
ing parchment and reads*) "Whereas, his Highness, Prince
Florimond, heir to the Kingdom of Calydon, will call upon the

Queen this afternoon to deliver a letter from his royal father,
I have arranged the following reception.   At four-fifteen this
Proclamation will be read."   (*He consults his watch*)   Dear
me!   Five minutes late already!   I shall have to alter it.
(*And with a sigh he makes the correction with a gold pencil*)
"At four-*twenty* precisely this Proclamation will be read.
At four-thirty Prince Florimond will arrive, and be shown at
once to the throne-room by — ahem — myself.   The Maids
of Honor will dance to amuse his Highness until the Queen is
announced, when they will immediately retire.   By order of
me, Sir Dandiprat Bombas, Court Chamberlain.

"Signed, Yours very truly,

"Sir Dandiprat Bombas.

"P. S.   Her Majesty the Queen regrets that, owing to her
duties in the kitchen, Princess Snow White will be unable to
attend."   You understand, young ladies?

ROSALYS.   Perfectly, Sir Dandiprat.

SIR DANDIPRAT.   You have eight minutes and thirty-one seconds
to prepare.

[*And he trips busily away again, followed by the Flunkies.*

ASTOLAINE.   Gracious!   I can't possibly learn that dance in
eight minutes and thirty-one seconds!

CHRISTABLE.   And we *must* dance in pairs!

ERMENGARDE.   What *shall* we do?

ROSALYS (*calling to Snow White, who is still hidden behind the
throne*).   Princess Snow White, what *shall* we do?

[*There is no answer.*

ASTOLAINE.   It's all right, Princess.   Sir Dandiprat has gone.

[*Still there is no answer; and puzzled, the little Maids call, one
after another.*

ROSALYS.   Princess Snow White!

CHRISTABEL.   Princess Snow White!

GUINIVERE.   Princess Snow White!

[*Still no answer.   Rosalys runs behind the throne.*

ROSALYS.   Oh, she's crying!   Oh, dear Princess!

[*They all run to Snow White, and find her hiding her face and
sobbing silently.*

MAIDS OF HONOR (*surrounding and embracing her*). Oh, what's the matter? . . . Please don't cry! If you cry, we shall cry, too!

SNOW WHITE. I didn't mean to cry. A Princess should *never* cry. (*She smiles resolutely*) There! But I did so want to see Prince Florimond again. He sends me a valentine every year; and long ago, when his father came to visit mine, we were wheeled about in the same baby-carriage. He must be grown up now.

ASTOLAINE. I think it's an outrageous shame!

SNOW WHITE. But you heard. (*Quoting*) "P. S. Her Majesty regrets that the Princess will be unable to attend."

ASTOLAINE. If I were a Princess, I'd do what I chose; and if the old Queen didn't like it I'd . . .

MAIDS OF HONOR (*apprehensively*). Astolaine! Hush!

ASTOLAINE. I'm tired of hushing.

SNOW WHITE. She's right. I am a King's daughter after all; and if I am always meek and do just what I'm told, I'll stay in that hateful kitchen all my life. Oh, wouldn't I like to march right in before everybody, and say, "Prince Florimond, I'm your cousin, Snow White. I apologize for my frock, but it's all I have; and you can't kiss my hand because it's covered with flour. But I did want to see you again after riding with you in a baby-carriage when you were two and I was a half — and I have! Good-bye!" And then I'd march back to my kitchen.

MAIDS OF HONOR. Oh, please, please don't, dear Princess!

ROSALYS. The Queen would be so angry . . .

ASTOLAINE (*struck with an idea*). Wait! The Queen won't be here when we dance for the Prince?

ROSALYS. No. Why?

ASTOLAINE. Then why can't the Princess dance in my place? She could pull my veil over her face, and I'd say afterward that I had — oh, freckles, or something spotty.

CHRISTABEL (*in delight*). Oh, Astolaine!

[*She runs to hug her for the suggestion.*

SNOW WHITE. Oh, dear, I wish it were possible, but my frock!

ROSALYS. Why can't we *all* lend her something?

CHRISTABEL. Why not? We have on heaps more than we need.

ROSALYS. She could have my overskirt!

[*She pulls it up to show an underskirt almost as elaborate.*

CHRISTABEL. And my guimpe.

AMELOTTE. And my lace jacket.

ERMENGARDE. And my cap and pearls.

ROSALYS. We could dress her perfectly!

[*They all hop up and down with squeaks of delight.*

ASTOLAINE. Will you do it, Princess? Oh, will you?

SNOW WHITE. You darlings! I suppose I oughtn't — but I will!

[*And she runs behind the throne to dress, with Guinivere to help her. The other little Maids unpin and unhook and twist and turn to reach hard buttons, at a great rate, as you can judge from the things they say.*

MAIDS OF HONOR. Here's my veil! . . . Oh, she doesn't want a veil first; help me with this skirt. I can't unhook me! . . . These pearls just *won't* untangle! . . . Please come and unpin this. . . . No, me first. . . . I won't go to either if you don't decide! . . . She's ready for the skirt now. . . . You unhook while I squeeze. Now: One, two, three! There isn't room for all our fingers on one little hook! . . . Here's the jacket!

[*And now they're all behind the throne, helping Snow White on with the new things, except poor Christabel, who is left writhing to reach a pin at the back of her neck.*

CHRISTABEL. I think you're just mean! I know it will prick! There — it did!

ROSALYS (*dancing out, waving Snow White's black frock*). Here's her little black dress. What shall I do with it?

ASTOLAINE (*following*). Oh, put it anywhere!

ROSALYS. But where *is* anywhere?

ASTOLAINE. Here, stuff it under this cushion on the throne. (*She does so*) They'll never find it there. *Won't* it be a joke when the Queen sits on it!

ROSALYS.   Oh, why did you say that?   Now I shall just giggle and giggle!

[*They run behind the throne again.   Snow White is almost dressed now; and the little Maids one after another tiptoe away from the throne, whispering.*

CHRISTABEL.   Oh, she looks like a bride, and she's perfectly sweet!

ERMENGARDE.   All silver and white from her head to her feet!

ROSALYS.   Her lips red as blood, and her hair black as night!

ASTOLAINE.   She's lovely, she's lovely, our Princess Snow White!

[*They stand waiting for her.   There is a moment's pause, and then Rosalys calls.*

ROSALYS.   Aren't you coming, Princess?

SNOW WHITE (*from behind the throne*).   Just a moment, till I shake out my hair.   There!

[*She steps into sight.   The Maids sink down in involuntary curtsies at the sight of her.*

CHRISTABEL.   She is lovelier than apple blossoms.

ASTOLAINE.   Lovelier than anybody I ever saw.

ROSALYS (*in a hushed voice*).   More beautiful than the Queen!

CHRISTABEL (*whispering*).   The Queen must never see her like this.

GUINIVERE.   Never!

SNOW WHITE (*who has been putting the last touches to her dress, suddenly*).   Oh, look!   My feet!

[*And indeed her feet are bare!*

ASTOLAINE (*after a pause*).   Oh, I don't think it matters.   The Prince is a gentleman, and no gentleman would look at a lady's feet except to admire them.

SNOW WHITE.   But I'd be different.

ASTOLAINE.   Then let's *all* take off our shoes and stockings.

ROSALYS.   Of course!

[*They plump down on the floor; but a trumpet sounds from the end of the terrace.*

SNOW WHITE.   There's the Prince now!

ASTOLAINE.   We can't stay here.   Let's run into the anteroom to finish.

SNOW WHITE. I am so afraid something may happen. Really I ought not to, but I do so want to see him!

MAIDS OF HONOR. Hurry! Hurry, dear Princess!

[*They hasten off, drawing Snow White with them. They are only just in time; for now music sounds on the terrace, and the throne room fills with Dukes and Duchesses, all dressed in their best robes and coronets. Then on struts Sir Dandiprat, more important than ever.*

SIR DANDIPRAT (*announcing*). His Highness, Prince Florimond, Heir Apparent to the Kingdom of Calydon.

[*The Prince appears, followed by his Pages, Valentine and Vivian. He bows politely to the kneeling Dukes and Duchesses as Sir Dandiprat ushers him to the throne.*

SIR DANDIPRAT. I regret, your Highness, that the Queen hasn't quite finished dressing. But she will be here in a moment. Meantime may the Maids of Honor entertain your Highness with a little dance?

THE PRINCE. It would give me great pleasure.

SIR DANDIPRAT. It is a very simple dance, your Highness, but considering their youth, the . . . (*but his eye falls upon a shoe that Guinivere has left behind. He picks it up and hides it under his coat-tails and stumbles on*) — the young persons do it very . . . er . . . very . . . (*and now he spies a stocking, and in hiding that the clumsy man lets the shoe fall. This confuses him still more, but he goes on*) — er, very creditably indeed. . . . (*And he sees a garter! This completes his embarrassment. He forgets the rest of his speech altogether, and cries*) Really they will drive me distracted! And where are they *now*? (*He dives about among the Dukes and Duchesses, hunting for them, just as they appear in the doorway*) Ah, here you are! Well, begin your dance at once!

[*And off he puffs to find the Queen, wiping his forehead alternately with the shoe and stocking as he goes.*

[*The Maids of Honor begin their Dance. They are all veiled and barefooted so that you couldn't tell Snow White from the others unless you happened to know that she was dressed in white and silver. But there is something about her that attracts the Prince from the first; and as the dance progresses he comes down from the throne to watch her more closely.   As the first figure ends he stands close beside her.*

THE PRINCE   (*to Snow White*).

> Lady, do you think that I
> Might dance too?   I'd like to try.

SNOW WHITE (*giving him her hand*).

> I was hoping you might be
> Tempted to join in — with me.

THE PRINCE.

> I shall learn with much more grace
> If you'll let me see your face.

SNOW WHITE.

> Oh, I oughtn't to; but — well . . .
> If you promise not to tell!

[*She puts back her veil.*

[*The Second Figure of the Dance begins.   Snow White now dancing with the Prince.   Once in a while we overhear what they are saying.*

SNOW WHITE.

> One would think that you (*we bow*)
> Never saw me until now.

THE PRINCE.

> Is it likely I'd forget
> If we two *had* ever met?

SNOW WHITE.

> Yet we once sat side by side,
> Speechless — till at last I cried!
>
> Oh, that's twice you've missed a turn.
> You don't seem to try to learn!

THE PRINCE.

> Do you know (*I did that bow*)
> Steps don't seem important now.

[*The dance ends, and a Trumpet sounds to announce the coming of the Queen.   But the Prince still holds Snow White's hand.*

SNOW WHITE.

> There's the Queen. She mustn't know!
> Please, my hand, sir! I must go!

THE PRINCE.

> Oh, not yet. I'll take the blame.
> I don't even know your name!

SNOW WHITE.

> Oh, don't keep me. I must fly —!
> I'm so sorry, but — good-bye!

[*And she runs off, surrounded by the Maids of Honor, who have been terribly frightened lest the Queen should spy her. Sir Dandiprat appears on the Terrace.*

SIR DANDIPRAT (*announcing*). Her Majesty the Queen!

[*To a blare of trumpets Queen Brangomar enters. She is very beautiful. She wears her crown, and her robes are embroidered in blues and greens like a peacock's tail. She holds out a jewelled hand for the Prince to kiss, and then sweeps to the throne.*

THE QUEEN. So you are Prince Florimond? I'm sorry you chose to-day to come. I'm not looking my best.

THE PRINCE. I have always heard of Queen Brangomar as the most beautiful . . .

THE QUEEN (*interrupting rudely*). Of course, of course! I am told you bring me a message from your father. What is it?

THE PRINCE. This letter. He said it was confidential.

THE QUEEN (*reading the letter*). M-m-m-m-m . . . wretched handwriting. . . . "My son Florimond, now of an age to marry . . ."

THE PRINCE (*startled*). Marry?

THE QUEEN. So your foolish old father is intending to marry you off, is he? I hope he isn't thinking of *me*. How many proposals would that make this week, Dandiprat?

SIR DANDIPRAT. Eleven, your Majesty — *including* those from the lunatic asylums.

THE QUEEN (*still reading*). What's this? To "his cousin the Princess Snow White"! To Snow White! (*She rises in anger*) To Snow White! (*Then, trying not to betray her jeal-*

ousy, she reseats herself with a bitter laugh) Really, my dear Florimond, of course I regret to say so, but Snow White isn't a *possible* choice. I'm sorry to disappoint you.

THE PRINCE (*interrupting*). But you don't, I . . .

THE QUEEN. *I* was speaking! Snow White is most ill-tempered; and so vulgar that she prefers to associate with kitchenmaids. Indeed, I believe she's in the kitchen at this moment. She wouldn't do for you at all.

THE PRINCE. Your Majesty has made me very happy!

THE QUEEN. Happy?

THE PRINCE. Five minutes ago what you say would have made me miserable, for even as a little boy I always dreamed of marrying Snow White when I grew up. But *now —!* You see, I've fallen in love with someone else meantime.

THE QUEEN. Meantime? When?

THE PRINCE. Here, just now, in this very room.

THE QUEEN (*with a pleased laugh*). Oh, my poor boy! Really, I'm so much older than you . . .

THE PRINCE. Oh, it's not your Majesty. She's one of Snow White's Maids of Honor.

THE QUEEN. A Maid of Honor? You don't mean to say you want to *marry* one of them! Your father would never consent. They're nice girls, and come of quite respectable families — daughters of dukes and earls and that class — but you can only marry a Princess.

THE PRINCE. I'd marry her without my father's consent, even if we had to set up housekeeping in a poor cottage!

THE QUEEN. Don't talk rubbish! What is the young person's name?

THE PRINCE. She . . . she didn't tell me. We danced together, that was all.

THE QUEEN (*sarcastically*). Are you quite sure you would know her again?

THE PRINCE. Your Majesty is unkind!

THE QUEEN. Apparently the only way to discover the young paragon is to summon *all* the Maids of Honor. (*She motions to Sir Dandiprat, who hurries off*) I am curious to know your taste. Stand here by me and point her out when she comes.

[*Sir Dandiprat reappears, and introduces the Maids of Honor. They are unveiled now; and as each is named she curtsies to the Prince.*

SIR DANDIPRAT. The Lady Rosalys. The Lady Amelotte. The Lady Ermengarde. The Lady Guinivere. The Lady Christabel. The Lady Astolaine. The Lady Ursula. The Lady Lynette.

THE PRINCE (*after a pause of astonishment*). But she's not there! There was another —!

THE QUEEN. Another? Eight — that's all.

SIR DANDIPRAT (*counting on his fingers*). Only eight, your Highness.

THE PRINCE. But there *was* another!

THE QUEEN (*suspiciously*). Another? What was she like?

THE PRINCE. Her hair was black as ebony; her skin was whiter than snow; her lips were redder than a drop of blood!

THE QUEEN (*in a terrible voice*). Snow White! Summon Snow White!

[*Snow White appears timidly in the entrance. I suspect she had been listening behind the curtains.*

SNOW WHITE. Your Majesty?

THE PRINCE. That is she! And oh, is she Snow White? You are Snow White!

THE QUEEN (*anger quite overcoming her as she sees Snow White's changed appearance*). Snow White! You! You dared . . .

[*She rushes toward the Princess; but suddenly, halfway, she falters and falls fainting.*

SIR DANDIPRAT (*hopping about in great excitement*). The Queen has fainted! The Queen has fainted! Oh, this is most important! Oh, Princess, see what you've done! Take her away, take her away! (*The Maids of Honor lead Snow White away; and Sir Dandiprat turns to the astonished Prince*) It's most distracting. Air, air! Out of the room, please! Give her air!

[*The Prince and the Courtiers hurry out. But no sooner is the*

Queen alone with Sir Dandiprat than she recovers from her pretended swoon.

SIR DANDIPRAT. Shall I fan your Majesty? Oh, I hope . . .

THE QUEEN. Where is the Prince?

SIR DANDIPRAT. On the terrace, your Majesty.

THE QUEEN. Keep him there till I ring.

SIR DANDIPRAT. Oh, pray don't anger him! Gain time! Gain time!

THE QUEEN. Get out, you idiot!

[*This rude exclamation so startles Sir Dandiprat that he stumbles backwards up the Terrace steps, and waddles out of sight as fast as his fat legs will carry him, leaving his staff behind.*

THE QUEEN (*alone*). The Witch! Witch Hex! I must summon her. She must help me now. [*She draws the curtains over both entrances so that she may not be seen at her magic. Then in a hushed, mysterious voice she chants.*

THE SPELL

From my eyebrow pluck a hair,
E — burrimee *boo*-row.
Blow it high up in the air,
E — burrimee hock.
Where it lands a circle trace,
E — burrimee *boo*-row.
Three times pace about the space,
and
Knock, knock, knock!

[*As she knocks smoke rises from the circle she has traced with Dandiprat's staff, and there is a sound of distant thunder.*

Thunder says the spell grows warm,
E — burrimee *boo*-row.
Now I speak the mystic Charm,
E — burrimee boo!

THE CHARM

Ee Eye-*sof*-o-gos.   Ee Eye-sof-a-giddle!
Ee Eye-*sof*-o-gos.   Ee Eye-sof-a-giddle.
Ee Eye-*sof*-o-gos!
Eee Eye-sof-o-*lof*-o-gos!
Ee Eye-*sof*-o-gos!
Ee Eye-sof-a-giddle!

[*The Charm sounds like nonsense, but it must be true magic, for the smoke increases as she chants it, and the thunder comes nearer.*

The spell's wound up, the charm is clear!
I summon thee, Witch Hex, appear!

[*Lo! through the floor Witch Hex does appear. She looks exactly like the witches in all fairy-tale pictures, with her pointed hat, red cloak, and crutched stick. It is evident that she is in a bad temper.*

THE WITCH. Help me out, help me out! (*The Queen helps her out of the smoking circle*) What's the meaning of this? I'm getting tired of being called up by you night and day. Last time I was in my nightgown and it was snowing! I was an idiot ever to teach you that Spell. Well, what is the matter now?

THE QUEEN. Don't be angry, dear godmother. You know how much I love you!

THE WITCH. Stuff! You don't love me. You don't love anybody but yourself. That's the matter with you. If you only knew the trouble I have to keep you beautiful! Your disposition keeps wearing through. If I should once say, "Bang! no more charms for that wretched Brangomar," how would you look then? (*She chuckles at the thought*) I believe you'd be uglier than I am.

THE QUEEN. I know, I know, dear Hex, but you wouldn't!

THE WITCH. Don't be too sure. Just summon me once too often, and you may find youself the *ugliest* woman in the Seven Kingdoms, for a change.

THE QUEEN.   Oh, tell me I am still the most beautiful!

THE WITCH.   You look all right yet.   But I warn you!   I'm using my strongest magic now.   You'd be much safer if you'd try to be good once in a while.   Well, who are you jealous of *this* time?

THE QUEEN.   Snow White.

THE WITCH.   Snow White?   She's only a child!

THE QUEEN.   So I thought till to-day, when I saw her for the first time prettily dressed.

THE WITCH.   Well, why in hop-scotch did you dress her up?

THE QUEEN.   I didn't.   She tricked me.

THE WITCH.   Who thought she was fairer than you?

THE QUEEN.   Prince Florimond.   He wants to marry her.

THE WITCH.   Florimond?   Pooh!   Mere boy!   Probably said it to plague you, knowing your wretched vanity.   But I've brought something with me that may help to keep you quiet. Just had time to snatch it when I felt you spelling away.   It's a Magic Mirror.

[*She takes from her pocket a hand Mirror, carved from a single crystal, that glows and gleams like an opal.*

THE QUEEN (*seizing the Mirror and gazing into it*).   Magic! . . . (*But suddenly she cries out in horror*)   Oh!

THE WITCH.   Ah, you see!   Reflects you as you really are.   If I stopped my spells that's what you'd look like.   Now it makes me quite decent looking.   That's because my character's better.

THE QUEEN.   Oh, the hateful thing!   I never saw anything so terrible.   Why, I looked almost funny!   Take it away! Take it away!

THE WITCH.   Wait!   That's not all its magic.   Hold it in your hand and say:

> Mirror, Mirror, in my hand,
> Who's the fairest in the land?

and it will answer truthfully.

THE QUEEN (*snatching it*). Oh, let me try! (*Shutting her eyes that she may not see her reflection, she asks*)

> Mirror, Mirror, in my hand,
> Who's the fairest in the land?

THE WITCH. Listen!

[*There is a faint strain of Music, and then a far-away voice that sounds like crystal bells, sings*

THE MIRROR.

> You who hold me in your hand,
> You were fairest in the land;
> But, to-day, I tell you true,
> Snow White is more fair than you!

[*With a scream of rage the Queen starts to dash the Mirror to the floor. The Witch rescues it just in time.*

THE WITCH. Stop! Stop! Gracious! Listen to me now! If you ever break that Mirror, you will become as ugly as you really are — and for life too! None of my spells can beauty you again either, for the Mirror is made with those same charms. I thought you knew enough common, every-day magic for that!

THE QUEEN (*pacing up and down, weeping with rage*). But Snow White is more beautiful than I! Snow White is more beautiful than I.

THE WITCH (*mocking her*). "Snow White is more beau-hoo-hoo-ti-ful than I!" Stop that wauling.

THE QUEEN. I can't bear it! Make a spell and turn her ugly — as ugly as a toad.

THE WITCH. Won't! Refuse to make any more bad spells. If you can't bear the sight of her, why not send her away somewhere, — say to boarding-school?

THE QUEEN. But she'd come back.

THE WITCH. Why should she? Suppose at boarding-school she got croup or mumps, or whatever those children's diseases are. . . .

THE QUEEN. Oh, I see! You'll make a spell and give her the disease.

THE WITCH.   No, no, no!   Won't do any more bad magic, I
tell you.   You must contrive to have her lost on the way to
boarding-school, and then just tell some tarradiddle to explain
why she doesn't come back — and there you are!   Everything permanently settled, and a little peace for me, I
hope.

THE QUEEN.   I might.   I could send Berthold, my Huntsman,
as if he were taking her to school, . . . and there . . .
oh! . . . in the deep forest . . . (*she whispers*) . . . he shall
put her to death.

THE WITCH (*starting*).   Goodness — gracious — mercy — me!
I never suggested anything like *that!*   Why, I hear she's quite
a nice child.

THE QUEEN.   I shall never know a happy hour while she's
alive.

THE WITCH.   Well, there's no arguing with *you.*   But can you
trust your Huntsman?

THE QUEEN.   I know a way to make him obey.

THE WITCH.   Glad you know something!   And look here!   If
you're *resolved* to have Snow White killed, there's a little favor
you might do me.   I'm making a new spell that's really *hard*
magic!   A hair restorer that will really restore hair.   Want
it for my own personal use.   (*She pops off her cap and shows a
perfectly bald head*)   I'd about given it up for want of the last
ingredient — the heart of a nice young girl.   Now I wouldn't
harm a nice young girl myself for anything; but if you're
determined to dispose of Snow White, I'd be obliged for her
heart.

THE QUEEN.   I promise.   Berthold shall bring it to me as a
proof.   And now good-bye, dear Hexy.   I must summon him
at once.

THE WITCH.   Hm!   It's always, "Good-bye, dear Hexy," as
soon as I've done what you want.   But I'm as glad to go as
you are to have me.   Say the "Quick Spell" and get me off.
Ready?

[*The Queen and the Witch join hands, shut their eyes and chant
in chorus.*

THE QUICK SPELL

THE QUEEN AND THE WITCH.

> Bangaboo-bar;
> Bangaboo-whack;
> Crow eat sun,
> Make all black!
> Mar-*oom*-bah!

[*Everything suddenly becomes dark, and in the darkness the two voices are heard still chanting.*

> Bangaboo-bar;
> Bangaboo-whack,
> Mole dig hole,
> Witch go back,
> Mar-*oom*-bah!

[*There is a queer sound, something like a very small earthquake. Then only the Queen's voice is heard.*

THE QUEEN.

> Bangaboo-bar!
> Bangaboo-whack!
> Witch is gone,
> Sun come back,
> Mar-*oom*-bah!

[*The light returns as suddenly as it went. The Witch has vanished. Quite calmly the Queen goes to the bell-cord.*

THE QUEEN. Let me see. I ring three times for the Huntsman.
[*She rings; but it is Sir Dandiprat who enters.*

SIR DANDIPRAT. Your Majesty rang for me?

THE QUEEN. Not for you, idiot, for Berthold. Give me a minute alone with him, and then summon the Prince and Snow White. Off with you! (*Sir Dandiprat hurries away just as Chief Huntsman Berthold enters. Berthold is tall and big. He has a kind, ruddy face*) Berthold, I have a task for you.

BERTHOLD. To take you a-hunting, your Majesty? Your

forests are full of game, wild pigs, deer — indeed there may even be a unicorn or two.

THE QUEEN. It's other game this time, Berthold. You have been a faithful Chief Huntsman. Suppose I promote you to be Lord High Admiral. As we have no navy, your duties would be light.

BERTHOLD. Oh, your Majesty, how can I thank you?

THE QUEEN. It depends upon your carrying out a task with absolute obedience. Come nearer. The Princess Snow White is to set out for boarding-school this afternoon. You will conduct her. At the Western Gates, you will take the old road that turns to the left . . .

BERTHOLD. But, your Majesty, that road leads into the deep wood.

THE QUEEN. You will take *that* road. When you have come to the very heart of the forest, then — (*and she hisses the words*) — you will kill the Princess.

BERTHOLD (*springing back*). Never, your Majesty, never!

THE QUEEN. She has disobeyed me. She must be punished.

BERTHOLD. Kill Snow White! My late King's daughter! The loveliest maid in the Seven Kingdoms! I would slay myself first. There is no man in your dominions base enough to do such a deed. Pray dismiss me.

[*He turns to go.*

THE QUEEN (*in a terrible voice*). Wait! I know how to make you obey. You have six small children, I believe?

BERTHOLD (*wonderingly*). Yes, your Majesty.

THE QUEEN. Suppose I lock them up in the Great Gray Tower.

BERTHOLD. Oh, your Majesty, have mercy!

THE QUEEN. Think! Can you not hear their voices calling to you from the dark? "We are hungry, papa!" they will cry, and they will beat on the door with their little hands.

BERTHOLD (*sinking to the ground*). Spare me! Spare me!

THE QUEEN. At last they will be too weak to cry or beat. Then when all has grown still within the Tower, I will say: "Berthold, here is the key. Go and see how Queen Brangomar punishes disobedience."

BERTHOLD (*rising with a cry*). Oh, I will obey, your Majesty! Heaven forgive me, but I cannot let my children starve.

THE QUEEN. That's *much* better, Berthold. You understand clearly?

BERTHOLD. Alas, too well!

THE QUEEN. What a tone of voice! Remember the motto, "A task cheerfully done is well done." And, oh, I almost forgot. You must bring me Snow White's heart before midnight, as a proof. Here comes the Prince. Do try to look more pleasant. [*Prince Florimond returns, ushered in by Sir Dandiprat, and followed by all the Courtiers, Pages, Maids of Honor, and Flunkies.*

THE PRINCE. I hope your Majesty has recovered.

THE QUEEN. Quite, thank you. I beg everybody's pardon. Something I had for lunch, no doubt. (*To Sir Dandiprat*) Where is the Princess Snow White?

SNOW WHITE (*appearing*). I am here, your Majesty.

THE QUEEN. My dear Snow White, Prince Florimond has come to ask your hand in marriage. What do you say?

SNOW WHITE (*drooping her head*). What may I say?

THE QUEEN. I was obliged to tell him how unfitted you are at present to become a Queen. Indeed, I've long been thinking of sending you away to some select boarding-school for backward Princesses. This seems the opportunity. You will remain at the school for a year and a day . . .

THE PRINCE. Oh, no, your Majesty!

THE QUEEN (*firmly*). And the Prince must promise not to see or write to you until the end of that time. Otherwise, I shall refuse my consent. Do you agree?

THE PRINCE. Since I must.

THE QUEEN. Then *that's* settled! Return here one year and one day hence, and we can then — (*and here she means more than she says*) — discuss the engagement. Now, Snow White, bid farewell to Prince Florimond. (*The Prince starts forward to kiss Snow White's hand, but the Queen intervenes*) No, no! A respectful bow and a curtsey will be quite sufficient. Goodbye, Prince Florimond. Give my regards to your father.

[*So the poor Prince bows himself out, followed by his Pages, but he looks back at Snow White as long as he can see her.*

THE QUEEN. Now, Snow White, I've arranged everything. You must leave immediately or you won't arrive at the school before nightfall. Berthold will conduct you. So say your good-byes quickly.

SNOW WHITE. Thank you so much, your Majesty. I'm not quite sure that I want to be a Queen, but I *should* like to be well educated. I'm very grateful.

[*She tries to take the Queen's hand, but the Queen withdraws it hastily.*

THE QUEEN. You are keeping Berthold waiting. Off with you at once.

SNOW WHITE (*turning to the Maids of Honor*). Good-bye, my little playmates! Good-bye, Amelotte and Ermengarde and Christabel and Rosalys. Don't cry, Rosalys; it will only be a year, and I promise not to come back so grown-up and princessy that you won't recognize me. Good-bye, dear Ladies and Gentlemen, who have all been so good to me! I kiss you all! (*She blows them a kiss. Then, slipping her little hand into Berthold's big one, says*) Now, Berthold!

[*And Berthold and the Princess Snow White go off along the Terrace toward the deep Forest, as —*

THE CURTAIN FALLS

SCENE II

IN THE FOREST

Great trees meet over a wild and overgrown path. It is after sunset, and the light is fading. A small brown Bird flies above the path, chirping a little call, and perches in a tree just out of sight. Snow White, running gaily, follows the bird.

SNOW WHITE. Yes, little brown bird, I hear you. You want another answer? Wait until I get my breath. (*She whistles an imitation of the bird's call*) What? Flying on again?

Where are you trying to lead us? (*She calls back to Berthold*)
Berthold, the brown bird seems to be trying to get me to
follow him. He's perched on that tree now. (*The Bird calls
again, and Snow White tries to imitate the call in words*)
"Come, Snow White! Come, Snow White!" Is that what
you are trying to say? Well, I'm coming!
[*And she runs on, following the bird.*
[*Berthold comes into sight. As he sees how lonely the spot is he
halts irresolutely and murmurs to himself.*

BERTHOLD. It may as well be here as anywhere. Mile after
mile I have put it off till the next turn or some more shadowed
spot. But that is no kindness to the Princess. Remember
your own children, man! It must be here! (*He calls after
Snow White and his voice is hoarse*) Princess! Come back!

SNOW WHITE (*answering*). What is it, Berthold? You want
me? (*She runs back to him*) There's the bird again. He
seems to know the way better than you do. Do you think
he can know that I'm going to boarding-school? (*The Bird
calls again, and she answers*) Don't be so impatient! What
did you want, Berthold?

BERTHOLD. Oh, dear Princess . . .
[*But he cannot go on.*

SNOW WHITE. Why are you so pale? Have you hurt yourself?
[*She tries to take his hand, but he draws it away.*

BERTHOLD. Oh, forgive me, Princess!
[*He kneels before her in anguish.*

SNOW WHITE (*wonderingly*). Forgive you? For what? (*She
tries to raise his head so that she may see his face*) What is it,
Berthold?

BERTHOLD. Don't look at me, Princess! Don't look at me.
[*He puts his arms about her, and hides his face in her dress.*

SNOW WHITE. Oh, whatever it is, tell me! I am afraid!

BERTHOLD. The Queen . . .

SNOW WHITE. The Queen?

BERTHOLD. The Queen . . . has commanded me to . . .
kill you . . . here . . . in this forest . . . now!

SNOW WHITE (*looking down at him in wonder*). Kill me? I don't understand. You're taking me to school! . . . Oh, you're *joking!* I call that a silly joke. Look at me! No, look at me! (*Slowly she raises his head. She reads the truth in his face, and with a cry springs from him*) Oh, it's true, it's true! I know it! That was why the Queen . . .! But you won't, will you? See, Berthold, I don't run away. I come right to you. I creep into your arms. You won't hurt me, will you?

BERTHOLD. If it were my life alone that were at stake, I would suffer any torture rather than harm a hair of your head. But the Queen . . .

SNOW WHITE. Oh, you mean — that the Queen will kill you, unless . . .

BERTHOLD. Not me, Princess, but my children. She has shut them up in the Gray Tower, and she will starve them to death unless . . .

SNOW WHITE. Oh, Berthold! (*Then, after a little pause, she goes on softly*) I know your children. I've played with them. She would do it, too. (*She thinks a moment; then, with sudden resolution, goes on*) Kiss me good-bye, Berthold. I couldn't *live* and think of your children. See, I'm not crying — I'm not even very frightened. I'll turn away and shut my eyes. But please be quick!

BERTHOLD (*staggering to his feet, makes a fumbling movement for his knife, but as he touches it he sinks down again with a cry*). I cannot, Princess, I cannot!

SNOW WHITE. But you must, Berthold! How else can you save your children?

BERTHOLD. I will find some way — some way.

SNOW WHITE. No, it's not possible, Berthold!

BERTHOLD. It's not possible for me to — kill — your Highness. [*There is a silence.*

SNOW WHITE. Berthold, considering the way the Queen has behaved, do you think it would be very wrong to tell her a story?

BERTHOLD (*dazed*). Wrong?

SNOW WHITE. Because, if it weren't wrong, mightn't you *tell* her that you'd killed me without doing it?

BERTHOLD. But the proof! She has commanded me to bring her your — heart — before midnight.

SNOW WHITE. My heart? I've never seen a heart. I don't suppose a little piece of beefsteak would look at all like it, would it?

BERTHOLD. No, but . . . (*He springs up*) Why not the heart of some beast? I might catch a wild pig here in the forest, and . . . (*Suddenly his voice drops*) But I couldn't leave you here alone. You would starve.

SNOW WHITE. Couldn't I live like the birds, on berries?

BERTHOLD. But the winter will come — and — oh, your Highness, there are savage beasts in this wood.

SNOW WHITE. I haven't seen a living creature but the little brown bird.

BERTHOLD. It was daytime, and I was with you; but it is growing dark, and at night . . .

SNOW WHITE. But if you don't take the heart to the Queen before midnight, you know what she will do. And you must catch the wild pig before it is too dark to see.

BERTHOLD. No! I dare not leave your Highness!

SNOW WHITE (*pretending to be struck with a new idea*). Berthold, could you find this place again?

BERTHOLD. Find it? Every inch of the way is branded on my brain!

SNOW WHITE. Then, to-morrow, hide some food in your tunic and come back again and we can plan.

BERTHOLD (*slowly*). I might . . . but . . .

SNOW WHITE. Oh, please! There is *no* other hope, is there?

BERTHOLD. None that I can see.

SNOW WHITE. Then hurry. It's getting darker every moment. Kiss me good-bye quickly. (*She puts her face up to him*) Until to-morrow, dear Berthold!

BERTHOLD. My Princess! Heaven keep you! Until to-morrow!

[*He hastens away.*

SNOW WHITE (*calling after him*). Good-bye, dearest Berthold! (*Then to herself*) Poor Berthold, does he think the Queen will ever let him out of her sight again? She will shut him up in prison for fear he might tell. He will never come back! Good-bye forever, Berthold! (*A sudden terror seizes her*) Oh, it's good-bye forever, *everybody!* (*She starts after him, crying*) Berthold, come back! (*But remembering, she clasps her hands over her mouth to stifle the cry*) Hush! Think of his children, Snow White, think of his children! (*With a little moan, she sinks to the ground*) But what shall I do? I'm afraid — afraid! (*And she hides her face among the leaves. The call of the brown Bird is heard, almost overhead. At first Snow White does not hear, and the Bird repeats the cry that sounds almost like "Come, Snow White!" Snow White looks up in wonder*) Oh, little bird, are you still here? I think you are my friend. (*The Bird flies off a little way, and then perches and repeats his call*) Are you telling me to follow you, as you did before? But where? I have nowhere to go. (*Again the Bird calls, and Snow White rises and follows where he flies*) Yes, I will follow. I trust you. (*She runs out of sight among the trees, calling as she goes*) I am coming! I am following, little bird!

THE CURTAIN FALLS

SCENE III

IN THE HOUSE OF THE SEVEN DWARFS

The Dwarfs' House is very tiny. It is built of rough stones and logs, and niched into a hillside in the depths of the great wood. It has but one room, with a single wide window and one low door. Along one side of the room are ranged seven small beds of different sizes. On the other is a stone fireplace for cooking, and a pump with a barrel under the spout. In the middle of the floor stands a table with seven places laid for supper. A single candle on the table lights the room. Through the window we see the forest, dim in the moonlight.

Presently the brown Bird flies past and perches on a branch just outside, still calling for Snow White to follow. They have come a long way and she is very tired and hungry; but as she sees the house and realizes where the brown Bird was leading her, she runs up to peep in through the window.

SNOW WHITE. Oh, was it toward this light you were leading me, brown bird? Why, it's a little house! Are you flying away now? Please let me thank you first. I blow you a kiss! He's gone. Perhaps birds don't like kisses, their faces are so sharp. (*Calling after him*) Good-bye, little friend! (*She looks cautiously through the window into the house*) What a queer little room! Seven beds and all so small. There must be lots of children in the family. Nobody with so many children could be wicked. (*She calls*) May I come in? (*As there is no answer she knocks at the door, then opens it a crack*) Please, may I come in to rest just for a moment? I'm lost in the forest. (*Still no answer. She steals into the room and looks about*) Nobody at home. But they couldn't mind if I sat down, just a minute. Oh, there's the children's supper all laid out. I'm so hungry! If I took just a tiny bit from each place, I'm sure they wouldn't mind.

[*She goes to the table, and as she nibbles a morsel at each place she sings to herself.*

EATING SONG

A drink of water from this cup,
Of porridge just a single sup;
Of honey just a drop to spread
Over this bit of crusty bread.
One corner of this barley-cake,
One nut — and for dessert I'll take
A single cherry of these four,
And not a single mouthful more, —
No, not a single mouthful more!

Now I ought to do something to pay for my supper. There's plenty to be done. It isn't at all a tidy house. (*She yawns;*

and then, shaking herself) Wake up, Snow White! You mustn't get sleepy yet; not till the people come home. (*But she cannot stifle another yawn*) There's a broom. Suppose I sweep a little. (*She begins, but the broom raises such a cloud of dust that she has to stop*) Dear me, that only makes things worse. This floor needs a good scrubbing. I might make up the beds. (*She goes to the biggest bed, but she is so tired that she sits down on it a moment before beginning*) This one looks as if it hadn't been made for years and years and years. I wonder if it's as humpy to lie on as it is to sit on. (*She lies down to try it*) Oh, it's more . . . It's humpy and bumpy . . . and bumpy and humpy . . . and . . .

[*Her voice trails away into silence. She has fallen asleep.*

[*For a time all is quiet in the room. Then from underground is a sound of distant knocking. It comes nearer till it sounds just under the house. Finally a stone slab in the floor is pushed up slowly, and from an underground passage that leads from the house into the deep mines, six Dwarfs clamber into sight. They are very small — the tallest hardly above your waist — but they are very old and their beards are long and gray. Each carries a lighted lantern and a pickaxe, and bears a heavy sack over his shoulder. As soon as the last is in the room, they form in line, with Blick, the eldest, at the head.*

BLICK. Now, brothers, evening roll-call. (*He calls his own name*) Blick! (*And answers*) Here! (*Then he calls each of the others by name — " Flick! Glick! Snick! Plick! and Whick!" and each answers, "Here!" Last of all Blick calls*) Quee! (*There is no answer. Blick shakes his head sadly*) Late, as usual! He's been stealing again. Whatever shall we do with that boy? (*All the Dwarfs sigh, and hang their heads with shame at Quee's conduct. But Blick goes on*) Well, brothers, what result of to-day's work? Half a ton of gold nuggets for mine.

[*He takes a handful of enormous nuggets from his sack. The others also exhibit their treasures as they name them.*

FLICK. A hundredweight of silver dust.

GLICK. Fifty pounds of diamonds.

SNICK. A bushel of rubies.

PLICK. A gallon of emeralds.

WHICK. A peck of opals.

BLICK. Fair, fair ! But we ought to work longer hours.

FLICK. Yes, what's the good of coming home — except to sleep.

GLICK. And have supper.

FLICK (*with scorn*). Oh, that supper !

BLICK. I know. It's wretched. If we cook it at night, it's too hot to eat ; if we cook it in the morning, it's cold and dusty by night. But what else can we do ?

GLICK. And I'd rather sleep underground than in those beds.

ALL. So would we !

BLICK. I know ! They haven't been made for years. But it doesn't pay to take time from digging diamonds to make beds, so what can we do ?

ALL (*sighing*). Nothing.

SNICK. But if we didn't come home to supper we wouldn't have to wash.

BLICK (*shocked*). Oh, brothers ! Washing is a duty. Hush ! I think I hear Quee. (*They all cock their heads sidewise, like robins, and listen*) Yes, that's Quee. He *has* been stealing again ! We must scold him soundly.

FLICK. It never does any good.

BLICK. But we must bring him up in the way he should go. He is the youngest of us ; he's only ninety-nine next April. Clear away and ready for him.

[*They pile their sacks in a corner, and squat on the floor in a semi-circle, with Blick, like a presiding judge, in the center.*

[*Quee creeps up stealthily through the underground passage. He is much the smallest, but graybearded like the others. As he faces his brothers one finger creeps into his mouth. Blick greets him sternly.*

BLICK. Quee, you are late again ! (*Quee nods*) Been stealing as usual, I suppose ?

[*Quee nods.*

ALL (*shaking their fingers at him reprovingly*). Oh !

BLICK. You know it's wrong!

ALL. Very, very wrong!

[*Quee nods.*

BLICK. Did anybody catch you at it? (*Quee shakes his head*) That's good — as far as it goes.

FLICK. Did you get me a mouse-trap?

[*Quee nods.*

GLICK. And my candles?

[*Quee nods.*

FLICK. And a pin? (*Quee nods*) I'm glad of that. I've always wanted a pin.

BLICK. Of course you understand, Quee, that stealing is a sin, and that your conduct makes us very sad?

ALL. Very, very sad!

BLICK. Will you promise to reform and . . .

FLICK (*interrupting hastily*). Wait, wait! Give him the list of things to get to-morrow first!

BLICK. Dear me, I almost forgot! Quee, tie a string round your finger to remember by. Now, what do you all want?

THE DWARFS.

[*Speaking in rapid succession; each names one article.*

A chain. A plane. A weather-vane.
A hat. A mat. A pussy-cat.
A pound of brass.
A pane of glass.
A crock. A lock. An eight-day clock.

A can. A pan. A palm-leaf fan.
A tack. A sack. An almanac.
A can of soup.
A chicken-coop.
A map. A cap. A snappy trap.

A pole. A bowl. A baker's roll.
A rake. A cake. A pound of steak.
A peck of meal.
A pickled eel.
A slate. A plate. A ten-pound weight.

BLICK.   That's all for to-morrow.   But remember, young man, if "It's a sin to steal a pin," how much worse it must be to steal a ten-pound weight.   You realize that?   (*Quee nods sadly*)   Brothers, we shall have to correct him again to-morrow night.   He is incorrigible.

ALL (*mournfully*).   In-cor-rig-ible!

BLICK.   Now for the evening washing.   Get the basin, Quee. [*Glad that his daily scolding is over, Quee runs cheerfully and fetches a basin of water, a big sponge and a towel.*   "No flinching now, brothers," *cries Blick.*   "Line up!   Right faces!" *All except Quee stand close together, and thrust their faces over one another's shoulders, with eyes closed.   Running down the line, Quee washes all their right cheeks with one long sweep of his sponge.*   "Reverse!" *cries Blick.   They all turn and face in the opposite direction; and Quee, running back up the line, washes all their other cheeks.*   "Right faces!"   *cries Blick. With a single sweep of his towel, Quee dries all their right cheeks; and when Blick commands* "Reverse," *he dries the opposite sides in the same neat and speedy way.   And so the Evening Washing is finished.*

BLICK.   There!   That's over for another twenty-four hours.

ALL.   Thank goodness!

BLICK.   Oh, come!   It's quick and comparatively painless. Only — Quee gets dirtier and dirtier every year.

FLICK.   *Somebody* must wash the others.

GLICK.   He's the youngest.

WHICK.   It's his duty.

BLICK.   Nevertheless, he's a disgrace to the family. [*Quee bows his head in shame.*

GLICK.   And now — (*with a heavy sigh*) — supper!

ALL (*sadly*).   Supper!

FLICK.   No hurry!   It's been getting cold ever since breakfast. [*With lagging feet they march to the table, and are about to eat, when Blick starts back in surprise.*

BLICK.   I say!
        Some one's been drinking from my cup!

FLICK.   Some one has eat my porridge up!

GLICK.   And took my honey!

SNICK.   See, they spread
          It all across my crust of bread!

PLICK.   Some one's been at my barley-cake!

WHICK.   Eaten my nut; — and dared to take
          The biggest cherry of Quee's four!

ALL.   And, goodness-gracious! how much more?

[*They gaze at each other in amazement.*

BLICK (*whispering*).   Brothers, there must be Robbers in the
house!

FLICK.   Or Pirates!

GLICK.   Or Burglars!

BLICK.   Probably burglars. If so, they're under the beds;
burglars always are. Hush! Let every man look under his
own bed.

[*Each Dwarf creeps to his bed, and peers cautiously under it.
Then, one after the other, they rise, shaking their heads and saying:* "Nobody under my bed!" "Nobody under my bed!"
"Nobody under my bed!" *Blick is the last. But as he rises
he sees Snow White, and exclaims in a tense whisper,* "But —
there's something in it! Look, brothers!" *The Dwarfs creep
about Blick's bed, and, holding their lanterns high, gaze down
upon the sleeping Snow White.*

GLICK (*whispering*).   What is it?

FLICK.   I know! It's a child.

BLICK.   No, it's a girl. I saw one once.

FLICK.   Well, girl or child, it's the most beautiful thing I ever
saw.

GLICK.   Is it tame, or will it fly away like a bird when it wakes
up?

FLICK.   Oh, children are tame — and they can talk.

ALL (*in rapture*).   Oh!

BLICK.   But this isn't a child, it's a girl. I don't think *girls*
can talk.

[*They all heave a sigh of disappointment.*

FLICK. I wish she'd stay with us just so that we could look at her.

BLICK. She won't.

GLICK. Why not?

BLICK. Of *course* she won't. Are we handsome, or young, or tall? In fact, aren't we dwarfs?
[*They all hang their heads.*

FLICK. But if we didn't tell her that?

BLICK. Flick, I wonder at you! Besides, she might find it out.

GLICK. She's beautifully white and clean. Look, she's been trying to sweep.

FLICK. I can't bear to think of her leaving us.

BLICK. I'm going to stay up all night just to watch her.

GLICK. Do you think there's any way we could persuade her to stay?

BLICK. I'm afraid not.

FLICK. Even if we laid presents on her bed?

BLICK. What kind of presents? Gold and diamonds?

FLICK. Oh, not common things like that! Really valuable things like — my jack-knife!

BLICK. Oh, things like *that!* It might. But I'm afraid not.

FLICK. We might try, anyhow. Let each man give the most valuable thing he has in the world.

BLICK (*collecting the gifts. Each names his present lovingly as he takes it from his pocket*). My thimble!

SNICK. My almanac.

PLICK. My empty bottle.

GLICK. And — my pet frog.

BLICK (*laying the gifts gently on the foot of Snow White's bed*). There, that may help. But no! It's no use, brothers. There is Quee!

ALL (*hopelessly*). Yes! There is Quee!

FLICK. We might hide him?

BLICK. She'd be sure to find him sooner or later.

GLICK. He might reform.

BLICK. But we never could pretend he wasn't dirty. He hasn't been washed for fifty years.

FLICK (*with a sudden inspiration*).   Brothers, why not wash him now?

GLICK.   We might !

ALL.   We *will !*

BLICK.   It must be done at once or he won't be dry by morning. Get the utensils.

BLICK (*marching to the pump*).   Here's the pump to douse him with !

SNICK (*fetching the basin*).   Here are suds to souse him with !

FLICK (*bringing the sponge*).   Here's the sponge to sop him with !

PLICK (*hurrying with the broom*).   Here's the broom to mop him with !

GLICK (*running with the soap*).   Here's the soap to scrub him with !

WHICK (*waving the towel*).   Here's the cloth to rub him with !
[*They surround Quee.*

BLICK.   Quee, you are going to be . . .

ALL (*in a tremendous whisper*).   *Washed !*
[*They carry him to the barrel, plump him in with a great splash, and pump on him.   Then, as they scrub and rub and soap and stir him about in the water, they chant in chorus :*

THE DWARFS.

> Here's the pump to *douse* him with !
> Here are suds to *souse* him with !
> Here's the sponge to *sop* him with !
> Here's the broom to *mop* him with !
> Here's the soap to *scrub* him with !
> Here's the cloth to *rub* him with !
> Rub ! Scrub ! Mop ! Sop ! Souse ! Douse !
> Rub !
> Scrub !
> Mop !
> Sop !
> Souse !
> Douse !

[*In their excitement they forget to be quiet.   Snow White stirs in her sleep; then wakes and sits up.*

SNOW WHITE. Where is this? Oh, there are the children that live here. Why, they're *not* children. They're queer, little old men. They'll never let me stay with them. (*She rises, and standing by the bed says shyly*) I beg your pardon. (*The Dwarfs turn suddenly. Snow White makes a little curtsey*) I'm sorry if I've disturbed you; but I was lost in the forest, and when I saw your house I was so tired and hungry I came in and took a little food — without asking. Then I'm afraid I fell asleep. (*She waits for an answer, but the Dwarfs gaze at her in silence, so she falters on*) I'd pay for it, but I haven't any money. (*She stops. Again a silence*) So all I can do is to say, "Thank you — and — good-night." (*She moves reluctantly to the door. The Dwarfs sigh deeply. She turns for a farewell curtsey*) Thank you *very* much. (*She half shuts the door behind her, then re-opens it to repeat*) Good-night! (*There is no answer except another heavy sigh from the Dwarfs. With sudden pity she bursts out*) Oh, you're not dumb, are you?

BLICK (*clearing his throat*). No, we're not dumb; but you're a girl, aren't you?

SNOW WHITE (*wonderingly*). Yes — I'm a girl.

BLICK. Or a child?

SNOW WHITE. Well, I'm not very old.

BLICK. We don't know how to talk to young people.

SNOW WHITE. Well, most grown people begin, "Why, how you've grown!" And usually the next thing is, "How do you like your school?"

BLICK. "How you've grown."

FLICK. "How do you like your school?"

SNOW WHITE (*smiling, but a little embarrassed*). Well — perhaps it *is* a little late for conversation. It's long past bedtime, isn't it?

BLICK. Long past.

SNOW WHITE. There are six of you and — seven beds, aren't there?

BLICK (*hastily putting the cover on the barrel*). Yes, there are seven beds.

SNOW WHITE. Oh, before I go, perhaps I ought to tidy the one I slept in. (*She goes to the bed*) What are these things on it? Oh! One's a frog. It's alive.

GLICK. He *was* my frog. He's perfectly tame.

SNOW WHITE. What a funny thing to put on a bed.

BLICK (*edging toward her eagerly*). They were meant to be presents.

SNOW WHITE. Oh — somebody's birthday?

FLICK. No, it's nobody's birthday.

SNOW WHITE. Then I don't see — ?

BLICK. They were meant to be presents for you.

SNOW WHITE. For me?

FLICK. We were afraid you wouldn't like them.

BLICK. I knew you wouldn't like them.

SNOW WHITE. But I *do* like them. Do you mean that you're not angry with me?

FLICK. Angry with you!

BLICK. We think you're the most wonderful thing we've ever seen!

SNOW WHITE. Oh, you darlings! Oh, I beg your pardon. Perhaps that wasn't respectful.

BLICK. Nobody ever called us "darlings" before, so we don't know.

FLICK. But it *sounds* nice.

SNOW WHITE. And you wouldn't mind if I should stay to-night, — only just to-night?

BLICK. We wouldn't mind if you should stay forever, — only just forever!

SNOW WHITE. Forever?

FLICK. Oh, will you?

SNOW WHITE. Oh, will you let me? Please let me live with you. I could be so useful.

BLICK. But our housekeeping . . .

SNOW WHITE. That's just how I could be useful. I can cook and sweep and make beds, and — oh, lots of things.

BLICK (*solemnly*). Will you excuse us a moment, please? (*He beckons the Dwarfs together and whispers*) Did I hear right? Did she say she would stay?

ALL (*eagerly*). She did!

BLICK. Whatever shall we say?

ALL (*perplexed*). *We* don't know.

BLICK (*turning to Snow White*). Er — could you tell us what it's usual to say when you're so glad that it almost *bursts* you?

SNOW WHITE. Would "Hip-hip-hurrah!" do?

BLICK. It *sounds* right. (*Slowly*) Hip-hip-hurrah.

ALL (*solemnly trying the new word*). Hip-hip-hurrah. (*Then, deciding that it does fit their feelings, they shout it in a joyous outburst*) Hip-hip-hurrah!

SNOW WHITE (*clapping her hands*). Oh, please, may I say "Hip-hip-hurrah!" too? I am so glad and grateful.

ALL. Hip-hip-hurrah!

SNOW WHITE (*remembering*). But — you may not want me when I tell you who I am. It may be dangerous . . .

BLICK (*hopefully*). Do *you* steal?

SNOW WHITE. No, not so bad as that. My name is Snow White.

BLICK. It sounds extremely clean.

SNOW WHITE. This morning I was a princess.

[*She sits on Blick's bed to tell her story. She is getting sleepy again.*

FLICK. What's a princess?

SNOW WHITE. Why, the daughter of a king and queen. My stepmother is Queen Brangomar. She hates me so much that I'm afraid there must be something horrid about me. . . . (*She is very drowsy now*) But I'm sure Prince Florimond did not like me . . . for . . . (*She sinks back on to the bed and her eyes close. The Dwarfs put their fingers to their lips. Then she revives a little and murmurs*) — for a year and a day . . . what was I saying? Oh, I'm so sleepy. Please, mayn't I tell you to-morrow morning? All I can think of now is "good-night!"

BLICK (*softly*). Good-night, Snow White!

SNOW WHITE (*almost asleep*). Good-night!

FLICK. Good-night, Snow White.

SNOW WHITE. Good — night.

GLICK.   Good-night, Snow White.

SNOW WHITE.   Good . . .

[*There is a silence.*

BLICK (*whispering*).   Brothers, she's asleep.   But she'll stay, she'll stay!

ALL (*whispering*).   Hip-hip-hurrah!

FLICK.   I'm so happy I'm sad!

GLICK (*wiping away a tear with his beard*).   I'm so happy it's making me cry!

SNICK.   We're all so happy!

[*They all wipe their eyes with their beards.*

BLICK.   We mustn't wake her.   Not a sound now.   We'll be quietest in bed.

[*Each Dwarf creeps toward his bed.*

BLICK.   But she's in my bed!   Well, I'll take Flick's.

[*He moves to the next bed, jumps in and pulls the clothes over his head — Dwarfs always sleep with the bedclothes over their heads. So each of the others has to move up one bed.   As they pop in, one after another, and cover their heads, they cry:*

FLICK.   I'll take Glick's.

GLICK.   I'll take Snick's.

SNICK.   I'll take Plick's.

PLICK.   I'll take Whick's.

WHICK.   I'll take Quee's.

BLICK (*sitting up suddenly*).   Brothers, we've forgotten Quee!

[*They all sit bolt upright.   Then in a whisper they call.*

ALL.   Q—u—e—e!

[*The cover over the water-barrel is pushed up and Quee's head appears.   He is very wet, but washed as clean as a new doll.*

BLICK.   Quee, she'll stay, but you'll have to sleep in the barrel.

QUEE.   Hip-hip-hurrah!

[*He disappears again into the barrel, and —*

THE CURTAIN FALLS

SCENE IV

WHERE THE WITCH LIVES

Witch Hex lives in a queer dark place like a cavern, with walls of black moss. Yet it can't be underground, for looking out through the single entrance that serves both for door and window you can see the Moon, very low and big, and always shining day and night. A great fire blazes in the middle of the floor, and over it stands a boiling cauldron. Against the wall is a large chest, carved with strange signs, in which the Witch keeps her Magic Things.

The Witch's three black Cats, Long Tail, Short Tail, and Lack Tail, are watching the cauldron, and occasionally stir the brew. They are extraordinarily large for cats — almost as large as little boys.

After a moment a shadow crosses the Moon, and Witch Hex flies home, riding on her broomstick, a basket on her arm.

THE WITCH (*alighting and setting her broomstick away*). There! Glad to be home at last. Where is Queen Brangomar? I thought she'd be here before me with Snow White's heart. I had to go half-way to the Moon for the other ingredients for that Magic hair-restorer; but I've got them all — safe in my basket. Now help me mix it. We must put all the other ingredients in before Brangomar comes.

[*The Witch and her Cats dance round and round the cauldron in a mystic circle; and as Hex throws the various things she has collected into the brew she chants.*

THE MAGIC MIXTURE

THE WITCH.

A hair from the tail of the ride-a-cock Horse;
A lace from the Old Woman's shoe,
A bit of the tuffet
Of Little Miss Muffet;
The blast that the Little Boy Blue.
A tear of the Kittens who lost all their mittens
When they began to cry.
A sniff from Miss Mary
When she was contrary;
The plum from Jack Horner's pie.

A slice of green cheese from the Man in the Moon;
  The tails of the Three Blind Mice;
    A bone from the cupboard
    Of old Mother Hubbard;
  And little girls' sugar and spice.

A tick from the clock of hi-diccory Dock;
  The tails of the sheep of Bo-peep;
    The eye of the Fly
    That saw Cock Robin die;
  And a "baa" from the Baa-black Sheep.

[*When she has finished the mixture, the Witch sniffs the steam from the cauldron, and then sips a little of the brew from the ladle.*

THE WITCH. Tastes good, and hot enough. Yes, the ladle is red hot. Now that's all except the heart. Set the kettle away to cool.

[*The Cats take the cauldron from the fire and set it in a corner.*

THE WITCH. I'm chilly! It's cold up by the Moon. (*She tucks up her skirts and sits down comfortably on the blazing fire*) Ah, that feels good! Nothing to do now but wait for Snow White's heart. But *then* you shall see what you shall see — a beautiful head of long, wavy hair for me. Ah, here's Brangomar at last!

[*Queen Brangomar enters. The Cats bow low to her.*

THE QUEEN. Sorry to be late, dear Hexy, but Berthold didn't return till morning, and then I personally had to see that he was locked up in the Gray Tower. He made a frightful fuss.

THE WITCH. Did he bring the heart?

THE QUEEN. Yes, here it is. Oh, how I hated that child!

THE WITCH. Hair restorer's just ready for it. Help me up. Don't like to sit on the fire *too* long. I dozed off the other day and boiled over. Now the heart. (*She takes it and hobbles to the cauldron*) Receipt says that when I add this the brew will turn a beautiful pink. Then I dip in my head, and presto! long and lovely hair. Now watch!

[*She drops the heart into the cauldron, which steams vigorously.*

THE WITCH (*dancing with delight*). See it steam!

THE QUEEN. But it's turning green, not pink.

THE WITCH. So it is! Still, there can't be any mistake; I was most careful. Well, here goes for a handsome head of hair. You'll hardly know me when you see me again. (*She dips her head into the steaming cauldron, and then raises it proudly*) How's that? Pretty fine, eh?

[*Something has surely sprouted on the Witch's bald pate. The Queen looks carefully, and then bursts into a peal of laughter; and the Cats roll on the ground in mirth.*

THE WITCH. What are you laughing at? Feels very thick and curly. Stop that cackling!

THE QUEEN (*hardly able to speak*). Oh, my dear Hex! Ha, ha, ha! You have — ha, ha, ha! — a headful of pig-tails!

THE WITCH. Pig-tails? (*She feels them*) Nonsense! It's short and curly.

THE QUEEN. Not pig-tails, Hexy! Your head is covered with little white, curly tails of pigs!

THE WITCH. Tails of pigs? Tails of pigs? (*She feels the growth carefully*) By hop-scotch, they *are* pigs' tails! Stop laughing! If the joke's on anybody, it's on *you*. Instead of a *human* heart, your precious huntsman has brought back the heart of a pig; and Miss Snow White is alive at this moment. Ha, ha, for *you!*

THE QUEEN (*her laughter broken off short*). What? Snow White alive?

THE WITCH. If these are pig's tails, that was a pig's heart. Ask your Magic Mirror if Snow White's not alive.

THE QUEEN (*seizing the Mirror which hangs from her girdle*).

> Mirror, mirror, in my hand,
> Who's the fairest in the land?

THE MIRROR (*answering*).

> You, who hold me in your hand,
> You *were* fairest in the land;
> But to-day, I answer true,
> Snow White is more fair than you.

THE QUEEN. Snow White alive!

[*She starts to dash the Mirror to the ground.*

THE WITCH (*seizing it*). Be careful of that Mirror, I tell you!

> Mirror, mirror, truly tell,
> Where does Princess Snow White dwell?

THE MIRROR.

> 'Mid the ancient forest dells,
> With the Seven Dwarfs she dwells.

THE WITCH. You see? It's perfectly clear. That huntsman of yours let Snow White escape, and brought back a pig's heart to fool us with. Snow White has found the house of the Seven Dwarfs — and there you are, my merry lady!

THE QUEEN. The Seven Dwarfs? Who are they?

THE WITCH. Rather nice little men; sort of gnomes. Live all alone.

THE QUEEN (*wrapping her cloak about her*). Where?

THE WITCH. Oh, ho! Intend to deal with Snow White yourself this time, do you?

THE QUEEN. Where do they live?

THE WITCH. The usual way is about twenty miles over the mountains, but there's a short cut through my back yard. Less than a mile that way.

THE QUEEN. Give me a knife or a dagger, quickly!

THE WITCH. What? Walk into the Dwarfs' house, knife in hand, and crown on your head like that? *I'd* sooner dance on a hornet's nest.

THE QUEEN. But what shall I do? She's alive! She's more beautiful than I! Oh, my heart will burn itself out of my body! Tell me some way!

THE WITCH. Deary me! Have I got to plan it all out for you again? You're a nuisance.

THE QUEEN. How? How?

THE WITCH. There's only one safe way . . .

THE QUEEN. Yes?

THE WITCH. First, I must transform you into a different-looking person altogether.

THE QUEEN. And then?

THE WITCH. And then give you some means of disposing of Snow White. Long Tail, fetch me the magic Killing Things.

THE QUEEN. Yes — yes!

[*The Cats fetch a box full of strange articles from the chest.*

THE WITCH (*examining them*). Almost none left. The dancing slippers. When you put those on you dance yourself to death. But they're too big for her. The doll you stick pins in. That would take too long. Oh, here are two good ones. The poisoned apple. (*She holds it up*) Beautiful, isn't it? The red side is poisoned, but the other is perfectly good. If you want to tempt anybody, eat the white side yourself. But if they swallow the least bit of the red side, down they drop. Then, if they lie still while you count one hundred, they're as dead as a tombstone. Or, here's the poisoned comb.

THE QUEEN. Let me see it!

[*She seizes the jewelled comb.*

THE WITCH. Put that in Snow White's hair and all's over with her. It works instantly. Which do you want?

THE QUEEN. Let me have both. If I fail with one, I'll try the other. Oh, how my fingers itch to set this in her black hair! Now what disguise?

THE WITCH. Disguise? Oh, yes! Long Tail, bring me the Transformation Mixtures.

[*Long Tail brings from the chest an odd-shaped bottle filled with purple liquid.*

THE WITCH. Is this the only one left? My entire stock of magic is running out. It's lucky I'm going to retire from business next year.

THE QUEEN (*attempting to snatch the bottle*). Let me see . . .

THE WITCH. Don't snatch! Wretched manners! *I'll* read the label. (*She reads*) "One teaspoonful before eating." Well, I declare, I've written out the dose most carefully, but totally forgotten what it changes people into. But that's easily remedied. A drop in the cauldron, and you'll see for yourself. Now watch!

[*She pours a few drops into the cauldron. Instantly a cloud of steam rises; and in the steam — dimly at first and then quite clearly — appears the figure of an old and wrinkled hag in thread-bare garments. She carries a large basket filled with ribbons, laces, needles, and such articles.*

THE WITCH. I remember. The Old Pedlar-Woman disguise. Just the thing! You could pretend to be selling Snow White the comb.

THE QUEEN. I'd hate to look so ugly.

THE WITCH. Vanity is always getting in your way. Well, it's all I've got. (*She reads from the bottle*) "Dose, one tea-spoonful, with a peppermint after." I haven't got a pepper-mint, but that was only to take away the taste.

[*She produces a spoon and uncorks the bottle.*

THE QUEEN (*hesitating*). Is the taste very bad?

THE WITCH. Vile! Really, one of the nastiest tastes I ever made. Open your mouth.

THE QUEEN (*shrinking*). Er — is being transformed painful?

THE WITCH. No - o-o-o, but unpleasant. Feels as though you were being turned inside out like a glove. Open your mouth.

THE QUEEN. I think, on the whole, I'll wait till to-morrow. You see, I have an important tea-party at Court this after-noon, and . . .

THE WITCH. Oh, ho! Cowardy, cowardy custard! Here, Cats, here's sport for you. Get the black mantle.

[*From the chest the Cats whisk a large black cloth embroidered with strange symbols, and advance toward the Queen.*

THE QUEEN. What are they going to do?

THE WITCH. Wrap you up so that you can't scratch while I pour this down your throat.

THE QUEEN. But I'm not ready; I must go-home first!

[*She makes a dash for the door, but the Cats are before her. Then begins a lively chase about the cave, the Queen running and dodg-ing, the Cats following and trying to throw the mantle over her head. The Witch enjoys it all hugely, crying: "Run, Brango-mar!" "Catch her, Long Tail!" "Catch her, Lack Tail!" and slapping her knees with delight till she is quite out of breath. At last the Cats succeed in cornering the Queen, and throw the mantle over her head.*

THE WITCH. Well done, Cats, well done! Trip her up and hold her down.

[*This the Cats do. Then the Witch sits on the squirming Queen; and, humming happily to herself, pours out a spoonful of the mixture.*

THE WITCH. Now, where *is* her mouth?

THE QUEEN (*in a smothered voice*). I won't take it! I won't!

THE WITCH. Oh, *there* it is! Thank you, Brangomar. (*She pours the dose through the cloth into the Queen's mouth; and as the Queen writhes she goes on*) I know it tastes bad, but nothing to make such a fuss about. (*Suddenly she holds up a warning finger*) I feel her changing! Do you? (*The Cats nod*) Done! Up with her, off with the mantle, and let's see the result.

[*The Cats draw off the mantle. Lo! the Queen has been transformed into the likeness of the old Pedlar-Woman, just as it appeared in the steam, basket of wares and all.*

THE WITCH. Splendid! Wouldn't recognize you myself, Brangomar. Wasn't half as bad as you thought it would be, was it?

THE PEDLAR-WOMAN (*crossly*). It was awful! Why — is this *my* voice?

THE WITCH. Of course. Different voice with every disguise.

THE PEDLAR-WOMAN. I'm all cramps, too. How do I change back?

THE WITCH. Dear me; lucky you thought to ask. I might have forgotten. Just sing:

"Peas porridge hot,
Peas porridge cold —"

but sing it backwards, like this:

"Old days nine,
Pot in the porridge peas,
Cold porridge peas,
Hot porridge peas."

That turns you right side out again.

THE PEDLAR-WOMAN. I must remember. Let me see : — "Old days nine . . ."

[*But the Witch claps her hand over Brangomar's mouth.*

THE WITCH. Gracious, woman, don't say it yet! We'd have all this to do over again. Really, you are the most senseless —! Here, take the apple and the comb and be off with you. I've had quite enough of you for one day.

THE PEDLAR-WOMAN. Now for Snow White! Oh, Hex, once I see her lying dead — dead before my own eyes . . .

THE WITCH (*interrupting*). If you use the apple, don't forget to count one hundred!

THE PEDLAR-WOMAN. It will be the happiest moment of my life!

THE WITCH. Nasty disposition!

THE PEDLAR-WOMAN (*going to the door*). You sha'n't escape me this time, my little beauty! You have no foolish Berthold to deal with now, but Brangomar, Brangomar her very self!"

[*And off she strides toward the house of the Seven Dwarfs.*

[*Left alone with her Cats, the Witch goes to the blazing fire and again sits down upon it.*

THE WITCH. Poor little Snow White! I'm really sorry for her. *I* don't bear her any ill will in spite of my pigs' tails. Long Tail, my looking-glass. (*Long Tail brings the looking-glass, and Witch Hex studies her new appearance carefully*) Oh, not so bad, after all! They're quite becoming; sure to keep their curl in the dampest weather, and certainly the very *latest* thing!

THE CURTAIN FALLS

SCENE V

IN THE HOUSE OF THE SEVEN DWARFS

The room is the same as before, but quite transformed by Snow White's housekeeping. It shines with cleanness. There are white coverlets on all the beds, curtains at the window, and flowers on the window-sill. Snow White's silver dress has been carefully put away, and she wears a frock of squirrel skins, trimmed with bright leaves.

It is early in the morning, and the Dwarfs are just starting off for the day's work. Each carries a neat basket of luncheon, which Snow White has put up; and each wears a bright bow tie which she has made. They are so proud of these ties that they part their beards over their shoulders to show them.

Snow White has just finished tying Quee's bow. She pats it into shape, kisses him, and says:

SNOW WHITE. There! Off you go!

BLICK. Couldn't you please give us all another kiss?

SNOW WHITE (*merrily*). No, indeed!

FLICK. Just one?

SNOW WHITE. Not one!

GLICK. A *little* one?

SNOW WHITE. No! That's the rule: one a day, morning *or* night, but not both.

BLICK. You see none of us ever, er — should I say "ate" or "tasted"? — a kiss till you came; so perhaps we *are* a little eager about them.

SNOW WHITE. I should say you were! Why, you're perfect children about kisses and games.

BLICK. That comes of our being dwarfs. You see, no dwarf is ever born till he's fifty. So, as we've never been young, we enjoy games all the more now.

SNOW WHITE. Oh, I understand; but I mustn't spoil you. And that reminds me, you're not to come home any more in the middle of the morning to play games. Tuesday you came back at eleven, Wednesday at ten, and yesterday at nine! What sort of a way to work is that?

BLICK (*penitently*). I know, but . . .

SNOW WHITE. Now not a moment before five to-day, because — (*she beckons them together and whispers*) — this is a secret — I'm going to make a cake with pink sugar frosting for supper. Now, off with you!

BLICK. Well, brothers, ready ! To-day we go into the forest for firewood. March !

[*In their usual military file the Dwarfs march off into the forest. Snow White stands in the doorway, waving her hand after them till they are out of sight. Then with a sigh of content she returns to the room.*

SNOW WHITE. Oh, I'm so happy here. I've never been so happy in all my life. Of course, I miss my dear Maids of Honor and the others; but the Dwarfs are so funny and loving and kind. (*She looks out of the door again*) It's a beautiful day. (*With a little pensive sigh*) I wonder if I shall ever see Prince Florimond again. (*But she checks herself sharply*) Stop that, Snow White ! You wonder about him much too often ! Remember, you're not a Princess any more, only just housekeeper to the Seven Dwarfs. You must forget all about the other things. Now for that cake !

[*And she fetches the mixing bowl. As she turns away Queen Brangomar, disguised as the old Pedlar-Woman, peers cautiously through the window. Seeing that Snow White is alone, she leans over the sill.*

THE PEDLAR-WOMAN. Good morning, dearie.

SNOW WHITE (*her hand springing to her heart*). Oh — !

THE PEDLAR-WOMAN. Did I frighten you, dearie ? No harm in an old pedlar-woman.

SNOW WHITE. You *did* startle me.

THE PEDLAR-WOMAN. So that's the way you pass your time in the forest, is it ? — cooking and eating and eating and cooking ! What a thing it is to be rich.

SNOW WHITE. But I'm not rich. I suppose I'm very poor.

THE PEDLAR-WOMAN. I've come a weary way. I'm that worn and footsore . . .

SNOW WHITE. Oh, *do* come in ! I'm so sorry.

THE PEDLAR-WOMAN (*entering*). Thank you, dearie. I'll just bar the door behind me for fear of the rheumatic drafts. I've been wandering days and days in this forest, and never met a soul to buy the least trinket of me.

SNOW WHITE.   I'm afraid I don't think a deserted forest *is* a very good place to sell things.

THE PEDLAR-WOMAN.   But *you'll* buy some little thing, my pet; some pretty little thing.

SNOW WHITE.   I'm awfully sorry, but . . .

THE PEDLAR-WOMAN.   Don't any of my wares tempt you? And cheap! — really costs more to sell 'em than they're worth. Look, sweetheart!

> Here's ribbons and laces,
> And gentlemen's braces,
>   A feather as white as foam;
> An outfit for cross-stitch,
> The egg of an ostrich,
>   And oh, what a beautiful comb,
>   That comb!
>   Just see, what a beautiful comb!

> Here's powder and patches,
> And Lucifer matches,
>   A motto with "Home Sweet Home,"
> And trimmings for frockings,
> And stockings with clockings;
>   But nothing so fine as this comb,
>   This comb!
>   Just look, what a beautiful comb!

SNOW WHITE.   They're very attractive, but I've no money.

THE PEDLAR-WOMAN.   Now that's too bad, dearie. I don't hardly feel as if I *could* go without leaving some little thing behind me. Rather make you a present than . . .

SNOW WHITE.   Oh, I couldn't take a present from you. I ought to be giving *you* something instead.

THE PEDLAR-WOMAN.   You gave me kind words and bid me in friendly. I'll tell you what, if you've no money I'll make you a free gift, sweetheart.

SNOW WHITE.   I couldn't really!

THE PEDLAR-WOMAN.   I'm set on it, my lamb, set on it! Name

your choice and yours it shall be. Now what do you say to this comb?

SNOW WHITE. That? Why, that's the *finest* thing you have.

THE PEDLAR-WOMAN. Just why I give it to you, my dear. And lovely it will look, a-shining in your black hair.

SNOW WHITE (*shrinking away*). No, no! I couldn't take anything so valuable!

THE PEDLAR-WOMAN. Come, dearie, just let me put it in for you, and *then* if you don't like the look of it — well, I'll say no more and be on my way.

SNOW WHITE. I *should* like to see how it looks — just for fun.

THE PEDLAR-WOMAN. That's my sweetheart. Now sit you down — (*Snow White sits on a stool*) — and shut your eyes so you sha'n't peep till it's in. Are they shut?

SNOW WHITE (*laughing*). Yes, tight shut!

THE PEDLAR-WOMAN. Then, here goes!

[*But just as she is about to insert the comb, Snow White springs up again.*

SNOW WHITE. No! I'd better not even see how it looks. I'd be tempted to keep it, and I mustn't. No-thank-you-very-much!

THE PEDLAR-WOMAN. Oh, dearie! Don't break my heart with your ingratitude.

SNOW WHITE. Well, if you're really *set* on giving me something, I'll take — a spool of thread.

THE PEDLAR-WOMAN. Wait, wait! I've something better than that. Look — a lovely apple, with a cheek as red as your own! I'd like a bite of it myself. You'd not be too proud to divide with an old pedlar-woman, would you, my lamb? Here, you take the pretty red half, and I'll take the white. (*She splits the apple, and gives Snow White one part*) Now that's what I call an apple! Taste it, dearie.

SNOW WHITE. I don't usually eat between meals, but — well, thank you.

[*She bites the apple. Suddenly she grasps her throat, whirls about once, falls, and then lies quite still.*

THE PEDLAR-WOMAN (*watches her for a moment, then cries exult-*

ingly). Ah, ha! So, my dear step-daughter, Queen Brango-mar laughs last, after all! Now to count one hundred while the poison works. (*And she begins to count*) One, two, three, four, five — (*Suddenly she stops to listen*) What's that?

[*Steps are heard outside the little house. They come nearer. There is a knock at the door.*

BLICK (*outside*). Snow White, it's us, the Dwarfs. Open the door.

[*He knocks again.*

THE PEDLAR-WOMAN (*in terror*). The Dwarfs! They'll tear me to pieces if they find me here. I must hide her! Where, where?

[*She looks about for a place to hide Snow White, then drags the big table over her and pulls the tablecloth down. Meantime the Dwarfs are knocking more and more impatiently.*

BLICK. Please open, Snow White. We haven't come back for games, honestly. We want to go down into the mines.

[*The Pedlar-Woman crouches along the wall, looking for some way to escape.*

FLICK (*outside, calling*). Snow White!

GLICK (*calling*). Snow White!

ALL THE DWARFS (*calling together*). Snow White!

BLICK. Brothers, there's something wrong! The window!

[*The Dwarfs run to the window and look in. They see the crouching Pedlar-Woman.*

PEDLAR-WOMAN (*realizing that she is caught, ducking and curtsey-ing*). Oh, it's *you*, my little gentlemen!

BLICK. Open the door!

PEDLAR-WOMAN. Yes, indeed, your honors! At once, your honors! (*But as she goes to unbar the door she continues to count under her breath*) Twenty-one, twenty-two, twenty-three, twenty-four . . .

BLICK (*beating on the door*). Quickly, I tell you!

THE PEDLAR-WOMAN. Yes, your honors!

[*She throws the door open. The Dwarfs rush in fiercely, their knives drawn, and surround her.*

BLICK. What are you doing here?

FLICK.   Where is Snow White?

THE PEDLAR-WOMAN.   Safe and sound, my little gentleman. But I've scarce breath to tell you. Just give me thirty seconds — or thirty-one or thirty-two or thirty-three . . .

BLICK.   What are you mumbling?

THE PEDLAR-WOMAN.   I was passing by with my basket o' wares — (*Blick makes a threatening gesture and she hurries on with a little cry*) — just passing — when your sweet little lady calls me to step in.

BLICK.   Where is she now?

THE PEDLAR-WOMAN.   She went into the forest on an errand, and bid me mind the house till she got back.

BLICK.   Errand? What errand?

PLICK.   She'd never leave the house with you!

FLICK.   How long has she been gone?

THE PEDLAR-WOMAN.   A matter of seconds, your honor. Fifty seconds, maybe, or fifty-one or fifty-two or fifty-three or fifty-four. . . .

BLICK.   Well, you need stay no longer. Go!

THE PEDLAR-WOMAN.   Yes, your honors. Certainly, your honors. (*She goes curtseying to the door, but turns to say*) Could you tell a poor peddling body how far it might be to the next town? Is it fifty-five miles now, or fifty-six, or fifty-seven, or . . .

BLICK (*starting toward her fiercely*).   Be off, or we'll lay hands on you!

[*With a little scream the Pedlar-Woman darts out and shuts the door; but she sticks her head in again to say:*

THE PEDLAR-WOMAN.   Before I go, my kind little gentlemen, let me give you an old gypsy-woman's blessing. It's a little rhyme, like. (*And she chants*)

> "Old days nine,
> Pot the in porridge peas,
> Cold porridge peas,
> Hot porridge peas."

[*As she says the last words she claps the door shut. But the transforming charm works instantly; and it is Queen Brango-mar in her royal robes who, with a mocking laugh, sweeps past the window and rushes off into the forest, still counting as she goes: "Fifty-eight, fifty-nine, sixty . . ." till her voice dies away in the distance. For a moment the Dwarfs stand amazed. Then Blick cries out.*

BLICK.   Brothers! That wasn't a pedlar-woman!

FLICK.   It looked like a queen!

BLICK.   Was it magic? Brothers, something is wrong! You, you and you follow, and seize her! And you, you and you search for Snow White. I will stay here in case she might come back.

[Six of the Dwarfs rush out, leaving Blick alone.

BLICK.   But it's not *like* Snow White to be frightened and run away. I wonder . . .

[Suddenly he spies something on the floor near the table. It is one of Snow White's slippers that came off when she fell.

BLICK.   What's that? Her slipper! (*He calls loudly*) Brothers, brothers! She is here! Here is her slipper! Search the house!

[The Dwarfs rush back into the room and begin to seek under the beds and behind the pump; but Flick pulls up the tablecloth, and cries out.

FLICK.   Look! Here she is!

[They move the table away and kneel about Snow White. Blick raises her head on his knee.

GLICK.   Is she hurt?

PLICK.   She has fainted.

GLICK.   Unlace her bodice.

BLICK.   It is loose. Is she breathing?

GLICK.   Water! Get water! Quick!

THE CURTAIN FALLS RAPIDLY

[After a moment it rises again. It is moonlight now; and the Dwarfs, with lighted lanterns, are grouped around the bed on which they have laid Snow White. All day long they have tried to revive her. They have bathed her face with water and wine,

and chafed her hands and feet without avail.   After a long silence Blick speaks.

BLICK.   There is no hope, my brothers.   There is nothing more to do.   Our Snow White is dead.

[*Another stillness.*

FLICK.   Yet see, her lips have not paled, and her skin is still as fair as snow.   I cannot bear to think of hiding her away in the black ground.

WHICK.   Nor I.

BLICK.   Brothers, let us make her a coffin all of crystal, so that we may see her always.

FLICK.   Yes.   And set it in the dell where she used to go for flowers.

BLICK.   And watch over her there, day and night, all our lives long.

FLICK.   This we will do.

BLICK.   We will never leave you, Snow White!

[*One by one they kneel about her silently.*

AGAIN THE CURTAIN FALLS

SCENE VI

THE THRONE ROOM OF THE PALACE

Sir Dandiprat is standing in the middle of the room, surrounded by all the Maids of Honor.   He looks puzzled and distressed.

ROSALYS (*to Sir Dandiprat*).   Of *course* it's to-day that Snow White is coming home.   That's why we're wearing our best clothes.

AMELOTTE.   It's a year and a day to-day.

CHRISTABEL.   We thought you knew.

SIR DANDIPRAT.   Dear me!   Are you sure?   It's most important.

CHRISTABEL.   She went away to school on the twentieth of June.

ROSALYS.   Last year.

ASTOLAINE. And to-day is the twenty-first.

ROSALYS. This year.

CHRISTABEL. So it *must* be a year and a day to-day.

SIR DANDIPRAT. Pooh, that's not the way to reckon it. It ought to be done by arithmetic. Let me see — (*He shuts his eyes and repeats*)

> "Thirty days hath September,
> April, June and . . ."

CHRISTABEL. That's no use !

SIR DANDIPRAT. Oh, I know — I know now ! How many days are there in a year ?

ROSALYS (*hiding a smile*). Three hundred and sixty-five, usually.

SIR DANDIPRAT. I've got it now ! Quiet ! Quiet ! I take June twentieth — (*he writes on his tablet with his gold pencil*), and add three hundred and sixty-five. She ought to arrive on June the three-hundred-and-eighty-fifth. Hm — that can't be right. It's most puzzling !

ROSALYS. Prince Florimond comes to-day, too.

SIR DANDIPRAT. What ? Prince Florimond, *too* ?

ASTOLAINE. Of course — to be engaged to Snow White.

SIR DANDIPRAT. The Prince coming, and nothing arranged — nothing ! Nobody ever tells me anything at this Court. He may be here any moment, and all the army out hunting for Berthold, and the Dukes and Duchesses scattered all over the lawn playing croquet ! Where are they ? I shall go distracted ! I shall go distracted !

[*He hurries out onto the Terrace, and turns first to the right, then to the left, then to the right again, before he can make up his foolish old mind, and waddles out of sight.*

ASTOLAINE. I didn't really believe a year and a day would *ever* be over. Did you ?

ROSALYS. Just think how much Snow White will know.

CHRISTABEL. I hope she'll know more than the Queen.

ASTOLAINE. And asks questions the Queen can't answer.

ERMENGARDE. Wouldn't that be fun !

CHRISTABEL. I hope she gets here before the Prince does. What do you think he'll say to Snow White when he does come?

ROSALYS. Why, of course, he'll say, "Princess, I love you to distractedness. I should like to marry you at once, please."

GUINIVERE. Oh! And what will *she* say?

ROSALYS. Probably she'll say, "I should be very much obliged."

ASTOLAINE. And that's that!

[*Sir Dandiprat's voice is heard on the Terrace, exclaiming, "Really, I shall go distracted!" and he bustles in again, followed by all the Dukes and Duchesses, whom he hastily arranges in their proper places about the room.*

SIR DANDIPRAT. The Prince is here! The Prince is here! We're keeping his Highness waiting! Quickly, quickly, my dear Dukes and Duchesses. Quickly, quickly!

[*A trumpet sounds, and Prince Florimond enters, followed by his Pages. The Courtiers bow low.*

SIR DANDIPRAT. I'm sorry to have kept your Highness waiting. I'll inform the Queen at once. She's been expecting you all the morning. Just a moment, your Highness. (*As he makes for the door he whispers to Christabel*) Where is the Queen?

CHRISTABEL. Try in front of all the looking-glasses!

SIR DANDIPRAT (*shocked*). Most disrespectful! You will drive me distracted — distracted!

[*He waddles off to find the Queen.*

THE PRINCE. Has the Princess returned?

ROSALYS (*curtseying*). Not yet, your Highness, but we expect her every moment.

THE PRINCE. Is she well?

ROSALYS. I don't know, your Highness. She hasn't written to us since she went away.

THE PRINCE. Not a single letter?

[*Sir Dandiprat re-appears and announces.*

SIR DANDIPRAT. Her Majesty, the Queen.

[*Queen Brangomar enters; and with a haughty nod to the Prince, sweeps to the throne.*

SNOW WHITE AND THE SEVEN DWARFS

Scene vi

Berthold. — "Guarding her, day and night, were Seven Dwarfs."

THE QUEEN. I totally forgot you were coming to-day, Florimond. Stupid of me. Poor boy, I've sad news for you. I
ought to have written, but I hated to distress you. I deeply
regret to say that Snow White is dead.

THE PRINCE. Snow White — dead . . .!

THE QUEEN. It happened at boarding-school.

THE PRINCE (*crying out*). Snow White . . . dead . . .?

THE QUEEN. I sent at least eighteen doctors, but it was useless.
[*The Prince sinks sobbing on the steps of the throne.*

THE QUEEN. Pray don't distress yourself. Everything possible has been done. I built a splendid monument over her
grave, a tall, gilded shaft surrounded by four groups of —
(*Suddenly she sees the stern figure of Berthold. He has been
standing silent and unnoticed in the doorway. She cries out*)
Berthold!

BERTHOLD (*advancing*). Yes, Berthold! Berthold, come to
punish you!

THE QUEEN. Seize him! Arrest him! Dandiprat, the soldiers!

SIR DANDIPRAT. I'm awfully sorry, your Majesty, but the
soldiers are all out hunting for him!

BERTHOLD. I fear neither your soldiers nor your witchcraft
now. No army, no court, no kingdom will be yours when I
have told my tale.

THE QUEEN (*shrieking*). Don't listen to him! He is mad!
I imprisoned him because he was mad.

BERTHOLD. No, for fear that I should tell of your wickedness.
But I escaped. I tunnelled under the tower, and fled back
to the forest to search for Snow White. Last night, in a
secret dell, I found —
[*His voice falters.*

THE PRINCE (*rising with a cry*). You found her?

BERTHOLD. Yes. But she lay in a coffin all made of shining
crystal, as fair as if she were but asleep. And guarding her,
day and night, were Seven Dwarfs.

THE QUEEN. But she is dead?

BERTHOLD. Yes, and you did the deed!

THE QUEEN (*trying to regain her self-control*). Nonsense! The man is quite mad. Snow White died at boarding-school. I tell you, I made the arrangements myself.

BERTHOLD. With that lie on your lips, — look!

[*The Seven Dwarfs appear on the Terrace bearing Snow White's crystal coffin covered with a pall of flowers. They march slowly into the room.*

THE QUEEN (*cowering on her throne*). The Dwarfs! Merciful stars, what are they bringing? No! No! Take it away! Take it away! You shall not bring her here! You shall not!

[*Rushing from the throne, the Queen hurls herself on the Dwarfs to prevent their setting down the coffin. So sudden is her on-slaught that they cannot resist; and with a crash of crystal the coffin is overturned. With a cry of horror the Dwarfs surround it, and the Courtiers crowd about them.*

[*For a moment the Queen stands apart. She seizes the Magic Mirror that hangs at her girdle, and with trembling lips whispers.*

THE QUEEN.

> Mirror, Mirror, in my hand,
> Who's the fairest in the land?

[*What the Mirror answers will never be known, for hardly has it begun to speak when, with a cry of rage, the Queen dashes it into a thousand pieces on the floor. Suddenly she clasps her hands over her face, sinks to her knees with a moan, and draws her veil close.*

[*And now there is a gasp of wonder from the Courtiers, and Rosalys' voice cries.*

ROSALYS. Oh, look! Snow White! She's breathing!

[*The group parts, and Snow White, half supported by the Dwarfs, is seen to stir.*

THE PRINCE (*rushing to her*). Snow White! My beloved!

[*He kneels beside her and raises her head.*

SNOW WHITE (*with a deep sigh*). Oh, it was such a long dream. I dreamed that I was dead. It was all dark and still. I could not move or see. Then, just now, came a great crash,

and this loosened in my throat — why, see! It's a little
piece of apple! — and I woke up. Or am I dreaming now?
No, there are my Dwarfs. And Rosalys and Christabel and
. . . Where am I? (*With a cry of fear she struggles to her
feet*) This is the palace! The Queen will find me! Hide
me, brothers, I'm afraid!

BERTHOLD (*pouncing upon the cowering Queen*). She shall
never harm you again, my Princess! What shall her punishment be? Let us starve her in the Gray Tower as she would
have starved my children.

BLICK. I'll make her a pair of red-hot iron shoes to dance in at
your wedding.

DANDIPRAT. If *I* might suggest . . .

[*But the Queen, writhing from Berthold's grasp, creeps to Snow
White and makes an imploring gesture.*

SNOW WHITE. Hush, please. I think she wants to speak to me.

THE QUEEN. Yes, to you alone!

SNOW WHITE. She wants to speak to me alone. Please let her.

BERTHOLD. Be careful, Princess!

SNOW WHITE. I'm not afraid any more.

[*The others withdraw a little, leaving Snow White and the Queen
together.*

THE QUEEN (*in a muffled voice*). Oh, Snow White, my punishment has come! I broke the Mirror, and my beauty is
gone forever!

SNOW WHITE. The Mirror?

THE QUEEN. Oh, forgive me. I shall never be jealous of you
again. Only let me go away where no one can ever see my
face. You shall be Queen now. Here is the crown.

[*She thrusts it into Snow White's hand.*

SNOW WHITE (*wonderingly*). I to be Queen? But you . . . ?

THE QUEEN. You don't believe me? Then look, — but oh, let
no one else see!

[*She lifts her veil a little, so that Snow White alone can see her
face.*

SNOW WHITE. Oh, how dreadful! Poor Brangomar! I forgive you. I pity you from the bottom of my heart! (*She*

turns to the others) Please let the Queen go away. She wants to go far away.

BERTHOLD (*barring the way*). Unpunished? Never, your Highness!

ALL. Never, never!

SNOW WHITE. I beseech you. She will never harm any one again. I answer for her. Let her go.

[*Reluctantly the Courtiers make way. The Queen kisses the hem of Snow White's dress; and then, her veil drawn close, stumbles toward the door.*

[*But just as she reaches the Terrace, who should appear there but Witch Hex. She looks very different now. Instead of her red cloak and pointed hat she wears a neat black-silk dress and bonnet. On her arm she carries a basket in which are three ordinary-sized black cats.*

THE WITCH (*stopping the Queen*). Highty-tighty, what's all this?

THE QUEEN (*clinging to her*). Oh, Witch Hex!

ALL (*in consternation*). Witch Hex! The Witch!

THE WITCH. Don't be frightened; not *Witch* Hex any more! Just Miss Hex now. Gave up magic for good and all day before yesterday, burned all my charms, shrunk my cats to their natural size and retired. Perfectly respectable old lady now. But whatever have you been doing to Brangomar?

THE QUEEN. Oh, Hex, I broke the Magic Mirror.

THE WITCH. And turned ugly, eh? I told you you would some day. Well, serves you right. Let's see.

[*She tries to lift the Queen's veil.*

THE QUEEN (*preventing her*). Oh, no, no, no!

THE WITCH. Oh, yes, yes, yes! You were fond enough of showing your face before. Turn about's fair play.

[*She snatches off the veil.*

[*The Queen has surely turned ugly, but it is a funny kind of ugliness. None of her features have changed except her nose, but that has grown enormous — almost a foot long, and very red.*

THE WITCH (*cackling with laughter*). My stars and garters! What a nose! *What* a nose!

SNOW WHITE (*appealingly*). Don't laugh at her!

THE QUEEN. Oh, Hex, can't you help me?

THE WITCH. Afraid not. The only way to be beautiful without magic is to be good. Who are all these fine folks?

SIR DANDIPRAT (*strutting forward importantly*). Allow me to present —

THE WITCH (*waving him away*). Shoo! old turkey-cock!

[*Meantime the Queen creeps quietly away, and is never seen or heard of again.*

THE WITCH. You must be Snow White. However did you come alive? Brangomar told me you ate the poisoned apple. Glad it didn't work, but why didn't it?

SNOW WHITE (*smiling*). I think the greedy bite I took must have stuck in my throat; and just now something happened, and it got joggled out.

THE WITCH. Glad of it. Always was sorry for you. Who's this nice boy? Oh, Prince Florimond, of course. I can guess why *you're* here. Well, is the betrothal all arranged? (*Snow White hangs her head, and the Prince blushes furiously*) Embarrassed, eh? Well, I don't know of any better use for bold old people than to help shy young people. Where's the ring, young man? Oh, come! I'll wager you've been carrying it about for a year. (*Shyly Prince Florimond produces the ring*) Your hand, Snow White!

SNOW WHITE. Please, do you think I ought to — yet? You see, I didn't get to school to be educated and . . .

THE WITCH. What has education got to do with marrying? I know almost everything, and here I am, single as a lamp-post! Put the ring on, Florimond. (*The Prince does so*) Now, young man, lead her to the throne and crown her properly, and we'll all swear allegiance to our new little Queen.

[*With stately grace the Prince leads Snow White to the throne, and reverently sets the crown on her head. Then he kneels before her, and all the Courtiers follow his example, and all the trumpets in the palace blare. Rising and unsheathing his sword, the Prince cries.*

THE PRINCE. Love and homage to our little Queen!

ALL (*in a great shout*).   Love and homage to our little Queen!

SNOW WHITE (*brushing away a happy tear*).   Oh, please . . .
please!

[*During all this the Dwarfs have withdrawn shyly to the farthest
corner of the room; but now Blick, clearing his throat and sum-
moning all his courage, cries.*

BLICK.   Brothers! March!

[*In military order the Dwarfs march to the throne. Some of
them think they ought to kneel, and some of them think not; so
they wobble for a moment and then stand still.*

BLICK (*stammering*).   Your — er — er — your — (*He gives it
up, and bursts out*) Please tell us what to call you? You
see, we've never met a Queen before.

SNOW WHITE.   Oh, brothers, call me only Snow White — always
and always!

BLICK.   Snow White, may we go now?

SNOW WHITE.   Go? Where?

BLICK.   To fetch you our wedding present — all our gold and
jewels. We'll make you the richest Queen in the whole
world.

SNICK.   And then back to our lonely house.

FLICK.   And those suppers!

GLICK.   And those beds!

SNOW WHITE.   No, no! You must stay with me always.

BLICK (*hanging his head*).   But we are — dwarfs.

SNOW WHITE.   There are no braver men in my kingdom! You
shall be my bodyguard, and Berthold shall be your Captain.

BLICK.   What do you say, brothers?

QUEE.   *I* say, "Hip, hip, hurrah!"

ALL THE DWARFS.   Hip, hip, hurrah!

THE WITCH.   Dear me! I quite enjoy being respectable. And
I can't see why you shouldn't live happily ever after.

ROSALYS.   Oh, Princess, if I don't dance, I shall just *die!*

CHRISTABEL.   And so shall I!

ALL THE MAIDS OF HONOR.   So shall I! So shall I!

SNOW WHITE (*to the Prince*).   May Queens dance, too, when they
are very, very happy?

THE PRINCE.   Do you remember the first words I ever said **to** you?

> "Lady, do you think that I
> Might dance too?   I'd like to try."

SNOW WHITE.   And I answered:

> "I was hoping you might be
> Tempted to join in — with me."

[*She gives him her hand, and they all whirl off into a gay and happy Dance; even the Dwarfs — who never could learn — hopping solemnly for joy, as —*

THE CURTAIN FALLS

P. S.   Snow White and Prince Florimond did *live happily ever after, as the Witch had predicted.*

THE FATHER OF CHRISTOPHER ROBIN

ONCE upon a time — not so very long ago — there were several Rear-Admirals of the United States Navy, several Justices of the Supreme Court, several Governors of several States, and several Major-Generals of the United States Army, and a number of authors, educators and critics, and actors — both moving-picture and otherwise — and ministers, and business men, and aviators, and musicians, and several hundreds of thousands of other people all reading a little book. And, after they had put it down, they went forth, and, at luncheon and dinner tables, at parties and dances and motor meets, — everywhere they went, in fact, they began reciting pages of that little book. And the more they recited, the more recruits went and bought the little book, until it seemed as though there never was a wee volume that had ever made such a noise — and a good noise too — throughout England and America.

And the reason of it was that there was a little boy who had a father : and the little boy's name was Christopher Robin, and his father's name was A. A. Milne, and both of them — in a way — were authors of this book, which they called "When We Were Very Young." I suppose the King of England was as delighted with it as was the President of the United States. I suppose Mr. Milne was as surprised as his publishers over the unstinted praise for this book which came from all sides. While Christopher Robin, who probably passed on all the poems before any one else saw them, very likely said to his father, "I told you so." For they gave him joy as they were written.

There is nothing more to say about "When We Were Very Young." It's the kind of book that's not written very often; I suppose it wasn't really written but sang itself into being on demand. But now that it is in print, it is likely to step cheerily into a niche which will keep it alive for all time. And the name of Mr. Milne is just a little magic.

Now, "Make-Believe" is a play that was written before "When We Were Very Young" was thought of. But there is in it all the quaintness that marks its little relative, and it is warranted to entertain with just as much spirit of revelry. Mr. Nigel Playfair, who produced it on the stage, did the most he could, by way of assembling the scenery, to impress his on-lookers that here was a very imaginative play, where, by the mere gift of make-believe, people could be transported here and there at will, and escape the commonplace world, with its myriad prescriptions. He wrote for it a Prologue, which, since it is not Mr. Milne's, is not printed with the play, but is men-cioned in the program.

There is a lot more to know about Mr. Milne — he is a dramatist, an essayist, a novelist; he fought in the Great War, and helped to edit the English *Punch*. But only Christopher Robin and "Make-Believe" concern us here.

Of course, we can give you a poor imitation:

> The Editor asked
> The Publisher, and
> The Publisher asked
> The Author:
> "May we have your drama for
> Our Treasury of Plays?"
> The Publisher asked
> The Author.
> The Author
> Said, "Probably,
> I'll go and ask
> My one
> Son,
> And tell you what he says."

He must have said "Yes", for here's "Make-Believe."

MAKE–BELIEVE

A CHILDREN'S PLAY IN A PROLOGUE
AND THREE ACTS

By A. A. MILNE

Applications regarding amateur productions of this play must be made to Samuel French, 25 West 45th St., New York City.

Reprinted by permission of the author from "Second Plays", published by Chatto & Windus, London.

MAKE–BELIEVE

A CHILDREN'S REVIEW AND PANTOMIME

As Produced by Nigel Playfair at the Lyric Theatre,
Hammersmith, London, England, December 24, 1918

Introduction by the Producer

SCISSORS	*Daughters of the Muse of the*	Angela Baddeley
PASTE	*Drama*	Hermione Baddeley
THE QUEEN OF MELODY		Carmen Judah
SOME OF THE AUDIENCE		Marjory Holman, Mary Rose, Audrey Betts, etc. Roy Lennol, Frank Worth, Ben Wordy, etc.

THE PLAY

BY A. A. MILNE

ACT I

The Princess and the Woodcutter

THE WOODCUTTER	John Barclay
THE PRINCESS	Marjory Holman
THE KING	Kinsey Peile
THE QUEEN	Rosa Lynd
THE BLUE PRINCE	Stanley Drewitt
THE RED PRINCE	Herbert Marshall
THE YELLOW PRINCE	Ivan Berlyn

Courtiers, etc.

ACT II

Oliver's Island

Scene I — The Heal Nursery

OLIVER	Roy Lennol
JILL	Marjory Holman
MISS PINNIGER	Jean Cadell
THE REV. LEMUEL SMILAX	Stanley Drewitt
THE DOCTOR	Kinsey Peile
AUNT JANE	Rosa Lynd

Furniture and Decorations by Heal & Sons, Tottenham Court Road.

Scene II — The Island

OLIVER	Roy Lennol
JILL	Marjory Holman
THE PIRATE CHIEF	John Barclay
FIRST PIRATE	Herbert Marshall
SECOND PIRATE	Stephen Thomas
THIRD PIRATE	Ivan Berlyn
STEWARD	Frank Worth
DUSKY MAIDEN	Betty Chester
MISS PINNIGER	Jean Cadell
FLUFFKINS	Kinsey Peile
JANE	Rosa Lynd
THE MISSIONARY	Stanley Drewitt
THE CASSIOWARY	Hannah Hart
THE CANNIBAL	H. Gordon

Pirates, Dusky Maidens, Fireflies, etc.

ACT III

Father Christmas and the Hubbard Family

Scene I — The House of the Hubbards

MR. HUBBARD	Kinsey Peile
MRS. HUBBARD	Rosa Lynd

Scene II — Outside the House of the Hubbards

PETER ABLEWAYS	John Barclay
JONAS HUMPHREY	Ford Hamilton
JENNIFER LING	Carmen Judah
MARTHA POWITT	Maude Miller
MR. HUBBARD	Kinsey Peile
LIZ	Betty Chester
BILL (*a burglar*)	Herbert Marshall
A POLICEMAN	Stanley Drewitt

Scene III — The House of the Hubbards

MR. HUBBARD	Kinsey Peile
MRS. HUBBARD	Rosa Lynd

Scene IV — The Hall of Father Christmas

FATHER CHRISTMAS	John Barclay
MR. HUBBARD	Kinsey Peile
MRS. HUBBARD	Rosa Lynd
FIRST USHER	H. Gordon
SECOND USHER	L. Barber
BARON BLUEBEARD	Herbert Marshall
MR. ROBINSON CRUSOE	Roy Lennol
GOLDILOCKS	Joan Wooller
RED RIDING HOOD	Marjory Holman
PUNCHINELLO	Hannah Hart
A CRACKER	Oliver Blossom Bangs

Toys, etc.

[Scenery painted by Mr. Mapleson. Wigs by Clarkson. Dresses designed and executed by Miss Hill Clarke.]

[This program is taken from Mr. Nigel Playfair's entertaining "Story of the Lyric Theatre, Hammersmith." London: Chatto and Windus. 1925. The Introduction by the Producer is omitted here.]

MAKE-BELIEVE

The playroom of the Hubbard family — nine of them. Counting Mr. and Mrs. Hubbard, we realize that there are eleven Hubbards in all, and you would think that one at least of the two people we see in the room would be a Hubbard of sorts. But no. The tall manly figure is James, the Hubbards' butler, for the Hubbards are able to afford a butler now. How different from the time when Old Mother Hubbard — called "old" because she was at least twenty-two and "mother" because she had a passion for children — could not even find a bone for her faithful terrier; but, of course, that was before Henry went into work. Well, the tall figure is James, the butler, and the little one is Rosemary, a friend of the Hubbard family. Rosemary is going in for literature this afternoon, as it's raining, and James is making her quite comfortable first with pens and ink and blotting-paper — always so important when one wants to write. He has even thought of a stick of violet sealing-wax; after that there can be no excuse.

ROSEMARY. Thank you, James. (*She sits down*) If any one calls I am not at home.

JAMES. Yes, Miss.

ROSEMARY. You may add that I am engaged in writing my auto — autobiography.

JAMES. Yes, Miss.

ROSEMARY. It's what every one writes, isn't it, James?

JAMES. I believe so, Miss.

ROSEMARY. Thank you. (*He goes to the door*) Oh, James?

JAMES. Yes, Miss?

ROSEMARY. What *is* an autobiography?

JAMES. Well, I couldn't rightly say, Miss — not to explain it properly.

ROSEMARY (*dismayed*). Oh, James! . . . I thought you knew everything.

JAMES. In the ordinary way, yes, Miss, but every now and then —

ROSEMARY. It's very upsetting.

JAMES. Yes, Miss. . . . How would it be to write a play instead? Very easy work, they tell me.

ROSEMARY (*nodding*). Yes, that's much better. I'll write a play. Thank you, James.

JAMES. Not at all, Miss.

[*He goes out.*

[*Rosemary bites her pen, and thinks deeply. At last the inspiration comes.*

ROSEMARY (*as she writes*). Make-Believe. M-a-k-e hyphen B-e-l —(*she stops and frowns*) Now which way *is* it? (*She tries it on the blotting-paper*) *That* looks wrong. (*She tries it again*) So does that. Oh, dear!

[*She rings the bell . . . James returns.*

JAMES. Yes, Miss?

ROSEMARY. James, I have decided to call my play Make-Believe.

JAMES. Yes, Miss.

ROSEMARY (*carelessly*). When you spell "believe," it *is* "i-e," isn't it?

JAMES. Yes, Miss.

ROSEMARY. I thought at first it was "e-i."

JAMES. Now you mention it, I think it is, Miss.

ROSEMARY (*reproachfully*). Oh, James! Aren't you certain?

JAMES. M-a-k-e, make, B-e-l —

[*He stops and scratches his whiskers.*

ROSEMARY. Yes. *I* got as far as that.

JAMES. B-e-l —

ROSEMARY. You see, James, it spoils the play if you have an accident to the very first word of it.

JAMES. Yes, Miss. B-e-l — I've noticed sometimes that if one writes a word careless-like on the blotting-paper, and then looks at it with the head on one side, there's a sort of instinct

comes over one, as makes one say (*with a shake of the head*)
"Rotten." One can then write it the other way more hope-
ful.

ROSEMARY. I've tried that.

JAMES. Then might I suggest, Miss, that you give it another
name altogether? As it might be, "Susan's Saturday Night",
all easy words to spell, or "Red Revenge", or —

ROSEMARY. I *must* call it Make-Believe, because it's all of the
play I've thought of so far.

JAMES. Quite so, Miss. Then how would it be to spell it wrong
on purpose? It comes funnier that way sometimes.

ROSEMARY. Does it?

JAMES. Yes, Miss. Makes 'em laugh.

ROSEMARY. Oh! . . . Well, which *is* the wrong way?

JAMES. Ah, there you've got me again, Miss.

ROSEMARY (*inspired*). I know what I'll do. I'll spell it "i-e";
and if it's right, then I'm right, and if it's wrong, then I'm
funny.

JAMES. Yes, Miss. That's the safest.

ROSEMARY. Thank you, James.

JAMES. Not at all, Miss.

[*He goes out.*

ROSEMARY (*writing*). Make-Believe. A Christmas Entertain-
ment —(*She stops and thinks, and then shakes her head*)
No, play — a Christmas Play in three acts. Er —
[*She is stuck.*
[*Enter James.*

JAMES. Beg pardon, Miss, but the Misses and Masters Hubbard are without, and crave admittance.

ROSEMARY. All nine of them?

JAMES. Without having counted them, Miss, I should say that
the majority of them were present.

ROSEMARY. Did you say that I was not at home?

JAMES. Yes, Miss. They said that, this being their house,
and you being a visitor, if you *had* been at home, then you
wouldn't have been here. Yumour on the part of Master
Bertram, Miss.

ROSEMARY.   It's very upsetting when you're writing a play.

JAMES.   Yes, Miss.   Perhaps they could help you with it. The more the merrier, as you might say.

ROSEMARY.   What a good idea, James.   Admit them.

JAMES.   Yes, Miss.   (*He opens the door and says very rapidly*) The Misses Ada, Caroline, Elsie, Gwendoline, and Isabel Hubbard, The Masters Bertram, Dennis, Frank, and Harold Hubbard.

[*They come in.*

ROSEMARY.   How do you do?

ADA.   Rosemary, darling, what *are* you doing?

BERTRAM.   It's like your cheek, bagging our room.

CAROLINE (*primly*).   Hush, Bertram.   We ought always to be polite to our visitors when they stay with us.   I am sure, if Rosemary wants our room —

DENNIS.   Oh, chuck it!

ADA (*at Rosemary's shoulder*).   Oh, I say, she's writing a play! [*Uproar and turmoil, as they all rush at Rosemary.*

{ THE BOYS.   Coo!   I say, shove me into it.   What's it about?   Bet it's awful rot.

{ THE GIRLS.   Oh, Rosemary!   Am *I* in it?   Do tell us about it.   Is it for Christmas?

ROSEMARY (*in alarm*).   James, could you —?

JAMES (*firmly*).   Quiet, there, quiet!   Down, Master Dennis, down!   Miss Gwendoline, if you wouldn't mind — (*He picks her up and places her on the floor*)   Thank you.

[*Order is restored.*

ROSEMARY.   Thank you, James. . . .   Yes, it's a play for Christmas, and it is called "Make-Believe", and that's all I'm certain about yet, except that we're all going to be in it.

BERTRAM.   Then I vote we have a desert island —

DENNIS.   And pirates —

FRANK.   And cannibals —

HAROLD (*gloatingly*).   Cannibals eating people — Oo!

CAROLINE (*shocked*).   Harold!   How would *you* like to be eaten by a cannibal?

DENNIS. Oh, chuck it! How would *you* like to be a cannibal and have nobody to eat?

[*Caroline is silent, never having thought of this before.*

ADA. Let it be a fairy-story, Rosemary, darling. It's so much *prettier*.

ELSIE. With a lovely princess —

GWENDOLINE. And a humble woodcutter who marries her —

ISABEL (*her only contribution*). P'itty P'incess.

BERTRAM. Princesses are rot.

ELSIE (*with spirit*). So are pirates!

[*Deadlock.*

CAROLINE. *I* should like something about Father Christmas, and snow, and waits, and a lovely ball, and everybody getting nice presents and things.

DENNIS (*selfishly, I'm afraid*). Bags I all the presents.

[*Of course, the others aren't going to have that. They all say so together.*

ROSEMARY (*above the turmoil*). James, I *must* have silence.

JAMES. Silence, all!

ROSEMARY. Thank you. . . . You will be interested to hear that I have decided to have a Fairy Story *and* a Desert Island *and* a Father Christmas.

ALL. Good!

[*Or words to that effect.*

ROSEMARY (*biting her pen*). I shall begin with the Fairy Story. (*There is an anxious silence. None of them has ever seen anybody writing a play before. How does one do it? Alas, Rosemary herself doesn't know. She appeals to James*) James, how *do* you begin a play? I mean when you've *got* the title.

JAMES (*a man of genius*). Well, Miss Rosemary, seeing that it's to be called "Make-Believe", why not make-believe as it's written already?

ROSEMARY. What a good idea, James!

JAMES. All that is necessary is for the company to think **very** hard of what they want, and — there we are! Saves all the bother of writing and spelling and what not.

ROSEMARY (*admiringly*). James, how clever you are!

JAMES. So-so, Miss Rosemary.

ROSEMARY. Now then, let's all think together. Are you all ready?

ALL. Yes!

[*They clench their hands.*

ROSEMARY. Then one, two, three — Go!

[*They think. . . . The truth is that James, who wasn't really meant to be in it, thinks too. If there is anything in the play which you don't like, it is James thinking.*

ACT I

THE PRINCESS AND THE WOODCUTTER

The Woodcutter is discovered singing at his work, in a glade of the forest outside his hut. He is tall and strong, and brave and handsome; all that a woodcutter ought to be. Now it happened that the Princess was passing, and as soon as his song is finished, sure enough, on she comes.

PRINCESS. Good morning, Woodcutter.

WOODCUTTER. Good morning.

[*But he goes on with his work.*

PRINCESS (*after a pause*). Good morning, Woodcutter.

WOODCUTTER. Good morning.

PRINCESS. Don't you ever say anything except good morning?

WOODCUTTER. Sometimes I say good-bye.

PRINCESS. You *are* a cross woodcutter to-day.

WOODCUTTER. I have work to do.

PRINCESS. You are still cutting wood? Don't you ever do anything else?

WOODCUTTER. Well, you are still a Princess; don't *you* ever do anything else?

PRINCESS (*reproachfully*). Now, that's not fair, Woodcutter. You can't say I was a Princess yesterday, when I came and helped you stack your wood. Or the day before, when I tied up your hand where you had cut it. Or the day before that, when we had our meal together on the grass. Was I a Princess then?

WOODCUTTER. Somehow I think you were. Somehow I think you were saying to yourself, "Isn't it sweet of a Princess to treat a mere woodcutter like this?"

PRINCESS. I think you're perfectly horrid. I've a good mind never to speak to you again. And — and I would, if only I could be sure that you would notice I wasn't speaking to you.

WOODCUTTER. After all, I'm just as bad as you. Only yesterday I was thinking to myself how unselfish I was to interrupt my work in order to talk to a mere Princess.

PRINCESS. Yes, but the trouble is that you *don't* interrupt your work.

WOODCUTTER (*interrupting it and going up to her with a smile*). Madam, I am at your service.

PRINCESS. I wish I thought you were.

WOODCUTTER. Surely you have enough people at your service already. Princes and Chancellors and Chamberlains and Waiting Maids.

PRINCESS. Yes, that's just it. That's why I want your help. Particularly in the matter of the Princes.

WOODCUTTER. Why, has a suitor come for the hand of her Royal Highness?

PRINCESS. Three suitors. And I hate them all.

WOODCUTTER. And which are you going to marry?

PRINCESS. I don't know. Father hasn't made up his mind yet.

WOODCUTTER. And this is a matter which father — which His Majesty decides for himself?

PRINCESS. Why, of course! You should read the History Books, Woodcutter. The suitors to the hand of a Princess are always set some trial of strength or test of quality by the King, and the winner marries his daughter.

WOODCUTTER. Well, I don't live in a Palace, and I think my own thoughts about these things. I'd better get back to my work.

[*He goes on with his chopping.*

PRINCESS (*gently, after a pause*). Woodcutter!

WOODCUTTER (*looking up*). Oh, are you there? I thought you were married by this time.

PRINCESS (*meekly*). I don't want to be married. (*Hastily*) I mean, not to any of those three.

WOODCUTTER. You can't help yourself.

PRINCESS. I know. That's why I wanted *you* to help me.

WOODCUTTER (*going up to her*). Can a simple woodcutter help a Princess?

PRINCESS. Well, perhaps a simple one couldn't, but a clever one might.

WOODCUTTER. What would his reward be?

PRINCESS. His reward would be that the Princess, not being married to any of her three suitors, would still be able to help him chop his wood in the mornings. . . . I *am* helping you, aren't I?

WOODCUTTER (*smiling*). Oh, decidedly.

PRINCESS (*nodding*). I thought I was.

WOODCUTTER. It is kind of a great lady like yourself to help so humble a fellow as I.

PRINCESS (*meekly*). I'm not *very* great.

[*And she isn't. She is the smallest, daintiest little Princess that ever you saw.*

WOODCUTTER. There's enough of you to make a hundred men unhappy.

PRINCESS. And one man happy?

WOODCUTTER. And one man very, very happy.

PRINCESS (*innocently*). I wonder who he'll be. . . . Woodcutter, if *you* were a Prince, would you be my suitor?

WOODCUTTER (*scornfully*). One of three?

PRINCESS (*excitedly*). Oo, would you kill the others? With that axe?

WOODCUTTER. I would not kill them, in order to help His Majesty make up his mind about his son-in-law. But if the Princess had made up her mind — and wanted me —

PRINCESS. Yes?

WOODCUTTER. Then I would marry her, however many suitors she had.

PRINCESS. Well, she's only got three at present.

WOODCUTTER. What is that to me?

PRINCESS. Oh, I just thought you might want to be doing something to your axe.

WOODCUTTER. My axe?

PRINCESS. Yes. You see, she *has* made up her mind.

WOODCUTTER (*amazed*). You mean — But — but I'm only a woodcutter.

PRINCESS. That's where you'll have the advantage of them, when it comes to axes.

WOODCUTTER. Princess! (*He takes her in his arms*) My Princess!

PRINCESS. Woodcutter! My Woodcutter! My, oh so very, very slow and uncomprehending, but entirely adorable Woodcutter!

[*They sing together. They just happen to feel like that.*

WOODCUTTER (*the song finished*). But what will His Majesty say?

PRINCESS. All sorts of things. . . . Do you really love me, Woodcutter, or have I proposed to you under a misapprehension?

WOODCUTTER. I adore you!

PRINCESS (*nodding*). I thought you did. But I wanted to hear you say it. If I had been a simple peasant, I suppose you would have said it a long time ago?

WOODCUTTER. I expect so.

PRINCESS (*nodding*). Yes. . . . Well, now we must think of a plan for making Mother like you.

WOODCUTTER. Might I just kiss you again before we begin?

PRINCESS. Well, I don't quite see how I am to stop you.

[*The Woodcutter picks her up in his arms and kisses her.*

WOODCUTTER. There!

PRINCESS (*in his arms*). Oh, Woodcutter, Woodcutter, why didn't you do that the first day I saw you? Then I needn't have had the bother of proposing to you. (*He puts her down suddenly*) What is it?

WOODCUTTER (*listening*). Somebody coming. (*He peers through the trees and then says in surprise*) The King!

PRINCESS. Oh! I must fly!

WOODCUTTER. But you'll come back?

PRINCESS. Perhaps.

[*She disappears quickly through the trees. The Woodcutter goes on with his work and is discovered at it a minute later by the King and Queen.*

KING (*puffing*). Ah! and a seat all ready for us. How satisfying.

[*They sit down, a distinguished couple — reading from left to right, "King, Queen" — on a bench outside the Woodcutter's hut.*

QUEEN (*crossly — she was like that*). I don't know why you dragged me here.

KING. As I told you, my love, to be alone.

QUEEN. Well, you aren't alone.

[*She indicates the Woodcutter.*

KING. Pooh, he doesn't matter. . . . Well now, about these three Princes. They are getting on my mind rather. It is time we decided which one of them is to marry our beloved child. The trouble is to choose between them.

QUEEN. As regards appetite, there is nothing to choose between them. They are three of the heartiest eaters I have met for some time.

KING. You are right. The sooner we choose one of them, and send the other two about their business, the better. (*Reflectively*) There were six peaches on the breakfast-table this morning. Did I get one? No.

QUEEN. Did *I* get one? No.

KING. Did our darling child get one — not that it matters? No.

QUEEN. It is a pity that the seven-headed bull died last year.

KING. Yes, he had a way of sorting out competitors for the hand of our beloved one that was beyond all praise. One could have felt quite sure that, had the three competitors been introduced to him, only one of them would have taken any further interest in the matter.

QUEEN (*always the housekeeper*). And even he mightn't have taken any interest in his meals.

KING (*with a sigh*). However, those days are over. We must think of a new test. Somehow I think that, in a son-in-law, moral worth is even more to be desired than mere brute strength. Now my suggestion is this: that you should disguise yourself as a beggar woman and approach each of the three princes in turn, supplicating their charity. In this way we shall discover which of the three has the kindest heart. What do you say, my dear?

QUEEN. An excellent plan. If you remember, I suggested it myself yesterday.

KING (*annoyed*). Well, of course, it had been in my mind for some time. I don't claim that the idea is original; it has often been done in our family. (*Getting up*) Well then, if you will get ready, my dear, I will go and find our three friends and see that they come this way.

[*They go out together. As soon as they are out of sight the Princess comes back.*

PRINCESS. Well, Woodcutter, what did I tell you?

WOODCUTTER. What did you tell me?

PRINCESS. Didn't you listen to what they said?

WOODCUTTER. I didn't listen, but I couldn't help hearing.

PRINCESS. Well, *I* couldn't help listening. And unless you stop it somehow, I shall be married to one of them to-night.

WOODCUTTER. Which one?

PRINCESS. The one with the kindest heart — whichever that is.

WOODCUTTER. Supposing they all three have kind hearts?

PRINCESS (*confidentially*). They won't. They never have. In our circles when three Princes come together, one of them has a kind heart and the other two haven't. (*Surprised*) Haven't you read any History at all?

WOODCUTTER. I have no time for reading. But I think it's time History was altered a little. We'll alter it this afternoon.

PRINCESS. What do you mean?

WOODCUTTER. Leave this to me. I've got an idea.

PRINCESS (*clapping her hands*). Oh, how clever of you! But what do you want me to do?

WOODCUTTER (*pointing*). You know the glade over there where the brook runs through it? Wait for me there.

PRINCESS. I obey my lord's commands.

[*She blows him a kiss and runs off.*

[*The Woodcutter resumes his work. By and by the Red Prince comes along. He is a — well, you will see for yourself what he is like.*

RED PRINCE. Ah, fellow . . . Fellow! . . . I said fellow!

[*Yes, that sort of man.*

WOODCUTTER (*looking up*). Were you speaking to me, my lord?

RED PRINCE. There is no other fellow here that I can see.

[*The Woodcutter looks round to make sure, peers behind a tree or two, and comes back to the Prince.*

WOODCUTTER. Yes, you must have meant me.

RED PRINCE. Yes, of course I meant you, fellow. Have you seen the Princess come past this way? I was told she was waiting for me here.

WOODCUTTER. She is not here, my lord. (*Looking round to see that they are alone*) My lord, are you one of the Princes who is seeking the hand of the Princess?

RED PRINCE (*complacently*). I am, fellow.

WOODCUTTER. His Majesty the King was here a while ago. He is to make his decision between you this afternoon. (*Meaningly*) I think I can help you to be the lucky one, my lord.

RED PRINCE. You suggest that I take an unfair advantage over my fellow-competitors?

WOODCUTTER. I suggest nothing, my lord. I only say that I can help you.

RED PRINCE (*magnanimously*). Well, I will allow you to help me.

WOODCUTTER. Thank you. Then I will give you this advice. If a beggar woman asks you for a crust of bread this afternoon, remember — it is the test!

RED PRINCE (*staggered*). The test! But I haven't *got* a crust of bread!

WOODCUTTER. Wait here and I will get you one.

[*He goes into the hut.*

RED PRINCE (*speaking after him as he goes*). My good fellow, I am extremely obliged to you, and if ever I can do anything for you, such as returning a crust to you of similar size or even lending you another slightly smaller one, or — (*The Wood-cutter comes back with the crust*) Ah, thank you, my man, thank you.

WOODCUTTER. I would suggest, my lord, that you should take a short walk in this direction (*pointing to the opposite direc-tion to that which the Princess has taken*), and stroll back casu-ally in a few minutes' time when the Queen is here.

RED PRINCE. Thank you, my man, thank you.

[*He puts the crust in his pocket and goes off. The Woodcutter goes on with his work. The Blue Prince comes in and stands watching him in silence for some moments.*

WOODCUTTER (*looking up*). Hullo!

BLUE PRINCE. Hullo!

WOODCUTTER. What do you want?

BLUE PRINCE. The Princess.

WOODCUTTER. She's not here.

BLUE PRINCE. Oh!

[*The Woodcutter goes on with his work and the Prince goes on looking at him.*

WOODCUTTER (*struck with an idea*). Are you one of the Princes who is wooing the Princess?

BLUE PRINCE. Yes.

WOODCUTTER (*coming towards him*). I believe I could help your Royal Highness.

BLUE PRINCE. Do.

WOODCUTTER (*doubtfully*). It would perhaps be not quite fair to the others.

BLUE PRINCE. Don't mind.

WOODCUTTER. Well then, listen.

[*He pauses a moment and looks round to see that they are alone.*

BLUE PRINCE. I'm listening.

WOODCUTTER. If you come back in five minutes, you will see a beggar woman sitting here. She will ask you for a crust of bread. You must give it to her, for it is the way His Majesty has chosen of testing your kindness of heart.

BLUE PRINCE (*feeling in his pockets*). No bread.

WOODCUTTER. I will give you some.

BLUE PRINCE. Do.

WOODCUTTER (*taking a piece from his pocket*). Here you are.

BLUE PRINCE. Thanks.

WOODCUTTER. Not at all, I'm very glad to have been able to help you.

[*He goes on with his work. The Blue Prince remains looking at him.*

BLUE PRINCE (*with a great effort*). Thanks.

[*He goes slowly away. A moment later the Yellow Prince makes a graceful and languid entry.*

YELLOW PRINCE. Ah, come hither, my man, come hither.

WOODCUTTER (*stopping his work and looking up*). You want me, sir?

YELLOW PRINCE. Come hither, my man. Tell me, has her Royal Highness the Princess passed this way lately?

WOODCUTTER. The Princess?

YELLOW PRINCE. Yes, the Princess, my bumpkin. But perhaps you have been too much concerned in your own earthy affairs to have noticed her. You — ah — cut wood, I see.

WOODCUTTER. Yes, sir, I am a woodcutter.

YELLOW PRINCE. A most absorbing life. Some day we must have a long talk about it. But just now I have other business waiting for me. With your permission, good friend, I will leave you to your faggots.

[*He starts to go.*

WOODCUTTER. Beg your pardon, sir, but are you one of those Princes that want to marry our Princess?

YELLOW PRINCE. I had hoped, good friend, to obtain your permission to do so. I beg you not to refuse it.

WOODCUTTER. You are making fun of me, sir.

YELLOW PRINCE. Discerning creature.

WOODCUTTER. All the same, I *can* help you.

YELLOW PRINCE. Then pray do so, log-chopper, and earn my everlasting gratitude.

WOODCUTTER. The King has decided that whichever of you three Princes has the kindest heart shall marry his daughter.

YELLOW PRINCE. Then you will be able to bear witness to him that I have already wasted several minutes of my valuable time in condescending to a mere faggot-splitter. Tell him this and the prize is mine. (*Kissing the tips of his fingers*) Princess, I embrace you.

WOODCUTTER. The King will not listen to me. But if you return here in five minutes, you will find an old woman begging for bread. It is the test which their Majesties have arranged for you. If you share your last crust with her —

YELLOW PRINCE. Yes, but do I look as if I carried a last crust about with me?

WOODCUTTER. But see, I will give you one.

YELLOW PRINCE (*taking it between the tips of his fingers*). Yes, but —

WOODCUTTER. Put it in your pocket, and when —

YELLOW PRINCE. But, my dear bark-scraper, have you no feeling for clothes at all? How can I put a thing like this in my pocket? (*Handing it back to him*) I beg you to wrap it up. Here, take this. (*Gives him a scarf*) Neatly, I pray you. (*Taking an orange ribbon out of his pocket*) Perhaps a little of this round it would make it more tolerable. You think so? I leave it to you. I trust your taste entirely. . . . Leaving a loop for the little finger, I entreat you . . . so. (*He hangs it on his little finger*) In about five minutes, you said? We will be there. (*With a bow*) We thank you. [*He departs delicately. The Woodcutter smiles to himself, puts down his axe and goes off to the Princess. And just in time. For behold! the King and Queen return. At least we think it is the Queen, but she is so heavily disguised by a cloak which she wears over her Court dress, that for a moment we are not quite sure.*

KING. Now then, my love, if you will sit down on that log there — (*placing her*) — excellent — I think perhaps you should remove the crown. (*Removes it*) There! Now the disguise is perfect.

QUEEN. You're sure they are coming? It's a very uncomfortable seat.

KING. I told them that the Princess was waiting for them here. Their natural disappointment at finding I was mistaken will make the test of their good nature an even more exacting one. My own impression is that the Yellow Prince will be the victor.

QUEEN. Oh, I hate that man.

KING (*soothingly*). Well, well, perhaps it will be the Blue one.

QUEEN. If anything, I dislike him *more* intensely.

KING. Or even the Red.

QUEEN. Ugh! I can't bear him.

KING. Fortunately, dear, you are not called upon to marry any of them. It is for our darling that we are making the great decision. Listen! I hear one coming. I will hide in the cottage and take note of what happens.

[*He disappears into the cottage as the Blue Prince comes in.*

QUEEN. Oh, sir, can you kindly spare a crust of bread for a poor old woman! Please, pretty gentleman!

BLUE PRINCE (*standing stolidly in front of her and feeling in his pocket*). Bread . . . Bread . . . Ah! Bread!

[*He offers it.*

QUEEN. Oh, thank you, sir. May you be rewarded for your gentle heart.

BLUE PRINCE. Thank you.

[*He stands gazing at her. There is an awkward pause.*

QUEEN. A blessing on you, sir.

BLUE PRINCE. Thank you. (*He indicates the crust*) Bread.

QUEEN. Ah, you have saved the life of a poor old woman —

BLUE PRINCE. Eat it.

QUEEN (*embarrassed*). I — er — you — er —

[*She takes a bite and mumbles something.*

BLUE PRINCE. What?

QUEEN (*swallowing with great difficulty*). I'm almost too happy to eat, sir. Leave a poor old woman alone with her happiness, and —

BLUE PRINCE. Not too happy. Too weak. Help you eat. (*He breaks off a piece and holds it to her mouth. With a great effort the Queen disposes of it*) Good! . . . Again! (*She does it again*) Now! (*She swallows another piece*) Last piece! (*She takes it in. He pats her kindly on the back, and she nearly chokes*) Good. . . . Better now?

QUEEN (*weakly*). Much.

BLUE PRINCE. Good day.

QUEEN (*with an effort*). Good day, kind gentleman.

[*He goes out.*

[*The King is just coming from the cottage, when he returns suddenly. The King slips back again.*

BLUE PRINCE. Small piece left over. (*He gives it to her. She looks hopelessly at him*) Good-bye.

[*He goes.*

QUEEN (*throwing the piece down violently*). Ugh! What a man!

KING (*coming out*). Well, well, my dear, we have discovered the winner.

QUEEN (*from the heart*). Detestable person!

KING. The rest of the competition is of course more in the nature of a formality —

QUEEN. Thank goodness.

KING. However, I think that it will prevent unnecessary discussion afterwards if we — Take care, here is another one.

[*He hurries back. Enter the Red Prince.*

QUEEN (*with not nearly so much conviction*). Could you spare a crust of bread, sir, for a poor hungry old woman?

RED PRINCE. A crust of bread, madam? Certainly. As luck will have it, I have a crust on me. My last one, but—your need is greater than mine. Eat, I pray.

QUEEN. Th-thank you, sir.

RED PRINCE. Not at all. Come, eat. Let me have the pleasure of seeing you eating.

QUEEN. M-might I take it home with me, pretty gentleman?

RED PRINCE (*firmly*). No, no. I must see you eating. Come! I will take no denial.

QUEEN. Th-thank you, sir. (*Hopefully*) Won't you share it with me?

RED PRINCE. No, I insist on your having it all. I am in the mood to be generous. Oblige me by eating it now for I am in a hurry; yet I will not go until you have eaten. (*She does her best*) You eat but slowly. (*Sternly*) Did you deceive me when you said you were hungry?

QUEEN. N-no. I'm very hungry.

[*She eats.*

RED PRINCE. That's better. Now understand — however poor I am, I can always find a crust of bread for an old woman. Always! Remember this when next you are hungry. . . . You spoke? (*She shakes her head and goes on eating*) Finished?

QUEEN (*with great difficulty*). Yes, thank you, pretty gentleman.

RED PRINCE. There's a piece on the ground there that you dropped. (*She eats it in dumb agony*) Finished?

QUEEN (*huskily*). Yes, thank you, pretty gentleman.

RED PRINCE. Then I will leave you, madam. Good morning.

[*He goes out.*

[*The Queen rises in fury. The King is about to come out of the cottage, when the Yellow Prince enters. The Queen sits down again and mumbles something. It is certainly not an appeal for bread, but the Yellow Prince is not to be denied.*

YELLOW PRINCE (*gallantly*). My poor woman, you are in distress. It pains me to see it, madam, it pains me terribly. Can it be that you are hungry? I thought so, I thought so. Give me the great pleasure, madam, of relieving your hunger. See (*holding up his finger*), my own poor meal. Take it! It is yours.

QUEEN (*with difficulty*). I am not hungry.

YELLOW PRINCE. Ah, madam, I see what it is. You do not wish to deprive me. You tell yourself, perchance, that it is not fitting that one in your station of life should partake of the meals of the highly born. You are not used, you say, to the food of Princes. Your rougher palate —

QUEEN (*hopefully*). Did you say food of Princes?

YELLOW PRINCE. Where was I, madam? You interrupted me. No matter — eat. (*She takes the scarf and unties the ribbon*) Ah, now I remember. I was saying that your rougher palate —

QUEEN (*discovering the worst*). No! No! Not bread!

YELLOW PRINCE. Bread, madam, the staff of life. Come, madam, will you not eat? (*She tries desperately*) What can be more delightful than a crust of bread by the wayside?

[*The Queen shrieks and falls back in a swoon. The King rushes out to her.*

KING (*to Yellow Prince*). Quick, quick, find the Princess.

YELLOW PRINCE. The Princess — find the Princess!

[*He goes vaguely off and we shall not see him again. But the Woodcutter and the Princess do not need to be found. They are here.*

WOODCUTTER (*to Princess*). Go to her, but don't show that you know me.

[*He goes into the cottage, and the Princess hastens to her father.*

PRINCESS. Father!

KING. Ah, my dear, you're just in time. Your mother —

PRINCESS. My mother?

KING. Yes, yes. A little plan of mine — of hers — your poor mother. Dear, dear!

PRINCESS. But what's the matter?

KING. She is suffering from a surfeit of bread, and —

[*The Woodcutter comes up with a flagon of wine.*

WOODCUTTER. Poor old woman! She has fainted from exhaustion. Let me give her some —

QUEEN (*shrieking*). No, no, not bread! I will *not* have any more bread.

WOODCUTTER. Drink this, my poor woman.

QUEEN (*opening her eyes*). Did you say drink?

[*She seizes the flagon and drinks.*

PRINCESS. Oh, sir, you have saved my mother's life!

WOODCUTTER. Not at all.

KING. I thank you, my man, I thank you.

QUEEN. My deliverer! Tell me who you are!

PRINCESS. It is my mother, the Queen, who asks you.

WOODCUTTER (*amazed, as well he may be*). The Queen!

KING. Yes, yes. Certainly, the Queen.

WOODCUTTER (*taking off his hat*). Pardon, your Majesty. I am a woodcutter, who lives alone here, far away from Courts.

QUEEN. Well, you've got more sense in your head than any of the Princes that *I've* seen lately. You'd better come to Court.

PRINCESS (*shyly*). You will be very welcome, sir.

QUEEN. And you'd better marry the Princess.

KING. Isn't that perhaps going a *little* too far, dear?

QUEEN. Well, you wanted kindness of heart in your son-in-law, and you've got it. And he's got common sense too. (*To Woodcutter*) Tell me, what do you think of bread as — as a form of nourishment?

WOODCUTTER (*cautiously*). One can have too much of it.

QUEEN. Exactly my view. (*To King*) There you are, you see.

KING. Well, if you insist. The great thing, of course, is that our darling child should be happy.

PRINCESS. I will do my best, father.

[*She takes the Woodcutter's hand.*

KING. Then the marriage will take place this evening. (*With a wave of his wand*) Let the revels begin.

[*They begin.*

ACT II

OLIVER'S ISLAND

SCENE I. *The Schoolroom* (*Ugh!*)

Oliver is discovered lying flat on his — well, lying flat on the floor, deep in a book. The Curate puts his head in at the door.

CURATE. Ah, our young friend, Oliver! And how are we this morning, dear lad?

OLIVER (*mumbling*). All right, thanks.

CURATE. That's well, that's well. Deep in our studies, I see, deep in our studies. And what branch of Knowledge are we pursuing this morning?

OLIVER (*without looking up*). "Marooned in the Pacific; or, The Pirate's Bride."

CURATE. Dear, dear, what will Miss Pinniger say to this interruption of our studies?

OLIVER. Silly old beast.

CURATE. Tut-tut, dear lad, that is not the way to speak of our mentors and preceptors. So refined and intelligent a lady as Miss Pinniger. Indeed I came here to see her this morning on a little matter of embroidered vestments. Where is she, dear lad?

OLIVER. It isn't nine yet.

CURATE (*looking at his watch*). Past nine, past nine.

OLIVER (*jumping up*). Je-hoshaphat!

CURATE. Oliver! Oliver! My dear lad! Swearing at *your* age! Really, I almost feel it my duty to inform your aunt —

OLIVER. Fat lot of swearing in just mentioning one of the Kings of Israel.

CURATE. Of Judah, dear boy, of Judah. To be ignorant on such a vital matter makes it even more reprehensible. I cannot believe that our dear Miss Pinniger has so neglected your education that —

[*Enter our dear Miss Pinniger, the Governess.*

GOVERNESS. Ah, Mr. Smilax; how pleasant to see you!

CURATE. My dear Miss Pinniger! You will forgive me for interrupting you in your labours, but there is a small matter of — ah! —

GOVERNESS. Certainly, Mr. Smilax. I will walk down to the gate with you. Oliver, where is Geraldine?

OLIVER. Aunt Jane wanted her.

GOVERNESS. Well, you should be at your lessons. It's nine o'clock. The fact that I am momentarily absent from the room should make no difference to your zeal.

OLIVER (*without conviction*). No, Miss Pinniger.

[*He sits down at his desk, putting "Marooned in the Pacific" inside it.*

CURATE (*playfully*). For men must work, Oliver, men must work. How doth the little busy bee — Yes, Miss Pinniger, I am with you.

[*They go out.*

OLIVER (*opening his poetry book and saying it to himself*). It was a summer evening — It was a summer evening — (*He stops, refers to the book, and then goes on to himself*) Old Kaspar's work was done. It was a summer evening, Old Kaspar's work was done —

[*Enter Geraldine — or Jill.*

JILL. Where's Pin?

OLIVER. Hallo, Jill. Gone off with Dearly Belovéd. Her momentary absence from the room should make no difference to your zeal, my dear Geraldine. And what are we studying this morning, dear child? (*To himself*) It was a summer evening, Old Kaspar's work was done.

JILL (*giggling*). Is that Pin?

OLIVER. Pin and Dearly Belovéd between them. She's a bit batey this morning.

JILL (*at her desk*). And all my sums have done themselves wrong. (*Hard at it with paper and pencil*) What's nine times seven, Oliver?

OLIVER. Fifty-six. Old Kaspar's work was done. Jolly well wish mine was. And he before his cottage door. Fat lot of good my learning this stuff if I'm going to be a sailor. I bet Beatty didn't mind what happened to rotten old Kaspar when he saw a German submarine.

JILL. Six and carry five Aunt Jane has sent for the doctor to look at my chest.

OLIVER. What's the matter with your chest?

JILL. I blew my nose rather loud at prayers this morning.

OLIVER. I say, Jill, you *are* going it!

JILL. It wasn't my fault, Oliver. Aunt Jane turned over two pages at once and made me laugh, so I had to turn it into a blow.

OLIVER. Bet you what you like she knew.

JILL. Of course she did, and she'll tell the doctor, and he'll be as beastly as he can. What did she say to you for being late?

OLIVER. I said somebody had bagged my sponge, and she wouldn't like me to come down to prayers all unsponged, and she said, "Excuses, Oliver, *always* excuses! Leave me. I will see you later." Suppose that means I've got to go to bed this afternoon. Jill, if I do, be sporty and bring me up "Marooned in the Pacific."

JILL. They'll lock the door. They always do.

OLIVER. Then I shall jolly well go up for a handkerchief this morning, and shove it in the bed, just in case. Cavé — here's Pin.

[*Miss Pinniger returns to find them full of zeal.*

GOVERNESS (*sitting down at her desk*). Well, Oliver, have you learnt your piece of poetry?

OLIVER (*nervously*). I — I think so, Miss Pinniger.

GOVERNESS. Close the book, and stand up and say it. (*Oliver takes a last despairing look, and stands up*) Well?

OLIVER. It was a summer evening —

GOVERNESS. The title and the author first, Oliver. Everything in its proper order.

OLIVER. Oh, I say, I didn't know I had to learn the title.

JILL (*in a whisper*). After Blenheim.

GOVERNESS. Geraldine, kindly attend to your own work.

OLIVER. After Blenheim. It was a summer evening.

GOVERNESS. After Blenheim, by Robert Southey. One of our greatest poets.

OLIVER. After Blenheim, by Robert Southey, one of our greatest poets. It was a summer evening, Old Kaspar's work was done — er — Old Kaspar's work was done — er — work was done, er. . . .

GOVERNESS. And he before —

OLIVER. Oh yes, of course. And he before — er — and he before — er — It was a summer evening, Old Kaspar's work was done, and he before — er — and he before — Er, it *was* a summer evening —

GOVERNESS. So you have already said, Oliver.

OLIVER. I just seem to have forgotten this bit, Miss Pinniger. And he before —

GOVERNESS. Well, what was he before?

OLIVER (*hopefully*). Blenheim? Oh no, it was *after* Blenheim.

GOVERNESS (*wearily*). His cottage door.

OLIVER. Oo, yes. And he before his cottage door was sitting in the sun. (*He clears his throat*) Was sitting in the sun. Er — (*he coughs again*) — er —

GOVERNESS. You have a cough, Oliver. Perhaps the doctor had better see you when he comes to see Geraldine.

OLIVER. It was just something tickling my throat, Miss Pinniger. Er — it was a summer evening.

GOVERNESS. You haven't learnt it, Oliver?

OLIVER. Yes, I have, Miss Pinniger, only I can't quite remember it. And he before his cottage door —

GOVERNESS. Is it any good, Geraldine, asking you if you have got any of your sums right?

JILL. I've got one, Miss Pinniger . . . nearly right . . . except for some of the figures.

GOVERNESS. Well, we shall have to spend more time at our lessons, that's all. This afternoon — ah — er —

[*She stands up as Aunt Jane and the Doctor come in.*

AUNT JANE. I'm sorry to interrupt lessons, Miss Pinniger, but I have brought the Doctor to see Geraldine. (*To Doctor*) You will like her to go to her room?

DOCTOR. No, no, dear lady. There is no need. Her pulse — (*he feels it*) — dear, dear! Her tongue — (*she puts it out*) — tut-tut! A milk diet, plenty of rice-pudding, and perhaps she would do well to go to bed this afternoon.

AUNT JANE. I will see to it, doctor.

JILL (*mutinously*). I *feel* quite well.

DOCTOR (*to Aunt Jane*). A dangerous symptom. *Plenty* of rice-pudding.

GOVERNESS. Oliver was coughing just now.

OLIVER (*to himself*). Shut up!

DOCTOR (*turning to Oliver*). Ah! His pulse — (*feels it*) — tut-tut! His tongue — (*Oliver puts it out*) Dear, dear! The same treatment, dear lady, as prescribed in the other case.

OLIVER (*under his breath*). Beast!

AUNT JANE. Castor-oil, liquorice-powder, ammoniated quinine — anything of that nature, doctor?

DOCTOR. *As* necessary, dear lady, *as* necessary. The system must be stimulated. Nature must be reinforced.

AUNT JANE (*to Governess*). Which do they dislike least?

OLIVER AND JILL (*hastily*). Liquorice-powder!

DOCTOR. Then concentrate on the other two, dear lady.

AUNT JANE. Thank you, doctor.

[*They go out.*

GOVERNESS. We will now go on with our lessons. Oliver, you will have opportunities in your bedroom this afternoon of learning your poetry. By the way, I had better have that book which you were reading when I came in just now.

OLIVER (*trying to be surprised*). Which book?

JILL (*nobly doing her best to save the situation*). Miss Pinniger, if you're multiplying rods, poles, or perches by nine, does it matter if —

GOVERNESS. I am talking to Oliver, Geraldine. Where is that book, Oliver?

OLIVER. Oh, *I* know the one you mean. I must have put it down somewhere.

[*He looks vaguely about the room.*

GOVERNESS. Perhaps you put it in your desk.

OLIVER. My desk?

JILL (*going up to Miss Pinniger with her work*). You see, it's all gone wrong here, and I think I must have multiplied — (*Moving in front of her as she moves*) I think I must have multiplied —

[*Under cover of this, Oliver makes a great effort to get the book into Jill's desk, but it is no good.*

GOVERNESS (*brushing aside Jill and advancing on Oliver*). Thank you, *I* will take it.

OLIVER (*looking at the title*). Oh yes, this is the one.

GOVERNESS. And I will speak to your aunt at *once* about the behaviour of both of you.

[*She goes out.*

OLIVER (*gallantly*). *I* don't care.

JILL. I did try to help you, Oliver.

OLIVER. You wait. Won't I jolly well bag something of hers one day, just when she wants it.

JILL. I'm afraid you'll find the afternoon rather tiring without your book. What will you do?

OLIVER. I suppose I shall have to think.

JILL. What shall you think about?

OLIVER. I shall think I'm on my desert island.

JILL. Which desert island?

OLIVER. The one I always pretend I'm on when I'm thinking.

JILL. Isn't there any one else on it ever?

OLIVER. Oo, lots of pirates and Dyaks and cannibals and — other people.

JILL. What sort of other people?

OLIVER. I sha'n't tell you. This is a special think I thought last night. As soon as I thought of it, I decided to keep it for (*impressively*) a moment of great emergency.

JILL (*silenced*). Oh! . . . Oliver?

OLIVER. Yes?

JILL. Let me be on your desert island this time. Because I did try to help you.

OLIVER. Well — well — (*Generously*) Well, you can if you like.

JILL. Oh, thank you, Oliver. Won't you tell me what it's about, and then we can both think it together this afternoon.

OLIVER. I expect you'll think all sorts of silly things that *never* happen on a desert island.

JILL. I'll try not to, Oliver, if you tell me.

OLIVER. All right.

JILL (*coming close to him*). Go on.

OLIVER. Well, you see, I've been wrecked, you see, and the ship has foundered with all hands, you see, and I've been cast ashore on a desert island, you see.

JILL. Haven't I been cast ashore too?

OLIVER. Well, you will be this afternoon, of course. Well, you see, we land on the island, you see, and it's a perfectly ripping island, you see, and — and we land on it, you see, and . . .

· · · · · · · · · ·

[*But we are getting on too fast. When the good ship crashed upon the rock and split in twain, it seemed like that all aboard must perish. Fortunately Oliver was made of stern mettle. Hastily constructing a raft and placing the now unconscious Jill upon it, he launched it into the seething maelstrom of waters and pushed off. Tossed like a cockle-shell upon the mountainous waves, the tiny craft with its precious freight was in imminent danger of foundering. But Oliver was made of stern mettle. With dauntless courage he rigged a jury-mast, and placed a telescope to his eye. "Pull for the lagoon, Jill," cried the dauntless Oliver, and in another moment. . . .*

As the raft glides into the still waters beyond the reef, we can see it more clearly. Can it be Jill's bed, with Oliver in his pyjamas perched on the rail, and holding up his bath-towel? Does he shorten sail for a moment to thump his chest and say, "But Oliver was made of stern mettle"? Or is it —

But the sun is sinking behind the swamp where the rattlesnakes bask. For a moment longer the sail gleams like copper in its rays, and then — fizz-z — we have lost it. See! Is that speck on the inky black waters the dauntless Oliver? It is. Let us follow to the island and see what adventures befall him.

Scene II

It is the island which we have dreamed about all our lives. But at present we cannot see it properly, for it is dark. In one of those tropical darknesses which can be felt rather than seen Oliver hands Jill out of the boat.

OLIVER. Tread carefully, Jill, there are lots of deadly rattle-snakes about.

JILL (*stepping hastily back into the boat*). Oli-ver!

⟨OLIV⟩ER. You hear the noise of their rattles sometimes when ⟨the su⟩n is sinking behind the swamp. (*The deadly rattle of ⟨a rattle⟩snake is heard*) There!

JILL.   Oh, Oliver, are they very deadly? Because if they are, I don't think I shall like your island.

OLIVER.   Those aren't. I always have their teeth taken out when ladies are coming. Besides, it's daylight now.
[*With a rapidity common in the tropics — although it may just be Oliver's gallantry — the sun climbs out of the sea, and floods the island. Jill, no longer frightened, steps out of the boat, and they walk up to the clearing in the middle.*

JILL (*looking about her*).   Oh, what a lovely island! I think it's lovely, Oliver.

OLIVER (*modestly*).   It's pretty decent, isn't it? Won't you lie down? I generally lie down here and watch the turtles coming out of the sea to deposit their eggs on the sand.

JILL (*lying down*).   How many do they de-deposit usually, Oliver?

OLIVER.   Oh, three — or a hundred. Just depends how hungry I am. Have a bull's-eye, won't you?

JILL (*excitedly*).   Oh, did you bring some?

OLIVER (*annoyed*).   Bring some? (*Brightening up*) Oh, you mean from the wreck?

JILL (*hastily*).   Yes, from the wreck. I mean besides the axe and the bag of nails and the gunpowder.

OLIVER.   Couldn't. The ship sank with all hands before I could get them. But it doesn't matter, because (*going up to one of the trees*) I recognize this as the bull's-eye tree.
[*He picks a couple of bull's-eyes and gives one to her.*

JILL.   Oh, Oliver, how lovely! Thank you.
[*She puts it in her mouth.*

OLIVER (*sucking hard*).   There was nothing but breadfruit trees here the first time I was marooned on it. Rotten things to have on a decent island. So I planted a bull's-eye tree, and a barley-sugar-cane grove, and one or two other things, and made a jolly ripping place of it.

JILL (*pointing*).   What's that tree over there?

OLIVER.   That one? Rice-pudding tree.

JILL (*getting up indignantly*).   Oliver! Take me back boat at once.

shut up, Jill.   You didn't think I meant it for

e's only you and me on the island.
hat about the domestic animals?   I suppose *they've*

w lovely!   Have we got a goat and a parrot, and

ch better than that.   Look in that cage there.
at a cage?   I never noticed it.   What do I do?
it).   Here, I'll show you.   (*He draws the blind,*
is exposed sitting on a stump of wood and blink-
n light)   What do you think of that?

I thought of that in bed one night.   Spiffing
've got some other ones in the plantation over
good specimens.   I feed 'em on rice-pudding.
one talk?
teaching it.   (*Stirring it up with a stick*)   Come

bling).   Ninety-nine, ninety-nine . . .
s all it can say at present.   I'm going to give it
lagoon to-morrow.   I want to see if there are
there aren't, then we can bathe there after-

a name yet?   I think I should like to

t, Fluffkins.   Time little doctors

it's a lovely island.
thing you want, you
s or anything like
irsty.
nk you.
't ever

JILL (*still on her back with her eyes shut*).   I hadn't
it much, Oliver dear.

OLIVER.   Because I can get you an awfully dece
like, and if I was his brother-in-law it would be ri
often been marooned with him, of course, but
brother-in-law.

JILL.   Why don't you marry his daughter and h
law?

OLIVER.   He hasn't got a daughter.

JILL.   Well, you could think him one.

OLIVER.   I don't want to.   If ever I'm such
marry, which I'm jolly well not going to be
— a dusky maiden.   Jill, be sporty.   All
married some time.   It's different with me

JILL.   Very well, Oliver.   I don't want to spo

OLIVER.   Good biz.

[*He stands up, shuts his eyes and waves his han*
[*Enter the Pirate Chief.*

PIRATE CHIEF (*with a flourish*).   Gentles, your s
modore Crookshank, at your service.   Better k
Spanish Main as One-eared Eric.

OLIVER.   Glad to meet you, Commodore.   I'
toed Thomas, the Terror of the Dyaks.
me Oliver, if you like.   This is my sister
the Pampas.

PIRATE CHIEF (*with another bow*).   Cha

JILL (*politely*).   Don't mention it, C

OLIVER.   My sister wants to ma
[*He moves a little away from*

JILL (*sitting down and ind*
you sit down, Commo

PIRATE CHIEF.   Than
I shall hear bette
[*He sits down o*

JILL.   Oh

PIRAT

I

I was an ear short and he was a head short. It was considered in the family that I had won.

[*There is an awkward pause.*

JILL (*shyly*). Well, Commodore?

PIRATE CHIEF. Won't you call me Eric?

JILL. I am waiting, Eric.

PIRATE CHIEF. Madam, I am not a marrying man, not to any extent, but if you would care to be Mrs. Crookshank, I'd undertake on my part to have the deck swabbed every morning, and to put a polish on the four-pounder that you could see your pretty face in.

JILL. Eric, how sweet of you. But I think you must speak to my brother in the library first. Oli-ver!

OLIVER (*coming up*). Hallo! Settled it?

JILL. It's all settled, Oliver, between Eric and myself, but you will want to ask him about his prospects, won't you?

OLIVER. Yes, yes, of course.

PIRATE. I shall be very glad to tell you anything I can, sir. I think I may say that I am doing fairly well in my profession.

OLIVER. What's your ship? A sloop or a frigate?

PIRATE. A brigantine.

JILL (*excited*). Oh, that's what Oliver puts on his hair when he goes to a party.

OLIVER (*annoyed*). Shut up, Jill! A brigantine? Ah yes, a rakish craft, eh, Commodore?

PIRATE (*earnestly*). Extremely rakish.

OLIVER. And how many pieces of eight have you?

PIRATE. Nine thousand.

OLIVER. Ah! (*To Jill*) What's nine times eight?

JILL (*to herself*). Nine times eight.

OLIVER (*to himself*). Nine times eight.

PIRATE (*to himself*). Nine times eight.

JILL. Seventy-two.

PIRATE. I made it seventy-one, but I expect you're right.

OLIVER. Then you've seventy-two thousand pieces altogether?

PIRATE. Yes, sir, about that.

OLIVER. Any doubloons?

PIRATE. Hundreds of 'em.

OLIVER. Ingots of gold?

PIRATES. Lashings of 'em.

JILL. And he's going to polish up the four-pounder until I can see my face in it.

OLIVER. I was just going to ask you about your guns. You've got 'em fore and aft, of course?

PIRATE. Yes, sir. A four-pounder fore and a half-pounder haft.

OLIVER (*little embarrassed*). And do you ever have brothers-in-law in your ship?

PIRATE. Well, I never have had yet, but I have always been looking about for one.

JILL. Oh, Oliver, isn't Eric a *nice* man?

OLIVER (*casually*). I suppose the captain's brother-in-law is generally the first man to board the Spaniard with his cutlass between his teeth?

PIRATE. You might almost say always. Many a ship on the Spanish Main I've had to leave unboarded through want of a brother-in-law. They're touchy about it somehow. Unless the captain's brother-in-law comes first they get complaining.

OLIVER (*bashfully*). And there's just one other thing. If the brigantine happened to put in at an island for water, and the captain's brother-in-law happened — just happened — to be a silly ass and go and marry a dusky maiden, whom he met on the beach —

PIRATE. Bless you, it's always happening to a captain's brother-in-law.

OLIVER (*in a magnificent manner*). Then, Captain Crookshank, you may take my sister!

JILL. Thank you, Oliver.

[*It is not every day that one-eared Eric, that famous chieftain, marries into the family of the Terror of the Dyaks. Naturally the occasion is celebrated by the whole pirate crew with a rousing chorus, followed by a dance in which the dusky maidens of the Island join. At the end of it, Jill finds herself alone with Tua-Heeta, the Dusky Princess.*]

JILL (*fashionably*). I'm so pleased to meet my brother's future wife. It's so nice of you to come to see me. You will have some tea, won't you? (*She puts out her hand and presses an imaginary bell*) I wanted to see you, because I can tell you so many little things about my brother, which I think you ought to know. You see, Eric — my husband —

TUA-HEETA. Ereec?

JILL. Yes. I wish you could see him. He's so nice-looking. But I'm afraid he won't be home to tea. That's the worst of marrying a sailor. They are away so much. Well, I was telling you about Oliver. I think it would be better if you knew at once that — he doesn't like rice-pudding.

TUA-HEETA. Rice-poodeeng?

JILL. Yes, he hates it. It is very important that you should remember that. Then there's another thing — (*An untidy looking servant comes in. Can it be — can it possibly be Aunt Jane? Horrors!*) He dislikes — Oh, there you are, Jane. You've been a very long time answering the bell.

AUNT JANE. I'm so sorry, ma'am, I was just dressing.

JILL. Excuses, Jane, always excuses. Leave me. Take a week's notice. (*To Tua-Heeta*) You must excuse my maid. She's very stupid. Tea at once, Jane. (*Aunt Jane sniffs and goes off*) What was I saying? Oh yes, about Oliver. He doesn't care for cod-liver oil in the way that some men do. You would be wise not to force it on him just at first. . . . Have you any idea where you are going to live?

TUA-HEETA. Live?

[*These dusky maidens are no conversationalists.*

JILL. I expect Oliver will wish to reside at Hammersmith, so convenient for the City. You'll like Hammersmith. You'll go to St. Paul's Church, I expect. The Vicar will be sure to call. (*Enter Aunt Jane with small tea-table*) Ah, here's tea. (*To Jane*) You're very slow, Jane.

AUNT JANE. I'm sorry, ma'am.

JILL. It's no good being sorry. Take another week's notice. (*To Tua-Heeta*) You must forgive my talking to my maid. She wants such a lot of looking after. (*Jane puts down the table*) That will do, Jane. (*Jane bumps against the table*) Dear, dear, how clumsy you are. What wages am I giving you now?

AUNT JANE. A shilling a month, ma'am.

JILL. Well, we'd better make it ninepence. (*Jane goes out in tears*) Servants are a great nuisance, aren't they? Jane is a peculiarly stupid person. She used to be aunt to my brother, and I have only taken her on out of charity. (*She pours out from an imaginary tea-pot*) Milk? Sugar?

[*She puts them in and hands the imaginary cup to Tua-Heeta.*

TUA-HEETA. Thank you.

[*Drinks.*

JILL (*pouring herself a cup*). I hope you like China. (*She drinks, and then rings an imaginary bell*) Well, as I was saying — (*Enter Aunt Jane*) You can clear away, Jane.

AUNT JANE. Yes, ma'am.

[*She clears away the tea and Tua-Heeta and — very quickly — herself, as Oliver comes back. Oliver has been discussing boarding-tactics with his brother-in-law. Captain Crookshank belongs to the now old-fashioned Marlinspike School; Oliver is for well-primed pistols.*

JILL. Oh, Oliver, I love your island. I've been thinking things all by myself. You're married to Tua-heeta. You don't mind, do you?

OLIVER. Not at all, Jill. Make yourself at home. I've just been trying the doctor in the lagoon. There *were* sharks there, after all, so we'll have to find another place for bathing. Oh, and I shot an elephant. What would you like to do now?

JILL. Just let's lie here and see what happens. (*What happens is that a cassowary comes along*) Oh, what a lovely bird! Is it an ostrich?

[*The cassowary sniffs the air, puts its beak to the ground and goes off again.*

OLIVER. Silly! It's a cassowary, of course.

JILL. What's a cassowary?

OLIVER. Jill! Don't you remember the rhyme?

I wish I were a cassowary
  Upon the plains of Timbuctoo,
And then I'd eat a missionary —
  And hat and gloves and hymn-book too!

JILL. Is that all they're for?

OLIVER. Well, what else would you want them for?
[*A Missionary, pith-helmet, gloves, hymn-book, umbrella, all complete — creeps cautiously up. He bears a strong likeness to the Curate, the Reverend Smilax.*

MISSIONARY. I am sorry to intrude upon your privacy, dear friends, but have you observed a cassowary on this island, apparently looking for something?

OLIVER. Yes, we saw one just now.

MISSIONARY (*shuddering*). Dear, dear, dear. You didn't happen to ask him what was the object of his researches?

JILL. He went so quickly.

MISSIONARY (*coming out of the undergrowth to them*). I wonder if you have ever heard of a little rhyme which apparently attributes to the bird in question, when residing in the level pastures of Timbuctoo, an unholy lust for the body and appurtenances thereto of an unnamed clerical gentleman?

OLIVER AND JILL (*shouting together*). Yes! Rather!

MISSIONARY. Dear, dear! Fortunately — I say fortunately — this is not Timbuctoo! (*Oliver slips away and comes back with a notice-board "Timbuctoo," which he places at the edge of the trees, unseen by the Missionary, who goes on talking to Jill*) I take it that a cassowary residing in other latitudes is of a more temperate habit. His appetite, I venture to suggest, dear lady, would be under better restraint. That being so, I may perhaps safely — (*He begins to move off, and comes suddenly up to the notice-board*) Dear, dear, dear, dear, dear! This is terrible! You said, I think, that the — ah — bird in question was moving in *this* direction?

OLIVER. That's right.

MISSIONARY. Then I shall move, hastily yet with all due precaution, in *that* direction. (*He walks off on tiptoe, looking over*

his shoulder in case the cassowary should reappear. *Consequently, he does not observe the enormous Cannibal who has
appeared from the trees on the right, until he bumps into
him)* I beg your — *(He looks up)* Dear, dear, dear, dear,
dear !

CANNIBAL. Boria, boria, boo !

MISSIONARY. Yes, my dear sir, it is as you say, a beautiful
morning.

CANNIBAL. Boria, boria, boo !

MISSIONARY. But I was just going a little walk — in this
direction — if you will permit me.

CANNIBAL *(threateningly)*. Boria, boria, boo !

MISSIONARY. I have noticed it, my dear sir, I have often made
that very observation to my parishioners.

CANNIBAL *(very threateningly)*. Boria, boria, boo !

MISSIONARY. Oh, what's he saying ?

OLIVER. He says it's his birthday to-morrow.

CANNIBAL. Wurra, wurra wug !

OLIVER. And will you come to the party ?

MISSIONARY *(to Cannibal)*. My dear sir, it is most kind of you to
invite me, but a prior engagement in a different part of the
country — a totally unexpected call upon me in another
locality — will unfortunately —

[*While he is talking, the cassowary comes back, sidles up to him,
and taps with his beak on the Missionary's pith-helmet.*

MISSIONARY *(absently, without looking round)*. Come in ! . . .
As I was saying, my dear sir — *(The bird taps again.* *The
Missionary turns round annoyed)* Can't you see I'm engaged
— Oh dear, dear, dear, dear, dear !

[*He clasps the Cannibal in his anguish, recoils from the Cannibal
and clasps the cassowary.* *The three of them go off together,
Oliver and Jill following eagerly behind to see who gets most.*

[*The Pirates come back, each carrying a small wooden ammuni-
tion-box, and sit round in a semicircle, the Pirate Chief in the
middle.*

PIRATE. Steward ! Steward !

STEWARD *(hurrying in)*. Yes, sir, coming, sir.

CHIEF. Now then, tumble up, my lad. I would carouse. Circulate the dry ginger.

STEWARD (*hurrying out*). Yes, sir, going, sir.

CHIEF. Look lively, my lad, look lively.

STEWARD (*hurrying in*). Yes, sir, coming, sir.

[*He hands round mugs to them all.*

CHIEF (*rising*). Gentlemen! (*They all stand up*) The crew of the *Cocktail* will carouse — (*They all take one step to the right, one back, and one left — which brings them behind their boxes — and then place their right feet on the boxes together*) One! (*They raise their mugs*) Two! (*They drink*) Three! (*They bang down their mugs*) Four! (*They wipe their mouths with the backs of their hands*) So! . . . Steward!

STEWARD. Yes, sir, here, sir.

CHIEF. The carouse is over.

STEWARD. Yes, sir.

[*He collects the mugs and goes out.*

[*The Pirates sit down again.*

CHIEF (*addressing the men*). Having passed an hour thus in feasting and song —

[*Hark! is it the voice of our dear Miss Pinniger? It is.*

GOVERNESS (*off*). Oliver! Oliver! Jill! You may get up now and come down to tea.

CHIEF. Having, as I say, slept off our carouse —

GOVERNESS (*off*). Oliver! Jill! (*She comes in*) Oh, I beg your pardon, I — er —

[*All the Pirates rise and draw their weapons.*

CHIEF. Pray do not mention it. (*Polishing his pistol lovingly*) You were asking —

GOVERNESS. I — I was l-looking for a small boy — Oliver —

CHIEF. Oliver? (*To 1st Pirate*) Have we any Olivers on board?

1ST PIRATE. No, Captain. Only Bath Olivers.

CHIEF (*to Governess*). You cannot be referring to my brother-in-law, hight Two-Toed Thomas, the Terror of the Dyaks?

GOVERNESS. Oh no, no — just a small boy and his sister — Jill.

CHIEF (*to 2nd Pirate*). Have we any Jills on board?

2ND PIRATE. No, Captain. Only gills of rum.

CHIEF (*to Governess*). You cannot be referring to Mrs. Crookshank, styled the Pride of the Pampas?

GOVERNESS. Oh no, no, I am so sorry. Perhaps I — er —

CHIEF. Wait, woman. (*To 6th Pirate*) Ernest, offer your seat to the lady.

[*The 6th Pirate stands up.*

GOVERNESS (*nervously*). Oh, please don't trouble, I'm getting out at the next station — I mean I —

6TH PIRATE (*thunderously*). Sit down!

[*She sits down tremblingly and he stands by her with his pistol.*

CHIEF. Thank you. (*To 1st Pirate*) Cecil, have you your pencil and note-book with you?

1ST PIRATE (*producing them*). Ay, ay, Captain.

CHIEF. Then we will cross-examine the prisoner. (*To Governess*) Name?

GOVERNESS. Pinniger.

1ST PIRATE (*writing*). Pincher.

CHIEF. Christian names, if any?

GOVERNESS. Letitia.

1ST PIRATE (*writing*). Letisher — how would you spell it, Captain?

CHIEF. Spell it like a sneeze. Age?

GOVERNESS. Twenty-three.

CHIEF (*to 1st Pirate*). Habits — untruthful. Appearance — against her. Got that?

1ST PIRATE. Yes, sir.

CHIEF (*to Governess*). And what are you for?

GOVERNESS. I teach. Oliver and Jill, you know.

CHIEF. And what do you teach them?

GOVERNESS. Oh, everything. Arithmetic, French, Geography, History, Dancing —

CHIEF (*holding up his hand*). A moment! I would take counsel with Percy. (*To 2nd Pirate*) Percy, what shall we ask her in Arithmetic? (*The 2nd Pirate whispers to him*) Excellent. (*To her*) If you really are a teacher, as you say, answer me this question. The brigantine *Cocktail* is in longitude 40° 39′ latitude 22° 50′, sailing closehauled on the port tack at 8 knots in a 15-knot nor'-nor' westerly breeze — how soon before she sights the Azores?

GOVERNESS. I — I — I'm afraid I — You see — I —

CHIEF (*to 1st Pirate*). Arithmetic rotten.

1ST PIRATE (*writing*). Arithmetic rotten.

CHIEF (*to 3rd Pirate*). Basil, ask her a question in French.

3RD PIRATE. What would the mate of a French frigate say if he wanted to say in French, "Avast there, ye lubbering swab" to a friend like?

GOVERNESS. Oh, but I hardly — I —

CHIEF (*to 1st Pirate*). French futile.

1ST PIRATE (*writing*). French futile.

CHIEF (*to 4th Pirate*). I don't suppose it's much use, Francis. But try her in Geography.

4TH PIRATE. Well now, lady. If you was wanting a nice creek to lay up cosy in, atween Dago Point and the Tortofitas, where would you run to?

GOVERNESS. R-run to? But that isn't — of course I —

CHIEF (*to 1st Pirate*). Geography ghastly.

1ST PIRATE (*writing*). Geography ghastly.

CHIEF (*to 5th Pirate*). Give her a last chance, Mervyn. See if she knows any history.

5TH PIRATE. I suppose you couldn't tell me what year it was when old John Cann took the *Saucy Codfish* over Black Tooth Reef and laid her alongside the Spaniard in the harbour there, and up comes the Don in his nightcap. "Shiver my timbers," he says in Spanish, "but there's only one man in the whole of the Spanish Main," he says, "and that's John Cann," he says, "who could —"

[*The Governess looks dumbly at him.*

CHIEF. She couldn't. History hopeless.

1ST PIRATE. History hopeless.

CHIEF (*to Governess*). What else do you teach?

GOVERNESS. Music, dancing — er — but I don't think —

CHIEF. Steward!

STEWARD (*coming in*).   Yes, sir, coming, sir.

CHIEF.   Concertina.

STEWARD (*going out*).   Yes, sir, going, sir.

CHIEF (*to Governess*).   Can you dance a hornpipe?

GOVERNESS.   No, I —

CHIEF.   Dancing dubious.

1ST PIRATE (*writing*).   Dancing dubious.

STEWARD (*coming in*).   Concertina, sir.

CHIEF.   Give it to the woman.

[*He takes it to her.*

GOVERNESS.   I'm afraid I —

[*She produces one ghastly noise and drops the concertina in alarm.*

1ST PIRATE (*writing*).   What shall I say, sir?   Music mouldy or music measly?

CHIEF (*standing up*).   Gentlemen, I think you will agree with me that the woman Pinniger has proved that she is utterly incapable of teaching anybody anything.   Twenty-five years, man and boy, I have sailed the Spanish Main, and, with the possible exception of a dumb and half-witted negro whom I shipped as cook in '64, I have never met any one so profoundly lacking in intellect.   I propose, therefore, that for the space of twenty-four hours the woman Pinniger should be incarcerated in the smuggler's cave, in the company of a black beetle of friendly temperament.

GOVERNESS.   Mercy!   Mercy!

1ST PIRATE.   I should like to second that.

CHIEF.   Those in favour — ay!   (*They all say "Ay"*)   Contrary — No!   (*The Governess says "No"*)   The motion is carried.

[*One of the Pirates opens the door of the cave.   The Governess rushes to the Chief and throws herself at his feet.   Oliver and Jill appear in the nick of time.*

OLIVER.   A maiden in distress!   I will rescue her.   (*She looks up and Oliver recognizes her*)   Oh!   Carry on, Commodore.

[*The Governess is lowered into the cave and the door is shut.*

CHIEF (*to his men*).   Go, find that black beetle, and having found it, introduce it circumspectly by the back door.

PIRATES. Ay, ay, sir.

[*They go out.*

OLIVER. All the same, you know, I jolly well should like to rescue somebody.

JILL (*excitedly*). Oo, rescue me, Oliver.

CHIEF (*solemnly*). Two-toed Thomas, Terror of the Dyaks, and Pest of the North Pacific, truly thou art a well-plucked one. Wilt fight me for the wench?

[*He puts an arm round Jill.*

OLIVER. I will.

CHIEF. Swords?

OLIVER. Pistols.

CHIEF. At twenty paces?

OLIVER. Across a handkerchief.

CHIEF. Done! (*Feeling in his pockets*) Have you got a handkerchief? I think I must have left mine on the dressing-table.

OLIVER (*bringing out his and putting it hastily back again*). Mine's rather — Jill, haven't you got one?

JILL (*feeling*). I know I had one, but I —

CHIEF. This is an ill business. Five-and-thirty duels have I fought — and never before been delayed for lack of a handkerchief.

JILL. Ah, here it is.

[*She produces a very small one and lays it on the ground. They stand one each side of it, pistols ready.*

OLIVER. Jill, you must give the word.

JILL. Are you ready?

[*The sound of a gong is heard.*

CHIEF. Listen! (*The gong is heard again*) The Spanish Fleet is engaged!

JILL. *I* thought it was our tea gong.

CHIEF. Ah, perhaps you're right.

OLIVER. I say, we oughtn't to miss tea. (*Holding out his hand to her*) Come on, Jill.

CHIEF. But you'll come back? We shall always be waiting here for you whenever you want us.

JILL. Yes, we'll come back, won't we, Oliver?

OLIVER. Oo, rather.

[*The whole population of the Island, Animals, Pirates, and Dusky Maidens, come on. They sing as they wave good-bye to the children who are making their way to the boat.*

JILL (*from the boat*). Good-bye, good-bye.

OLIVER. Good-bye, you chaps.

JILL (*politely*). And thank you all for a very pleasant afternoon.

[*They are all singing as the boat pushes off. Night comes on with tropical suddenness. The singing dies slowly down.*

ACT III

FATHER CHRISTMAS AND THE HUBBARD FAMILY

SCENE I

The drawing-room of the Hubbards before Fame and Prosperity came to them. It is simply furnished with a deal table and two cane chairs.

Mr. and Mrs. Hubbard, in faultless evening dress, are at home, Mr. Hubbard reading a magazine, Mrs. Hubbard with her hands in her lap. She sighs.

MR. HUBBARD (*impetuously throwing down his magazine*). Dearest, you sighed?

MRS. HUBBARD (*quickly*). No, no, Henry. In a luxurious and well-appointed home such as this, why should I sigh?

MR. HUBBARD. True, dear. Not only is it artistically furnished, as you say, but it is also blessed with that most precious of all things — (*he lifts up the magazine*) — a library.

MRS. HUBBARD. Yes, yes, Henry, we have much to be thankful for.

MR. HUBBARD. We have indeed. But I am selfish. Would you care to read?

[*He tears out a page of the magazine and hands it to her.*

MRS. HUBBARD. Thank you, thank you, Henry.

[*They both sit in silence for a little. She sighs again.*

MR. HUBBARD. Darling, you did sigh. Tell me what grieves you.

MRS. HUBBARD. Little Isabel. Her cough troubles me.

MR. HUBBARD (*thoughtfully*). Isabel?

MRS. HUBBARD. Yes, dear, our youngest. Don't you remember, she comes after Harold?

MR. HUBBARD (*counting on his fingers*). A, B, C, D, E, F, G, H, I — dear me, have we got nine already?

MRS. HUBBARD (*imploringly*). Darling, say you don't think it's too many.

MR. HUBBARD. Oh no, no, not at all, my love. . . . After all, it isn't as if they were real children.

MRS. HUBBARD (*indignantly*). Henry! How can you say they are not real?

MR. HUBBARD. Well, I mean they're only the children we thought we'd like to have if Father Christmas gave us any.

MRS. HUBBARD. They are just as real to me as if they were here in the house. Ada, Bertram, Caroline, the high-spirited Dennis, pretty Elsie with the golden ringlets, dear little fair-haired Frank —

MR. HUBBARD (*firmly*). Darling one, Frank has curly brown hair. It was an understood thing that you should choose the girls, and *I* should choose the boys. When we decided to take — A, B, C, D, E, F — a sixth child, it was my turn for a boy, and I selected Frank. He has curly brown hair and a fondness for animals.

MRS. HUBBARD. I daresay you're right, dear. Of course it is a little confusing when you never see your children.

MR. HUBBARD. Well, well, perhaps some day Father Christmas will give us some.

MRS. HUBBARD. Why does he neglect us so, Henry? We hang up our stockings every year, but he never seems to notice them. Even a diamond necklace or a few oranges or a five-shilling postal order would be something.

MR. HUBBARD. It is very strange. Possibly the fact that the chimney has not been swept for some years may have something to do with it. Or he may have forgotten our change of address. I cannot help feeling that if he knew how we had been left to starve in this way he would be very much annoyed.

MRS. HUBBARD. And clothes. I have literally nothing but what I am standing up in — I mean sitting down in.

MR. HUBBARD. Nor I, my love. But at least it will be written of us in the papers that the Hubbards perished in faultless evening dress. We are a proud race, and if Father Christmas deliberately cuts us off in this way, let us go down proudly. . . . Shall we go on reading or would you like to walk up and down the room? Fortunately these simple pleasures are left to us.

MRS. HUBBARD. I've finished this page.

MR. HUBBARD (*tearing out one*). Have another, my love.

[*They read for a little while, until interrupted by a knock at the door.*

MRS. HUBBARD. Some one at the door! Who could it be?

MR. HUBBARD (*getting up*). Just make the room look a little more homey, dear, in case it's any one important.

[*He goes out, leaving her to alter the position of the chairs slightly.*

MRS. HUBBARD. Well?

MR. HUBBARD (*coming in*). A letter.

[*He opens it.*

MRS. HUBBARD. Quick!

MR. HUBBARD (*whistling with surprise*). Father Christmas! An invitation to Court! (*Reading*) "Father Christmas at Home, 25th December. Jollifications, 11:59 P.M." My love, he has found us at last!

[*They embrace each other.*

MRS. HUBBARD. Henry, how gratifying!

MR. HUBBARD. Yes. (*Sadly, after a pause*) But we can't go.

MRS. HUBBARD (*sadly*). No, I have no clothes.

MR. HUBBARD. Nor I.

MRS. HUBBARD. How can I possibly go without a diamond necklace? None of the Montmorency-Smythe women has ever been to Court without a diamond necklace.

MR. HUBBARD. The Hubbards are a proud race. No male Hubbard would dream of appearing at Court without a gentleman's gold Albert watch-chain. . . . Besides, there is another thing. There will be many footmen at Father Christmas's Court, who will doubtless require coppers pressed into their palms. My honour would be seriously affected, were I compelled to whisper to them that I had no coppers.

MRS. HUBBARD. It is very unfortunate. Father Christmas may have hundreds of presents waiting for us.

MR. HUBBARD. True. But how would it be to hang up our stockings again this evening — now that we know he knows we are here? I would suggest tied on to the door-knocker, to save him the trouble of coming down the chimney.

MRS. HUBBARD (*excitedly*). Henry, I wonder! But of course we will.

[*They begin to take off — the one a sock, the other a stocking.*

MR. HUBBARD. I almost wish now that my last suit had been a knickerbocker one. However, we must do what we can with a sock.

MRS. HUBBARD (*holding up her stocking and looking at it a little anxiously*). I hope Father Christmas won't give me a bicycle. A stocking never sets so well after it has had a bicycle in it.

MR. HUBBARD (*taking it from her*). Now, dear, I will go down and put them in position. Let us hope that fortune will be kind to us.

MRS. HUBBARD. Let us hope so, darling. And quickly. For (*picking up her page of the magazine*) it is a trifle cold.

[*He goes out and she is left reading.*

SCENE II

Outside the house the snow lies deep. The stocking and sock are tied on to the door-knocker. There is a light in the window. A party of carol-singers, with lanterns, come by and halt in the snow outside the house.

PETER ABLEWAYS. Friends, are we all assembled?

JONAS HUMPHREY. Ay, ay, Peter Ableways, assembled and met together in a congregation, for the purpose of lifting up our voices in joyous thanksgiving, videlicet the singing of a carol or other wintry melody.

JENNIFER LING. Keep your breath for your song, Master Humphrey. That last "Alleluia" of yours was a poor windy thing, lacking grievously in substance.

JONAS (*sadly*). It is so. I never made much of an Alleluia. It is not in my nature somehow. 'Tis a vain boastful thing an Alleluia.

MARTHA PORRITT. Are we to begin soon, Master Ableways? My feet are cold.

JONAS. What matter the feet, Martha Porritt, if the heart be warm with loving-kindness and seasonable emotions?

MARTHA. Well, nothing of me will be warm soon.

JENNIFER. Ay, let's begin, Peter Ableways, while we carry the tune in our heads. It is ill searching for the notes in the middle of the carol, as some singers do.

PETER. Well spoken, Mistress Jennifer. Now listen all, while I unfold the nature of the entertainment. *Item* — A carol or birth song to draw the attention of all folk to the company here assembled and the occasion celebrated. *Item* — Applause and the clapping of hands. *Item* — A carol or song of thanksgiving. *Item* — A collection.

JONAS. An entertainment well devised, Master Ableways, sobeit the words of the second song remain with me after I am delivered of the first.

MARTHA. Are we to begin soon, Master Ableways? My feet are cold.

PETER. Are we all ready, friends? I will say one — two — three — and at "three" I pray you all to give it off in a hearty manner from the chest. One — two —

JONAS. Hold, hold, Master Ableways! Does it begin — No, that's the other one. (*Jennifer whispers the first line to him*) Ay, ay — I have it now — and bursting to get out of me. Proceed, Peter Ableways.

PETER. One — two — three —
[*They carol.*

PETER. Well sung, all.

HUMPHREY. The applause followed, good Master Peter, as ordained. Moreover, I have the tune of the second song ready within me. Likewise a la-la-la or two to replace such words as I have forgotten.

MARTHA. Don't forget the collection, Master Ableways.

PETER. Ay, the collection.

[*He takes off his hat and places it on the ground.*

HUMPHREY. Nay, not so fast, Master Peter. It would be ill if the good folk thought that our success this night were to be estimated by an empty hat. Place some of our money in it, Master Ableways. Where money is, money will come.

JENNIFER. Ay, it makes a pleasing clink.

PETER. True, Mistress Jennifer. Master Humphrey speaks true.

[*He pours some coppers from his pockets into his hat.*

MARTHA. Are we to go on, Master Ableways? My feet are cold.

PETER (*shaking the hat*). So, a warming noise.

HUMPHREY. To it again, gentles.

PETER. Are all ready? One — two — three!

[*They carol.*

PETER. Well sung, all.

HUMPHREY. Have you the hat, Master Peter?

PETER (*picking it up*). Ay, friend, all is ready.

[*The door opens and Mr. Hubbard appears at the entrance.*

MR. HUBBARD. Good evening, friends.

PETER. Good evening, sir.

[*He holds out the hat.*

MR. HUBBARD (*looking at it*). What is this? (*Peter shakes it*) Aha! Money!

PETER. Remember the carol singers, sir.

MR. HUBBARD (*helping himself*). My dear friends, I will always remember you. This is most generous. I shall never forget your kindness. This is most unexpected. But not the less welcome, not the less — I think there's a ha'penny down there that I missed — thank you. As I was saying, unexpected but welcome. I thank you heartily. Good evening, friends.

[*He goes in and shuts the door.*

PETER (*who has been too surprised to do anything but keep his mouth open*). Well! . . . Well! . . . Well, friends, let us to the next house. We have got all that we can get here. [*They trail off silently.*

MARTHA (*as they go off*). Master Ableways!

PETER. Ay, lass!

MARTHA. My feet aren't so cold now.
[*But this is to be an exciting night. As soon as they are gone, a Burglar and a Burglaress steal into view.*

BILL. Wotcher get, Liz? (*She holds up a gold watch and chain. He nods and holds up a diamond necklace*) 'Ow's that?

LIZ (*starting suddenly*). H'st!

BILL (*in a whisper*). What is it?

LIZ. Copper!

BILL (*desperately*). 'Ere, quick, get rid of these. 'Ide 'em in the snow, or —

LIZ. Bill! (*He turns round*) Look! (*She points to the stocking and sock hanging up*) We can come back for 'em as soon as 'e's gone.
[*Bill looks at them, and back at her, and grins. He drops the necklace into one and the watch into the other. As the Policeman approaches they strike up, "While shepherds watched their flock by night," with an air of great enthusiasm.*

POLICEMAN. Now then, move along there.
[*They move along. The Policeman flashes his light on the door to see that all is well. The stocking and sock are revealed. He beams sentimentally at them.*

Scene III

We are inside the house again. Mrs. Hubbard is still reading a page of the magazine. In dashes Mr. Hubbard with the sock and stocking.

MR. HUBBARD. My darling, what do you think? Father Christmas has sent you a little present.
[*He hands her the stocking.*

MRS. HUBBARD. Henry! Has he sent you one too?

MR. HUBBARD (*holding up his sock*). Observe!

MRS. HUBBARD. How sweet of him! I wonder what mine is. What is yours, darling?

MR. HUBBARD. I haven't looked yet, my love. Perhaps just a few nuts or something of that sort, with a card attached saying, "To wish you the old, old wish." We must try not to be disappointed, whatever it is, darling.

MRS. HUBBARD. Of course, Henry. After all, it is the kindly thought which really matters.

MR. HUBBARD. Certainly. All the same, I hope — Will you look in yours, dear, first, or shall I?

MRS. HUBBARD. I think I should like to, darling. (*Feeling it*) It feels so exciting. (*She brings out a diamond necklace*) Henry!

MR. HUBBARD. My love! (*They embrace*) Now you will be able to go to Court. You must say that your husband is unfortunately in bed with a bad cold. You can tell me all about it when you come home. I shall be able to amuse myself with —

[*He is feeling in his sock while talking, and now brings out the watch and chain.*

MRS. HUBBARD. Henry! My love!

MR. HUBBARD. A gentleman's gold hunter and Albert watch-chain. My darling!

[*They put down their presents on the table and embrace each other again.*

MRS. HUBBARD. Let's put them on at once, Henry, and see how they suit us.

MR. HUBBARD. Allow me, my love.

[*He fastens her necklace.*

MRS. HUBBARD (*happily*). Now I feel really dressed again! Oh, I wish we had a looking-glass.

MR. HUBBARD (*opening his gold watch*). Try in here, my darling.

MRS. HUBBARD (*surveying herself*). How perfectly sweet! . . . Now let me put your watch-chain on for you, dear.

[*She arranges it for him — Henry very proud.*

MR. HUBBARD. Does it suit me, darling?

MRS. HUBBARD.   You look fascinating, Henry!

[*They strut about the room with an air.*

MR. HUBBARD (*taking out his watch and looking at it ostentatiously*). Well, well, we ought to be starting. My watch makes it 11:58. (*He holds it to her ear*) Hasn't it got a sweet tick?

MRS. HUBBARD.   Sweet! But starting where, Henry? Do you mean we can really — But you haven't any money.

MR. HUBBARD.   Money? (*Taking out a handful*) Heaps of it.

MRS. HUBBARD.   Father Christmas?

MR. HUBBARD.   Undoubtedly, my love. Brought round to the front door just now by some of his messengers. By the way, dear — (*indicating the sock and stocking*) — hadn't we better put these on before we start?

MRS. HUBBARD.   Of course. How silly of me!

[*They sit down and put them on.*

MR. HUBBARD.   Really, this is a very handsome watch-chain.

MRS. HUBBARD.   It becomes you admirably, Henry.

MR. HUBBARD.   Thank you, dear. There's just one little point. Father Christmas is sometimes rather shy about acknowledging the presents he gives. He hates being thanked. If, therefore, he makes any comment on your magnificent necklace or my handsome watch-chain, we must say that they have been in the family for some years.

MRS. HUBBARD.   Of course, dear. [*They get up.*

MR. HUBBARD.   Well, now we're ready.

MRS. HUBBARD.   Darling one, don't you think we might bring the children?

MR. HUBBARD.   Of course, dear! How forgetful of me! . . . Children —'shun! (*Listen! Their heels click as they come to attention*) Number! (*Their voices — alternate boy and girl, one to nine — are heard*) Right *turn!*

MRS. HUBBARD.   Darling one, I almost seem to hear them!

MR. HUBBARD.   Are you ready, my love?

MRS. HUBBARD.   Yes, Henry.

MR. HUBBARD.   Quick march!

[*The children are heard tramping off. Very proudly Mr. and Mrs. Hubbard bring up the rear.*

Scene IV

The Court of Father Christmas. Shall we describe it? No. But there is everything there which any reasonable person could want, from ices to catapults. And the decorations, done in candy so that you can break off a piece whenever you are hungry, are superb.

1st USHER (*from the back*). Father Christmas!

SEVERAL USHERS (*from the front*). Father Christmas!

[*He comes in.*

FATHER CHRISTMAS (*genially*). Good evening, everybody.

[*I ought to have said that there are already some hundreds of people there, though how some of them got invitations — but, after all, that is not our business. Wishing to put them quite at their ease, Father Christmas, who has a very creditable baritone, gives them a song. After the applause which follows it, he retires to the throne at the back, and awaits his more important guests. The Ushers take up their places, one at the entrance, one close to the throne.*

1st USHER. Mr. and Mrs. Henry Hubbard!

[*They come in.*

MR. HUBBARD (*pressing twopence into his palm*). Thank you, my man, thank you.

2ND USHER. Mr. and Mrs. Henry Hubbard.

MR. HUBBARD (*handing out another twopence*). Not at all, my man, not at all.

[*Mrs. Hubbard curtsies and Mr. Hubbard bows to Father Christmas.*

FATHER CHRISTMAS. I am delighted to welcome you to my Court. How are you both?

MR. HUBBARD. Very well, thank you, sir. My wife has a slight cold in one foot, owing to —

MRS. HUBBARD (*hastily*). A touch of gout, sir, inherited from my ancestors, the Montmorency-Smythes.

FATHER CHRISTMAS. Dear me, it won't prevent you dancing, I hope?

MRS. HUBBARD. Oh no, sir.

FATHER CHRISTMAS. That's right. We shall have a few more

friends coming in soon. You have been giving each other presents already, I see. I congratulate you, madam, on your husband's taste.

MRS. HUBBARD (*touching her necklace*). Oh no, this is a very old heirloom of the Montmorency-Smythe family.

MR. HUBBARD. An ancestress of Mrs. Hubbard's — a lady-in-waiting at the Tottenham Court — at the Tudor Court — was fortunate enough to catch the eye of — er —

MRS. HUBBARD. Elizabeth.

MR. HUBBARD. Queen Elizabeth, and — er —

FATHER CHRISTMAS. I see. You are lucky, madam, to have such beautiful jewels. (*Turning to Mr. Hubbard*) And this delightful gold Albert watch-chain —

MR. HUBBARD. Presented to an ancestor of mine, Sir Humphrey de Hubbard, at the battle of — er —

MRS. HUBBARD. Agincourt.

MR. HUBBARD. As you say, dear, Agincourt. By King Richard the — I should say William the — well, by the King.

FATHER CHRISTMAS. How very interesting.

MR. HUBBARD. Yes. My ancestor clove a scurvy knave from the chaps to the chine. I don't quite know how you do that, but I gather that he inflicted some sort of a scratch upon his adversary, and the King rewarded him with this handsome watch-chain.

USHERS (*announcing*). Mr. Robinson Crusoe!
[*He comes in.*

FATHER CHRISTMAS. How do you do?

CRUSOE (*bowing*). I'm a little late, I'm afraid, sir. My raft was delayed by adverse gales.
[*Father Christmas introduces him to the Hubbards, who inform him that the weather is very seasonable.*

USHERS. Miss Riding Hood!
[*She comes in.*

FATHER CHRISTMAS. How do you do?

RIDING HOOD (*curtseying*). I hope I am in time, sir. I had to look in on my grandmother on the way here.
[*Father Christmas makes the necessary introductions.*

MRS. HUBBARD (*to Crusoe*). Do come and see me, Mr. Crusoe. Any Friday. I should like your advice about my parrot. He's moulting in all the wrong places.

MR. HUBBARD (*to Red Riding Hood*). I don't know if you're interested in wolves at all, Miss Hood. I heard a very good story about one the other day.

[*He begins to tell it, but she has hurried away before he can remember whether it was Thursday or Friday.*

USHERS. Baron Bluebeard!

[*He comes in.*

FATHER CHRISTMAS. How do you do?

BLUEBEARD (*bowing*). I trust you have not been waiting for me, sir. I had a slight argument with my wife before starting, which delayed me somewhat.

[*Father Christmas forgives him.*

USHERS. Princess Goldilocks!

FATHER CHRISTMAS. How do you do?

GOLDILOCKS (*curtseying*). I brought the youngest bear with me — do you mind? (*She introduces the youngest bear to Father Christmas and the other guests*) Say, how do you do, darling? (*To an Usher*) Will you give him a little porridge, please, and if you have got a nice bed where he could rest a little afterwards — he gets tired so quickly.

USHER. Certainly, your Royal Highness.

[*Music begins.*

GOLDILOCKS (*to Father Christmas*). Are we going to dance? How lovely!

FATHER CHRISTMAS (*to the Hubbards*). You will dance, won't you?

MRS. HUBBARD. I think not just at first, thank you.

GOLDILOCKS (*to Crusoe*). Come along!

CRUSOE. I am a little out of practice — er — but if you don't mind — er —

[*He comes.*

BLUEBEARD (*to Riding Hood*). May I have the pleasure?

MRS. HUBBARD (*to Riding Hood*). Be careful, dear; he has a very bad reputation.

RIDING HOOD (*to Bluebeard*).   You don't eat people, do you?

BLUEBEARD (*pained by this injustice*).   Never!

RIDING HOOD.   Oh then, I don't mind.   But I do hate being eaten.

[*Now we can't possibly describe the whole dance to you, for in every corner of the big ballroom couples were revolving and sliding, and making small talk with each other.   So we will just take two specimen conversations.*

CRUSOE (*nervous, poor man*).   Princess Goldilocks, may I speak to you on a matter of some importance to me?

GOLDILOCKS.   I wish you would.

CRUSOE (*looking across at Bluebeard and Red Riding Hood, who are revolving close by*)   Alone.

GOLDILOCKS (*to Bluebeard*).   Do you mind?   You can have your turn afterwards.

BLUEBEARD (*to Riding Hood*).   Shall we adjourn to the Buffet?

RIDING HOOD.   Oh, do let's.

[*They adjourn.*

CRUSOE (*bravely*).   Princess, I am a lonely man.

GOLDILOCKS (*encouragingly*).   Yes, Robinson?

CRUSOE.   I am not much of a one for society, and I don't quite know how to put these things, but — er — if you would like to share my island, I — I should so love to have you there.

GOLDILOCKS.   Oh, Robbie!

CRUSOE (*warming to it*).   I have a very comfortable house, and a man-servant, and an excellent view from the south windows, and several thousands of acres of good rough-shooting, and — oh, do say you'll come!

GOLDILOCKS.   May I bring my bears with me?

CRUSOE.   Of course!   I ought to have said that.   I have a great fondness for animals.

GOLDILOCKS.   How sweet of you!   But perhaps I ought to warn you that we all like porridge.   Have you —

CRUSOE.   I have a hundred acres of oats.

GOLDILOCKS.   Then, Robinson, I am yours.   (*They embrace*) There!   Now tell me — did you make all your clothes yourself?

CRUSOE (*proudly*). All of them.

GOLDILOCKS (*going off with him*). How wonderful of you! Really you hardly seem to want a wife.

[*They go out. Now it is the other couple's turn.*

[*Enter, then, Bluebeard and Riding Hood.*

BLUEBEARD. Perhaps I ought to tell you at once, Miss Riding Hood, that I have been married before.

RIDING HOOD. Yes?

BLUEBEARD. My last wife unfortunately died just before I started out here this evening.

RIDING HOOD (*calmly*). Did you kill her?

BLUEBEARD (*taken aback*). I — I — I —

RIDING HOOD. Are you quite a nice man, Bluebeard?

BLUEBEARD. W-what do you mean? I am a very *rich* man. If you will marry me, you will live in a wonderful castle, full of everything that you want.

RIDING HOOD. That will be rather jolly.

BLUEBEARD (*dramatically*). But there is one room into which you must never go. (*Holding up a key*) Here is the key of it.

[*He offers it to her.*

RIDING HOOD (*indifferently*). But if I'm never to go into it, I sha'n't want the key.

BLUEBEARD (*upset*). You — you *must* have the key.

RIDING HOOD. Why?

BLUEBEARD. The — the others all had it.

RIDING HOOD (*coldly*). Bluebeard, you aren't going to talk about your *other* wives all the time, are you?

BLUEBEARD. N — no.

RIDING HOOD. Then don't be silly. And take this key, and go and tidy up that ridiculous room of yours, and when it's nice and clean, and when you've shaved off that absurd beard, perhaps I'll marry you.

BLUEBEARD (*furiously drawing his sword*). Madam!

RIDING HOOD. Don't do it here. You'll want some hot water.

BLUEBEARD (*trying to put his sword back*). This is too much, this is —

RIDING HOOD.   You're putting it in the wrong way round.

BLUEBEARD (*stiffly*).   Thank you.

[*He manages to get it in.*

RIDING HOOD.   Well, do you want to marry me?

BLUEBEARD.   Yes!

RIDING HOOD.   Sure?

BLUEBEARD (*admiringly*).   More than ever.   You're the first woman I've met who hasn't been afraid of me.

RIDING HOOD (*surprised*).   Are you very alarming?   Wolves frighten me sometimes, but not just silly men. . . .   (*Giving him her hand*)   All right then.   But you'll do what I said?

BLUEBEARD.   Beloved one, I will do anything for you.

[*Crusoe and Goldilocks come back.   Probably it will occur to the four of them to sing a song indicative of the happy family life awaiting them.   On the other hand they may prefer to dance. . . .*

[*But enough of this.   Let us get on to the great event of the evening.   Ladies and gentlemen, are you all assembled?   Then silence, please, for Father Christmas.*

FATHER CHRISTMAS.   Ladies and gentlemen, it gives me great pleasure to see you here at my Court this evening; and in particular my friends Mr. and Mrs. Hubbard, of whom I have been too long neglectful.   However, I hope to make up for it to-night.   (*To an Usher*)   Disclose the Christmas Tree!

[*The Christmas Tree is disclosed, and — what do you think?   Children disguised as crackers are hanging from every branch!   Well, I never!*

FATHER CHRISTMAS (*quite calmly*).   Distribute the presents!

[*An Usher takes down the children one by one and places them in a row, reading from the labels on them, "Mrs. Hubbard, Mr. Hubbard" alternately.*

USHER (*handing list to Mr. Hubbard*).   Here is the nominal roll, sir.

MR. HUBBARD (*looking at it in amazement*).   What's this?   (*Mrs. Hubbard looks over his shoulder*)   Ada, Bertram, Caroline — My darling one!

MRS. HUBBARD.   Henry!   Our children at last!   Oh, are they all — *all* there?

MR. HUBBARD.   We'll soon see, dear.   Ada!

ADA· (*springing to attention*).   Father!

[*She stands at ease.*

MR. HUBBARD.   Bertram! . . .   (*And so on up to Elsie*) . . . Frank!

FRANK.   Father!

MR. HUBBARD.   There you are, darling, I told you he had curly brown hair. . . .   Gwendoline!

[*And so on.*

MRS. HUBBARD (*to Father Christmas*).   Oh thank you so much. It is sweet of you.

MR. HUBBARD (*to Father Christmas*).   We are slightly overcome. Do you mind if we just dance it off?   (*Father Christmas nods genially*)   Come on, children!

[*He holds out his hands, and he and his wife and the children dance round in a ring, singing, "Here we go round the Christmas Tree, all on a Christmas evening." . . .*

[*And then — But at this moment James and Rosemary and the Hubbard children stopped thinking, so of course the play came to an end.   And if there were one or two bits in it which the children didn't quite understand, that was James's fault.   He never ought to have been thinking at all, really.*

THE KING WITH THE IRON HEART

Mr. Stark Young is the author of a book of little dialogues entitled "Sweet Times and the Blue Policeman." They were originally written for the children of a college president, at a time when Mr. Young was a teacher, and evidently they were successfully played under the direction of Mr. Young himself. So simple are the dialogues that they may be made to fit several kinds of demands : either they may be easily read by the seven-year-older who is just beginning, or they may be acted by youngsters from seven to twelve who wish to give a few moments' entertainment; or they may be enacted by marionettes, if one is versed in the art of strings and the mysteries of wooden dolls. "The King with the Iron Heart" is a theme often met with in fairy tales. As Mr. Young handles it, the simplicity of it is sweetly lyrical. It is a moral dialogue in blossom, — nothing more.

THE KING WITH THE IRON HEART

By STARK YOUNG

Copyright, 1921, by McCall and Hearst's Company

Reprinted from *Theatre Arts* and *The McCall* . . . in book (Harcourt, Brace, Publisher)
by Stark Young. Copyright, New York.

THE KING WITH THE IRON HEART

A great chamber in the Palace of the King. The King sits on his throne, his golden crown on his head. Beside him stands the King's Wise Man. They are silent. The Herald stands at the door.

THE HERALD. Hear, every one, let every one give ear. This is the day of the King's Bounty. Let all people come that have boons to ask.

[*The Woman with the Crippled Boy enters and stands before the throne.*

THE HERALD. The Woman with the Crippled Boy, O King!

THE KING. What would you, Woman?

THE WOMAN. O King, will you not help me? I have no bread for my little boy and he is lame and can never walk. Mercy, O King, will you pity me?

THE KING. No, I do not pity you.

THE WISE MAN. The King cannot feel any pity for you, his heart is bound with iron. He cannot be sorry for any one.

THE KNIGHT WHOSE WHITE HORSE IS DEAD. O King of the East Country, pity me, and help me. I am the Knight whose White Horse is dead. Now I must walk and can win no glory. Do you not pity me from your heart, O King?

THE KING. I cannot feel pity in my heart, stand back and let others speak.

THE WOMAN. The King's heart is iron bound, no pity can swell the King's heart.

THE BLIND BEGGAR. O Most High Majesty of the East Country and of the High Hills and Silver Lakes, pity me. I am poor and hungry and old — and I do implore Your Majesty to unbind your heart and pity me.

THE KING. I feel no pity in my heart.

THE WISE MAN. That is not to be wondered at. The King

can feel no pity; for a magician once bound his heart with iron because the King forgot the birthday of his little son. His Majesty cannot feel sorry for any one.

THE KING. Let them all stand aside. I see my son drawing near.

THE WISE MAN. What will you ask of the King, O Royal Prince?

THE PRINCE. O Royal Father, the maiden I love is at the door. She is poor, but she is a king's daughter. I love her and beg you to permit me to marry her. Pity us at last.

THE KING. I do not pity you. You cannot marry her. She has no money.

THE WISE MAN. Speak, Prince. It may not be in vain. Her father is a king, though his kingdom has been taken from him by robber chiefs.

THE PRINCE. Your Royal Highness, I do love this princess, I shall die if you will not allow me to marry her.

THE KING. You may die. I shouldn't be sorry.

THE PRINCE. O Royal Father —

THE KING. Be silent.

THE PRINCE. Woe is me. Oh, that some one could break the charm and loose the iron from the King's heart.

THE WISE MAN. Oh, that some one knew the charm!

THE HERALD. The Old Woman of Dreams would stand before his Majesty the King.

THE KING. Let her come. What are dreams to me!

[*The Old Woman of Dreams enters.*

THE OLD WOMAN OF DREAMS. Your Most Royal Highness, King of the East Country and of the Shining Rivers of the Hills, may I speak my dream?

THE KING. Speak, Woman, or be silent, I care not.

THE OLD WOMAN OF DREAMS. Seven days ago I dreamed a dream of a king whose heart was bound in iron so that he could never feel sorry for any one that was unhappy. And the angel of my dreams sent a song upon my lips that might break the charm. And therefore have I walked seven days and seven nights from my own place, the Red City of the Rising Stars, to come unto the King and speak my dream.

THE KING. Speak then, woman.

THE OLD WOMAN OF DREAMS. I dreamed I heard these words upon the wind:

> I will lay you along my arm,
> O little golden heart:
> I will keep you from all harm,
> O little golden heart,
> O little heart.

THE WISE MAN. The King listens.

THE KING. Methinks I have heard that song before.

THE WISE MAN. Let the Old Woman of Dreams say the song again.

THE OLD WOMAN OF DREAMS.

> I will lay you along my arm,
> O little golden heart;
> I will keep you from all harm,
> O little golden heart,
> O little heart.

[A loud sound is heard like iron bands snapping. The King cries out.

THE KING. Oh, me, oh, me, the iron bursts from my heart! It is the song my mother used to sing me!

THE WISE MAN. Oh, blessed dream, his mother's song!

THE KING. Ah, me, ah, me, now I see the sorrow these poor people have felt! Let them come in—Let the Woman with the Crippled Boy come forward.

[The Woman enters.

THE KING. O Woman, I can be sorry for you now. Your boy shall have a donkey and a little cart to go about and up and down the highroad to see the market folk. And you, Knight whose White Horse is Dead, hear my promise. You shall have my own snow white steed, whose name is Windy Wings.

THE KNIGHT WHOSE WHITE HORSE IS DEAD. I shall win great battles, O King!

THE KING. And you, Blind Beggar, shall have my little page, who will go abroad with you, and into my gardens, and you shall live in my palace.

THE WISE MAN. Your Majesty will not forget your son?

THE KING. I come last to my own son. You, Great Wise Man, and you, Woman of Dreams, shall stay beside me and be my councillors.

THE PRINCE. O Royal Father, I am here.

THE KING. Where is the Poor Princess whose father's kingdom was taken from him by robber chiefs?

THE PRINCE. She is at the door, Father.

THE KING. Let her come in.

[*The beautiful young Princess enters.*

THE KING. Princess, you and my son may marry, and when I am old, my son will be king and wear my crown, and you will be his queen.

THE PRINCESS. Thanks, Your Majesty. Oh, I am so happy!

THE LITTLE CRIPPLED BOY. A donkey and cart — how jolly!

THE BLIND BEGGAR. My troubles are over!

THE PRINCE. We are all happy, Royal Father.

THE KING. But I am the happiest of all.

CURTAIN

HALT!
CHILDREN TURN BACK
PARENTS AND TEACHERS AND
LIBRARIANS READ AHEAD

AN INTRODUCTION WHICH IS AN APPENDIX

It is not a wise thing to offer advice before a goodly Table of Contents. What is much more circumspect is to go to the end of the Bright Road, and there deliver one's preachment without fear of dulling the entertainment. "Another Treasury of Plays for Children" has not been edited with any theories as to educational dramatics; there have not been asked within the gay walls of this book any upholders of special propagandas, and so those who desire dramatizations of health topics, those who seek pageants representing a crusade against tuberculosis, will probably be disappointed.

The same point of view has been maintained that characterized the first "Treasury of Plays for Children." The Editor has a great love for the theater; he does not believe in its conscious use for educational purposes. He considers a play largely from the angle of its appeal to an audience, — not of its being used for the object of self-expression. And while he has made compromises in a few instances by inserting between these covers little dramas which could be easily acted by children, or by young amateurs of an older age, he has ever had in mind plays for a theater in which young folk would be the audience — and by young folk he means youthful hearts from seven to seventy.

Any one who has experienced the barren search for suitable historical plays will appreciate the relief in finding such a drama as Mr. Drinkwater's "Abraham Lincoln", which, barring the interludes, is well within the comprehension of juvenile appreciation. The joy of being given a whole portrait rather than snipped-off incidents in the life of a great man is refreshment, after poring over stunted dialogues which portray Washington cutting down the cherry tree, or Grandpa ringing the bell for Liberty. A man's reach should exceed his grasp, and the sweep of events dealt with in this episodic drama should gather up and hold the interest of children.

In including a little play by Maria Edgeworth, the Editor has thought that maybe the quaintness of it would appeal in an age when manners are somehow discounted in democratic education, and gentleness has somewhat disappeared before the more rugged exercise of a Boy Scout or Camp Fire Girl chivalry. It has been a great regret on our part that no strictly religious drama has been found suitable for this collection. In the reverent dialogues which have come under observation, the piety has been too insistent for artistic needs, and the moral intention has been painfully stressed. We had a Processional ready for inclusion, written by a fervent poetess, but when we took it to a friendly musician for suggestions as to processional music, we witnessed the deadly dull reaction the little piece had upon him. And that was warning sufficient. The Editor had felt this himself and only needed such evidence of dreariness to seal the doom of a perfectly commendable but thoroughly undramatic endeavor.

The paucity of children's plays continues; yet the schoolroom, the club, the recreation groups still make their insistent demands. And where there is the demand, there is the supply. Sporadic attempts to found Children's Theaters are made here and there, but there does not seem to be the urge for one which would assure its permanent establishment. Nor does the professional theater deem it profitable even to meet the holiday spirit of youth at Christmas time, so the Pantomime is merely a dream talked of in this country, not a realization. Teachers are frantically teaching educational dramatics. Little bodies are being swathed in Dennison paper, little arms are being stretched in Dalcroze eurythmics, little minds are being crammed with innocuous dialogue. Wrong kinds of books are being written, demonstrating the easy methods of play production, by Professors of Athletics, who know nothing whatsoever about the theater, and recommend rules for acting that are totally absurd. Those who write children's plays have in mind all the limitations of the child's ability. It is a sad spectacle — the nursery making believe under grown-up guidance, rehearsing patriotic masques in which a State, robed to look like Columbia, receives with open arms animated oats, sweet beans and barley, stage properties easily supplied by the local grocer, and the plot drawn from the inspiring source of a commercial geography ! Teachers every year frantically search for short cuts to dramatic expression : how to become an actor in six lessons, how to make everything out of cheese-cloth, how to select plays that are so stretchable in their casts of characters that one or fifty pupils may have a part. You may have either one wild oat, or a whole primary class of them.

These educational requirements are having a devastating effect on the dramatic output, and the Editor has oftentimes been discouraged by the seeming indifference on the part of writers of children's plays to attempt anything of an artistic nature. One must be practical, one must bear in mind the isolated community, one must remember that not all schools have stages — there are a thousand and one limitations that dull the spirit of writing such plays. A group of youngsters live in a hog-growing section of the country. How appropriate to dramatize for them "This Little Pig Went to Market !" The Boy Scout Manual — that book of etiquette for the Daniel Boones of the land — must be made into a comedy of manners ! I have recently read a dramatization of "Little Red Riding Hood", French and English text — what might be profoundly called a "language drama" — wherein elements are introduced to send thrills of pleasure to the hearts of all lovers of the nursery tale. One feels instantly the appropriateness of the dramatization ! The characters stand at attention before the curtain line. Red Riding Hood and Grandmother — with all the other extraneous characters — cry, "We are saved ! All is well ! Long live Little Red Riding Hood ! Long live America ! Long live France !" And the curtain falls to the strains of the "Marseillaise !"

One is deeply touched by the tremendous artistic quality of this ! It is instinct with the true life of the nursery ! It is conducive to the higher things in the theater ! It shows such deep insight into the workings of the child mind! Surely you don't believe that. We are not considering the child one bit; we are satisfying an educational theory; we are attempting to justify a grown-up fallacy that the natural dramatic instinct of the child must be made to count in his education; that the tendency of a child to hitch his imagination to a star must be curbed within the bounds of useful service to State and Country. It is this condition of mind which is the bulwark against which attempts to write children's plays are shattered.

The Editor has the greatest respect for the dramatic instinct of children, for the imagination of the nursery, for the make-believe element. That is why he pleads so continually for the better play, and attempts to place before young readers some of the material he thinks worthy and of decided child interest. If what he gives happens to fit in with education, or if children wish to act in the plays, that is their concern and pleasure. Many a juvenile company has delighted fond parents with piping productions of Gilbert and Sullivan's "Mikado" and "Patience." Since the necessity for "expressing oneself" has been recognized by school boards, the Editor sympathizes with the teacher who has to "get up" a production for this or that occasion, and for just so many pupils. But this is not his concern in the assembling of his Table of Contents. He aims for a collection of plays literarily good and fancy free. There are dramas which he would have liked to include, like Maeterlinck's "The Blue Bird" and Tagore's "The Post Office" and Eleanor Gates's "The Poor Little Rich Girl." He has not exhausted the list of commendable plays by any means. Which shows that there *are* good dramas for a Children's Theater, if ever one takes root somehow and somewhere.

A child's play is a very sensitive thing. It is compounded of so many elements that have everything to do with art, and so little to do with educational dramatics. Watching the carefree spirit of children, their natural creativeness, their long flights of dreaming, I am resentful of catching these spontaneous expressions of well-being, as I am of catching a butterfly of gay color, hovering above Sweet Williams in the garden. "Hang it all," writes Mr. W. Graham Robertson — our good friend who gave us "Pinkie and the Fairies", and is again in his chair around the Table of Contents of this volume — "why improvement?" The children of his neighborhood — the delightful George Meredith country — asked him for a play "neither idyllic, infantine, nor improving." Which means that his plays have in them all three elements, as organic of the material as yeast is of dough — without effort, and with much grace, and with the tasty pinch of common sense to boot.

The whole danger confronting the writing of children's plays is that a physical standard has been set, and the dramatist has been told to go no further than the outward experience of the child can measure. This is all wrong: for the spiritual and imaginative experiences of children are in reach far beyond this. Heaven lies about us in our infancy; we should make the most of it, for, as matters are now organized, we won't have much time for heaven later on!

There are some writers who have a condescending stoop toward the young world. They feel themselves circumscribed! Circumscribed by what? I can see only one phase where they would have to be careful not to go beyond childhood in dealing with emotional experience. And that emotional experience narrows down largely to the one absorbing topic of adult literature to-day : sex.

We worry over how far advanced a child should be at a certain age, when we really have not taken full stock of what he is at that age. Do we know anything of his humor? Have we ever attempted to shape things in accord with that humor? It lurks in the gravity of children, in the profundity which marks their slim years. A child can put two absolute truths together, with an unconscious humor that is delightful. To whom? To grown people. You see, I take the full measure of a good children's play as being that which will interest their elders as well. Otherwise, where would "The Blue Bird" come in? or "Peter Pan"?

In their talk, young folks show the simplest methods by which they gain effects. My young son, when he was a trifle younger, said to me over the telephone, "Yes, I've been good. Oh, no, Daddy, I forgot, I've just been bad!" Two contrasting statements with their humorous value. He said to me, "I want to see a lion, a tiger, an elephant, and *a worm!*" He showed the artist's sense of line and proportion. I do not believe that those who are writing children's plays live in the atmosphere of "Let's pretend"; the myriad shades of contrasts and meanings in juvenile daily life still await discovery by them.

Until we understand the full approach, we will go on, I suppose, dramatizing for the physical inadequacy of childhood. Just so long as plays go well, are easily comprehensible, are no strain on the pocketbook for scenery and costume, are the *a-b-c* of thought sequence, it is all that is necessary. Whereas, plays for children should be shaped as beautiful vases are shaped; or written as all good plays are written — according to laws that make of drama an art.

MONTROSE J. MOSES

TOWN HILL
NEW HARTFORD
CONNECTICUT
June, 1926

A READING LIST

Considering the importance of the subject, writers about children and the dramatic instinct are still very hazy in their ideas. What they have to say is based largely on what their experience has been in the classroom, and they sound very thankful whenever they find their theories working. The Editor recalls attending a conference on children's plays in Cincinnati, and the eagerness with which teachers used their note-books indicated the pressing need there was for guidance in the subject.

The unfortunate thing was that advice of the character they most required was largely dependent on an adequate supply of plays with which to satisfy the dramatic instinct in the class-room. And this supply, to judge by the pitiable groping of these earnest workers, was accounted by all very slim indeed.

I have declared myself on the side of the drama that is written for children, regardless of their physical ability to act; but, nevertheless, I would be blind indeed were I to ignore either the existence of dramatics in the classroom, or the difficulties under-lying the handling of group expression. I am, therefore, includ-ing in this bibliography articles of all characters bearing upon the many problems the subject involves. Such a list cannot attempt to be selective, since there is so little to select from, but it can, by the very diversity of its matter, be suggestive to the discerning reader. Some of the topics interest merely because they point to one of the symptoms of the disease — the disease being the "low blood pressure" of our children's plays: acting, production, writing — all seem to be done with a mechanical regard for usefulness. Nowhere is there shown in these articles a picture of children enthralled by drama made palpitant. The Royal Road to Good Children's Plays, we still maintain, does not pass through the schoolroom.

Anderson, Madge. The Heroes of the Puppet Stage. New York: Harcourt, Brace & Company. 1923.

Andrews, Elsie V. Dramatization in the Grades. Boston: F. W. Faxon Co. 1919. (*Useful Reference Series*, Vol. 32, No. 22. See also Michigan State Normal College. Ypsilanti. *Library Bulletin*, No. 4.)

Armstrong, Martin D. The Puppet Show. Waltham Saint Lawrence, England: The Golden Cross Press. 1922.

Atlantic Book of Junior Plays, The. Edited by Charles Swain Thomas. Boston: Little, Brown, and Company.

Bell, Lady. The Cat and the Fiddle. Eight Dramatized Nursery Rhymes for Nursery Performers. New York: Longmans, Green & Co. 1922. (See also the same author's "Fairy Tales and How to Act Them." New York: Longmans, Green & Co. 1918.)

Blum, G. Departmental Coöperation in School Productions. *Drama*, Vol. 16, 101. December, 1925.

Books and Plays for Home Economics Entertainments. *Journal Home Economics*, Vol. 15, 726. December, 1923. (Such plays as "Omelet and Oatmelia" are recommended!)

Breneiser, S. G. Art Possibilities in Stagecraft. *School Arts*, Vol. 25, 103–106. October, 1925.

Burness, P. E. Stagecraft, an Extra Classroom Activity. *Industrial Arts*, Vol. 13, 152–154. April, 1924.

Carnegie Institute of Technology, Proceedings of the Conference on the Drama in American Universities and Little Theaters. Pittsburgh, 1925.

Carter, Huntley. Notes on the Newest Russian Theatre. *Drama*, Vol. 14, 248. May–June, 1924. (See also his "The New Theatre and Cinema of Soviet Russia.")

Children's Theatre. *Drama*, Vol. 16, 32–33. October, 1925.

Christmas Drama, Few Plays for. *Drama*, Vol. 14, 73–74. November, 1923.

Christmas Plays for Children and Young People. *Drama*, Vol. 16, 73–75. November, 1925.

Christmas Plays for Young People. *Playground*, Vol. 19, 513–514. December, 1925.

Crandall, L. W. Drama in the Schools. *Drama*, Vol. 16, 99–100. December, 1925.

Curtis, H. S. Renaissance of Drama. *School and Society*, Vol. 19, 513–516. May 3, 1924.

Darton, Frederick J. H. The Good Fairy; or, The Adventures of Sir Richard Whittington, R. Crusoe, Esqr., Master Jack Horner and others. With particular description of a theatre contrived by Albert Rutherstone. London: W. Gardner, Darton & Co. 1922.

De la Mare, Walter. Crossings. A Fairy Play. Music by C. Armstrong Gibbs. Illustrated by Dorothy P. Lathrop. New York: Alfred A. Knopf. 1923.

Eaton, Walter P. Amateur's Earnest Vacation. *Freeman*, Vol. 7, 519–520. August 8, 1923.

Effect of the New Stagecraft on Amateur Dramatics. *Playground*, Vol. 18, 425–426. October, 1924.

Farrar, John. The Magic Sea Shell and Other Plays for Children. New York: George H. Doran Co. 1923.

February Celebrations in Plays for Children, Special Suggestions for. *Drama*, Vol. 15, 90–91. January, 1925.

Ferrigni, P. A History of Puppets. By "Yorick." [*Pseud.*] *Mask*, Florence, 1912–1914. Vol. 5, 111–140, 303–322; Vol. 6, 17–32, 129–134, 205–220, 297–305.

Gregory, Lady. Three Wonder Plays. New York: G. P. Putnam's Sons. 1922.

Greppin, E. Lighting a Play. *School Arts*, Vol. 23, 548–553. May, 1924.

Hanes, E. F. Drama Course in the University High School. Bibliography. *School Review*, Vol. 29, 746–757. December, 1921.

Hazard, L. L. Dante in the Drama Class. *Poet Lore*, Vol. 33, 228–231.

Hazeltine, Alice I. Plays for Children. Chicago: American Library Association Publication Board. 1921. (See also *Monthly Bulletin*, St. Louis Public Library, August, 1918.)

Henderson, R. Children's Theatre: Murals of Fairy Tales. *International Studio*, Vol. 82, 61–66. October, 1925.

Higgins, B. H. Pageant in Rural Life. Bibliography. *School Arts*, Vol. 23, 561–564. May, 1924.

Holt, Roland. A List of Music for Plays and Pageants, with Practical Suggestions. New York: D. Appleton & Co. 1925.

Hughes, F. M. Survey of the Reading Interests of the Pupils of the Madison, Wis., High School. *Education*, Vol. 44, 437–448. March, 1924.

Hunter, R. C. Educational Dramatics: Reply to J. Dolman, Jr. *Quarterly Journal Speech Education*, Vol. 10, 274–276. June, 1924. (See *Q. J. S. E.*, for April, 1921.)

Irvine, H. Staging Shakespeare in Schools and Colleges. *Theatre*, Vol. 38, 41, 75. October, 1923.

Jackson, O. L. Practical Puppet Theatre. *School Arts*, Vol. 23, 558–560. May, 1924.

Jagendorf, M. One-Act Plays for Young Folks. New York: Brentano's. c. 1924.

Jaslow, M. B. High School, Junior, and Drama. *Education*, Vol. 42, 473–487. April, 1922.

Johnson, N. Handling of School Plays. *School Arts*, Vol. 23, 568–569. May, 1924.

Jones, Sybil E. Children's Theatre, A. *Theatre*, Vol. 35, 318–319, 344. May, 1922.

Joseph, Helen Haiman. A Book of Marionettes. New York: B. W. Huebsch. 1920.

Kreymborg, A. Writing for Puppets. *Theatre Arts*, Vol. 7, 302–316. October, 1923.

Lamb, Charles. A Masque of Days. From the Last Essays of Elia. Newly Dressed and Decorated by Walter Crane. New York: Cassell & Co. 1901.

Linnell, Gertrude. Stages in College Auditoriums. *Archaeolog. Forum*, Vol. 38, 59–62. February, 1923.

Little Theatre Play List. See monthly numbers of *Drama*, beginning October, 1925.

Lord, Katherine. Let's Give a Play! How to Select, Plan, and Stage an Amateur Production. *Delineator*, Vol. 104, 18, 61, 62. January, 1924.

—— How to Give an Outdoor Play. *Delineator*, Vol. 101, 64–65. August, 1922.

Mabie, E. C. More Compilation of Plays, *Quarterly Journal Speech Education*, Vol. 8, 308–310. June, 1922.

Mackay, Constance D. [Holt]. Art of Producing a Play. *Woman's Home Companion*, Vol. 50, 29. January, 1923.

—— Drama in Which Young People Can Participate: The School and the Community Celebration. *Drama*, Vol. 16, 32. October, 1925.

—— Fifty Plays without Royalties. *Woman's Home Companion*, Vol. 51, 11. November, 1924.

—— Graduation Plays. *Woman's Home Companion*, Vol. 50, 29, 46. April, 1923.

—— How to Produce Children's Plays. New York: Henry Holt and Company. 1915. (See also Barrett H. Clark's "How to Produce Amateur Plays." Boston: Little, Brown and Company. Revised Edition.)

—— What Play Shall We Give? *Woman's Home Companion*, Vol. 49, 37. February, 1922. (See also Mrs. Holt's article relating to the play in the Church, *Delineator*, Vol. 107, 5. December, 1925.)

McCabe, L. R. Children's Theatre: Making All the Fairy Tales Come True. Theatre of the Heckscher Foundation. *Arts and Decoration*, Vol. 18, 14–15, 98. December, 1922.

McIsaac, F. J. Marionettes and How to Make Them: a Book for Girls and Boys, illustrated by Tony Sarg, text by F. J. McIsaac, with two plays from home-made marionettes, by Anne Stoddard. London, 1923. (Also New York: B. W. Huebsch. 1921.)

McMillan, C. Growing Academic Recognition of Dramatic Production. *Quarterly Journal Speech Education*, Vol. 10, 23–29. February, 1924.

Merry, Glenn Newton. High School Plays. Iowa University. *Extension Bulletin*, No. 44. 1919.

Mick, H. L. Dressing and Stringing a Puppet. *Drama*, Vol. 13, 297–298. May, 1923.

—— Face of a Puppet. *Drama*, Vol. 13, 139–140. January, 1923.

—— How a Puppet Gets Its Head. *Drama*, Vol. 13, 173–174. February, 1923.

—— Puppets from the Neck Down. *Drama*, Vol. 13, 266–267. April, 1923.

Milne, A. A. If I May. New York: E. P. Dutton and Co. 1921. (Essay on "Children's Plays", pp. 68–73.)

Moore, Anne Carroll. The Three Owls: A Book about Children's Books, Their Authors, Artists, and Critics. New York: The Macmillan Co. 1925. ("Plays for Summer Days." Compiled by Harriet Sabra Wright, pp. 348–351; "Plays to Read and Plays to Act." By Harriet Sabra Wright, pp. 293–299; "Unwritten Plays for Children", pp. 299–301; "Czech Children at the Theatre." By Hana Muskova Shaw, pp. 302–306; "What American Children Are Missing", pp. 306–307.)

Moses, Montrose J. Let's Dramatize for Children. *Theatre Arts*, Vol. 8, 831–835. December, 1924.

—— Forgive Us Our Children's Plays. New York: *Herald-Tribune Books*, Sunday, March 7, 1926.

Nichols, W. H. Some General Considerations on Staging a High School Play. *School Arts*, Vol. 23, 522–527. May, 1924.

Nott, S. C. Penny Plain and Two Pence Coloured. *Drama*, Vol. 15, 145–147. April, 1925. (See under Stevenson. Also Brander Matthews' "A Book About the Theatre", chapter on "A Moral from a Toy Theatre.")

Oglebay, Kate. Plays for Children. Chicago: Drama League of America. 1915. (See also the revised edition, New York: H. W. Wilson Co. 1922.)

—— Is a Children's Theatre a Practical Possibility? *Theatre*, Vol. 39, 41. September, 1924.

Overton, Grace Sloan. Drama in Education. New York: The Century Co. 1926. (Emphasis on Religious Drama in Bibliography.)

Painton, Frederick C. The Marionette as a Correlator in the Public Schools. *School Arts*, Vol. 22, 204–209. 1922.

Park, J. G. Puppets. *School Arts*, Vol. 23, 570–572.

Patriotic Celebrations, Few Plays for. *Drama*, Vol. 16, 152, 155. January, 1926.

Patten, Cora Mel. Plays for Children. Chicago: Drama League of America. 1923.

—— Plays for Children. Bibliography. *Drama*, Vol. 16, 233–235. March, 1926.

Plays for Girls' and Women's Clubs. *Playground*, Vol. 15, 579–580, 648; Vol. 16, 121–122. December, 1921; January, 1922; June, 1922.

Punch and Judy. [New edition.] Introduction by Charles Hall Grandgent. Illustrations by George Cruikshank. Cambridge: Washburn & Thomas. 1925.

Puppets, How Tony Sarg Performs Miracles with Marionettes. *Current Opinion*, Vol. 72, 351–353. March, 1922.

Recent One-Act Plays with Mixed Casts for Schools. *Drama*, Vol. 16, 105. December, 1925.

Riley, Alice C. D. Ten Minutes by the Clock and Three Other Children's Plays for Out-Door and In-Door Production. New York: George H. Doran Co. c. 1923.

Russell, Mary M. Drama as a Factor in Social Education. New York: George H. Doran Co. 1924. (Containing a useful Bibliography. She also wrote "How to Produce Plays and Pageants." Doran, 1923.)

Sidgwick, Ethel. Four Plays for Children. London: Sidgwick & Jackson. 1913.

Stevenson, Robert Louis. Movements of Young Children. *Portfolio*, August, 1874. In "Juvenalia."

—— Child's Play. *Cornhill*, September, 1878. In "Virginibus Pueresque."

—— A Penny Plain and Two Pence Coloured. *Magazine of Art*, April, 1884. In "Memories and Portraits."

—— My First Book — Treasure Island. *The Tatler*, August, 1894. In "Juvenalia."

Stinchcomb, Mrs. H. Art Education and Dramatic Expression through Children's Plays. *Playground*, Vol. 19, 159. June, 1925.

Story of Joseph, Dramatized by the 6-B Pupils. *Education*, Vol. 43, 352–362. February, 1923.

Stratton, Clarence. High School Production Where the Stage Equipment Is Adequate. *Theatre*, Vol. 39, 40–42, 74. December, 1924. (The volume number, in N. Y. P. L., has been changed to 40.)

—— Presenting Plays with Meagre Equipment. *Theatre*, Vol. 39, 41, 74. November, 1924.

—— Producing in Little Theatres. New York: Henry Holt & Co. 1921.

Sutorius-Langley, Pauline. List of Plays for Thanksgiving, and Some Recent Volumes of Plays for Children. *Drama*, Vol. 16, 30. October, 1925.

Thackeray, William Makepeace. *Roundabout Papers*. "Round About the Christmas Tree." [Description of Pantomime.]

—— *Roundabout Papers*. "On a Lazy Idle Boy."

—— *Roundabout Papers*. "Ogres."

Thespians, Our Young, in Dead Earnest. *Literary Digest*, Vol. 85, 26–27. May 16, 1925.

Thorpe, C. D. Educational Function of High School Dramatics. *Quarterly Journal Speech Education*, Vol. 10, 116–127. April, 1924.

Webber, J. P., and H. H. Webster. One-Act Plays for Secondary Schools. Boston: Houghton, Mifflin Co. 1923.

Whanslaw, H. W. Everybody's Theatre and How to Make It. Introduction by Edward Shanks. London: W. Gardner, Darton & Co.

Wilson, S. A. Drama and Crops. *Playground*, Vol. 16, 361–362. November, 1922.

Willson, W. Children's Theatre: Where Fairy Tales Come True. *St. Nicholas*, Vol. 50, 562–569. April, 1923.

Wise, C. M. Dramatics for the School and Community. Cincinnati: Stewart Kidd Co. 1923. (See particularly "A Book List for Dramatization in School Work", pp. 113–115. D. Appleton now issues this book.)

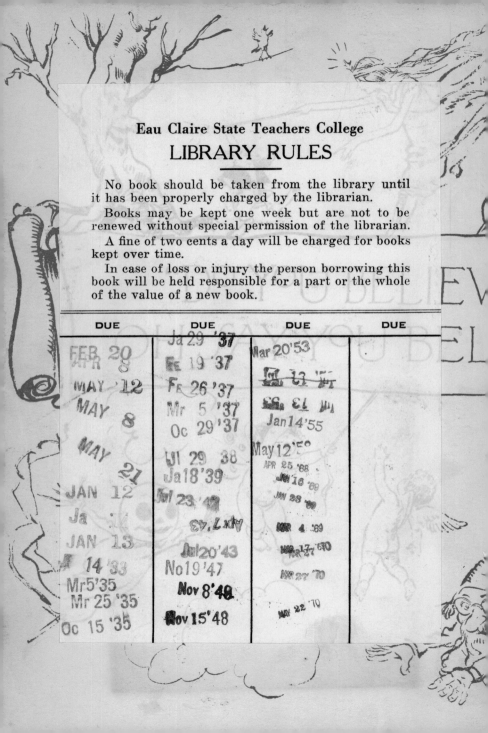

Eau Claire State Teachers College
LIBRARY RULES

No book should be taken from the library until it has been properly charged by the librarian.

Books may be kept one week but are not to be renewed without special permission of the librarian.

A fine of two cents a day will be charged for books kept over time.

In case of loss or injury the person borrowing this book will be held responsible for a part or the whole of the value of a new book.

DUE	DUE	DUE	DUE
FEB 20	Ja 29 '37	Mar 20 '53	
APR 8	Fe 19 '37		
MAY 12	Fe 26 '37	Fe 13 '54	
MAY 8	Mr 5 '37	Se 13 '54	
	Oc 29 '37	Jan 14 '55	
MAY 21	Jl 29 38	May 12 '59	
JAN 12	Ja 18 '39	APR 25 '68	
Ja	Jl 23 '42	JAN 16 '69	
JAN 13	Apr 7 '43	JAN 23 '69	
Ja 14 '33	Jul 20 '43	MR 4 '69	
Mr 5 '35	No 19 '47	MR 17 '70	
Mr 25 '35	Nov 8 '48	MR 27 '70	
Oc 15 '35	Nov 15 '48	MAY 22 '70	